flame- or arc-resistance testing of a fabric. When the fabric is used to manufacture an arc-rated suit, however, compliance might not rely on the fabric testing but on the testing addressed in the standard for the entire suit, including the zipper, buttons, logos, thread, face shield, and so forth. The correct standard must be referenced on the label.

Employers must also be able to identify markings that indicate equipment has not been properly evaluated. For example, no PPE should be labeled as "NFPA approved" or as complying with NFPA *70E*.

Case Study
130.7(C)(14)

Scenario

Ian was an electrician for an electrical contracting firm. He arrived at a worksite to conduct tasks assigned by the host employer. A documented meeting was held between the two. The host employer provided information on the electrical hazards within the equipment and the documentation regarding the risk assessments for the equipment and tasks.

Ian's initial task was a voltage measurement in a 600-volt motor control center. The risk assessment provided by the host employer and the equipment label indicated an incident energy of 5.1 cal/cm² at a distance of 18 inches Ian donned the 8 cal/cm² PPE that was provided by his employer. During the act of measuring the terminal voltage, an arc flash occurred. Ian was nonresponsive when the plant supervisor found him, and his PPE was severely damaged. Ian was rushed to the hospital.

Results

Ian sustained third-degree burns over nearly 60 percent of his body. The injury was so severe that he died 3 weeks later.

Investigation

It was not determined what initiated the incident. Investigation after the incident determined that both the risk assessment provided to Ian and the information on the equipment label were appropriate for the task. Inspection of the label on his arc-rated PPE indicated a rating of 8 cal/cm², presumably based on the specified testing standards. The work procedure was deemed to be sufficient.

From the label information and manufacturer's documentation, it was determined that the PPE was counterfeit, the arc rating of the PPE had not been properly evaluated, and the PPE was not capable of withstanding the marked incident energy exposure. It is unclear if the inappropriate PPE exacerbated Ian's injury.

Analysis

Ian's employer failed in its responsibility to protect him from the electrical hazards present for his assigned tasks. Ian's employer might not have had the qualifications necessary to determine if the PPE issued to him was appropriate or capable of providing the protection necessary to save his life.

Relevant NFPA *70E* Requirements

If Ian's employer had followed the requirements of NFPA *70E*, Ian might not have been k... employer failed to meet in...

- Provide employees
- The PPE used must 130.7(C)(9)].
- PPE must conform t 130.7(C)(14)(a)].

Δ **(15) Arc Flash PPE Category Method.** The requirements of 130.7(C)(15) shall appl the arc flash PPE category method is used for the selection of arc flash PPE.

If the arc flash risk assessment is conducted using the incident energy calcul method, the tables referenced in 130.7(C)(15)(a) and (C)(15)(b) are not permitted used to determine the required PPE.

When conducting the arc flash risk assessment using the PPE category metho tables must be used in the following sequence:

1. Considering site-specific factors, it must be determined if an arc flash is likely f tasks specified in Table 130.5(C).
2. If an arc flash is likely, the hierarchy of risk controls in 110.5(H)(3) must be exha before determining the necessary PPE.

Exhibit 120.1 illustrates some of the basic differences between a simple lockout and a complex lockout procedure.

(b) All complex lockout/tagout procedures shall require a written plan of execution that identifies the person in charge.

If one or more of the conditions listed in 120.4(A)(5)(a) exist, the lockout is defined as complex, and a person in charge must be assigned. The primary responsibility of the person in charge is directly implementing a complex lockout procedure.

(c) The complex lockout/tagout procedure shall vest primary responsibility in an authorized employee for employees working under the protection of a group lockout or tagout device, such as an operation lock or lockbox. The person in charge shall be held accountable for safe execution of the complex lockout/tagout.

EXHIBIT 120.1

One example of a simple lockout — Single energy source

One example of a complex lockout — Multiple energy sources — Person in charge with only key to energy sources — Written procedure required — Key locked in group lockout device — Each authorized employee has own lockout device

...and a complex lockout procedure.

...Workplace 2021

99

NFPA *70E* Summary of Technical Changes: 2021

2021 Section	Comments	FR/SR/SCR Reference
130.2 [2018]	Relocated the requirement to de-energize from former Section 130.2 to Article 110 to emphasize that de-energizing is a requirement of electrical safety programs.	FR-93
130.1, 130.2, 130.3	Rewrote Sections 130.1 and 130.2 to accommodate the relocation of information from former 130.2(A) to 110.3. Focused Article 130 on requirements related to work involving electrical hazards.	FR-41, FR-43, SR-20
Table 130.5(C)	Revised table to include initial CB and switch operation and after-maintenance because each has a higher likelihood of an arc flash event. Removed normal operating conditions from the table because it is redundant with 130.2(A)(4). Changed voltage testing to electrical testing to accommodate other testing tasks.	FR-45, SR-22
Table 130.5(G)	Added Footnote d, which permits the use of footwear that has been tested to demonstrate no ignition, melting, or dripping at the estimated incident energy exposure. Added Footnote e to clarify the required arc rating of outer layers.	FR-46, SR-23
130.6 [2018]	Relocated to 130.8.	FR-60, FR-61, FR-62, FR-63, FR-64, FR-65, FR-68
Table 130.7(C)(7)(a)	New table provides maximum use voltages for rubber insulating gloves and provides ready access to users of this standard and for the proper application of 130.7(C)(7)(a).	FR-49
130.7(C)(9)(b)	Added sentence to clarify the required arc rating of outer layers.	SR-24

MW00633817

Handbook for Electrical Safety in the Workplace

SIXTH EDITION

Edited by

Christopher D. Coache

With the complete text of the 2021 edition of NFPA *70E®, Standard for Electrical Safety in the Workplace®*

NATIONAL FIRE PROTECTION ASSOCIATION
The leading information and knowledge resource on fire, electrical and related hazards

Product Management: Debra Rose
Development and Production: Ken Ritchie
Copyediting: Maeghan Connor
Interior Design: Cheryl Lang way

Cover Design: Scott Robinson
Composition: Cenveo Publisher Services
Printing/Binding: Webcrafters, Inc.

Copyright © 2020
National Fire Protection Association®
One Batterymarch Park
Quincy, Massachusetts 02169-7471

Important Notices and Disclaimers: Publication of this handbook is for the purpose of circulating information and opinion among those concerned for fire and electrical safety and related subjects. While every effort has been made to achieve a work of high quality, neither the NFPA® nor the contributors to this handbook guarantee or warrantee the accuracy or completeness of or assume any liability in connection with the information and opinions contained in this handbook. The NFPA and the contributors shall in no event be liable for any personal injury, property, or other damages of any nature whatsoever, whether special, indirect, consequential, or compensatory, directly or indirectly resulting from the publication, use of, or reliance upon this handbook.

This handbook is published with the understanding that the NFPA and the contributors to this handbook are supplying information and opinion but are not attempting to render engineering or other professional services. If such services are required, the assistance of an appropriate professional should be sought.

NFPA 70E®, *Standard for Electrical Safety in the Workplace*® ("NFPA 70E®"), is, like all NFPA codes, standards, recommended practices, and guides ("NFPA Standards"), made available for use subject to Important Notices and Legal Disclaimers, which appear at the end of this handbook and can also be viewed at *www.nfpa.org/disclaimers*.

Notice Concerning Code Interpretations: This sixth edition of the *Handbook for Electrical Safety in the Workplace* is based on the 2021 edition of NFPA 70E. All NFPA codes, standards, recommended practices, and guides ("NFPA Standards") are developed in accordance with the published procedures of the NFPA by technical committees comprised of volunteers drawn from a broad array of relevant interests. The handbook contains the complete text of NFPA 70E and any applicable Formal Interpretations issued by the NFPA at the time of publication. This NFPA Standard is accompanied by explanatory commentary and other supplementary materials.

The commentary and supplementary materials in this handbook are not a part of the NFPA Standard and do not constitute Formal Interpretations of the NFPA (which can be obtained only through requests processed by the responsible technical committees in accordance with the published procedures of the NFPA). The commentary and supplementary materials, therefore, solely reflect the personal opinions of the editor or other contributors and do not necessarily represent the official position of the NFPA or its technical committees.

REMINDER: UPDATING OF NFPA STANDARDS

NFPA 70E®, *Standard for Electrical Safety in the Workplace*®, like all NFPA codes, standards, recommended practices, and guides ("NFPA Standards"), may be amended from time to time through the issuance of Tentative Interim Amendments or corrected by Errata. An official NFPA Standard at any point in time consists of the current edition of the document together with any Tentative Interim Amendment and any Errata then in effect. In order to determine whether an NFPA Standard has been amended through the issuance of Tentative Interim Amendments or corrected by Errata, visit the "Codes & Standards" section on NFPA's website. There, the document information pages located at the "List of NFPA Codes & Standards" provide up-to-date, document-specific information, including any issued Tentative Interim Amendments and Errata. To view the document information page for a specific NFPA Standard, go to http://www.nfpa.org/docinfo to choose from the list of NFPA Standards, or use the search feature to select the NFPA Standard number (e.g., NFPA 70E). The document information page includes postings of all existing Tentative Interim Amendments and Errata. It also includes the option to register for an "Alert" feature to receive an automatic email notification when new updates and other information are posted regarding the document.

The following are registered trademarks of the National Fire Protection Association:

National Fire Protection Association®
NFPA®
National Electrical Code®, NFPA 70®, and NEC®
Standard for Electrical Safety in the Workplace® and NFPA 70E®

NFPA No.: 70EHB21
ISBN (book): 978-1-4559-2589-6
ISSN: 2691-7203

Printed in the United States of America

20   21   22   23   24   5   4   3   2   1

Dedication

A standard such as NFPA *70E*®, *Standard for Electrical Safety in the Workplace*®, starts with an idea. It is well documented that electrical incidents cause fatalities. Before 1979, more than 600 workers were electrocuted annually in the workplace. At that time, there was no consensus on how to properly protect employees working on or near energized electrical equipment. A small group of industry professionals felt something had to be done to remedy the situation.

Standards are developed by volunteers who have the passion and commitment to make something better. They come from different backgrounds with different viewpoints. Volunteers spend countless hours debating what is a best practice and what should be a standard requirement. Every few years, volunteers meet to improve the standard by addressing changes in the industry and changes requested by the public. They draft the standard so that it can be reviewed by the public before it is issued as an American National Standard.

It has been over 40 years since the first group of volunteers dedicated their time, expense, and experience to help save the lives of workers exposed to electrical hazards. Since then, hundreds of volunteers have spent thousands of hours working in the background to help prevent workplace electrical injuries and fatalities. Electrical safety in the workplace has been greatly improved through their contributions. Although the volunteers are overlooked by users of the standard, they are the bedrock upon which the standard is developed. Volunteers are listed in the front of each NFPA *70E* edition (though they're not included in this handbook). This edition of the handbook is dedicated to past and present NFPA *70E* technical committee members, for without their tireless efforts, many more families would be devastated by the loss of a loved one.

Contents

Preface   vii

About the Editor   xi

NFPA *70E* Summary of Technical Changes: 2021   T1

PART 1

NFPA 70E®, Standard for Electrical Safety in the Workplace®,
with Commentary   1

ARTICLE 90
Introduction   3

CHAPTER 1

Safety-Related Work Practices   11

- **100** Definitions   13
- **105** Application of Safety-Related Work Practices and Procedures   43
- **110** General Requirements for Electrical Safety-Related Work Practices   46
- **120** Establishing an Electrically Safe Work Condition   91
- **130** Work Involving Electrical Hazards   118

CHAPTER 2

Safety-Related Maintenance Requirements   187

- **200** Introduction   189
- **205** General Maintenance Requirements   191
- **210** Substations, Switchgear Assemblies, Switchboards, Panelboards, Motor Control Centers, and Disconnect Switches   199
- **215** Premises Wiring   201
- **220** Controller Equipment   203
- **225** Fuses and Circuit Breakers   204
- **230** Rotating Equipment   207
- **235** Hazardous (Classified) Locations   208
- **240** Batteries and Battery Rooms   210

Contents

245   Portable Electric Tools and Equipment   211
250   Personal Safety and Protective Equipment   212

CHAPTER 3

Safety Requirements for Special Equipment   215

300   Introduction   216
310   Safety-Related Work Practices for Electrolytic Cells   217
320   Safety Requirements Related to Batteries and Battery Rooms   224
330   Safety-Related Work Practices: Lasers   231
340   Safety-Related Work Practices: Power Electronic Equipment   235
350   Safety-Related Work Requirements: Research and Development Laboratories   239
360   Safety-Related Requirements for Capacitors   244

INFORMATIVE ANNEXES

A   Informative Publications   249
B   Reserved   255
C   Limits of Approach   257
D   Incident Energy and Arc Flash Boundary Calculation Methods   261
E   Electrical Safety Program   273
F   Risk Assessment and Risk Control   275
G   Sample Lockout/Tagout Program   289
H   Guidance on Selection of Protective Clothing and Other Personal Protective Equipment (PPE)   295
I   Job Briefing and Job Safety Planning Checklist   301
J   Energized Electrical Work Permit   305
K   General Categories of Electrical Hazards   309
L   Typical Application of Safeguards in the Cell Line Working Zone   315
M   Layering of Protective Clothing and Total System Arc Rating   317
N   Example Industrial Procedures and Policies for Working Near Overhead Electrical Lines and Equipment   319
O   Safety-Related Design Requirements   325
P   Aligning Implementation of This Standard with Occupational Health and Safety Management Standards   331
Q   Human Performance and Workplace Electrical Safety   335
R   Working with Capacitors   345

PART 2

Supplements   363

1   *National Electrical Code* Requirements Associated with Safety-Related Work Practices   365
2   Electrical Preventive Maintenance Programs   371
3   Typical Safety Procedure (Procedure for Selection, Inspection, and Care of Rubber Insulating Gloves and Leather Protectors)   379

Index   391

Important Notices and Legal Disclaimers   399

Preface

The 2021 edition of the *Handbook for Electrical Safety in the Workplace* contains the latest information on electrical safety. More than 120 years have passed since March 18,1896, when a group of 23 people representing a wide range of organizations met at the headquarters of the American Society of Mechanical Engineers in New York City. Their purpose was to develop a national code of rules for electrical construction and operation. It was the first national effort to develop electrical installation rules for the United States. That successful effort resulted in the *National Electrical Code® (NEC®)*, the installation code used throughout the United States and in many countries around the world.

The *NEC* addresses electrical installations and provides requirements for the safe operation of installed electrical equipment. NFPA *70E®, Standard for Electrical Safety in the Workplace®,* arose from the need to address the electrical safety of employees when they interact with energized electrical equipment. Since its inception, NFPA *70E* has been tied to the Occupational Safety and Health Administration (OSHA). To understand how OSHA and NFPA *70E* are related and interact, it is important to understand the history of the Occupational Safety and Health Act (OSH Act). 29 CFR Section 1910.3(b)(1) addresses the historical relationship between the Act and the National Fire Protection Association (NFPA): "The relevant legislative history of the Act indicates congressional recognition of the American National Standards Institute and the National Fire Protection Association as the major sources of national consensus standards. National consensus standards adopted on May 29, 1971, pursuant to section 6(a) of the Act are from those two sources."

In 1970, Congress responded to the public's demand for safer workplaces and passed the OSH Act. Under this Act, employers are responsible for providing safe and healthful workplaces for their employees. In general, the OSH Act covers all employers and their employees in all 50 states, the District of Columbia, Puerto Rico, and other US territories.

The OSH Act was signed into law by President Richard Nixon on December 29, 1970, and it created three independent branches. The first branch is OSHA, the administrative and prosecutorial branch under the US Department of Labor. OSHA's role is to ensure safe and healthful workplaces for America's working men and women by setting and enforcing standards and providing training, education, and assistance. The second branch is the Occupational Safety and Health Review Commission (OSHRC), which is the independent federal agency created to process contested citations or penalties resulting from OSHA inspections of American workplaces. The third branch is the National Institute for Safety and Health (NIOSH), which helps ensure safe and healthful working conditions by providing research, information, education, and training in the field of occupational safety and health.

Originally, OSHA adopted the *NEC* as its electrical safety standard by reference. Later, OSHA was confronted with several issues when attempting to use the *NEC* to prepare updated electrical safety standards that would serve OSHA's needs. In addition to installation standards derived from the *NEC,* there was a need for electrical safety-related work practices and guidelines for the maintenance of electrical systems considered critical to safety. A separate standard became necessary to provide requirements for safe work practices for people who might be exposed to electrical hazards.

In May 1975, a meeting was held between the National Electrical Manufacturers Association (NEMA) and the US Department of Labor to discuss a new approach to updating the Electrical Occupational Safety and Health Standards (Subpart S of Part 1910). That meeting led to the concept of a document being put together by extracting suitable portions from the NEC and other documents applicable to electrical safety. A proposal was presented to the NFPA Electrical Section, which unanimously supported the development of a document to be used as the basis for evaluating electrical safety in the workplace.

On January 7, 1976, the Standards Council of NFPA appointed the Committee on Electrical Safety Requirements for Employee Workplaces. The standard was visualized as consisting of four major parts: Part I, Installation Safety Requirements; Part II, Safety-Related Work Practices; Part III, Safety-Related Maintenance Requirements; and Part IV, Safety Requirements for Special Equipment. Each part was recognized as being an important aspect of electrical safety in the workplace, but the parts were sufficiently independent of each other to permit their separate publication. The first edition of NFPA 70E (1979) included only Part I, which dealt primarily with those electrical installation requirements from the NEC that were most directly tied to worker safety.

On January 16, 1981, OSHA revised its electrical installation standard for general industry by replacing the references to the 1971 *NEC* with the relevant requirements from Part I of the 1979 edition of NFPA *70E*. This simplified and clarified the electrical standard. The OSHA standard was written mainly in performance-based language versus the prescriptive-based language found in NFPA *70E* to reduce the need for frequent revision and to avoid technological obsolescence.

The electrical standards at the time in Subpart S of the General Industry Standards covered electrical equipment and installations rather than work practices. Although unsafe work practices appeared to be involved in most workplace electrocutions, OSHA had very few regulations addressing the work practices necessary for electrical safety. Because of this, OSHA determined that standards were needed to minimize these hazards. OSHA's *Electrical Safety-Related Work Practices* went into effect on December 4, 1990 and were based on Part II of the 1983 edition of NFPA *70E*. The new standards, written mainly in performance-based language, addressed the practices and procedures necessary to protect employees working on or near exposed energized and de-energized parts of electric equipment.

A violation of the General Duty Clause, Section 5(a)(1) of the OSH Act, exists if an employer fails to create a workplace that is free from recognized hazards that cause or are likely to cause death or serious physical injury. The General Duty Clause is not used to enforce the requirements of consensus standards. Employers are required to follow the OSHA regulations and not nonmandatory standards. However, consensus standards can help employers recognize hazards and provide feasible means to mitigate injuries from those hazards. Following national consensus standards can help employers meet their obligations under OSHA requirements.

OSHA looks to NFPA *70E* to fill out the performance-based requirements included in their standards, especially since NFPA *70E* is the American National Standard on the subject and sets the bar for safe work practices. This creates a symbiotic relationship between NFPA *70E* and the OSHA standards for electrical safety.

Acknowledgments

Electricity can be a very dangerous occupational hazard. Almost all members of the workforce are exposed to electrical energy every day as they perform their duties. NFPA *70E* not only addresses those that institute electrical safety programs but also the employees who must implement those programs to prevent injury. Since the creation of NFPA *70E,* employees have become more aware of the hazards of electricity and how to protect themselves. Fatalities due to electrical contact in the workplace have decreased by nearly 75 percent since the issuance of the first edition of NFPA *70E.* However, there are still too many electrical injuries and deaths, and there is still work to do. This edition contains the latest consensus on the requirements to prevent electrical injuries.

Handbooks are a team effort, and I have been supported by an outstanding team of professionals. I acknowledge the exceptional work of Ken Ritchie, Content Development Manager, who supported me every step of the way. I also acknowledge the contributions of former NFPA staff who served as staff liaisons to the committee and gratefully acknowledge the work of the editors who assembled previous editions of this handbook. The collective electrical safety expertise of former editors provided the solid foundation on which the 2021 edition of this handbook was built. This edition would not be possible without the tireless work of the dedicated professionals who serve on the Committee on Electrical Safety in the Workplace. Their work has saved and will save countless lives.

I thank my family, Heidi and Rebecca, for their patience, help, and support during the development of this edition. I thank Rusty and Liesl for their companionship through the difficult start to 2020.

—*Christopher D. Coache*

About the Editor

Christopher D. Coache

Christopher is a senior electrical engineer at NFPA. Prior to joining NFPA, he was employed in several industries as an electrical engineer responsible for electrical safety, from the design of equipment to worker safety. Chris serves as the staff liaison for NFPA 73, *Standard for Electrical Inspections for Existing Dwellings-,* NFPA 110, *Standard for Emergency and Standby Power Systems;* NFPA 111, *Standard on Stored Electrical Energy Emergency and Standby Power Systems* ', NFPA 780, *Standard for the Installation of Lightning Protection Systems;* and *NFPA 70E®, Standard for Electrical Safety in the Workplace®.* He is also an editor of the *National Electrical Code® Handbook* and the *National Fire Alarm and Signaling Code Handbook.* Chris is a member of the International Association of Electrical Inspectors (IAEI) and IEEE.

NFPA *70E* Summary of Technical Changes: 2021

This table provides an overview of changes from the 2018 edition to the 2021 edition of NFPA *70E*, *Standard for Electrical Safety in the Workplace*. For more information on the reason(s) for each change, visit www.nfpa.org/70E. The first revision (FR), second revision (SR), and second correlating revision (SCR) numbers are provided in the third column of this table for reference to the official documentation of the technical committee's actions.

2021 Section	Comments	FR/SR/SCR Reference
Article 100	Deleted several definitions of terms not used within NFPA *70E*.	**FR-1, FR-2, FR-6**
Article 100	Added informational note to the term *electrically safe work condition* to clarify the definition.	**FR-9, SCR-1**
Article 100	Added informational note to the term *fault current, available* to clarify that available fault current varies by location in the circuit.	**FR-10**
Article 100	Added the word *exposed* to the definition of the term *shock hazard* to indicate that parts must be exposed to be a hazard.	**FR-13**
Article 110	Re-organized Article 110 for a logical progression through the requirements.	**FR-90**
110.1	Revised Informational Note No. 2 to clarify hazard elimination in relation to an electrically safe work condition.	**SR-2**
110.2	Relocated lockout/tagout general principles from 120.2(A) to Article 110, General Requirements for Electrical Safety-Related Work Practices.	**FR-17, SR-7**
110.3, 110.4	Relocated from former Sections 130.2 and 130.2(A), as the requirement is part of an electrical safety program.	**FR-93**
110.5(K)	New subsection requires electrical safety programs to include a policy on establishing an electrically safe work condition.	**FR-30**
110.5(L)	New subsection clarifies that the lockout or tagout program must be either part of the electrical safety program or must reference the lockout or tagout program.	**FR-24, SR-9**
110.12	New section clarifies that electrical safety is predicated on all the equipment being used in accordance with the instructions provided by the manufacturer.	**FR-37**
120.3(C)(3)	Revised to align with OSHA 1910.333(b)(2)(iii)(E).	**FR-39**

2021 Section	Comments	FR/SR/SCR Reference
130.2 [2018]	Relocated the requirement to de-energize from former Section 130.2 to Article 110 to emphasize that de-energizing is a requirement of electrical safety programs.	FR-93
130.1, 130.2, 130.3	Rewrote Sections 130.1 and 130.2 to accommodate the relocation of information from former 130.2(A) to 110.3. Focused Article 130 on requirements related to work involving electrical hazards.	FR-41, FR-43, SR-20
Table 130.5(C)	Revised table to include initial CB and switch operation and after-maintenance because each has a higher likelihood of an arc flash event. Removed normal operating conditions from the table because it is redundant with 130.2(A)(4). Changed voltage testing to electrical testing to accommodate other testing tasks.	FR-45, SR-22
Table 130.5(G)	Added Footnote d, which permits the use of footwear that has been tested to demonstrate no ignition, melting, or dripping at the estimated incident energy exposure. Added Footnote e to clarify the required arc rating of outer layers.	FR-46, SR-23
130.6 [2018]	Relocated to 130.8.	FR-60, FR-61, FR-62, FR-63, FR-64, FR-65, FR-68
Table 130.7(C)(7)(a)	New table provides maximum use voltages for rubber insulating gloves and provides ready access to users of this standard and for the proper application of 130.7(C)(7)(a).	FR-49
130.7(C)(9)(b)	Added sentence to clarify the required arc rating of outer layers.	SR-24
130.7(C)(10)	Added footwear that has been tested to demonstrate no ignition, melting, or dripping at the estimated incident energy exposure.	FR-51
Table 130.7(C)(15)(a) Table	Added all arc-resistant equipment to the table. Added Footnote e, which permits the use of footwear that has been tested to demonstrate no ignition, melting, or dripping at the estimated incident energy exposure. Added Footnote f to clarify the required arc rating of outer layers.	FR-54, SR-25
Table 130.7(C)(15)(c)	Revised glove requirements and Table Note (d) to correlate with Table 130.5(G). Added table footnote that permits the use of footwear that has been tested to demonstrate no ignition, melting, or dripping at the estimated incident energy exposure.	FR-55, SR-25
130.7(D)(1)	Simplified the language regarding the requirement to use insulated tools and equipment. Simplified the language regarding the use of barriers. Simplified and changed the applicable boundary from the limited approach boundary to the restricted approach boundary to clarify the difference between the use of barriers per 130.7(D) and barricades per 130.7(E).	FR-67
130.7(E)(4) [2018]	Relocated to 130.12, as cutting conductors is not related to alerting techniques.	FR-57
130.8	Relocated from 130.6.	FR-68, SR-17, SR-18
130.12	Relocated from 130.7(D)(4).	FR-57, SR-19
320.3(C) [2018]	Deleted former 320.3(C), DC Ground Fault Detection, because it addressed design and installation considerations, not work practices.	FR-75

2021 Section	Comments	FR/SR/SCR Reference
350.9	Revised energy thresholds to accurately reflect the information in the informational note's resource document. Deleted the capacitive circuit threshold to prevent duplication and potential confusion with new Article 360.	**FR-77, SR-35**
Article 360	New article for safety-related requirements for capacitors.	**FR-88, SCR-4,**
Table D.1	Added limitations of IEEE 1584-2018.	**SR-41**
D.4	Revised to align with IEEE 1584-2018.	**SR-39**
F.7	New section provides guidance to users on selecting PPE using a battery risk assessment process when multiple hazards are or might be present.	**FR-72**
1.2	New checklist for job safety planning.	**FR-91, SR-42**
0.2.3(5)	Added a description of energy-reducing line side isolation.	**FR-86**
Annex R	New annex provides information regarding working with capacitors.	**FR-89, SR-47**

NFPA *70E*®, *Standard for Electrical Safety in the Workplace*®, with Commentary

Part 1 of this handbook includes the complete text and figures of the 2021 edition of NFPA *70E*®, *Standard for Electrical Safety in the Workplace*®. The text, tables, and figures from the standard are printed in black and are the official requirements of NFPA *70E*. Illustrations from the standard are labeled as Figures. Additions, deletions, and changes to the code are indicated by text shading and icons. See page 2 for information on the revision symbols used to identify changes from the previous edition of NFPA *70E*.

Part 1 also includes explanatory commentary to provide insight and other background information for specific sections of the standard. The commentary can help provide a clear understanding of how the requirements can be properly applied. Given a particular requirement, the associated commentary could take the reader behind the scenes into the reasons for the requirement, or it could delve deeper into the subject of the requirement. Commentary text is printed on a color screen to help the reader easily distinguish it from the text of the standard. Line drawings, graphs, and photographs in the commentary are labeled as Exhibits.

This edition of the handbook includes a list of Technical Changes, which precedes Part I. This provides the user with an overview of the major code changes from the 2018 to the 2021 edition of NFPA *70E*. In addition to the commentary text and exhibits, the following are some of the features that have been developed to help the reader understand certain concepts or see them from a different perspective:

- **Case Studies**—Woven throughout the commentary, Case Studies provide real-world summaries of electrical injury incidents, including analysis and discussion of the role of NFPA *70E*.
- **OSHA Connections**—The OSHA Connection feature shows how the Occupational Safety and Health Administration's (OSHA's) electrical safety standards correspond with certain NFPA *70E* requirements.

- **Worker Alerts**—The Worker Alert feature is positioned beside certain requirements to highlight electrical safety information that is especially crucial for employees to be aware of and to understand.

The focus of NFPA *70E* is protecting the employees who might be at risk of injury from electrical hazards. For the employer, it means proactively implementing the requirements before an employee is put at risk. An employer who implements the requirements after an employee injury or fatality has not met their mandated obligation to provide a safe work environment. For employees, it means they must be knowledgeable of the requirements, which should be provided with proper training. An employee's electrical safety training must be more than following the labeling of equipment and using personal protective equipment (PPE). Without fully understanding their roles, options, and personal impact on safety, employees may blindly take on undue risk of injury.

Electrical safety is not limited to those in electrical trades. Any task conducted in the vicinity of energized circuits puts employees at risk. However, many employers and employees tend to believe that NFPA *70E* only applies to those in the electrical industry. Trades that have been mistakenly believed to be exempt from electrical safety requirements have suffered fatalities. Painters, machine operators, groundskeepers, roofers, well drillers, dump truck drivers, welders, and boom truck operators are common victims of electrical injuries. It is foreseeable that employees in other trades could be exposed to electrical hazards. Employers are responsible for the safety of their employees, even when their work environment is a residence, production line, field, roadway, or rooftop.

REVISION SYMBOLS IDENTIFYING CHANGES FROM THE PREVIOUS EDITION

Text revisions are shaded. A Δ before a section number indicates that words within that section were deleted and a Δ to the left of a table or figure number indicates a revision to an existing table or figure. When a chapter was heavily revised, the entire chapter is marked throughout with the Δ symbol. Where one or more sections were deleted, a • is placed between the remaining sections. Chapters, annexes, sections, figures, and tables that are new are indicated with an *N*.

Note that these indicators are a guide. Rearrangement of sections may not be captured in the markup, but users can view complete revision details in the First and Second Draft Reports located in the archived revision information section of each code at www.nfpa.org/docinfo. Any subsequent changes from the NFPA Technical Meeting, Tentative Interim Amendments, and Errata are also located there.

Shaded text = Revisions   Δ = Text deletions and figure/table revisions   • =Section deletions   *N* = New material

Introduction

NFPA *70E®, Standard for Electrical Safety in the Workplace®*, provides enforceable responsibilities for employers and employees to protect against electrical hazards to which employees might be exposed. It is an internationally accepted American National Standard that defines electrical safety-related work practices. The requirements at the heart of NFPA 70E are suitable for adoption and implementation by agencies and employers charged with the responsibility of electrical safety plan development, implementation, and maintenance.

Following and fostering basic installation safety, maintenance, and prudent work procedure rules are essential to employee safety. This can be accomplished by installing electrical systems in accordance with NFPA *70®, National Electrical Code® (NEC®)*; by maintaining electrical systems in accordance with NFPA 70B, *Recommended Practice for Electrical Equipment Maintenance* (in the absence of the specific manufacturer's instructions); and by following the safety policies, procedures, and process controls identified in NFPA *70E*. The technical committees for the NEC, NFPA *70E,* and NFPA 70B all report to the National Fire Protection Association (NFPA) via the NEC Correlating Committee. This promotes consistency between the safety-related work procedures, installation requirements, and recommended maintenance procedures contained in the documents.

NFPA *70E* does not include design requirements, but system design considerations can have a significant impact on worker safety during the installation, inspection, operation, maintenance, and demolition of electrical systems and components. When considered at the electrical system design stage, the use of elimination or substitution—as required by the hierarchy of risk control methods in 110.5(H) and explained in Informative Annex F—can often remove the hazard or lower the risk. The type and location of disconnect switches, for example, can play a role in the need for use of PPE when creating an electrically safe work condition. It is easier and less costly to implement safety features during the design phase than during (or after) the installation phase. Early discussions between engineers, designers, installers, maintainers, owners, and users of electrical systems can facilitate the implementation of safety features and enhance safe work practices.

The Occupational Safety and Health Administration (OSHA) looks to the prescriptive-based requirements of NFPA *70E* to fulfill the performance-based requirements included in its standards, especially since NFPA *70E* is the American National Standard on the subject and sets the bar for safe work practices. This symbiotic relationship between NFPA *70E* and OSHA electrical safety standards helps to increase safety in the workplace.

Typically, NFPA *70E* is not adopted via legislation. It is most often used by employers voluntarily to help fulfill their obligations to OSHA. Compliance with federal regulations is often not verified until an injury occurs. By default, both the employer and employee play the role of the authority having jurisdiction (AHJ) when it comes to proactively implementing and enforcing the requirements of NFPA *70E*.

Article 90, Introduction, should be the starting point for use of the standard, as it identifies the purpose, scope, and arrangement of the document. This information is essential for establishing a framework to apply the standard. The administrative topics of Purpose (90.1) and Scope (90.2) set the ground rules by which the standard is enforced. Users must first determine the standard's applicability to their situation, and Article 90 provides the information necessary to determine when the standard applies to a workplace and to ensure proper compliance.

90.1 Purpose.

The purpose of this standard is to provide a practical safe working area for employees relative to the hazards arising from the use of electricity.

The purpose of NFPA *70E* is to provide a working area for employees that is safe from the risk associated with the use of electricity in the workplace. Using an appropriate mix of risk controls from the hierarchy of risk control methods—as required by 110.5(H) and explained in Informative Annex F—can reduce the risks associated with the use of electricity to an acceptable level.

Work that is performed on exposed energized electrical conductors or circuit parts is dangerous. NFPA *70E,* like many safety standards, defines requirements based on the risk controls identified in the hierarchy of risk control methods, starting with the most effective risk control and ending with what is considered the least effective risk control. This standard utilizes or identifies all of the risk controls in this hierarchy, but the primary protective strategy when an electrical hazard is present must be establishing an electrically safe work condition. After this strategy is executed, all electrical energy has been removed from all conductors and circuit parts to which the employee could be exposed. Only under limited circumstances is energized electrical work allowed to be performed without creating an electrically safe work condition.

NFPA 70E establishes safety processes that use policies, procedures, and program controls to reduce the risk associated with the use of electricity to an acceptable level. The core objective is practical, accomplishable electrical safety that results in employees going home safe at the end of the day. The risk controls discussed in this standard are not impractical or unrealistic; they are sound, viable, and workable applications of safety procedures and policies to be implemented by the employer and employee.

When electrical equipment has been properly installed and maintained and is used in accordance with its listings and the manufacturer's instructions, the risk of injury from the use of electricity should be minimal, especially under normal operating conditions. Safety can only be what is reasonably actionable, and all the risk associated with the use of electricity in the workplace might not be eliminated. The risk, however, must be reduced to an acceptable level. By reducing the risks associated with the use of electricity to an acceptable level, injuries—including fatalities—from the use of electricity in the workplace can be managed to the extent that they are virtually eliminated.

Prudent decision-making is necessary to help employees steer clear of situations where the risk of injury is unacceptable. Proper training and supervision can help educate employees on how to avoid potentially dangerous situations.

As is the very nature of a standard, each requirement contained within might not be the best practice that can be employed for a specific condition, but it is the minimum threshold of what must be done. A standard cannot cover all the conditions that exist for every piece of equipment, it cannot foresee every hazard present at every installation, and it cannot anticipate the actions of every employee at every company. Users should not limit themselves to meeting the minimum requirements—they should consider appropriate additional precautions beyond those provided in the standard to address their specific situations.

90.2 Scope.

The scope describes in general terms what this standard covers and includes sufficient details to explain the range or limit of what is covered. It is important to understand that the *NEC* applies to electrical installations (premises wiring systems) and NFPA *70E* applies to employee workplaces that are located on premises that have premises wiring systems. Premises are locations that consist of any combination of buildings, structures, or grounds. When locations become employee workplaces, 90.2 clarifies which premises are covered by the work policies, procedures, and process controls in this document

(A) Covered. This standard addresses electrical safety-related work practices, safety-related maintenance requirements, and other administrative controls for employee workplaces that are necessary for the practical safeguarding of employees relative to the hazards associated with electrical energy during activities such as the installation, removal, inspection, operation, maintenance, and demolition of electric conductors, electric equipment, signaling and communications conductors and equipment, and raceways. This standard also includes safe work practices for employees performing other work activities that can expose them to electrical hazards as well as safe work practices for the following:

(1) Installation of conductors and equipment that connect to the supply of electricity
(2) Installations used by the electric utility, such as office buildings, warehouses, garages, machine shops, and recreational buildings that are not an integral part of a generating plant, substation, or control center

Informational Note: This standard addresses safety of workers whose job responsibilities involve interaction with energized electrical equipment and systems with potential exposure to electrical hazards. Concepts in this standard are often adapted to other workers whose exposure to electrical hazards is unintentional or not recognized as part of their job responsibilities. The highest risk for injury from electrical hazards for other workers involve unintentional contact with overhead power lines and electric shock from machines, tools, and appliances.

Section 90.2(A) defines employee activities that require realistic safety-related work procedures. These activities include planned interaction with the electrical distribution system and connected equipment (such as installation, inspection, operation, maintenance, and demolition) and can also include unanticipated interactions (such as when employees are painting, tree trimming, or using lifts or ladders). This standard is also intended to cover employees when they are interacting with electrically powered machines, tools, and appliances.

Some complexes—such as college campuses and industrial, military, or multi-unit type facilities—frequently include utility-type generating facilities, utility-type substations, or utility-type electrical distribution systems. Often, these installations are not electrically self-sufficient and are connected to utility power systems. The point of connection between a utility power system and an owner's electrical system is defined as the service point. The *NEC, NFPA 70E,* and NFPA 70B are applicable to conductors and equipment on the load side of the service point. On the load side, the facility is responsible for the installation, operation, and maintenance during electrical equipment's full life cycle, from initial installation, through operation and maintenance, and up to and including its decommissioning and legal disposal.

Maintenance on the line side of the service point is the responsibility of the utility company. On the line side of the service point, workers often use utility-type safety rules, such as those included in ANSI C2, *National Electrical Safety Code®*. Although not required by NFPA *70E,* an employee on the line side of the service point that is not qualified to follow the utility-type safety rules is required by OSHA to follow the safety procedures identified in its general industry safety standards and as defined by NFPA *70E.*

The utility support facility (e.g., the administration building, the maintenance shop, the vehicle garage) and the customer-owned substation are included within the scope of NFPA *70E.* Utilization-type distribution systems in a power plant—including building services such as lighting and heating, ventilation, and air conditioning (HVAC)—are also included within the scope of NFPA *70E.* These systems are typically not wired as integral parts of the electric power generation installation. Various electrical equipment within the same area of a generating facility might or might not be covered by NFPA *70E,* as shown in Exhibit 90.1.

Dwelling units (residences) that become employee workplaces are included within the scope of this standard (and OSFIA's electrical safety-related work procedure rules). A contractor working on a dwelling unit's backup generator, solar panels, or HVAC system is in a dwelling unit workplace. Even though permanent existing wiring of a dwelling

OSHA Connection

The U.S. Department of Labor's Mine Safety and Health Administration (MSHA), in agreement with OSHA, endorsed the application of NFPA *70E* for "Arc Flash Accident Prevention Best Practices." This made it clear that NFPA *70E* applies to the mining industry workplace.

OSHA Connection

29 CFR 1910.269
The OSHA note to 29 CFR 1910.269(a)(1)(i)(A) considers equivalent generation, transmission, and distribution installations of industrial establishments that follow OSHA's rules regarding utility-type systems in 29 CFR 1910.269 effectively to be utility companies.

OSHA Connection

29 CFR 1910.269
Appendix A-2
OSHA provides a flowchart in 1910.269 Appendix A-2 for the application of 1910.269 (Electric Power Generation, Transmission, and Distribution) and Subpart S (Electrical) to the electrical safety-related work practices of qualified and unqualified utility workers.

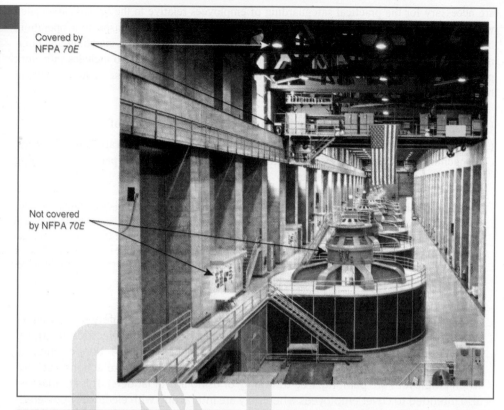

Covered by
NFPA *70E*

Not covered
by NFPA *70E*

unit is not covered by OSHA electrical safety standards, OSHA safety-related work practices must be followed during a renovation to protect employees from the recognized hazards presented by electrical installations. In addition, equipment—such as portable tools and extension cord sets connected to permanent wiring—is covered by OSHA electrical safety standards.

(B) Not Covered. This standard does not cover safety-related work practices for the following:

(1) Installations in ships, watercraft other than floating buildings, railway rolling stock, aircraft, or automotive vehicles other than mobile homes and recreational vehicles

All of the workplaces indicated in this exemption concern movement and the transportation of people or material. Because such facilities might have special features and requirements, the electrical distribution systems in them do not have to be installed in accordance with the *NEC,* and they are not required to follow the safe work procedures included in this document. However, if the employer determines that the required level of safety can be achieved by following the rules in this document, the employer is not precluded from following them.

(2) Installations of railways for generation, transformation, transmission, or distribution of power used exclusively for operation of rolling stock or installations used exclusively for signaling and communications purposes

Note that the exemption in 90.2(B)(2) applies only to utility-type systems used solely for rolling stock and not for premises wiring systems. For example, general lighting for a railroad yard is covered by this standard. If an employer in a railroad yard determines that the desired level of safety can be achieved by following the rules in this document, the employer is not precluded from following them.

(3) Installations of communications equipment under the exclusive control of communications utilities located outdoors or in building spaces used exclusively for such installations

Communication equipment installations under the control of private entities that are not utilities and premises wiring systems within building spaces used by utilities solely for communications equipment do not fall under the exemption in 90.2(B)(3). Interaction with this equipment is not exempt from the safe work practices of this standard.

(4) Installations under the exclusive control of an electric utility where such installations:

    a. Consist of service drops or service laterals, and associated metering, or

    b. Are located in legally established easements or rights-of-way designated by or recognized by public service commissions, utility commissions, or other regulatory agencies having jurisdiction for such installations, or

    c. Are on property owned or leased by the electric utility for the purpose of communications, metering, generation, control, transformation, transmission, or distribution of electric energy, or

    d. Are located by other written agreements either designated by or recognized by public service commissions, utility commissions, or other regulatory agencies having jurisdiction for such installations. These written agreements shall be limited to installations for the purpose of communications, metering, generation, control, transformation, transmission, or distribution of electric energy where legally established easements or rights-of-way cannot be obtained. These installations shall be limited to federal lands, Native American reservations through the U.S. Department of the Interior Bureau of Indian Affairs, military bases, lands controlled by port authorities and state agencies and departments, and lands owned by railroads.

Wherever an apparatus is owned by and is under the sole control of a utility company, the utility exemption in 90.2(B)(4) goes into effect, and the utility company is not required to follow the safe work procedures for qualified persons in this standard. However, for persons who are not qualified to work under the work procedures specifically applicable to a utility, OSHA's general industry safety-related work procedure rules would apply and, therefore, the safe work rules in this standard would apply.

90.3 Standard Arrangement.

This standard is divided into the introduction and three chapters, as shown in Figure 90.3. Chapter 1 applies generally, Chapter 2 addresses safety-related maintenance requirements, and Chapter 3 supplements or modifies Chapter 1 with safety requirements for special equipment.

    Informative annexes are not part of the requirements of this standard but are included for informational purposes only.

The arrangement of this standard is such that the purpose and scope are given up front, followed by the common rules with support material, and then the rules for more defined subject areas. At the end of the standard are the informative annexes, which include explanatory material covering specific subjects in detail.

    Chapter 1, Safety-Related Work Practices, is the heart of the standard. It provides general definitions, rules, and guidelines for electrically safe work practices. Chapter 2 deals with the maintenance necessary to ensure electrical safety from potential exposure to electrical hazards. The requirements contained in Chapter 1 and Chapter 2 generally apply to electrical safety in all workplaces.

    Chapter 3 covers the unique and distinctive types of electrical equipment and systems in the workplace, as well as unique and distinctive workplace locations that call for specialized procedures. When the rules identified in Chapter 1 might result in unsafe

OSHA Connection

29 CFR 1910.269 Appendix A-2
Subpart S (Electrical) applies to unqualified utility workers (as defined in 1910.399) not covered under 1910.269 (Electric Power Generation, Transmission, and Distribution).

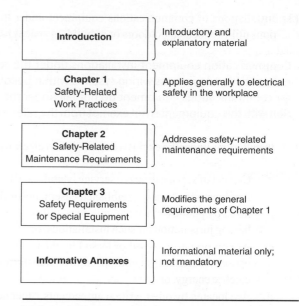

FIGURE 90.3 *Standard Arrangement.*

conditions due to unique or unusual situations, Chapter 3 changes or modifies the work procedures to achieve the same goal—establishing safe work practices for employees while accommodating unique or unusual circumstances.

The informative annexes provide additional, nonmandatory, explanatory material. Each informative annex covers a separate and distinctive subject area.

90.4 Mandatory Rules, Permissive Rules, and Explanatory Material.

(A) Mandatory Rules. Mandatory rules of this standard are those that identify actions that are specifically required or prohibited and are characterized by the use of the terms *shall* or *shall not.*

Mandatory rules either compel or bar an action by the employee or by the employer. Mandatory rules in NFPA *70E* are necessary to keep employees safe in work environments. They are particularly important when the risk of an incident caused by electrical hazards is determined to be unacceptable.

(B) Permissive Rules. Permissive rules of this standard are those that identify actions that are allowed but not required, are normally used to describe options or alternative methods, and are characterized by the use of the terms *shall be permitted or shall not be required.*

Permissive rules are options or alternative methods for achieving equivalent safety; they are not requirements. Permissive rules use mandatory language and, as such, constitute rules by using phrases such as "shall be permitted" or "shall not be required." A close reading of permissive phrases is important because permissive rules are often misinterpreted. For example, the permissive phrase "shall be permitted" can be mistaken for a requirement. Substituting "[method A] is allowed" for "[method A] shall be permitted" generally clarifies the interpretation. When evaluating choices among the options permitted, employers should make sure that the option they select does not increase the risk of injury from a potential electrical hazard above what is considered to be acceptable.

CHAPTER

1

Safety-Related Work Practices

ARTICLE 100 Definitions

ARTICLE 105 Application of Safety-Related Work Practices and Procedures

ARTICLE 110 General Requirements for Electrical Safety-Related Work Practices

ARTICLE 120 Establishing an Electrically Safe Work Condition

ARTICLE 130 Work Involving Electrical Hazards

Employees interacting with or working near energized electrical conductors and circuit parts can be exposed to an unacceptable level of risk of injury from electrical hazards. This exposure can result in an electrical shock injury, electrocution, an arc flash burn or thermal burn, injury from molten metal, a shrapnel or pressure blast, or a secondary injury as the result of a fall or from trying to avoid exposure.

Where electricity is used in the workplace, NFPA *70E®, Standard for Electrical Safety in the Workplace®,* provides the safety-related work rules necessary to eliminate or reduce the risk associated with potential exposure to electrical hazards to an acceptable level. A hazard (or source of possible injury) is separate from a risk (a combination of the likelihood and severity of an injury). Not all hazards present risk to employees. Not all levels of risk are unacceptable. The hazard and risk terminology in NFPA *70E* is consistent with other national and international standards.

Electrical safety is like a three-legged stool. One leg depends on a safe installation. *NFPA 70®, National Electrical Code® (NEC®),* stipulates the installation rules necessary to ensure that an electrical installation is safe to operate. The NEC establishes safe installation rules for premises wiring systems for residential, commercial, institutional, industrial, and certain utility facilities.

For the second leg of the stool, these electrical installations are kept safe by following the preventive maintenance recommendations required by the manufacturer or those included in NFPA 70B, *Recommended Practice for Electrical Equipment Maintenance.* The preventive maintenance program for a facility must include an inspection and testing program that is overseen by competent personnel. Electrical equipment must be maintained for it to be safely operated under normal conditions.

The third leg of the stool is NFPA *70E,* which addresses the protection of workers when they are exposed to electrical hazards. NFPA *70E* provides the employer with the direction required to create an electrical safety program (ESP) for the facility. With the employer's ESP following the rules laid out in NFPA *70E,* the employees should be able to select and execute the safety-related work procedures required when the electrical equipment they are interacting with is in other than a normal operating condition.

NFPA 70®
National Electrical Code®
Stipulates the **installation rules** necessary to assure that an electrical installation is safe to operate.

NFPA 70B
Recommended Practice for Electrical Equipment Maintenance
Provides **preventive maintenance** recommendations for electrical systems and equipment

NFPA 70E®
Standard for Electrical Safety in the Workplace®
Provides the requirements to establish a **practical safe working area** for employees relative to the hazards arising from the use of electricity.

Chapter 1 of NFPA *70E* consists of five articles that include the necessary information and essential safety-related work procedures required for employees to work safely where there is an unacceptable risk of injury from exposure to electrical hazards in the workplace. The information and safety-related work procedures included in NFPA *70E* should form the basis of the employer's ESP. The following is a brief description of each article:

- Article 100 offers the terms and definitions necessary to understand this standard.
- Article 105 establishes the overall scope, purpose, and organization of Chapter 1 and distinguishes the responsibilities of employers and employees.
- Article 110 covers the overall requirements for formulating and implementing an electrical safety program, including policies, risk assessments, employee training, program and field auditing, documenting, and the relationships between the types of employers.
- Article 120 provides the information necessary to create an electrically safe work condition (ESWC). It provides the requirements to establish a lockout/tagout program for a facility where electrical hazards are present.
- Article 130 defines the situations under which an ESWC must be established. It also describes the situations under which energized electrical work can be justified and the requirements for working safely with energized electrical equipment.

Definitions

Article 100 contains the definitions of technical terms considered fundamental to the proper understanding of key requirements in this standard. Although these terms might be used or defined differently in another standard, these definitions apply within the scope of NFPA *70E®, Standard for Electrical Safety in the Workplace®*. Understanding the vocabulary used in this standard is crucial to comprehending its requirements. When discussing a requirement, the parties involved must know the intended meaning of each term. This common understanding can increase electrical safety in the workplace. Many of the defined terms included in NFPA *70E* are taken directly from NFPA *70®, National Electrical Code®* (*NEC®*). The definition of each term extracted from the NEC is identified by a bracketed reference of [**70**:100], which indicates that it comes from Article 100 of that document.

Scope. This article contains only those definitions essential to the proper application of this standard. It is not intended to include commonly defined general terms or commonly defined technical terms from related codes and standards. In general, only those terms that are used in two or more articles are defined in Article 100. Other definitions are included in the article in which they are used but may be referenced in Article 100. The definitions in this article shall apply wherever the terms are used throughout this standard.

Official NFPA definitions are under the purview of the NFPA Standards Council, not the committee that is responsible for this document. Official definitions are the same in all NFPA documents. Many NFPA documents rely on or cross-reference each other, and having official definitions facilitates consistency across documents. Commonly defined general terms are not defined in NFPA *70E* unless they are used in a unique or restricted manner. General terms can be found in nontechnical dictionaries. Commonly defined technical terms, such as volt and ampere, can be found in ANSI/IEEE 100, *IEEE Standard Dictionary of Electrical and Electronics Terms*.

Not all definitions are included in Article 100. Additional definitions can be found in Chapters 2 and 3 within the articles in which they are used. For example, the definitions applicable to lasers can be found in 330.2, Definitions. An understanding of the definitions is paramount to understanding the rules in this standard.

Accessible (as applied to equipment). Admitting close approach; not guarded by locked doors, elevation, or other effective means. [**70**:100]

Access to equipment is necessary for operation, maintenance, and service, but this definition can also be used to identify equipment that is accessible to unqualified persons. If a person has no impediment to reaching a piece of equipment, the equipment is considered accessible.

Approved. Acceptable to the authority having jurisdiction

This is an NFPA official definition. See the definition for the term *authority having jurisdiction (AHJ)* for a better understanding of the approval process. An understanding of terms such as *listed* and *labeled* can help the user understand the approval process. Typically, approval of listed equipment is more readily given by an AHJ where the authority accepts a laboratory's listing mark. Other options might be available for the jurisdiction to approve equipment, including evaluation by the inspection authority or field evaluation by a qualified laboratory or individual. NFPA 790, *Standard for Competency of Third-Party Field Evaluation Bodies,* can be used to qualify evaluation services. NFPA 791, *Recommended Practice and Procedures for Uniabeled Electrical Equipment Evaluation,* can be used to evaluate unlabeled equipment in accordance with nationally recognized standards and the requirements of the AHJ.

The importance of the role of the AHJ in the North American safety system cannot be overstated. The AHJ verifies that an installation complies with the standard, or, in the case of NFPA *70E,* that the established work procedure complies with the standard. The definition of the term *authority having jurisdiction* and its accompanying informational note can help users understand code enforcement and the inspection process.

Arc Flash Hazard. A source of possible injury or damage to health associated with the release of energy caused by an electric arc.

> Informational Note No. 1: The likelihood of occurrence of an arc flash incident increases when energized electrical conductors or circuit parts are exposed or when they are within equipment in a guarded or enclosed condition, provided a person is interacting with the equipment in such a manner that could cause an electric arc. An arc flash incident is not likely to occur under normal operating conditions when enclosed energized equipment has been properly installed and maintained. See 110.4(D) for further information.

> Informational Note No. 2: See Table 130.5(C) for examples of tasks that increase the likelihood of an arc flash incident occurring.

An arc flash hazard exists if a person is or might be exposed to a significant thermal hazard. A significant thermal hazard is one with an incident (thermal) energy of 1.2 cal/cm² or more. Note that 1.2 cal/cm² is considered to be the energy level necessary for the onset of a second-degree burn. The minimum requirements of this consensus standard use 1.2 cal/cm² because there is a probability that the affected employee will not suffer a permanent physical injury.

Merriam-Webster's Collegiate Dictionary defines a second-degree burn as "a burn marked by pain, blistering, and superficial destruction of dermis with edema and hyperemia of the tissues beneath the burn." This type of burn results in red, white, or splotchy skin, as well as swelling, pain, and blisters. A second-degree burn penetrates the second layer of skin. When the first layer is destroyed, it separates from the second layer. The raw nerves in the second skin layer make this burn painful. If a second-degree burn is larger than 3 inches in diameter or is on a person's hands, feet, face, groin, buttocks, or a major joint, the Mayo Clinic suggests treating it as a major burn and seeking immediate medical help. Exhibit 100.1 illustrates the damage to the skin layers resulting from a second-degree burn caused by an arc flash.

Exhibit 100.2 shows an arc flash incident from the initial fault to the expiration of the arc. An arc flash incident can result in intense heat, shrapnel, molten metal, intense light, poisonous oxides, and pressure waves.

Arc Flash Suit. A complete arc-rated clothing and equipment system that covers the entire body, except for the hands and feet.

> Informational Note: An arc flash suit may include pants or overalls, a jacket or a coverall, and a beekeeper-type hood fitted with a face shield.

EXHIBIT 100.1

Skin damage from a second-degree burn.

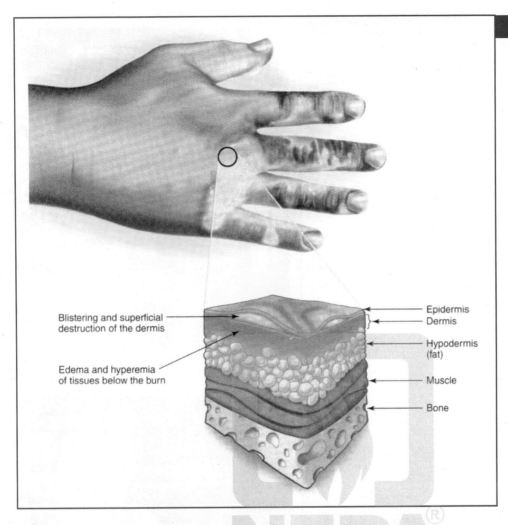

Blistering and superficial destruction of the dermis

Edema and hyperemia of tissues below the burn

Epidermis
Dermis
Hypodermis (fat)
Muscle
Bone

An arc flash suit is a complete system that must be evaluated. The suit is not a combination of components that have been evaluated individually. Exhibit 100.3 shows an employee in a 40 cal/cm² arc flash suit with other necessary PPE for the assigned task. An arc flash suit does not provide protection for an employee's hands and feet, which must also be covered by adequate arc-fault protective equipment as shown in the exhibit.

Δ **Arc Rating.** The value attributed to materials that describes their performance to exposure to an electrical arc discharge. The arc rating is expressed in cal/cm² and is derived from the determined value of the arc thermal performance value (ATPV) or energy of breakopen threshold (E_{BT}) (should a material system exhibit a breakopen response below the ATPV value). Arc rating is reported as either ATPV or E_{BT}, whichever is the lower value.

> Informational Note No. 1: Arc-rated clothing or equipment indicates that it has been tested for exposure to an electric arc. Flame-resistant clothing without an arc rating has not been tested for exposure to an electric arc. All arc-rated clothing is also flame resistant.

> Informational Note No. 2: ATPV is defined in ASTM F1959/F1959M, *Standard Test Method for Determining the Arc Rating of Materials for Clothing,* as the incident energy (cal/cm²) on a material or a multilayer system of materials that results in a 50 percent probability that sufficient heat transfer through the tested specimen is predicted to cause the onset of a second degree skin burn injury based on the Stoll curve.

Worker Alert

Arc-rated PPE does not necessarily prevent injury. Arc-rated PPE that conforms to the applicable standards and that is properly rated for the anticipated incident energy should mitigate any burn injury you might receive from an arc flash incident so it is not permanent.

EXHIBIT 100.2

Photos of an arc flash.
(Courtesy of Westex)

Informational Note No. 3: E_{BT} is defined in ASTM F1959/F1959M, *Standard Test Method for Determining the Arc Rating of Materials for Clothing,* as the incident energy (cal/cm^2) on a material or a material system that results in a 50 percent probability of breakopen. Breakopen is a material response evidenced by the formation of one or more holes of a defined size [an area of 1.6 cm^2 (0.5 in.^{2}) or an opening of 2.5 cm (1.0 in.) in any dimension] in the innermost layer of arc-rated material that would allow thermal energy to pass through the material.

This definition correlates with the definitions in ASTM F1506, *Standard Performance Specification for Flame Resistant Textile Materials for Wearing Apparel for Use by Electrical Workers Exposed to Momentary Electric Arc and Related Thermal Hazards,* and ASTM F1891, *Standard Specification for Arc and Flame Resistant Rainwear.* The term *arc rated* (AR) is consistent with the terminology used in these ASTM standards and provides consistency for the selection of protective apparel.

Workers must wear AR clothing when within the arc flash boundary to reduce the risk of serious injury or death caused by an arc flash. Although all AR clothing is also flame resistant (FR), the inverse is not always true. FR clothing might not provide adequate protection against an arc flash. For electrical hazards, AR PPE is necessary rather than FR apparel because it has been specifically tested for protection against the thermal effects of an arc flash event.

Manufacturers determine the arc and flame ratings for protective equipment. For clothing to be considered flame resistant, the material must withstand ignition or self-extinguish. Additional tests are required to achieve an arc rating. For example, the material must be exposed to arc flashes to determine how much energy the material repels before the wearer would be subjected to a second-degree burn.

Labels on arc-rated clothing should include the rating, as shown in Exhibit 100.3. The arc rating should be visibly marked to ensure that the correctly rated gear is used. An arc flash PPE category marking alone (such as 1 or 3) is not an arc rating and is only appropriate when the arc flash risk assessment is conducted using the arc flash PPE category method.

Informational Notes No. 2 and No. 3 provide guidance on how the arc thermal performance value (ATPV) and the energy of the breakopen threshold (EBT) relate to the testing that is performed in accordance with ASTM F1959, *Standard Test Method for Determining the Arc Rating of Materials for Clothing.* The lower of these two values, as determined by testing, is the one that must be used to label the PPE. Arc flash PPE testing determines the incident energy level at which the PPE has a 50 percent probability of successfully preventing a second-degree burn. Properly rated PPE should limit the employee's injury to a second-degree burn when the PPE does not successfully withstand the incident energy presented. When arc-rated equipment is exposed to less than its rating, there can be a substantial increase in the probability of success.

Attachment Plug (Plug Cap) (Plug). A device that, by insertion in a receptacle, establishes a connection between the conductors of the attached flexible cord and the conductors connected permanently to the receptacle. [70:100]

The contact blades of general-purpose attachment plugs have specific shapes, sizes, and configurations so that the plug cannot be inserted into a receptacle or cord connector of a different voltage or current rating. Locking and non-locking attachment plugs are available with options such as integral switches, fuses, or ground-fault circuit-interrupter protection

Authority Having Jurisdiction (AHJ). An organization, office, or individual responsible for enforcing the requirements of a code or standard, or for approving equipment, materials, an installation, or a procedure

Informational Note: The phrase "authority having jurisdiction," or its acronym AHJ, is used in NFPA documents in a broad manner, since jurisdictions and approval agencies vary, as do their responsibilities. Where public safety is primary, the authority having jurisdiction may be a federal, state, local, or other regional department or individual such as a fire chief; fire marshal; chief of a fire prevciovn bureau, labor department, or health department; building official; electrical inspector; or others having statutory authority. For insurance purposes, an insurance inspection department, rating bureau, or other insurance company representative may be the authority having jurisdiction. In many circumstances, the property owner or his or her designated agent assumes the role of the authority having jurisdiction; at government installations, the commanding officer or departmental official may be the authority having jurisdiction.

This is an NFPA official definition. The AHJ, where electrical safety of employees is concerned, is the party (or parties) responsible for enforcing the electrical safety requirements of NFPA *70E*. This could be the designee of a federal or state governmental agency, the commanding officer of a military base, a party designated by the owner or operator of a facility, a party designated by an employer, a party from an insurance company inspection department, the employer or employee themselves, or a combination of several of these.

Typically, NFPA *70E* is not adopted as legislation; it is most often used voluntarily by employers to help fulfill their obligations to OSHA. Compliance with federal regulations is often not verified until an injury occurs. Throughout organizations, there are many people responsible for the various NFPA *70E* requirements. Employers must provide safety-related work practices and training for their employees. Employers must also verify that the appropriate PPE is issued to their employees.

Notwithstanding, employees are required to implement their employer's training and practices. They are also responsible for their own actions. By default, both the employer *and* the employee play the role of the AHJ when it comes to proactively implementing and enforcing the requirements of NFPA *70E*. Electrical safety is everyone's job

---

Worker Alert

Regardless of your employer's safety plan, it is you who has the biggest impact on your personal safety. You are responsible for your own actions, and ultimately, you are the AHJ solely responsible for final assurance that a task can be and is performed safely.

In some regard, everyone could be considered the AHJ at a facility, whether they are upper management, middle management, a supervisor, or an employee.

Automatic. Performing a function without the necessity of human intervention.

An automatic function or operation can be initiated mechanically. For instance, a high-pressure cutoff switch requires no human interaction to open the circuit when it detects high pressure.

△ **Balaclava.** An arc-rated head-protective fabric that protects the neck and head except for a small portion of the facial area.

> Informational Note: Some balaclava designs protect the neck and head area except for the eyes while others leave the eyes and nose area unprotected.

An arc-rated balaclava is shown in Exhibit 100.4. It fits tightly against the wearer's head and neck, leaving few air pockets between the balaclava and the wearer's skin. Only balaclavas having a tested arc rating in cal/cm^2 can be used to meet the requirements of NFPA *70 E*. Balaclavas intended only for warmth must not be worn as arc flash protection.

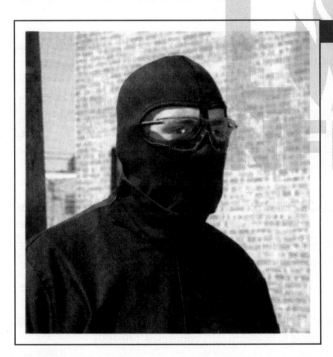

EXHIBIT 100.4

A balaclava sock hood made from two layers of rib knit material with an arc thermal performance value (ATPV) rating of 28 cal/cm^2. (Courtesy of Salisbury by Honeywell)

Barricade. A physical obstruction such as tapes, cones, or A-frame-type wood or metal structures intended to provide a warning and to limit access.

The purpose of a barricade is to provide a warning to approaching individuals that a hazardous condition exists. It is intended to limit the approach of persons to an unsafe area (see the definition of barrier). A barricade might consist of warning tape and cones as shown in Exhibit 100.5.

EXHIBIT 100.5

A barricade used to keep unqualified persons from an area. (Courtesy of The T-CAP/ www.TheTCap.com)

Δ **Barrier.** A physical obstruction that is intended to prevent contact with equipment or energized electrical conductors and circuit parts.

A barrier must have sufficient integrity to eliminate the chance of unsafe contact. A barrier constructed from voltage-rated materials might be in physical contact with an energized conductor. Barriers constructed of other materials—such as wood, metal, or fiberglass—are installed to prevent contact with energized conductors or circuit parts.

Bonded (Bonding). Connected to establish electrical continuity and conductivity. [**70**:100]

Bonding is establishing an electrical connection between the conductive elements of an electrical installation. Bonding does not necessarily rely on the presence of a ground connection

Bonding Conductor or Jumper. A reliable conductor to ensure the required electrical conductivity between metal parts required to be electrically connected. [**70**:100]

Either of the terms *bonding conductor or jumper* can be used. A bonding jumper is an electrical conductor that is installed to join discontinuous or potentially discontinuous portions of conductive elements. The primary purpose of a bonding jumper is to ensure electrical conductivity between two conductive bodies, such as a box and a metal raceway. The term *bonding jumper* is sometimes interpreted to mean a short conductor, although some bonding jumpers can be several feet in length.

Boundary, Arc Flash. When an arc flash hazard exists, an approach limit from an arc source at which incident energy equals 1.2 cal/cm^2 (5 J/cm^2).

> Informational Note: According to the Stoll skin burn injury model, the onset of a second degree burn on unprotected skin is likely to occur at an exposure of 1.2 cal/cm^2 (5 J/cm^2) for one second.

The arc flash boundary is determined either via calculation or by using the PPE category method tables. The arc flash boundary separates an area in which a person is likely to be exposed to a second-degree burn from an area in which the potential for injury does not likely include a second-degree burn. Arc flash burns can still occur outside the arc flash boundary, but they aren't likely to be second-degree burns or worse. The arc flash boundary can be thought of as existing when electrical equipment is in other than a normal operating state.

The minimum requirements of NFPA *70E* use 1.2 cal/cm^2 to set the arc flash boundary because that is the distance at which there is a probability that the employee will not suffer a permanent physical injury. See the commentary associated with the term *arc flash hazard* for further information regarding the arc flash hazard and second-degree burns.

All body parts that cross into the arc flash boundary must be protected from the potential thermal effects of the hazard. The arc flash boundary is independent of the shock protection limited approach and restricted approach boundaries. See 130.4(E) and its associated informational note for more information.

Exhibit 100.6 illustrates the three boundaries that must be determined using the risk assessments required by NFPA *70E*. The arc flash boundary might not always be the first boundary an employee crosses when assigned a task.

Boundary, Limited Approach. An approach limit at a distance from an exposed energized electrical conductor or circuit part within which a shock hazard exists.

The limited approach boundary is a shock protection boundary that is not related to arc flash or incident energy. The arc flash boundary might be greater than, less than, or equal to the limited approach boundary. This shock protection boundary is the approach limit for unqualified employees and is intended to eliminate the risk of contact with an exposed energized electrical conductor or circuit part. Exhibit 100.6 illustrates the three boundaries that must be determined using the risk assessments required by NFPA *70E*.

Boundary, Restricted Approach. An approach limit at a distance from an exposed energized electrical conductor or circuit part within which there is an increased likelihood of electric shock, due to electrical arc-over combined with inadvertent movement

The restricted approach boundary is a shock protection boundary that is not related to arc flash or incident energy. The arc flash boundary might be greater than, less than, or equal to the restricted approach boundary. This shock protection boundary is the approach limit for qualified employees. If a qualified employee crosses the restricted approach boundary, they must be protected from unexpected contact with the conductors or circuit parts that are energized and exposed. Exhibit 100.6 illustrates the three boundaries that must be determined using the risk assessments required by NFPA *70E*.

Building. A structure that stands alone or that is cut off from adjoining structures by fire walls with all openings therein protected by approved fire doors. [**70**:100]

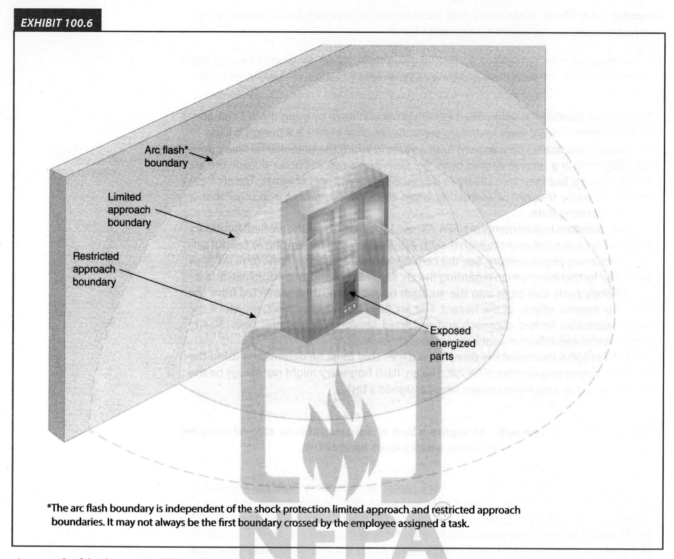

EXHIBIT 100.6

*The arc flash boundary is independent of the shock protection limited approach and restricted approach boundaries. It may not always be the first boundary crossed by the employee assigned a task.

An example of the three approach boundaries addressed by NFPA 70E.

Generally, a building is any roofed or walled structure that is intended to support or shelter any use or occupancy. However, a separate structure, such as a billboard or radio tower, might also be considered a building. In general, a fire wall is a wall with a fire resistance rating and structural stability that separates buildings or subdivides a building to prevent the spread of fire.

Cabinet. An enclosure that is designed for either surface mounting or flush mounting and is provided with a frame, mat, or trim in which a swinging door or doors are or can be hung. [**70:**100]

Cabinets are enclosures in which electrical assemblies, such as panelboards, are installed to enclose energized electrical conductors and circuit parts under normal equipment operating conditions.

Circuit Breaker. A device designed to open and close a circuit by nonautomatic means and to open the circuit automatically on a predetermined overcurrent without damage to itself when properly applied within its rating. [**70**:100]

> Informational Note: The automatic opening means can be integral, direct acting with the circuit breaker, or remote from the circuit breaker.

Conductive. Suitable for carrying electric current.

> The term *conductive* refers to any material that is capable of conducting an electrical current. If a material does not have an established voltage rating—as with voltage-rated rubber products—the material should be considered conductive.

Conductor, Bare. A conductor having no covering or electrical insulation whatsoever. [**70**:100]

Δ **Conductor, Covered.** A conductor encased within material of composition or thickness that is not recognized by *NFPA 70, National Electrical Code,* as electrical insulation. [**70**:100]

> An uninsulated grounded system conductor within an overall exterior jacket of a Type SE cable is an example of a covered conductor. Covered conductors often resemble insulated conductors, but they should always be treated as bare conductors because the covering does not have an assigned insulation or voltage rating. Examples of where covered conductors can be used include busbars and overhead service conductors. See the definition and commentary for conductor, insulated for more information.

Δ **Conductor, Insulated.** A conductor encased within material of composition and thickness that is recognized by *NFPA 70, National Electrical Code,* as electrical insulation. [**70**:100]

> For the covering of a conductor to be considered insulation, it must pass the minimum testing required by the appropriate product standard. One such product standard is UL 83, *Thermoplastic-Insulated Wires and Cables.* Only wires and cables that meet the minimum fire, electrical, and physical properties required by the applicable standards are permitted to be marked with the letter designations found in the *NEC.* Unless a voltage rating is marked on the insulation, a conductor should be considered a covered conductor.

Controller. A device or group of devices that serves to govern, in some predetermined manner, the electric power delivered to the apparatus to which it is connected. [**70**:100]

> A controller can be a remote-controlled magnetic contactor, variable frequency drive, switch, circuit breaker, or another device that is normally used to start and stop motors and other apparatus. Stop-and-start stations and similar control circuit components that do not open power conductors to the motor are not considered controllers.

Current-Limiting Overcurrent Protective Device. A device that, when interrupting currents in its current-limiting range, reduces the current flowing in the faulted circuit to a magnitude substantially less than that obtainable in the same circuit if the device were replaced with a solid conductor having comparable impedance.

One important circuit characteristic that affects incident energy is the level of the arcing current, which is dependent on the available fault current. Limiting the amount of current (energy) that is permitted through an overcurrent device during a faulted condition reduces the amount of available incident energy during an arcing fault. Installing a current-limiting overcurrent protective device is one method to reduce incident energy.

The *NEC* recognizes two levels of overcurrent protection: branch-circuit overcurrent protection and supplementary overcurrent protection. Contrary to the name, branch-circuit overcurrent protective devices are used to protect service, feeder, and branch circuits. Supplementary devices are always used in addition to branch-circuit overcurrent protective devices.

Cutout. An assembly of a fuse support with either a fuseholder, fuse carrier, or disconnecting blade. The fuseholder or fuse carrier may include a conducting element (fuse link), or may act as the disconnecting blade by the inclusion of a nonfusible member.

A cutout is usually associated with the protection of a distribution conductor similar to those commonly used in utility distribution systems.

De-energized. Free from any electrical connection to a source of potential difference and from electrical charge; not having a potential different from that of the earth.

The term *de-energized* describes the condition of electrical equipment and should not be used for other purposes. De-energized does not describe a safe condition.

Device. A unit of an electrical system, other than a conductor, that carries or controls electric energy as its principal function. [**70**:100]

Switches, circuit breakers, fuseholders, receptacles, attachment plugs, and lampholders that distribute or control but do not consume electricity are considered devices. Components that consume incidental amounts of energy, such as a ground-fault circuit-interrupter (GFCI) receptacle with a pilot light, are also considered devices

Disconnecting Means. A device, or group of devices, or other means by which the conductors of a circuit can be disconnected from their source of supply. [**70**:100]

Disconnecting means can be one or more switches, circuit breakers, or other rated devices that are used to disconnect electrical conductors from their source of energy. Only a disconnecting means that is load rated should be used to disconnect an operating load.

Disconnecting (or Isolating) Switch (Disconnector, Isolator). A mechanical switching device used for isolating a circuit or equipment from a source of power.

Disconnecting switches are intended to be operated after interrupting and removing the load current.

Dwelling Unit. A single unit providing complete and independent living facilities for one or more persons, including permanent provisions for living, sleeping, cooking, and sanitation. [**70**:100]

Electrical Hazard. A dangerous condition such that contact or equipment failure can result in electric shock, arc flash burn, thermal burn, or arc blast injury.

> Informational Note: Class 2 power supplies, listed low voltage lighting systems, and similar sources are examples of circuits or systems that are not considered an electrical hazard.

Although this definition includes four separate hazards, NFPA *70E* currently addresses only two of them directly—electric shock and arc flash burns. As part of the risk assessment, it is necessary to determine the need for and an appropriate method of protecting employees from the other hazards. Other known arcing fault hazards include flying parts, molten metal, intense light, poisonous oxides, and generated pressure waves (blasts). Additional electrical hazards could be associated with arcing faults.

Power-limited circuits are not normally considered electrical hazards, and electrical equipment energized at less than 50 volts is not normally considered an arc flash hazard. However, the effects of an arcing fault are related to the available incident energy. In some instances, such as with a 48-volt battery bank, the arcing fault hazard might be significant at a lower voltage.

> **Worker Alert**
>
> The requirements of this standard protect you from two of the recognized electrical hazards—electric shock and arc flash burn. There are other hazards associated with electrical energy, some of which are not fully understood. There is no public consensus on the methods for determining these other hazards or on the methods of protecting you from them.

Electrical Safety. Identifying hazards associated with the use of electrical energy and taking precautions to reduce the risk associated with those hazards.

Electrical safety is a condition that can be achieved by doing the following:

- Identifying all of the electrical hazards
- Generating a comprehensive plan to mitigate exposure to the hazards
- Providing protective schemes, including training for both qualified and unqualified persons

Electrical Safety Program. A documented system consisting of electrical safety principles, policies, procedures, and processes that directs activities appropriate for the risk associated with electrical hazards.

An electrical safety program is the all-encompassing term for an employer's documented system of evaluating hazards and providing the appropriate actions necessary to protect employees from electrical injuries. Refer to 110.5 for the required elements of an electrical safety program and Annex E for descriptions of safety principles, controls, and procedures.

Electrically Safe Work Condition. A state in which an electrical conductor or circuit part has been disconnected from energized parts, locked/tagged in accordance with established standards, tested to verify the absence of voltage, and, if necessary, temporarily grounded for personnel protection.

> Informational Note: An electrically safe work condition is not a procedure, it is a state wherein all hazardous electrical conductors or circuit parts to which a worker might be exposed are maintained in a de-energized state for the purpose of temporarily eliminating electrical hazards for the period of time for which the state is maintained.

Establishing an electrically safe work condition (ESWC) is the only work procedure that ensures that an electrical injury will not occur. However, verifying the absence of voltage is an activity where the risk of injury from electrical hazards is unacceptable. Until an ESWC is established, an unacceptable risk of injury exists and employees must be protected from the hazards present.

Enclosed. Surrounded by a case, housing, fence, or wall(s) that prevents persons from unintentionally contacting energized parts.

Enclosure. The case or housing of apparatus—or the fence or walls surrounding an installation to prevent personnel from unintentionally contacting energized electrical conductors or circuit parts or to protect the equipment from physical damage.

Enclosures are required to be marked with numbers that identify the environmental conditions for which they can be used. NEC Table 110.28 summarizes the intended uses of the various standard types of enclosures rated 1000 volts nominal or less for nonhazardous locations. Enclosures that comply with the requirements for more than one type might be marked with multiple designations.

Energized. Electrically connected to, or is, a source of voltage. [**70:**100]

The term *energized* is associated with all voltage levels, not just those levels that present a shock hazard. Energized equipment and devices are also not limited to those that are connected to a source of electricity. Batteries, capacitors, circuits with induced voltages, and photovoltaic systems must also be considered energized. In addition, electrolytic processes are considered energized.

Equipment. A general term, including fittings, devices, appliances, luminaires, apparatus, machinery, and the like, used as a part of, or in connection with, an electrical installation. [**70:**100]

Equipment, Arc-Resistant. Equipment designed to withstand the effects of an internal arcing fault and that directs the internally released energy away from the employee.

> Informational Note No. 1: An example of a standard that provides information for arc-resistant equipment is IEEE C37.20.7, *Guide for Testing Switchgear Rated Up to 52 kV for Internal Arcing Faults.*
>
> Informational Note No. 2: See O.2.4(9) for information on arc-resistant equipment.

Only equipment specifically identified as being arc-resistant can provide protection from an internal arcing fault when the equipment is closed and operating normally. If doors and covers (including fasteners) are not completely closed, employees can be exposed to the hazards associated with an arcing fault just as if no arc-resistant rating existed. Exhibit 100.7 shows an example of arc-resistant equipment and metal-clad equipment.

Exposed (as applied to energized electrical conductors or circuit parts). Capable of being inadvertently touched or approached nearer than a safe distance by a person. It is applied to electrical conductors or circuit parts that are not suitably guarded, isolated, or insulated.

Arc-resistant switchgear   Metal-clad switchgear

Some electrical equipment contains conductors that are uncovered and guarded only by the enclosure. Wires and tools inserted through equipment ventilation openings could contact energized conductors; therefore, the level of exposure must be determined based on the equipment, the task to be performed, and the associated tools.

Some panelboards are equipped with an internal cover. Once the outer cover is removed, the wiring gutter is accessible. However, inadvertent contact cannot be prevented by the internal cover, and the conductors and circuit parts will still be considered exposed.

Exposed (as applied to wiring methods). On or attached to the surface or behind panels designed to allow access. [**70:**100]

Wiring methods located above lift-out ceiling panels are considered exposed.

Fault Current. The amount of current delivered at a point on the system during a short-circuit condition.

A fault current is a current that leaves the intended circuit path to return to the source of the supply. The term, as used in this standard, refers to an abnormal current beyond the usual range within the circuit. In the electrical industry, a fault current is often referred to as a short-circuit current.

Fault Current, Available. The largest amount of current capable of being delivered at a point on the system during a short-circuit condition.

Informational Note No. 1: A short circuit can occur during abnormal conditions such as a fault between circuit conductors or a ground fault. See Figure 100.0.

ac or dc supply source → Source

Available fault current →

Available fault current →

Equipment

Equipment with a short-circuit current rating →

OCPD

Overcurrent protective device with an interrupting rating →

Available fault current →

Load

△ **FIGURE 100.0** *Available Fault Current*

Informational Note No. 2: If the dc supply is a battery system, the term *available fault current* refers to the prospective short-circuit current.

Informational Note No. 3: The available fault current varies at different locations within the system due to the location of sources and system impedances.

Fitting. An accessory such as a locknut, bushing, or other part of a wiring system that is intended primarily to perform a mechanical rather than an electrical function. [**70:**100]

Examples of fittings include condulets, conduit couplings, electrical metallic tubing (EMT) couplings, and threadless connectors.

Fuse. An overcurrent protective device with a circuit-opening fusible part that is heated and severed by the passage of overcurrent through it.

Informational Note: A fuse comprises all the parts that form a unit capable of performing the prescribed functions. It may or may not be the complete device necessary to connect it into an electrical circuit.

Ground. The earth. [**70:**100]

The term *ground* is commonly used in North America. For installations within the scope of the *NEC*, ground literally refers to the earth, which is used as a reference point to establish system potential and to limit line surges. In some electronic circuits, the term is used to describe a reference point, which might not be the ground (earth).

Ground Fault. An unintentional, electrically conductive connection between an ungrounded conductor of an electrical circuit and the normally non-current-carrying conductors, metallic enclosures, metallic raceways, metallic equipment, or earth. [**70**:100]

Any fault is unintentional and normally unexpected. A fault results in an electrical current being imposed on an unintended circuit, which could include a person. One of the primary purposes of grounding an electrical system is to provide a path for a fault current that excludes a person.

Two types of faults can occur in an electrical circuit—a bolted fault and an arcing fault—and each type results in different hazardous conditions. An example of a bolted fault is a de-energized circuit with safety grounds installed for maintenance purposes that is then re-energized with the safety grounds still in place. The most common type of fault is an arcing fault, which might result from a conductive object falling into the circuit or from a component failure.

Bolted faults and arcing faults exhibit different characteristics and present different hazards. The primary hazard associated with a bolted fault is shock or electrocution. If a bolted fault exists for too long, the mechanical force or pressure produced by the current can cause conductors to move significantly, resulting in an arcing fault. An arcing fault is normally associated with a thermal and physical hazard. Arcing faults can also present a shock or electrocution hazard.

Grounded (Grounding). Connected (connecting) to ground or to a conductive body that extends the ground connection. [**70**:100]

Grounded, Solidly. Connected to ground without inserting any resistor or impedance device. [**70**:100]

Grounded Conductor. A system or circuit conductor that is intentionally grounded. [**70**:100]

In most instances, one conductor of an electrical circuit is intentionally connected to the earth. That conductor is the grounded conductor. A grounded system engages the overcurrent protective device in response to the first occurrence of a ground fault in a circuit. An equipment grounding conductor is not a grounded conductor.

Ground-Fault Circuit Interrupter (GFCI). A device intended for the protection of personnel that functions to de-energize a circuit or portion thereof within an established period of time when a current to ground exceeds the values established for a Class A device. [**70**:100]

Informational Note: Class A ground-fault circuit interrupters trip when the current to ground is 6 mA or higher and do not trip when the current to ground is less than 4 mA. For further information, see ANSI/UL 943, *Standard for Ground-Fault Circuit Interrupters.*

GFCI devices do not prevent shocks that could startle or cause the reflex action of a person. GFCI devices operate quickly in the 4 mA to 6 mA range to minimize the chance of electrocution or serious shock injury.

Exhibits 100.8 through 100.10 show examples of devices that provide GFCI protection.

A portable GFCI with open neutral protection that is designed for use on the line end of a flexible cord. (Courtesy of Legrand®)

A 15-ampere duplex receptacle with integral GFCI that also protects downstream loads. (Courtesy of Legrand®)

A temporary power outlet unit commonly used on construction sites with a variety of configurations, including GFCI protection. (Courtesy of Hubbeii Wiring Device-Kellems)

Grounding Conductor, Equipment (EGC). The conductive path(s) that provides a ground-fault current path and connects normally non-current-carrying metal parts of equipment together and to the system grounded conductor or to the grounding electrode conductor, or both. [**70**:100]

> Informational Note No. 1: It is recognized that the equipment grounding conductor also performs bonding.
>
> Informational Note No. 2: See 250.118 of *NFPA 70, National Electrical Code,* for a list of acceptable equipment grounding conductors.

Under normal conditions, a person typically must be exposed to a potential difference of 50 volts or more for a shock hazard to exist. One of the primary purposes of an EGC is reducing the potential difference (voltage) between surfaces that an employee is likely to touch, thereby minimizing the chance of shock injury or electrocution.

In a solidly grounded electrical system, the EGC also provides an effective ground-fault current path that facilitates the operation of circuit overcurrent protective devices when a ground fault occurs. This function of the EGC is extremely important for minimizing the duration of a ground fault in a circuit.

Grounding Electrode. A conducting object through which a direct connection to earth is established. [**70**:100]

Grounding Electrode Conductor. A conductor used to connect the system grounded conductor or the equipment to a grounding electrode or to a point on the grounding electrode system. [**70**:100

Guarded. Covered, shielded, fenced, enclosed, or otherwise protected by means of suitable covers, casings, barriers, rails, screens, mats, or platforms to remove the likelihood of approach or contact by persons or objects to a point of danger. [**70**:100]

It is unlikely that people or objects will contact equipment, circuits, or conductors that are guarded. Although guarding provides protection from exposure to shock or electrocution, it is still possible for persons to be exposed to arc flash hazards. The fenced-in substation shown in Exhibit 100.11 effectively removes the likelihood of approach or contact by unauthorized persons.

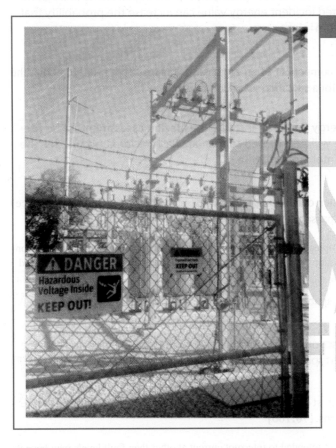

EXHIBIT 100.11

An equipment enclosure. This equipment is said to be guarded.

Hazard. A source of possible injury or damage to health.

Hazards can refer to all of the aspects of technology, environmental factors, and activities that create risk. In addition, ANSI/AIHA Z10, *American National Standard for Occupational Health and Safety Management Systems,* defines a hazard as a condition, set of circumstances, or inherent property that can cause injury, illness, or death.

Hazardous. Involving exposure to at least one hazard.

Incident Energy. The amount of thermal energy impressed on a surface, a certain distance from the source, generated during an electrical arc event. Incident energy is typically expressed in calories per square centimeter (cal/cm^2).

Science and testing have proven that an energy of 1.2 cal/cm² is sufficient to cause a 2nd-degree burn to exposed skin. NFPA *70E* covers electrical safety practices, and as such, it does not dictate the use of a particular method of calculating incident energy. Incident energy calculations are based on thermal energy only. ASTM standards require PPE ratings to be in calories per square centimeter (cal/cm²) rather than joules per square centimeter, joules per meter squared, or calories per square inch. Regardless of the unit of measurement, the selection of proper PPE dictates that the incident energy and PPE thermal ratings be expressed using the same unit.

Predicting the amount of available incident energy is crucial when selecting the appropriate PPE. Properly rated PPE can prevent injury, melting or burning of clothing, and direct skin exposure due to the increased temperature during an arcing fault. Using PPE rated above the calculated incident energy value can increase the probability that the employee is protected from injury.

Incident Energy Analysis. A component of an arc flash risk assessment used to predict the incident energy of an arc flash for a specified set of conditions.

The calculated incident energy from the installation-specific assessment is the predicted energy an employee will be exposed to if an arc flash incident occurs. See the commentary to 130.5(G) for more information.

Insulated. Separated from other conducting surfaces by a dielectric (including air space) offering a high resistance to the passage of current.

Informational Note: When an object is said to be insulated, it is understood to be insulated for the conditions to which it is normally subject. Otherwise, it is, within the purpose of these rules, uninsulated.

Interrupter Switch. A switch capable of making, carrying, and interrupting specified currents.

An interrupter switch is a disconnecting means rated to interrupt the load current. The manufacturer's product label typically provides the interrupting rating of the switch.

Interrupting Rating. The highest current at rated voltage that a device is identified to interrupt under standard test conditions. [**70**:100]

Informational Note: Equipment intended to interrupt current at other than fault levels may have its interrupting rating implied in other ratings, such as horsepower or locked rotor current.

An interrupting rating is generally expressed in root-mean-square (rms) symmetrical amperes and is specified as a fault current magnitude only. Where instantaneous phase trip elements are used, the interrupting capacity is the maximum rating of the device with no intentional delay. Where instantaneous phase trip elements are not used, the interrupting capacity is the maximum rating of the device for the rated time interval. Circuit breakers also have a short-time current rating, which is the ability of the breaker to remain closed for a specified time interval under high fault current conditions. The short-time rating is used to determine the ability of the circuit breaker to protect itself and other devices and to coordinate with other circuit breakers so the system will trip selectively. Exhibit 100.12 depicts the label of a 225-ampere frame circuit breaker, which shows the interrupting capacity ratings.

Isolated (as applied to location). Not readily accessible to persons unless special means for access are used. [**70**:100]

> Isolated conductors, devices, and equipment are protected from accidental contact by an unqualified person, as a special means, such as a tool or key, is required to gain access. Standard tools, such as Phillips head screwdrivers, are not considered to be special means.

Labeled. Equipment or materials to which has been attached a label, symbol, or other identifying mark of an organization that is acceptable to the authority having jurisdiction and concerned with product evaluation, that maintains periodic inspection of production of labeled equipment or materials, and by whose labeling the manufacturer indicates compliance with appropriate standards or performance in a specified manner.

> This is an NFPA official definition. Labeled equipment, devices, and conductors have identifying marks to indicate that they meet the requirements defined by the appropriate standards. These marks are most often third-party symbols used to indicate that not only an evaluated sample complied with the standard, but that the production units continue to comply. The mark must be of an organization acceptable to the AHJ. Labeled equipment must be approved and used in accordance with instructions supplied as part of the labeling or listing. Exhibit 100.13 shows a motor control center label indicating a third-party evaluation that meets both United States and Canadian product standards.

Listed. Equipment, materials, or services included in a list published by an organization that is acceptable to the authority having jurisdiction and concerned with evaluation of products or services, that maintains periodic inspection of production of listed equipment or materials or periodic evaluation of services, and whose listing states that either the equipment, material, or service meets appropriate designated standards or has been tested and found suitable for a specified purpose.

Informational Note: The means for identifying listed equipment may vary for each organization concerned with product evaluation; some organizations do not recognize equipment as listed unless it is also labeled. The authority having jurisdiction should utilize the system employed by the listing organization to identify a listed product.

OSHA Connection

29 CFR 1910.7(b)

The term *nationally recognized testing laboratory (NRTL)* means an organization that is recognized by OSHA to test for safety and to list, label, or accept equipment or materials.

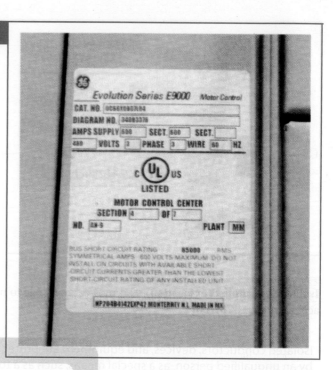

This is an NFPA official definition. Listing is the most common method of third-party evaluation of the safety of a product. These organizations evaluate equipment in accordance with the appropriate product standards and maintain lists of products that comply. NFPA codes and standards do not use the OSHA term *nationally recognized testing laboratory (NRTL)* because the acceptance of the listing organization is the responsibility of the AHJ. Even when not required by this standard, listed equipment is often employed to facilitate approval.

Luminaire. A complete lighting unit consisting of a light source, such as a lamp or lamps, together with the parts designed to position the light source and connect it to the power supply. It may also include parts to protect the light source or the ballast or to distribute the light. A lampholder itself is not a luminaire. [**70:**100]

Maintenance, Condition of. The state of the electrical equipment considering the manufacturers' instructions, manufacturers' recommendations, and applicable industry codes, standards, and recommended practices.

The condition of maintenance for a piece of equipment plays a major role in the safety of not only the maintenance employee, but also the person operating the equipment. Improperly maintained or damaged equipment cannot be assumed to function normally or to provide the protection for the operator that would be afforded by proper installation and maintenance.

Motor Control Center. An assembly of one or more enclosed sections having a common power bus and principally containing motor control units. [**70:**100]

A motor control center typically contains combination motor starters, fusible safety-disconnect switches, circuit breakers, power panels, solid-state drives, and similar components. A motor control center is not to be confused with switchgear or a switchboard. It is important to understand the difference when using Table 130.7(C)(15)(a) and Table 130.7(C)(15)(b) because the arc flash hazard PPE categories are based on the type of equipment and voltage level used.

Outlet. A point on the wiring system at which current is taken to supply utilization equipment. [**70**:100]

The term *outlet* is frequently misused to refer to receptacles. Although a receptacle is an outlet, not all outlets are receptacles. Other types of outlets include lighting outlets, smoke alarm outlets, and motor outlets.

Overcurrent. Any current in excess of the rated current of equipment or the ampacity of a conductor. It may result from overload, short circuit, or ground fault. [**70**:100]

> Informational Note: A current in excess of rating may be accommodated by certain equipment and conductors for a given set of conditions. Therefore, the rules for overcurrent protection are specific for particular situations.

Overload. Operation of equipment in excess of normal, full-load rating, or of a conductor in excess of rated ampacity that, when it persists for a sufficient length of time, would cause damage or dangerous overheating. A fault, such as a short circuit or ground fault, is not an overload. [**70**:100]

Panelboard. A single panel or group of panel units designed for assembly in the form of a single panel, including buses and automatic overcurrent devices, and equipped with or without switches for the control of light, heat, or power circuits; designed to be placed in a cabinet or cutout box placed in or against a wall, partition, or other support; and accessible only from the front. [**70**:100]

Premises Wiring (System). Interior and exterior wiring, including power, lighting, control, and signal circuit wiring together with all their associated hardware, fittings, and wiring devices, both permanently and temporarily installed. This includes: (a) wiring from the service point or power source to the outlets; or (b) wiring from and including the power source to the outlets where there is no service point.

Such wiring does not include wiring internal to appliances, luminaires, motors, controllers, motor control centers, and similar equipment. [**70**:100]

> Informational Note: Power sources include, but are not limited to, interconnected or stand-alone batteries, solar photovoltaic systems, other distributed generation systems, or generators.

Premises wiring includes all wiring downstream of the service point to the outlets. However, a premises wiring system does not have to be supplied by an electric utility. For example, a generator or photovoltaic system can supply a stand-alone premises wiring system. The premises wiring for these systems includes the power source as well as the wiring to the outlets.

Qualified Person. One who has demonstrated skills and knowledge related to the construction and operation of electrical equipment and installations and has received safety training to identify the hazards and reduce the associated risk.

In a broad context, any person doing any task should have the training necessary to perform that task, should know something about the equipment they are interacting with, and should understand how to avoid injury. Anyone interacting with or working around electrical equipment that is not under normal operating conditions [see 110.4(D) and the associated commentary] is at risk of injury from the use of electricity and should be qualified to perform their assigned tasks under the requirements of NFPA *70E*.

A qualified employee must understand the construction and operation of the equipment or circuit associated with a planned work task. An employee could be qualified to perform one work task and not be qualified to perform a different task on the same piece of equipment. An employee might also be qualified to work on one piece of equipment but not another similar piece of equipment.

Many state and local government licensing programs have training requirements that must be met for a person to be considered qualified. The applicant must be examined initially and then periodically after procuring a license. The license in and of itself does not make a person qualified, under the requirements of NFPA *70E,* for all the tasks or equipment they might encounter. For example, often, the licensing of electricians qualifies them to install electrical equipment in accordance with the *NEC,* but it might not qualify them to maintain that same equipment. Electrical work requires continuing education and demonstration of the skill necessary to work safely.

It might be helpful for employees to familiarize themselves with the following definitions:

- **Licensure.** The granting of licenses, especially to practice a profession or trade. *Note:* Licensure normally requires passing an examination and meeting certain qualifications. Where licensure is in effect, certain tasks or trades might only be performed by licensed individuals.

- **Certification.** The act of making something official. *Note:* Certification generally requires passing an examination and meeting certain qualifications. However, certifications are issued by private organizations, not by government entities; one example is the NFPA Certified Electrical Safety Compliance Professional certification. The value given to certification could depend upon the reputation of the organization issuing the certification.

- **Registration.** The act or process of adding names to an official list, thereby entitling the party to practice a profession, such as Registered Professional Electrical Engineer. *Note:* Registration is similar to licensure in that it requires passing an examination and meeting certain qualifications.

Part of being a qualified person is recognizing that energized electrical work is permitted only under the conditions specified in 110.4. A qualified person must understand the electrical hazards associated with the scheduled work task and must be able to react appropriately to all of the hazards associated with the task. They must be trained to understand and apply the details of the electrical safety program and procedures provided by their employer. A qualified person should also be able to understand risk assessments and the proper application and limitations of PPE. They must understand the limitations of test equipment, such as voltage testers; how to select the appropriate equipment; and how to apply that equipment to the planned work task.

The phrase "has demonstrated skills" requires that the person actually demonstrate the ability to perform a task. It might be necessary for them to demonstrate the ability to perform the task while using the appropriate PPE to ensure that the restricted lighting and field of view of the arc flash suit hood or the dexterity limitations of voltage-rated gloves with leather protectors do not hinder the employee

Raceway. An enclosed channel of metal or nonmetallic materials designed expressly for holding wires, cables, or busbars, with additional functions as permitted in this standard. [**70**:100]

Δ **Receptacle.** A contact device installed at the outlet for the connection of an attachment plug, or for the direct connection of electrical utilization equipment designed to mate with the corresponding contact device. A single receptacle is a single contact device with no other contact device on the same yoke. A multiple receptacle is two or more contact devices on the same yoke. [**70**:100]

The term receptacle is frequently misused. A receptacle is a device installed at an outlet. However, not all outlets are receptacle outlets. See the definition of outlet for more information

Risk. A combination of the likelihood of occurrence of injury or damage to health and the severity of injury or damage to health that results from a hazard.

Risk is not only the likelihood that an incident might occur but also includes the severity (i.e., seriousness) of the injury or damage that can result. A risk might have a high probability of an incident occurring, but the result could be a minor injury. Conversely, a risk might have a low likelihood of occurring but present the potential for severe injury. See the commentary on Informative Annex F for more information.

Risk Assessment. An overall process that identifies hazards, estimates the likelihood of occurrence of injury or damage to health, estimates the potential severity of injury or damage to health, and determines if protective measures are required.

Informational Note: As used in this standard, *arc flash risk assessment* and *shock risk assessment* are types of risk assessments.

A risk assessment is about risk mitigation, and it includes hazard identification. Implementing risk control requires the application of safety controls from the hierarchy of risk controls in accordance with the process required by 110.5(H)(3) and identified in Informative Annex F.

Service Drop. The overhead conductors between the utility electric supply system and the service point. [**70**:100]

The *NEC* contains requirements for the interface (service point) between the utility conductors (service drop or service lateral) and the premises conductors (overhead service conductors or overhead service entrance conductors).

Service Lateral. The underground conductors between the utility electric supply system and the service point. [**70**:100]

Service Point. The point of connection between the facilities of the serving utility and the premises wiring. [**70**:100]

Informational Note: The service point can be described as the point of demarcation between where the serving utility ends and the premises wiring begins. The serving utility generally specifies the location of the service point based on the conditions of service.

The service point is the point of demarcation on the wiring system where the serving utility ends and the premises wiring begins. It is the transition point where the rules of NFPA *70E* and the NEC apply. Only conductors physically located on the premises wiring side (load side) of the service point are covered by the NEC. The utility typically specifies the location of the service point. The exact location of a service point might vary from utility to utility, as well as from occupancy to occupancy. The service point might be at the transformer or substation for an industrial installation or at the weatherhead and drip loop for a small commercial occupancy. Exhibit 100.14 shows two examples of service point locations.

EXHIBIT 100.14

Examples of service point locations.

Shock Hazard. A source of possible injury or damage to health associated with current through the body caused by contact or approach to exposed energized electrical conductors or circuit parts.

Informational Note: Injury and damage to health resulting from shock is dependent on the magnitude of the electrical current, the power source frequency (e.g., 60 Hz, 50 Hz, dc), and the path and time duration of current through the body. The physiological reaction ranges from perception, muscular contractions, inability to let go, ventricular fibrillation, tissue bums, and death.

A person's tolerance to an electrical current through the body varies depending on the path of the current through the body and the applied voltage. The tolerance level also varies from person to person. A 60 Hz alternating electrical current occurring near 1 mA and 5 mA is the level typically considered to cause an involuntary reaction. Pain might be felt at a slightly higher current, and involuntary muscle contractions could occur around 20 mA. Direct current and higher frequencies can affect tolerance levels. Although exposure to any energized component can present a shock hazard, a shock hazard is generally considered to exist at a voltage of 50 volts or greater. For more information, see the commentary for 340.4, which focuses on the effects of electricity on the human body.

Short-Circuit Current Rating. The prospective symmetrical fault current at a nominal voltage to which an apparatus or system is able to be connected without sustaining damage exceeding defined acceptance criteria. [**70**:100]

The short-circuit current rating (SCCR) is marked on equipment, as shown in the bottom section of the label in Exhibit 100.13. The available input current must not exceed this rating. Wire, bus structures, switching, protection and disconnect devices, and distribution equipment will be damaged or destroyed if they exceed their short-circuit ratings.

Overcurrent protective devices should be selected to ensure that the let-through energy does not exceed the electrical equipment's SCCRs should a short circuit or high-level ground fault occur. The SCCR is the actual symmetrical root-mean-square (rms) fault current that equipment can withstand for a period of time. It could be 3 cycles, 15 cycles, 30 cycles, or some other time period depending upon the standard to which the equipment or component was tested.

Utility companies usually determine and provide information on the available short-circuit current levels at the service equipment. Literature on how to calculate short-circuit currents at each point in any electrical distribution system can be obtained by contacting the manufacturers of overcurrent protective devices.

Single-Line Diagram. A diagram that shows, by means of single lines and graphic symbols, the course of an electric circuit or system of circuits and the component devices or parts used in the circuit or system.

A single-line diagram illustrates a complete system or a portion of a system using graphic symbols. Recorded copies of this drawing should be marked using red-lining or some other method to illustrate all the changes made to the system. The availability of an up-to-date and accurate single-line diagram that identifies sources of energy and locations of disconnecting means is key to implementing procedures to establish an electrically safe work condition. Exhibit 205.1 and Figure D.2.2 both show examples of single-line diagrams.

Special Permission. The written consent of the authority having jurisdiction. [**70**:100]

Step Potential. A ground potential gradient difference that can cause current flow from foot to foot through the body.

Any current path through the body other than from foot to foot is considered touch potential. Exhibit 100.15 illustrates the difference between step and touch potential and the possible injuries that can result from an electric current passing through the human body. Although the insulating quality of voltage-rated gloves or footwear might be one component of a system to mitigate step and touch potential hazards, these cannot be used as the primary means of employee protection. See 130.7(C)(8) for more information on foot protection.

EXHIBIT 100.15

(a) Step potential   (b) Touch potential

Step and touch potential

Structure. That which is built or constructed. [**70**:100]

Switch, Isolating. A switch intended for isolating an electric circuit from the source of power. It has no interrupting rating, and it is intended to be operated only after the circuit has been opened by some other means. [**70**:100]

Isolating switches, while not intended nor rated to open circuits under load, can provide the means to install lockout devices after the load current is removed.

Switchboard. A large single panel, frame, or assembly of panels on which are mounted on the face, back, or both, switches, overcurrent and other protective devices, buses, and usually instruments. These assemblies are generally accessible from the rear as well as from the front and are not intended to be installed in cabinets. [**70**:100]

Switchgear or motor control centers do not meet this definition. However, many electrical employees incorrectly apply the term *switchgear* to switchboards and motor control centers. It is important to understand the difference when using Table 130.7(C)(15)(a) and Table 130.7(C)(15)(b) because the arc flash hazard PPE categories are based on the type of equipment being serviced and its voltage level.

Modern switchboards are totally enclosed to minimize the probability of spreading fire to adjacent combustible materials and to guard live parts. Service busbars are isolated from the remainder of the switchboard by barriers to avoid inadvertent contact by personnel or tools during maintenance.

Switchgear, Metal-Clad. A switchgear assembly completely enclosed on all sides and top with sheet metal, having drawout switching and interrupting devices, and all live parts enclosed within grounded metal compartments.

Switchgear, Metal-Enclosed. A switchgear assembly completely enclosed on all sides and top with sheet metal (except for ventilating openings and inspection windows), containing primary power circuit switching, interrupting devices, or both, with buses and connections. This assembly may include control and auxiliary devices. Access to the interior of the enclosure is provided by doors, removable covers, or both. Metal-enclosed switchgear is available in non-arc-resistant or arc-resistant constructions.

Switching Device. A device designed to close, open, or both, one or more electric circuits.

A switching device is any device that is rated for this use. Splicing devices located mid-conductor are sometimes rated for use as disconnecting devices and, therefore, are acceptable to use as switching devices

Touch Potential. A ground potential gradient difference that can cause current flow from hand to hand, hand to foot, or another path, other than foot to foot, through the body.

Any current path between two points of the body, other than from foot to foot, is called touch potential. (For more information, see Exhibit 100.15 and the commentary following the definition for the term *step potential*.)

Ungrounded. Not connected to ground or to a conductive body that extends the ground connection. [**70**:100]

Unqualified Person. A person who is not a qualified person.

Any person who has not received the specific training necessary to perform a task or to recognize when an electrical hazard exists and how to avoid that hazard or who has not demonstrated their ability to perform a task is an unqualified person. An employee qualified to perform a specific task might be unqualified to perform other tasks. The characteristics of being qualified and unqualified are task-dependent.

Worker Alert

Often, the most appropriate person to determine your qualification level for a given task is you. it is ultimately your responsibility to recognize if you do not have the skills necessary to perform a task safely.

Utilization Equipment. Equipment that utilizes electric energy for electronic, electro-mechanical, chemical, heating, lighting, or similar purposes. [**70**:100]

Voltage (of a Circuit). The greatest root-mean-square (rms) (effective) difference of potential between any two conductors of the circuit concerned. [**70**:100]

Informational Note: Some systems, such as three-phase 4-wire, single-phase 3-wire, and 3-wire direct-current, may have various circuits of various voltages.

Voltage, Nominal. A nominal value assigned to a circuit or system for the purpose of conveniently designating its voltage class (e.g., 120/240 volts, 480Y/277 volts, 600 volts). [**70**:100]

> Informational Note No. 1: The actual voltage at which a circuit operates can vary from the nominal within a range that permits satisfactory operation of equipment.

> Informational Note No. 2: See ANSI C84.1, *Electric Power Systems and Equipment—Voltage Ratings (60 Hz)*.

> Informational Note No. 3: Certain battery units are rated at nominal 48 volts dc but have a charging float voltage up to 58 volts. In dc applications, 60 volts is used to cover the entire range of float voltages.

Δ **Working Distance.** The distance between a person's face and chest area and a prospective arc source.

> Informational Note: Incident energy increases as the distance from the arc source decreases. See 130.5(C)(1) for further information

The required arc flash PPE is based on the incident energy at the working distance. Often, arms and hands are placed closer to the hazard than the chest. Additional arc flash protection might be necessary for any body part that is closer to the hazard than the specified working distance.

Working On (energized electrical conductors or circuit parts). Intentionally coming in contact with energized electrical conductors or circuit parts with the hands, feet, or other body parts, with tools, probes, or with test equipment, regardless of the personal protective equipment (PPE) a person is wearing. There are two categories of "working on": *Diagnostic (testing)* is taking readings or measurements of electrical equipment, conductors, or circuit parts with approved test equipment that does not require making any physical change to the electrical equipment, conductors, or circuit parts. *Repair* is any physical alteration of electrical equipment, conductors, or circuit parts (such as making or tightening connections, removing or replacing components, etc.).

A person required to perform a task involving intentional contact with an energized electrical conductor or circuit part is considered to be working on the energized part. That person is subject to all the associated requirements, including the selection of the appropriate level of PPE. Regardless of the use of PPE, measuring voltage with probes is an example of a diagnostic task involving working on energized parts that exposes an employee to an electrical hazard.

Two distinctly different types of tasks are included in this definition: diagnostic testing and repair. The two categories suggest that different procedural approaches might be necessary depending on the complexity of the task and the employee's exposure to electrical hazards.

Worker Alert

The protection afforded by this standard is based on this working distance. It is important to understand that your hands and arms are typically closer to an energized circuit. Leaning toward the equipment to gain a better viewpoint exposes your head and face to greater energy levels. These body parts must have additional protection that often exceeds the labeled protection level.

Application of Safety-Related Work Practices and Procedures

Article 105 establishes the overall scope, purpose, and organization of Chapter 1. It differentiates between the responsibilities of the employer and those of the employee. The employer has the responsibility of providing safety-related work procedures, training employees in those practices, supervising those employees, auditing, and documenting. The employees are responsible for applying the work procedures in accordance with their training and demonstrated ability.

OSHA's electrical safety standards are derived from NFPA *70E®, Standard for Electrical Safety in the Workplace®*. Since NFPA *70E* is the American National Standard for electrical safety in the workplace, it sets the minimum consensus requirements for safe electrical work procedures. NFPA *70E* establishes the minimum standard of care. OSHA's electrical safety standards are mainly performance based, whereas NFPA *70E* is mainly prescriptive based. NFPA *70E* fleshes out how the performance-based requirements in OSHA standards should be met by providing and defining the minimum standard industry practices necessary for electrical safety. OSHA is the law, but NFPA *70E* outlines how to comply with OSHA's electrical safety requirements.

105.1 Scope.

Chapter 1 covers electrical safety-related work practices and procedures for employees who are exposed to an electrical hazard in workplaces covered in the scope of this standard.

Chapter 1 outlines the electrical safety procedures necessary to protect employees from the dangers inherent in the use of electricity. The chapter also defines the employer's responsibility to create an electrical safety program (ESP) and implement the procedures of the program. An electrical safety procedure should include all the employees who interact with the systems, equipment, components, or parts that use electricity.

The requirements of NFPA *70E* are not limited to those in the electrical industry. NFPA *70E* does not deem a task as electrical or nonelectrical work. It requires that all employees be protected from electrical hazards. Electrical safety is not related to an employee's title, whether it be a mechanic, electrician, maintenance worker, technician, contractor, or painter. Instead, NFPA *70E* uses the terms *qualified person* and *unqualified person*.

Injuries associated with the use of electricity are not limited to unique employees, specific industries, or a particular segment of a specific industry. The applicability of this standard does not depend on the employee's craft; whether the facility is classified as residential, commercial, institutional, or industrial; whether or not the employee is qualified; the business of the employer; or the employees' level of training. For work locations covered by NFPA *70E*, no industry segment or work discipline is omitted. The fundamentals in this standard are intended to protect all types of employees in the identified workplaces, as well as those in other workplaces if the employer chooses to adopt the work procedures.

105.2 Purpose.

These practices and procedures are intended to provide for employee safety relative to electrical hazards in the workplace.

Informational Note: For general categories of electrical hazards, see Informative Annex K.

Employees might be exposed to an unacceptable level of risk of injury when interacting with energized electrical conductors and circuit parts that are not under normal operating conditions. When electrical equipment is not properly installed or maintained, even the risk associated with the normal operation of electrical equipment might be unacceptable.

The requirements of NFPA *70E* are not limited to the installation or maintenance of electrical equipment. NFPA *70E* covers the interaction of any employee with any electrical equipment. This standard specifies the electrical safety-related work procedures required to protect all types, categories, and classes of employees and others—whether or not they are qualified or unqualified to interact with energized electrical equipment—under normal or other than normal operating conditions. Normal operating conditions are defined in 110.4(D).

105.3 Responsibility.

(A) Employer Responsibility. The employer shall have the following responsibilities:

(1) Establish, document, and implement the safety-related work practices and procedures required by this standard.
(2) Provide employees with training in the employer's safety-related work practices and procedures.

Compliance with safety regulations is not just an employer responsibility. The Occupational Safety and Health Act of 1970 specifically requires that employees comply with the applicable OSHA regulations. The responsibilities are divided between employer and employee.

Employers are required to have an electrical safety program (ESP) for employees that includes the requirements identified in 110.6 and 110.7. Employees are required to put into practice the policies and procedures of the ESP, which includes training to perform the task at hand safely and the use of the required tools and safety equipment. The best results are achieved with collaboration and cooperation between labor and management, including the use of cross-functional teams and outside experts as necessary.

It is the employer's responsibility to create an ESP that includes policies, procedures, and process controls to document the program and to implement the program via training, auditing, and enforcement that is appropriate to the risk associated with the potential electrical hazards. The employer's ESP needs to address all the situations that can lead to the potential exposure of an employee to an electrical hazard. Where the employer has an overall occupational health and safety management system in place, the ESP is a component of such a program and needs to be integrated into the system.

The development and implementation of ESPs and their work procedures require the knowledge, expertise, and commitment of both management and their employees. Management must provide the assets necessary and coordinate planning, scheduling, and best practices. The required tasks are normally performed by employees who tend to have familiarity and expertise in the use of the actual systems and equipment. Sometimes, the required expertise is lacking and has to be developed. It is in the organization's interest and the interest of the individuals involved that every employee goes home safe and sound. The commitment of both parties is required.

Managers and supervisors must demonstrate the safety behaviors they expect their employees to follow. A comprehensive safety program can easily be rendered ineffective if management does not support the safety principles or does not encourage a safe culture. Management must allow the time necessary for employees to learn the documented safety procedures and must convey that safety takes precedence over speed. Employees who perceive the opposite will take shortcuts and expose themselves to an increased risk of injury.

(B) Employee Responsibility. The employee shall comply with the safety-related work practices and procedures provided by the employer.

NFPA *70E* is not just about the actions an employer took before an incident investigation. NFPA *70E* is about preventing workers from being injured. Regardless of an employer's electrical safety plan, it is the employee who has the biggest impact on his or her electrical safety.

Employers are required to provide safety-related work practices and training to their employees. The employer must teach the employees to be aware of the hazards and their actions and should instill in the employees a sense of self-discipline. An employer must also train the employees to perform tasks, recognize the hazards associated with those tasks, and understand the potential injuries that can be caused by those hazards, as well as how to protect themselves from those hazards.

Employees are responsible for implementing each of these safety practices into their work. An employer may train, audit, and retrain employees, but it is the employee who will make decisions and take actions that could result in injury. Employees have a responsibility to know their limitations—only they can determine if they are truly qualified to safely perform a task.

105.5 Organization.

Chapter 1 of this standard is divided into five articles. Article 100 provides definitions for terms used in one or more of the chapters of this document. Article 105 provides for application of safety-related work practices and procedures. Article 110 provides general requirements for electrical safety-related work practices and procedures. Article 120 provides requirements for establishing an electrically safe work condition. Article 130 provides requirements for work involving electrical hazards.

Article 105 defines the scope, purpose, and responsibilities of electrical safety for the parties involved. The practices and procedures contained in Article 110 must be established before an employee interacts with any electrical equipment or circuit parts. The requirements in Article 120 eliminate the hazards associated with the use of electricity by creating an electrically safe work condition through de-energizing, lockout, and verification that there is no voltage, as well as by temporarily grounding equipment as necessary. The practices and procedures in Article 130 cover justified interaction with and tasks performed near energized electrical equipment or circuit parts.

Worker Alert

In order for there to be an effective safety culture, you must incorporate the provided training, practices, and procedures. Taking shortcuts, skipping steps, or failing to don protective gear are risky decisions that lie with you, not your employer. You should work to improve safety by providing effective feedback on the training, practices, and procedures

OSHA Connection

Public Law 91-596, "Occupational Safety and Flealth Act of 1970"
SEC. 5.(b) Duties
Each employee must comply with occupational safety and health standards and all rules, regulations, and orders issued pursuant to this Act, which are applicable to his own actions and conduct.

Article 110 General Requirements for Electrical Safety-Related Work Practices

Work practices set the policy and direct employee activity in broad terms. They can be incorporated as part of an employer's overall occupational health and safety management system. Work practices should address planning all tasks and protecting employees from hazards. They should also incorporate the electrical safety work program, which explains how to put the practices to use. For example, work procedures might detail how an employee can maintain electrical equipment or use a specific test instrument. Principles of work practices should include the following:

- Establishing an electrically safe work condition
- Identifying the hazards and minimizing the risks
- Protecting the employees
- Planning all the tasks
- Anticipating unexpected events
- Ensuring employee qualifications and abilities
- Inspecting and maintaining electrical equipment
- Using the correct tools

110.1 Priority.

Hazard elimination shall be the first priority in the implementation of safety-related work practices.

> Informational Note No. 1: Elimination is the risk control method listed first in the hierarchy of risk control identified in 110.5(H)(3). See Annex F for examples of hazard elimination.

> Informational Note No. 2: An electrically safe work condition is a state wherein all hazardous electrical conductors or circuit parts to which a worker might be exposed are placed and maintained in a de-energized state, for the purpose of temporarily eliminating electrical hazards. See Article 120 for requirements to establish an electrically safe work condition for the period of time for which the state is maintained. See Informative Annex F for information regarding the hierarchy of risk control and hazard elimination.

Once a hazard has been identified, it should be determined if it can be eliminated. If there is no hazard, there is no risk of injury from a hazard. During the electrical system and equipment design stage, methods should be employed to eliminate the hazard in its entirety. In this first context, elimination is removal of the hazard entirely so that it never exists. This is often not an option for installed equipment.

Hazard elimination can also be achieved by applying other controls, such as through the establishment of an electrically safe work condition (ESWC), but the initial attempt should be to fully eliminate the hazard. The primary electrical safety procedure must be establishing an ESWC. The practice of hazard elimination must be employed regardless of other risk controls unless there is proper justification for energized electrical work.

110.2 General.

Electrical conductors and circuit parts shall not be considered to be in an electrically safe work condition until all of the requirements of Article 120 have been met.

Safe work practices applicable to the circuit voltage and energy level shall be used in accordance with Article 110 and Article 130 until such time that electrical conductors and circuit parts are in an electrically safe work condition.

Informational Note: See 120.5 for the steps to establish and verify an electrically safe work condition.

De-energized equipment is not in an electrically safe work condition (ESWC). Installing locks and tags does not ensure that electrical hazards have been removed. Until an ESWC has been properly established, employees must use work practices identical to those for working on or near exposed live parts. These work practices (including the use of PPE) should be appropriate for the voltage and energy level of the circuit as if it were known to be energized.

With a proper risk assessment and when performed under the conditions for normal operation, the act of establishing an ESWC should remove hazards before the equipment is opened. Although establishing an ESWC must be considered energized work, ideally, it should not expose the employee to any energized circuits. The ESWC voltage measurement should always be zero. This procedure, including the use of PPE, is necessary to protect workers in case something goes wrong.

Where an ESWC exists, there is no electrical energy in the proximity of the work task(s) and the elimination requirement of 110.1 has been met. The danger of injury from electrical hazards has been removed and neither protective equipment nor special safety training is required.

110.3 Electrically Safe Work Condition.

Energized electrical conductors and circuit parts operating at voltages equal to or greater than 50 volts shall be put into an electrically safe work condition before an employee performs work if any of the following conditions exist:

(1) The employee is within the limited approach boundary.

(2) The employee interacts with equipment where conductors or circuit parts are not exposed but an increased likelihood of injury from an exposure to an arc flash hazard exists.

Under both NFPA *70E®* and OSHA requirements, work is required to be performed in an electrically safe work condition (ESWC) unless energized work can be justified. If an employee is within the limited approach boundary or interacts with energized electrical equipment, conductors, or circuit parts in such a manner that there is a likelihood of injury from exposure to a potential arc flash event, the primary method of protection must be that energized conductors and circuit parts be put into an ESWC. The requirements for creating an ESWC can be found in Article 120. The act of creating an ESWC includes the risk controls of administration and elimination from the hierarchy of risk controls. Elimination established in this manner is considered the most effective form of risk control available through a work procedure.

The boundary for establishing an ESWC is the limited approach boundary. However, the point at which an energized electrical work permit is required is the restricted approach boundary or when there is potential exposure to an arc flash. Note that an ESWC is required to be established based on a shock protection boundary; it is not dependent upon the potential for an arc flash to occur. Unless energized work is justified, an employee must not be exposed to a shock hazard regardless of the use of PPE.

Worker Alert

When there is potential for you to be injured by electricity, the primary work practice must be to shut the equipment off. Under certain conditions (such as in a damp environment or with lacerated skin on your hands), shock or electrocution can occur at values below 50 volts.

OSHA Connection

29CFR 1910.333(a)(1)

Live parts must be de-energized before the employee works on or near them. Energized work requires the employer to demonstrate that de-energizing introduces additional or increased hazards or is infeasible due to equipment design or operational limitations. Live parts that operate at less than 50 volts to ground must be evaluated to determine if there is an increased exposure to electrical burns or to explosion due to electric arcs.

The phrase "interacting with the equipment" might include opening or closing a disconnecting means or pushing a reset button. However, if equipment is installed in accordance with the requirements of *NFPA 70®, National Electrical Code® (NEC®)*, and the manufacturer's instructions, and if it is properly maintained and operated normally, the chance of one of these actions initiating an arcing fault is remote. Normal operation of equipment involves interacting with it, but for most equipment, this does not meet the definition of *working on* as defined in Article 100. Normal operation of equipment is not expected to place an employee at an inherent risk of injury. An arc flash hazard is more likely to exist where a circuit breaker is racked in or out of switchgear, or where the equipment does not meet the normal operating conditions stated in 110.4(D).

Properly protecting employees from electrical hazards requires more than just using the various tables within NFPA *70E*. Many factors must be considered and many requirements applied before employees are put at risk of an injury. The flow chart in Exhibit 110.1 illustrates a sample of the necessary thought process. Exhibit 110.1, however, does not absolve users of their responsibility to read, understand, and properly apply the requirements.

110.4 Energized Work.

The primary protective strategy must be establishing an electrically safe work condition (ESWC), which is a form of risk control of administration (the use of procedures including lockout) from the hierarchy of risk controls to achieve the elimination of a hazard. [For more information, see 110.5(H)(3) and its associated commentary regarding the hierarchy of risk controls.] After this strategy has been executed, all of the electrical energy will have been removed from all the conductors and circuit parts to which the employee could be exposed. After an ESWC has been established, no PPE is required and unqualified persons are permitted to execute the remainder of the work. The only exception to this requirement is when working on exposed energized electrical conductors or circuit parts can be justified as described under one of the conditions listed in 110.4.

Employers are required to provide procedures to prevent injury to employees. Work near or on exposed conductors that are not in an ESWC will always expose employees to potential injury. Even with a company policy to place all equipment in an ESWC prior to work, the point at which an ESWC is verified is considered energized. Whether for verification of the ESWC or if the energized work is justified, a shock risk assessment and an arc flash risk assessment must be conducted. These assessments are independent of each other. Although an arc flash hazard might not be present where all energized work is performed, energized work typically presents a shock hazard.

Equipment that is considered to be operating normally is generally thought to be safe, barring any unusual circumstances. However, when electrical equipment changes state—such as when equipment is switched from energized to de-energized, when a circuit breaker is reset, or when the equipment does not meet the normal operating conditions—the result might be an arcing fault.

Until an ESWC is established, an unacceptable risk of injury exists and employees must continue to wear protective equipment. There is no way to establish an ESWC without some risk of exposure to a potential hazard. Until an employee is certain that no energy is present, it must be assumed that it is. With a proper risk assessment and under the conditions that permit normal operation, establishing an ESWC should remove the hazard before the voltage measurement is performed. Although establishing an ESWC must be considered energized work, it should not expose the employee to an energized circuit. The ESWC voltage measurement should always be zero. This process is in place to protect the employee if something goes wrong. After an ESWC has been established, employees can then remove gear worn to protect against electrical hazards. The approach boundaries no longer exist, and other employees in the vicinity are not at risk.

EXHIBIT 110.1

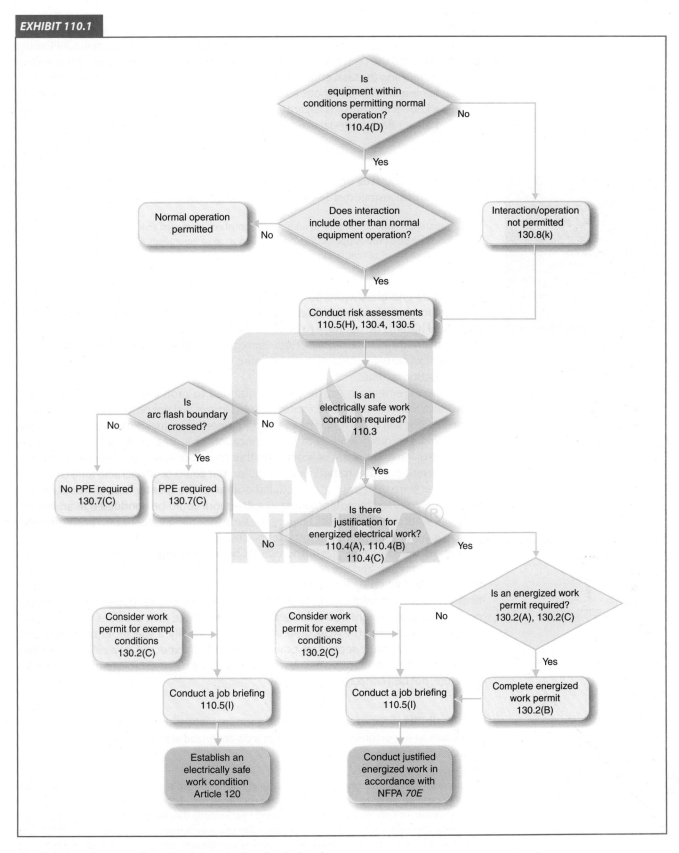

A sample thought process flow chart for conducting electrical work.

This is in contrast to justified energized work during which employees must continuously wear protective gear when they are within the approach boundaries. PPE must be worn up until the time the equipment is placed back into a normal operating condition. In performing the task, employees are constantly at risk of having an incident occur and sustaining an injury. Without an ESWC, PPE is being used to protect the employee against a known and present hazard while energized work is being performed. Anyone entering an arc flash boundary or a shock protection boundary is at risk and must be protected.

(A) Additional Hazards or Increased Risk. Energized work shall be permitted where the employer can demonstrate that de-energizing introduces additional hazards or increased risk.

Informational Note: Examples of additional hazards or increased risk include, but are not limited to, interruption of life-support equipment, deactivation of emergency alarm systems, and shutdown of hazardous location ventilation equipment.

Claiming de-energized work poses an increased risk or hazard does not provide justification for energized work. Documentation of the reasoning must be provided. The additional hazards do not have to be electrical hazards, and the increased risk does not have to from electrical hazards. Hazards might include chemical, mechanical, or environmental hazards—such as those associated with chemical plants, refineries, or ethanol production facilities.

The requirements in Article 130 are intended to protect employees when energized electrical work is justified. Protecting employees will not prevent an incident from occurring, nor will it prevent damage to equipment if an incident does occur. Before authorizing energized work with the justification of a greater hazard, consideration should be given to the result of an incident that could occur. Not only would equipment failure present a greater hazard, but the equipment could be inoperable for a considerably longer time than during a scheduled outage. If the greater hazard would not be immediately caused by equipment failure, the work could be conducted in an electrically safe work condition (ESWC) before the time that the greater hazard presents itself.

For example, the proposed justification could be that life support equipment must be worked on while energized. There must be an alternate plan if an incident does occur during repair and the equipment is rendered inoperative. How will life support be maintained when such an event occurs? Another example is a hazardous area ventilation system that might depend on the continuity of electrical power. However, temporary ventilation might be available. Often, the alternate plan provides the reasoning and ability to conduct the work de-energized. Additionally, if specific equipment is not supplied by automatic secondary power, a sudden, unexpected power loss is not the concern of the equipment owner. A scheduled outage by an established ESWC should, therefore, not be a concern.

(B) Infeasibility. Energized work shall be permitted where the employer can demonstrate that the task to be performed is infeasible in a de-energized state due to equipment design or operational limitations.

Informational Note: Examples of work that might be performed within the limited approach boundary of exposed energized electrical conductors or circuit parts because of infeasibility due to equipment design or operational limitations include performing diagnostics and testing (for example, start-up or troubleshooting) of electric circuits that can only be performed with the circuit energized and work on circuits that form an integral part of a continuous process that would otherwise need to be completely shut down in order to permit work on one circuit or piece of equipment.

Infeasible does not mean impractical. That it is infeasible to establish an electrically safe work condition is most often based on the task to be performed, not the equipment being worked on. In many situations, due to equipment design limitations, it is infeasible to perform diagnostic work such as voltage or temperature measurement, troubleshooting, and testing of electrical equipment without an employee being exposed to energized conductors and circuit parts. With the advent of remote programming and monitoring ports, however, what was considered infeasible might have changed. If it is feasible to install a remote programming port to program a motor control center bucket electronic overload relay, opening the door and exposing an employee to energized electrical conductors and circuit parts might no longer be justified.

What is considered infeasible for older equipment might not be infeasible for newly designed equipment. With the availability of remote racking systems, it might no longer be feasible for an employee to be in front of or even within the room when a task involves replacing a circuit breaker in switchgear.

(C) Equipment Operating at Less Than 50 Volts. Energized electrical conductors and circuit parts that operate at less than 50 volts shall not be required to be de-energized where the capacity of the source and any overcurrent protection between the energy source and the worker are considered and it is determined that there will be no increased exposure to electrical bums or to explosion due to electric arcs.

This justification for energized work essentially addresses only shock to employees. Under normal conditions, electrical conductors energized at a voltage less than 50 volts do not present an electrical shock hazard. This allowance does not apply to any system operating at 50 volts or less without first considering if there is a risk of exposure to electrical burns or explosions from electrical arcs. If there is the potential for arc flash or thermal burns to occur, working on an energized low-voltage circuit is not permitted unless it is justified by the allowances of 110.4(A) or 110.4(B).

A thermal hazard can exist in circuits that have a significant capacity to deliver energy, even when the voltage level is less than 50 volts. For instance, battery installations can be connected, so an arc resulting from a short circuit might present a significant thermal hazard. Burn injuries that can be caused by the use of electricity include the following three types:

- An electrical burn that occurs when sufficient electrical current flows through the body
- A thermal burn that results from the skin touching a hot surface or contacting clothing that has caught fire
- An arc flash burn caused by the radiation from an arc flash event

An arc flash event could occur provided there is a large enough battery (even if it is less than 50 volts) or as a result of discharge from a capacitor. If an uninsulated wrench is left across the terminals of a 12-volt battery for an extended period of time, it can become red hot and can easily burn skin if it is touched without the appropriate protection.

Many control circuits operate at a voltage level of less than 50 volts. Creating an open circuit or short circuit in one of these control circuits could result in a different type of hazard. An interruption or other unintended action within an industrial process can result in exposure to a chemical hazard or the creation of an unacceptable environmental condition.

(D) Normal Operating Condition. Normal operation of electric equipment shall be permitted where a normal operating condition exists. A normal operating condition exists when all of the following conditions are satisfied:

Normal operation of equipment involves interacting with it, but for most equipment, this does not meet the definition of working on as defined in Article 100. If equipment meets all of these criteria, there is no reason to assume that it is inherently unsafe. When equipment is operating normally or an employee is operating that equipment, the risk associated with normal operation is generally considered to be acceptable. Normal operation of equipment is typically conducted by someone other than a qualified person as defined by NFPA *70E*.

These normal operating conditions apply to the normal operation of equipment for its intended function. Normal operation of specific equipment is typically determined by the equipment manufacturer and does not include installation. For example, normal operation does not include the installation or removal of a circuit breaker; neither is considered normal operation of that circuit breaker for its intended purpose of overcurrent protection. Closed-door racking of a breaker might not adequately protect employees. PPE for the maximum possible hazard must be used during the installation or removal. Remote racking is a protective technique that can be used to keep employees outside of arc flash boundaries.

(1) The equipment is properly installed.

Much of the equipment that falls under the purview of NFPA *70E* does not have a governmental electrical inspector who verifies that its installation complies with applicable codes, standards, and instructions. Equipment is often installed by an employee or an outside contractor with no governmental oversight. Without proper installation, the equipment cannot be depended upon to operate correctly or to perform its required safety functions.

The employer/owner must determine how to enforce and determine compliance with the *NEC* for equipment installed under these circumstances. The employer/owner must also make sure that all the equipment is properly installed. If not, employees will be at risk of injury during normal operation of that equipment.

(2) The equipment is properly maintained.

At the time it is properly installed, equipment is in a new condition and everything is expected to be in order. After that point in time, equipment will slowly begin to show signs of wear and tear. Motors, circuit breakers, and even transformers are not pieces of equipment that should be ignored; they require maintenance. Most manufacturers will provide recommendations on what is minimally required to maintain their equipment. Some industries provide guidance on maintenance. NFPA 70B, *Recommended Practice for Electrical Equipment Maintenance,* contains a wealth of information on the subject.

Proper maintenance is not just the act of fixing, adjusting, or filling fluids. There is a time aspect that is just as important. A piece of equipment might only need proper maintenance every year or two in one installation, but that same piece of equipment might require monthly maintenance in another installation. The employer/owner must make sure that any equipment is properly maintained. If not, employees will be at risk of injury during normal operation.

(3) The equipment is used in accordance with instructions included in the listing and labeling and in accordance with manufacturer's instructions.

For employees to safely interact with equipment, they must understand the conditions, methods, functions, and sequences of safely operating the equipment. Equipment is supplied with its manufacturer's operating instructions. If the equipment is listed, these instructions typically include the specifics necessary to operate the equipment within the parameters of that listing. Operating equipment contrary to those instructions can put employees at risk of injury when operating that equipment.

(4) The equipment doors are closed and secured.

This requirement necessitates some judgment on the part of the employee at the time of equipment operation. For someone to gain access to an HID circuit breaker for normal operation, they must open a hinged door on the panelboard. This is different from an access door, which is intended to be closed and secure during the operation of a transformer. This differentiation requires proper training of the employees interacting with the equipment. If the wrong door is open, employees could be exposed to a risk of injury during normal operation of that equipment.

(5) All equipment covers are in place and secured.

This requirement necessitates some judgment on the part of the employee at the time of equipment operation. The bolted cover to which the hinged access door for a panelboard is attached is intended to stay in place when an employee is operating the breaker. This requires proper training of the employee interacting with the equipment. If the covers are absent or not secure, the employee could be exposed to a risk of injury during normal operation of that equipment.

(6) There is no evidence of impending failure.

Informational Note: The phrase *properly installed* means that the equipment is installed in accordance with applicable industry codes and standards and the manufacturer's recommendations. The phrase *properly maintained* means that the equipment has been maintained in accordance with the manufacturer's recommendations and applicable industry codes and standards. The phrase *evidence of impending failure* means that there is evidence such as arcing, overheating, loose or bound equipment parts, visible damage, or deterioration.

Typically, the employer/owner is not aware of the daily condition of equipment in the facility. The burden of determining the condition of the equipment is often the responsibility of the employee interacting with the equipment, as conditions can change on a daily basis. This employee must be trained to understand the potential failure modes and to identify the signs of impending failure of the equipment. These signs vary greatly depending on the type of electrical equipment in use. The smell of ozone, presence of smoke, sound of arcing, visible damage, or warning lights are all possible indications of equipment failure. There might also be some unusual cases that are undetectable, such as rodents or snakes getting into equipment through unsealed openings. If any of these signs are present, the employee could be at risk of injury during normal operation of that equipment.

110.5 Electrical Safety Program.

Electrical safety is not just for qualified persons or those working on electrical equipment. An employer's electrical safety program (ESP) needs to address all the situations that could lead to the potential exposure of an employee to an electrical hazard. Where electrical safety is involved, high ethical standards should exist and be enforced. As illustrated in Exhibit 110.2, an ESP includes many different components.

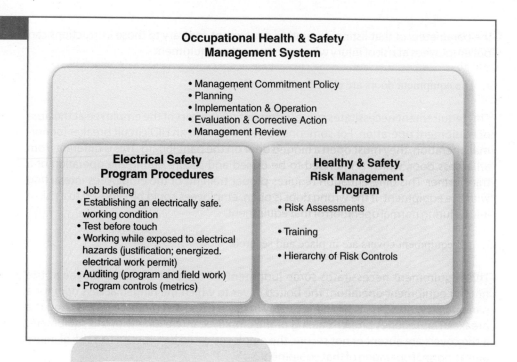

EXHIBIT 110.2

Components of an electrical safety program.

Δ **(A) General.** The employer shall implement and document an overall electrical safety program that directs activity appropriate to the risk associated with electrical hazards.

> Informational Note No. 1: Safety-related work practices such as verification of proper maintenance and installation, alerting techniques, auditing requirements, and training requirements provided in this standard are administrative controls and part of an overall electrical safety program.

> Informational Note No. 2: See Informative Annex P for information on implementing an electrical safety program within an employer's occupational health and safety management system.

> Informational Note No. 3: IEEE 3007.1, *Recommended Practice for the Operation and Management of Industrial and Commercial Power Systems,* provides additional guidance for the implementation of the electrical safety program.

> Informational Note No. 4: IEEE 3007.3, *Recommended Practice for Electrical Safety in Industrial and Commercial Power Systems,* provides additional guidance for electrical safety in the workplace.

It is the employer's responsibility to create and document an electrical safety program that includes policies, procedures, and process controls. The employer must implement the program through training, auditing, and enforcement that is appropriate to the risk associated with the potential electrical hazards. Where the employer has an overall occupational health and safety management system in place, the electrical safety program must be a component of this system.

An employer might develop an occupational health and safety management system in accordance with ANSI/AIHA Z10, *Occupational Health and Safety Management Systems.* In the same way that NFPA *70E* provides information on electrical safety-related work procedures, ANSI/AIHA Z10 provides guidance on developing and implementing an overall occupational safety management system. ANSI/AIHA Z10 provides a framework into which an electrical safety program can fit.

(B) Inspection. The electrical safety program shall include elements to verify that newly installed or modified electrical equipment or systems have been inspected to comply with applicable installation codes and standards prior to being placed into service.

Often, building systems are inspected by an authority outside of the employer/owner. Much of the equipment that falls under the purview of NFPA *70E* does not have a governmental electrical inspector who verifies that the installation complies with applicable codes, standards, and instructions. Equipment is often installed by an employee or outside contractor, with no governmental oversight. Without proper installation, equipment cannot be depended upon to operate correctly or to perform its required safety functions. The employer/owner must determine how to enforce and determine compliance with *NFPA 70, National Electrical Code* (*NEC*), for equipment installed under these circumstances.

Case Study

110.5

Scenario

Joe, a journeyman electrician with 28 years of experience, and Al, an electrical apprentice, were removing a set of circuit conductors from a circuit breaker installed in a 480Y/277-volt, 3-phase, 4-wire, 800-ampere main breaker service panelboard. The panelboard supplied power to the entire building. Due to the cost associated with having the utility company disconnect the power to the building, their employer decided to have them proceed with this task by simply placing the main circuit breaker into the off position to de-energize the panelboard busbars. However, the service conductors into the line-side terminals of the main circuit breaker were still energized and exposed.

Joe began removing the conductors from a branch circuit breaker in the upper left-hand side of the enclosure. Al was standing on a ladder 4 or 5 feet away and was manually supporting the conduit that contained the circuit conductors. The bare equipment grounding conductor they were removing was still connected to the equipment grounding terminal in the enclosure. As the conductors were being removed, the equipment ground conductor accidentally came into contact with an energized terminal on the main circuit breaker and an arc flash event ensued.

Result

Al saw a large flash and heard a loud noise, followed by two more rapid explosive noises. Then, Al noticed that Joe's synthetic clothing was in flames. Al patted out the flames on his partner with his hands and burned himself in the process. He then led Joe out of the smoke-filled room and called 911 for assistance.

Joe sustained second- and third-degree burns over nearly 50 percent of his body. He required surgery to remove destroyed skin, as well as restorative skin grafts. He needed physical therapy for a year and, after another year, returned to work full time. Al was treated for second-degree burns and released.

Analysis

Unless establishing an electrically safe work condition (ESWC) introduced a greater hazard or increased risk or was infeasible (neither of which was indicated), the employer should not have authorized the work. The facts suggest that the company placed a higher priority on the cost of the utility establishing an ESWC than the personal safety of Al and Joe. If an ESWC had been properly established prior to the removal of the circuit conductors, this incident would not have occurred.

An assumption was made that simply opening the main circuit breaker was enough protection for the assigned task rather than establishing an ESWC. Within the enclosure, there were exposed energized circuit parts that were not addressed. Proper risk assessments and work procedures would have identified that an electrical hazard existed within the enclosure—even with the load side of the circuit breaker de-energized. The work should have been considered energized work due to the presence of exposed electrical hazards within the enclosure. If the task had been properly justified, a written permit would have been necessary. The permit would have to have been approved by the owner, responsible management, or safety officer. The energized work permit would have specified the written procedures necessary to conduct the task safely and any necessary protective equipment, and it would have used the hierarchy of risk controls to address the exposed energized circuit parts. The exposed parts of the service conductors and the main circuit breaker could have been shielded by an appropriate insulating barrier. The exposed parts of the circuit conductors, including the equipment grounding conductor, could have been insulated. Also, appropriate PPE could have been used or worn.

(continued)

Relevant NFPA *70E* Requirements

This was not simply a case of the need for Joe and Al to don proper PPE. If the company had followed the requirements of NFPA *70E*, Al and Joe might not have been injured. The employer ignored the following primary safety principles:

- Create an electrical safety program [110.5],
- Establish an electrically safe work condition [110.3],
- Properly justify energized work [110.4].
- Conduct risk assessments [110.5(H)]

Joe and Al also hold some responsibility for the incident. As employees, they should have been aware of their responsibilities under NFPA *70E*. In addition to the requirements listed above, they should have been aware of the following:

- Their ability to meet the definition of a qualified person [100]
- Their need for awareness and self-discipline [110.5(D)]
- The training they should have received from their employer [110.6]

Worker Alert

When interacting with electrical equipment, you should be aware of equipment that has not been maintained. Maintenance personnel generally know if a company's priority is to maintain its high-value or production equipment rather than *all* of its electrical equipment. Without a comprehensive maintenance program, you could be at risk when operating or interacting with equipment.

(C) Condition of Maintenance. The electrical safety program shall include elements that consider condition of maintenance of electrical equipment and systems.

An electrical safety program must consider the condition of maintenance of the equipment and its component parts. Without proper maintenance, equipment cannot be depended upon to perform its required safety functions, such as interrupting fault currents within its characteristic time-current curves. Proper maintenance can be achieved using the manufacturer's instructions or the recommendations included in NFPA 70B, *Recommended Practice for Electrical Equipment Maintenance.*

Proper maintenance applies not only to the equipment where the task is being performed but also to any remote disconnect and the circuit's overcurrent device, for example.

Case Study   110.5(C)

Scenario

Ellen was an electrician at a chemical manufacturing facility. Carl, the senior electrician, was qualifying Ellen to perform energized tasks on production line equipment. The company had an established electric safety work program with documented procedures for each task to be performed. Routine maintenance was conducted on the production line equipment to minimize lost production time. Risk assessments were conducted and labels with the results were applied to the equipment. In order for Ellen to better understand the unique production line equipment, the first task scheduled was simple diagnostic testing. Even though the task was exempted by NFPA *70E*, company policy required that an energized work permit be completed prior to performing the task. A job briefing was held to make sure that Ellen fully understood the task and work procedures. Carl demonstrated how to visually inspect all the equipment necessary for the task.

The enclosure where the task was to be performed was labeled with an incident energy of 6.4 cal/cm² at a working distance of 18 inches. The label stated that a minimum PPE arc rating of 8 cal/cm² was required to work on the equipment. Both Carl and Ellen dressed in PPE because they would be within the 7-foot arc flash boundary. Although Ellen would be conducting the task, company policy required Carl to also wear shock PPE for safety even though he would not be within the restricted approach boundary.

After opening the access panel, Ellen proceeded to perform the diagnostic evaluation by connecting an analyzer to check the power quality. After the testing had begun, Ellen bumped into the side of the enclosure, knocking loose a nut that had been spot-welded to the inside of the enclosure to bolt the access panel in place. When Ellen reached deeper into the equipment to retrieve the nut, an arc flash occurred.

Result

Ellen suffered severe second-degree burns over the left side of her body from the face to the waist. She was released from the hospital after 3 days and returned to work after another 3 weeks. Carl was not injured during the incident.

Investigation

The incident primarily occurred as a result of human error. Ellen's impulse reaction to retrieve the nut by blindly reaching into the enclosure was the root cause. Although she was not yet qualified to perform the task on her own, Ellen should have had training that provided her with a better understanding of the risks and hazards associated with the energized equipment, not just those associated with the assigned task.

Subsequent investigation into the incident revealed the primary cause of the severity of the injury. Although Ellen's employer placed a priority on the maintenance of the production line equipment to maximize revenue, the electrical distribution equipment had not been maintained since its initial installation 16 years prior. The circuit breaker, which was meant to limit the incident energy, was found to have a fault clearing time nearly double that used for the incident energy calculation. Examination of the device revealed that the environment within the chemical facility had degraded the trip mechanism. Although the PPE worn by Ellen was rated for 10 cal/cm², it was subjected to an estimated incident energy level of 21.4 cal/cm².

Analysis

Although Ellen holds some responsibility for the incident because her blind reaching directly initiated the arc flash, her employer failed to protect her from the energized electrical hazards to which they subjected her. Maintenance of equipment as required by NFPA *70E* is not limited to only the equipment being worked on—it is applicable to all the overcurrent devices upstream from that equipment. This is true whether the policy is to establish an electrically safe work condition or to authorize justified energized work. Proper maintenance is necessary whether the arc flash analysis is conducted using the incident energy method or the PPE category method. Whenever an arc flash hazard exists, it is the proper function of protective devices that will limit the severity of the injury to a worker. Ellen was fortunate that the PPE she was wearing performed beyond its rating, thereby preventing permanent injury or death.

(D) Awareness and Self-Discipline. The electrical safety program shall be designed to provide an awareness of the potential electrical hazards to employees who work in an environment with the presence of electrical hazards. The program shall be developed to provide the required self-discipline for all employees who must perform work that may involve electrical hazards. The program shall instill safety principles and controls.

Human factors are generally recognized as being among the leading causes of injury. When employees are performing tasks, they are typically solely responsible for their actions. After employees have gone through training, received supervision, and been provided procedures to follow, it is their own actions (or lack thereof) that will impact their safety. In the hierarchy of risk controls, awareness generally means being able to recognize warning signs. In this section, awareness refers to attentiveness to oneself, others, and the situation. According to this section, awareness can apply to any of the following:

- Recognizing when the risk of a potential electrical hazard is unacceptable
- Understanding a possible sequence of events that could lead to exposure to an electrical hazard
- Being alert to other personnel who could enter the work area
- Realizing that work conditions could change
- Understanding that personal circumstances—such as weariness, exhaustion, boredom, or distraction—can affect performance and result in unsafe conditions

By learning awareness and self-discipline, employees will begin to accept that their own actions are often among the primary causes of injuries. Workers will start questioning the use of shortcuts, such as failing to don the appropriate PPE or conducting unjustified energized work. They will also begin to realize that the rush to complete a task before the end of a shift or fatigue from extended hours could put them at risk.

Aware and self-disciplined employees understand the potential harm certain actions might subject them to and realize that it is not worth the risk. They might also start to correct or point out the unsafe actions of other employees.

Having an electrical safety program is not enough, in itself; employees must follow the policies and effectively implement the procedures. The employer must provide the personal and other protective equipment required. The equipment owner must ensure that the warning labels required by 130.5(H) are attached to the equipment. However, employees have to be able to select, wear, and use the equipment appropriate for the specific hazards involved.

(E) Electrical Safety Program Principles. The electrical safety program shall identify the principles upon which it is based.

> Informational Note: For examples of typical electrical safety program principles, see Informative Annex E.

A company's primary safety and business objectives should guide the development of its safety program. Electrical safety program principles are the company's safety policies. As such, they are safety guidelines for the employees. These principles must direct employee activity.

An employee might not interact with electrical equipment safely if their employer favors keeping the production line running or getting power back on as quickly as possible. Unless the company's core safety principles and expectations of performing energized work safely are upheld, employees might justify taking shortcuts and engaging in substandard work practices to meet those goals.

An employer's policies might include the following:

- Identifying and minimizing electrical hazards
- Planning every job
- Documenting first-time procedures
- Anticipating unexpected events
- Reporting, investigating, and documenting all incidents

Examples of such policies can be found in the sample electrical safety program outline found in E.1 of Informative Annex E.

(F) Electrical Safety Program Controls. An electrical safety program shall identify the controls by which it is measured and monitored.

> Informational Note: For examples of typical electrical safety program controls, see Informative Annex E.

Electrical safety program controls are the company's electrical safety metrics for determining if a safety program is effective and efficient. Metrics are measurable points used to determine performance. They can also be used to determine if improvements to a safety program are required and, if so, what needs to be changed. Some program controls can be found in the sample electrical safety program outline found in E.2 of Informative Annex E.

There are two common metrics used to determine the effectiveness of something: lagging metrics and leading metrics. Lagging metrics provide a reactive view of a safety program. Lagging metrics for a safety program might include the total time lost to injuries, the money spent on worker compensation, or the amount of training an employee has received. Leading metrics are used to identify and correct contributing factors before an incident occurs. Leading metrics for a safety program might include the number of hazards identified and eliminated, the reduction in the number of energized work permits authorized, or the number of work procedures altered for de-energized work. Using a combination of these metrics can enhance a work safety program.

(G) Electrical Safety Program Procedures. An electrical safety program shall identify the procedures to be utilized before work is started by employees exposed to an electrical hazard.

> Informational Note: For an example of a typical electrical safety program procedure, see Informative Annex E.

A company's electrical safety program must be documented. It must include the policies, procedures, and process controls necessary for employees to work safely.

A procedure should be specific to a task. It should contain a defined scope, the required qualifications for and the number of employees involved, the hazards associated with the task, the limits of approach, the necessary safe work practices, and the required PPE, as well as its required tools and necessary precautionary techniques. Electrical diagrams, equipment preventative maintenance requirements, visual job aids, and manufacturer data sheets should also be provided where they are warranted. The procedure should be discussed and reviewed during the job briefing to ensure that it sufficiently addresses the scheduled task before work begins.

Electrical safety should be a continual improvement process, and all procedures should be reviewed periodically. A procedure is the best practice at a certain time; some companies use the term *standard operating procedure (SOP)*. Over time, situations can change and new methods can be developed. When situations change and the risk of injury exists, employees must be able to identify and implement the necessary procedures for safe work where the potential for electrical hazards exists.

(H) Risk Assessment Procedure. The electrical safety program shall include a risk assessment procedure and shall comply with 110.5(H)(1) through 110.5(H)(3).

The flowchart in Exhibit 110.3 on page 61 illustrates the process of conducting risk assessments. The chart references the main subsections pertinent to each type of assessment and those applicable to each leg of the chart. This exhibit is not intended to absolve users of their responsibility to read and understand the applicable NFPA *70E* requirements

---

> **Worker Alert**
>
> Your employer must provide you with documented procedures before you begin a task. You must review and understand the procedures before you start. Improvising in the field is dangerous.

Case Study   110.5(H)

Scenario

Steve's job one morning was to install a monitoring box on the outside of a switchgear, a job he had done more than a dozen times as a 29-year veteran electrician. After reviewing the project with the engineer, it was determined that the best place to install the monitor was an entrance cabinet that carried parallel 500-kcmil 480-volt feeder wires with no live exposed parts. Although the wires were not secured in the cabinet, there was more than 4 inches of clearance expected on the end of the gear he would be working on. Steve would use a self-tapping screw that would penetrate into the cabinet by less than half an inch. He considered the installation a "zero-risk job"—he would be on the outside of the switchgear, and the screws would fall at least 3½ inches from the live wires.

Steve stayed behind alone at the job site to conduct the task. He drilled the top left, then the top right, the bottom right, and finally the bottom left. As the last screw came to a stop against the box flange, he heard a loud boom inside the cabinet and a buzzing sound, which were followed by a spray of metal and fire. Instinctively, he ducked. The cabinet door was still closed. The arc flash had come through the side of the switchgear and the monitor box. Backing up to avoid the flames, he hit a wall.

(continued)

As Steve turned the corner, he realized he was on fire. After frantically ripping off his t-shirt and slapping out the flames, he looked down at his badly burned hands and felt an agonizing pain on his face. A warm feeling on the left side of his neck crept upward. When he looked down at his torso, he realized he was still on fire. He started whipping at the flames and finally put them out. At the hospital it was discovered that more than 30 percent of his body was burned. A helicopter then transported him to a hospital with a specialized burn unit.

Steve on the day of the accident, immediately after admission to the hospital. (Courtesy of the Lenz family)

Result

Nearly every day in the hospital, burn techs took Steve to a room and placed him in a large metal trough where they scrubbed the dead skin off his arms and chest. Steve's first surgery occurred a few days after arriving at the hospital. The surgeons removed more dead skin off his chest and sides and covered the areas with cadaver skin to protect him until he was ready to have grafts from his own body. A silver spongy material was then stapled directly to his skin. By the end of the third surgery, skin from his lower right leg and both his thighs now covered his arms, chest, and collarbone.

Steve received his nutrition through a tube that had been placed in his nose. He lost 20 pounds over the course of a month, a significant amount for someone his size. By the fourth surgery, the doctors took large amounts of skin from the back of his left thigh and calf and grafted it to the sides of his upper body. Finally, he was released from the hospital.

On his second day home, Steve blacked out in the shower and crashed through the shower door, landing in a pile of glass. The heat from the hot water, combined with his blood pressure medication and his low blood volume, had caused the blackout.

After hours in the emergency room and numerous stitches, Steve was back home. Steve became dependent on narcotics and gradually weaned himself off all medication. After 2 weeks, Steve was no longer dependent on pain medication, but he was in constant pain.

After 8 months and hundreds of thousands of dollars of medical bills, Steve had full mobility and faint scars, but his life is not the same. He carries the knowledge that if he had been wearing personal protective equipment (PPE), he might have returned home without a scratch that December day. "If I could change one thing, I would have worn the stupid $35 shirt," says Steve. "I would have put on the gloves; I would have put on the shield. One tiny mistake, one oversight, a fraction of a second, a dropped tool, somebody else's mistake—it doesn't matter, it's going to catch you. We all think that we are indestructible, and I learned that I'm not indestructible. Hopefully I won't have to prove that to my kids again."

Analysis

What happened to Steve emphasizes the importance of performing a thorough risk assessment. A risk assessment must identify hazards, assess risks, and apply risk controls. The fact that the switchgear was not placed into an electrically safe work condition (ESWC) warranted consideration of shock and arc-flash hazards. Blindly screwing into an energized enclosure should have triggered concern for exposure to electrical hazards. Although Steve was working on the exterior of an enclosure, the fact that he could not see what was behind the enclosure wall elevated the risk of exposure to an arc flash event.

It is probable that human error also played a role in this incident. The engineer may have assumed that conductors were routed in a specific way, given what was shown on the design drawing. Or the installer may have routed the conductors incorrectly. Additional risk resulted from not verifying the installation of the internal conductors and by performing the task under the assumption that sufficient clearance was present for insertion of the screw. It is possible that the engineer was not qualified to assess the hazards associated with that specific switchgear. Human error in assuming what should be rather than verifying what is put Steve at a greater risk of an injury.

The fact that an ESWC should have been established and the PPE should have been employed is moot in this situation. Without a proper risk assessment identifying the electrical hazards associated with a task, there is no way to properly protect an employee from injury. Without knowing the hazards and risks, it is possible for incorrect or insufficient controls from the hierarchy of risk controls methods to be employed. The act of establishing an ESWC on the switchgear would have put an employee at risk without first conducting a proper assessment. There is no safe way to utilize appropriate equipment or proper protection techniques without first knowing the risks and level of hazards.

EXHIBIT 110.3

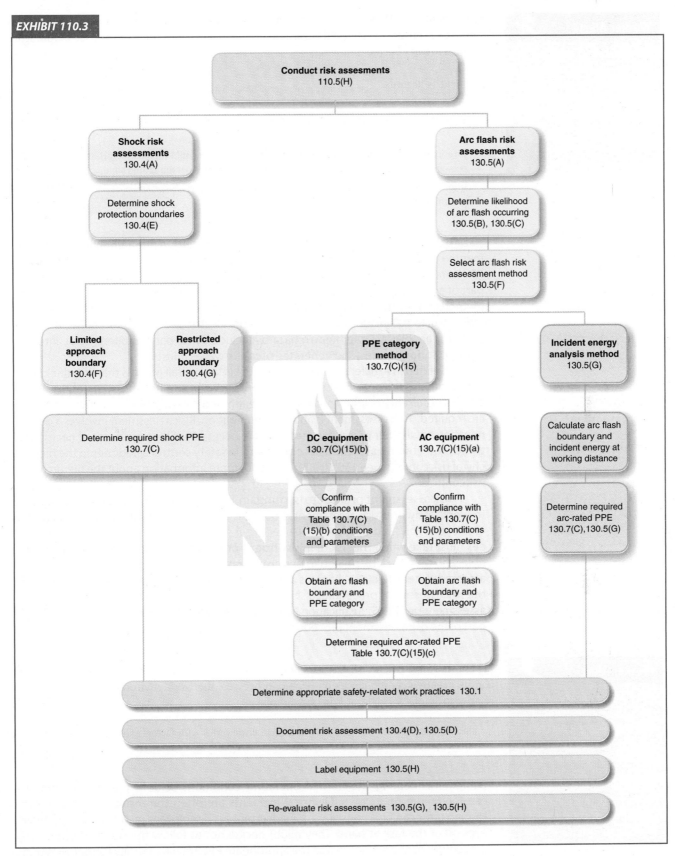

Risk assessment flow chart.

△ **(1) Elements of a Risk Assessment Procedure.** The risk assessment procedure shall address employee exposure to electrical hazards and shall identify the process to be used before work is started to carry out the following:

(1) Identify hazards
(2) Assess risks
(3) Implement risk control according to the hierarchy of risk control methods

> Informational Note No. 1: The risk assessment procedure could include identifying when a second person could be required and the training and equipment that person should have.
>
> Informational Note No. 2: For more information regarding risk assessment and the hierarchy of risk control, see Informative Annex F.

Hazards must first be recognized to reduce the risk of injury. A program should be implemented to identify hazards proactively and to identify, analyze, and minimize risks. NFPA *70E* currently addresses only two hazards directly: electric shock and arc flash burns. As part of a risk assessment, it is necessary to determine the need for and an appropriate method of protecting workers from all electrical hazards. The definition of electrical hazard in Article 100 includes any of the following: electric shock, arc flash burns, thermal burns, or arc blasts. Other known hazards include flying parts, molten metal, intense light, poisonous oxides, and generated pressure waves (blasts).

As defined in Article 100, a risk assessment is "an overall process that identifies hazards, estimates the potential severity of injury or damage to health, estimates the likelihood of occurrence of injury or damage to health, and determines if protective measures are required." Risk assessment is about risk mitigation. Risk assessment involves a determination of whether protective measures are necessary. If they are deemed necessary, these protective measures must come from the safety control categories in the hierarchy of risk controls. See 110.5(H)(3) and F.3 for more information about the hierarchy of risk controls.

A risk assessment procedure is a fundamental guideline for employees to follow to work safely. This risk assessment procedure must be documented and available to employees. For this procedure to be effective, it should point out the steps that employees must take when the risk of injury from a potential electrical hazard is unacceptable, and they must be trained to perform the procedure correctly each time the risk is assessed. Where electrical hazards are involved, there are at least two components to the risk assessment procedure: a shock risk assessment per 130.4 and an arc flash risk assessment per 130.5. Justification in accordance with 110.4 should also be considered part of the risk assessment procedure.

(2) Human Error. The risk assessment procedure shall address the potential for human error and its negative consequences on people, processes, the work environment, and equipment relative to the electrical hazards in the workplace.

> Informational Note: The potential for human error varies with factors such as tasks and the work environment. See Informative Annex Q.

Equipment meeting the normal operating conditions seldom presents an injury-causing failure on its own. Electrical incidents are often the result of human error. Human error can be a conscious or inadvertent act. Employees might slip or take their eyes off of the task at hand. They might decide not to follow the standard operating procedures or choose not to don the appropriate PPE. Training is a key factor in limiting these human errors.

If employers don't address employees taking shortcuts, skipping procedures, or routinely breaking rules, employees might begin to consider their actions acceptable. If an employer is aware of these issues, they must promote safety so employees don't assume they are permitted to continue using unsafe work practices.

Safe work practices help establish human behaviors, which, in turn, aid in preventing errors. A behavior-based safety approach is an important method of addressing electrical safety in the workplace. This approach can help employees recognize that such errors are a leading cause of injury and that they need to take responsibility for their own safety. As the process permeates throughout a facility, employees will correct actions taken by peers. Eventually, voluntary compliance with safe work practices will increase as employees realize that their decisions influence safety.

Case Study   110.5(H)(2)

Background

Scott was employed by an electrical contracting firm hired for the demolition and remodel of a commercial site. Safety considerations were considered during the planning and design phase of the job. A field manager/safety director reported to the company owner, and his safety duties included visits to each job site at least twice a week. A written safety program included safety rules, safe work procedures for specific settings, and a lockout program. Biweekly meetings that covered safety and other job-related topics were conducted by the field foreman, who was responsible for on-site job safety. The employer was committed to safety and loss prevention and was clear about an employee's responsibility to work safely. Working on energized conductors was not allowed by company policy. Employees not following safe work procedures were "written up."

On-the-job training was conducted under close supervision of the field foreman. Employees were checked on how well they performed expected tasks before being permitted to work alone. Training was reinforced by safety manuals, scheduled safety meetings, and printed materials. A field foreman was required to be at least a journeyman electrician. After 7 years of experience under the supervision of a master electrician and passing a test, a journeyman electrician was granted a master electrician license.

Scott, a 35-year-old male with 12 years' experience as master electrician, including 5 years operating his own business, had been with the employer for 4 months. He had worked with a senior field foreman during his first several weeks and had demonstrated sufficient skills to work alone as a field foreman. Scott was assigned as the field foreman on the site for the 3-month duration of the job and supervised three employees.

Scenario

On the day of the incident, all the work being conducted by contractors was required to be completed before the end-of-the-day inspection by the fire marshal. Scott was tasked with installing fluorescent lighting and emergency exit lights that had been added to the original job specifications. When he arrived

with the fixtures, the general contractor asked about an emergency light that did not appear to be charging. That light was on the same circuit to which Scott was to add the new fixtures. Scott closed the circuit at the service panel to verify that the installed light was charging. After confirming the light was functioning, the circuit may not have been locked out. The panel was capable of being locked out and Scott was holding one of two keys—the other key was inside the panel.

Scott returned to complete the process of adding a light fixture to a 277-volt circuit that provided power to other lighting fixtures in the building. He was working alone. Scott did not use personal protective equipment other than a wire-stripper with insulated handles. He was in the process of stripping insulation from the three conductors of Type MC cable that entered the hallway from an opening in the wall. Scott was standing on a dry concrete floor with the cable in one hand and the wire stripper in the other hand. While he was stripping the insulation, Scott contacted the energized conductor and some part of the cable.

Result

Scott was found on the hall floor by another subcontractor who came to borrow a tool. The worker noticed arcing at Scott's chest where he was clutching the cable and wire stripper. The worker called for others to de-energize the power and call 911. Another worker shut off the power to the building then came to Scott's aid and found him without a pulse. No one on site knew CPR. Within 5 minutes the police responded and the officer initiated CPR. The fire department medic unit arrived several minutes later and continued CPR while transporting Scott to the hospital where he was pronounced dead 70 minutes later.

Analysis

An employee is required to comply with the safety-related work practices provided by the employer. Although it appears as if the employer had a well-developed electrical safety program, Scott, a master electrician, was killed by contacting energized electrical parts. The apparent cause of the fatality is that Scott did not apply the training provided by his employer or follow

(continues)

the required procedures. Energized work was a violation of the employer policy. The reason the lockout program did not work may have been human error.

A contract employer is responsible for the safety of its employees regardless of the work location. Less obvious reasons for this fatality could lie with the employer's electrical safety program. An employer must document and implement safety-related work practices and train employees. The electrical safety program must specifically address risks and hazards associated with the tasks assigned. A contract employer may not have an electrical safety program or training program that addresses many different scenarios that put an employee at risk of injury when on-site. Energized equipment encountered during installation will not have NFPA *70E* required risk assessments conducted or safety labels in place. This often requires specific safety procedures for the individual job in order to address each hazard and risk appropriately.

The fact that Scott was a master electrician and was qualified as a foreman did not necessarily qualify him to perform the assigned task. Although energized electrical work was prohibited, a lockout program existed, and the employer was not aware of any previous violation of the policy, there is no indication that field audits were conducted to confirm compliance with or to evaluate current procedures. It is possible that a procedure for properly establishing an electrically safe work condition (ESWC) for the specific equipment, rather than a lockout procedure, did not exist. A general procedure for lockout often does not address the safety issues that Scott faced. For example, leaving the work site triggers a requirement to verify that an ESWC still exists before continuing work.

There are 29 CFR regulations that may have saved Scott's life. 29 CFR 1910.151(a) requires that the employer ensure the ready availability of medical personnel for advice and consultation on matters of plant health. 29 CFR 1910.151(b) states that in the absence of an infirmary, clinic, or hospital in near proximity to the workplace which is used for the treatment of all injured employees, a person or persons is required to be adequately trained to render first aid. Adequate first aid supplies must be readily available.

Relevant NFPA *70E* Requirements

From the perspective of Scott being able to have returned home that day safely, he should have been aware of the following:

- His responsibility to follow policies, procedures, and training [105.3]
- His own awareness and self-discipline [110.5(D)]
- How to properly conduct job safety planning and briefing [110.5(I)]
- His ability to be a qualified person for the assigned task [110.6(A)(1)]
- Required lockout procedure training [110.6(B)]
- How to properly establish an ESWC [Article 120]
- The proper selection and use of personal and other protective equipment [130.7]

The employer's electrical safety program may have been bolstered with the following requirements:

- Employer's responsibility for proper policies, procedures and training to employees [105.3(A)]
- The need for a proper risk assessment [110.5(H)]
- Auditing of the electrical safety program and procedures [110.5(M)]
- Training requirements necessary for a qualified person [110.6(A)(1)]
- Employer's responsibility in establishing an ESWC [120.1(B)]
- Need to retest for ESWC when job location is left unattended [120.4(B)(6)]
- What is involved in conducting proper risk assessments [130.1, 130.4, 130.5]
- The required PPE for employees [130.7]

Content source: National Institute for Occupational Safety and Health (NIOSH); Maryland FACE Program, Case 94022.

Worker Alert

If a risk assessment defaults to the category tables for PPE or does not include elements of control prior to PPE, you might be at a higher risk of severe injury than is necessary for a properly justified energized task. You should be aware of the other means or methods you could use to prevent or mitigate possible injuries.

△ **(3) Hierarchy of Risk Control Methods.** The risk assessment procedure shall require that preventive and protective risk control methods be implemented in accordance with the following hierarchy:

(1) Elimination
(2) Substitution
(3) Engineering controls
(4) Awareness
(5) Administrative controls
(6) PPE

Informational Note No. 1: Elimination, substitution, and engineering controls are the most effective methods to reduce risk as they are usually applied at the source of possible injury or damage to health and they are less likely to be affected by human error. Awareness, administrative controls, and PPE are the least effective methods to reduce risk as they are not applied at the source and they are more likely to be affected by human error.

Informational Note No. 2: See Informative Annex F for more information regarding the hierarchy of risk control methods and examples of those methods.

A risk assessment can not only determine a hazard, but, as the name suggests, it can also determine the risk associated with performing a task. Risk assessments must be conducted whether equipment will be placed into an electrically safe work condition (ESWC) or if justified energized electrical work will be authorized. The PPE category method does not remove the need to implement the hierarchy of risk controls. The assessments apply whether they use the PPE category method or the incident energy analysis method.

The hierarchy of risk controls is listed in order of the most effective to the least effective and must be applied in descending order for each risk assessment. Once a hazard has been identified, it must first be determined if the hazard can be eliminated.

Both installation and work practices impact electrical safety, but they are separate and distinct electrical industries. For electrical safety to progress, employers must utilize a holistic approach. The decision to install equipment in a particular manner can affect the safety of the employees responsible for maintaining that equipment since there is no limit to the amount of energy that a safe installation can contain. With a holistic approach to electrical safety, the installation considers employee exposure to hazards and the methods of controlling those hazards. It is easier in the electrical system design and equipment selection phase to utilize the most effective controls of elimination and substitution to limit the risk associated with anticipated justified energized work. Under that condition, an employee will not only be protected by work practices but also by the installation.

In this first context, elimination is the removal of a hazard so that it does not exist in the system. This removes the potential for human error when interacting with the equipment. Full elimination of a hazard is often not an option for installed equipment. Although elimination can also be achieved by applying other controls, such as by establishing an ESWC, these controls introduce the potential for human error. Therefore, the initial attempt should be full elimination of a hazard. Informative Annex F describes what is involved in conducting a risk assessment and the benefits of each control. It also explains the potential effects of the controls on a hazard and the associated risk.

Another aspect of elimination that is often overlooked is the removal of employees from the area containing the hazard. NFPA *70E* addresses safe work practices for employees conducting tasks where there are hazards. The risk of injury is substantially reduced when employees are not in the proximity of a hazard. For example, if the racking of an energized breaker is a justified task, then the use of a remote racking system would not place employees at risk of injury if an incident were to occur.

The result of each risk assessment should be evaluated to determine if the hierarchy of controls could be further employed to lower risk or reduce a hazard. Only after all the other risk controls have been exhausted should PPE be selected. PPE is considered the least effective and lowest level of safety control for employee protection and should not be the first or only control element used.

The primary method of worker protection required by NFPA 70E and OSFIA is for equipment to be placed in an ESWC when a hazard or risk of injury exists. When the result of a risk assessment determines that a hazard or risk of injury exists, it is unacceptable to justify energized work simply with the ability to utilize PPE. Properly rated arc flash PPE can limit the severity of an injury but does not necessarily prevent an injury if an incident occurs.

(I) Job Safety Planning and Job Briefing. Before starting each job that involves exposure to electrical hazards, the employee in charge shall complete a job safety plan and conduct a job briefing with the employees involved.

(1) Job Safety Planning. The job safety plan shall be in accordance with the following:

(1) Be completed by a qualified person
(2) Be documented
(3) Include the following information:

    a. A description of the job and the individual tasks
    b. Identification of the electrical hazards associated with each task
    c. A shock risk assessment in accordance with 130.4 for tasks involving a shock hazard
    d. An arc flash risk assessment in accordance with 130.5 for tasks involving an arc flash hazard
    e. Work procedures involved, special precautions, and energy source controls

Informational Note: For an example of a job safety planning checklist see Figure 1.2.

A task must be planned in detail in order for there to be an effective job briefing. If the task is being conducted for the first time, work procedures must be developed before the work begins. If the planning reveals shortcomings in the safe work program or procedure, these should be addressed before the task is performed. It should also be verified that the necessary equipment will be available to perform the task.

NFPA *70E* currently addresses only two hazards directly—electric shock and arc flash burns. As part of the risk assessment, it is necessary to determine the need for and an appropriate method of protecting employees from all electrical hazards. The definition of electrical hazard in Article 100 includes any of the following: electric shock, arc flash burns, thermal burns, or arc blasts. Other known hazards include flying parts, molten metal, intense light, poisonous oxides, and generated pressure waves (blasts).

(2) Job Briefing. The job briefing shall cover the job safety plan and the information on the energized electrical work permit, if a permit is required.

Where exposure to potential electrical hazards is involved, the employee in charge should be qualified to perform the specific task (i.e., for working at the applicable voltage). The job briefing and planning checklist located in Informative Annex I can be referenced as needed. The employee in charge must be able to communicate what is required to the employees involved. In some instances, this could require knowledge of a second language. If the tasks involved require the skills of a licensed electrician, then it might be wise for a licensed electrician to perform the job briefing.

The job briefing needs to be completed before employees start the tasks. However, it should not be performed so far ahead that the employees involved might forget what was covered. The job briefing should include a discussion of the work procedure so that all of the parties fully understand the procedure before beginning the task. The job briefing should also give employees the opportunity to express any concerns they have about the task, the procedure, and their safety.

Δ **(3) Change in Scope.** Additional job safety planning and job briefings shall be held if changes occur during the course of the work that might affect the safety of employees.

Informational Note: For an example of a job briefing checklist, see Figure 1.1.

Worker Alert

The job briefing must cover all aspects of an assigned task. Equipment, procedures, PPE, hazards, risk control methods, and so forth must all be addressed in a manner that you fully understand and agree with. The job briefing is your opportunity to address any safety concerns prior to starting a task.

Worker Alert

You might find a reason to change the scope of a task after work has begun, or someone else might request that you do additional work. Neither should occur without modifying the work plan. Additional unanticipated hazards could expose you to injury. Your protection from additional hazards or risks might not be addressed in the original work permit.

A deviation from the work plan might put workers at risk. Tightening a lug instead of establishing an electrically safe work condition or holding a flashlight while performing a task that requires temporary lighting can dramatically affect a work procedure or risk assessment. A wisp of smoke drifting from a ventilation opening or an employee gaining equipment access from another direction can dramatically alter the hazard or risk to which an employee is exposed. Any change in scope, procedure, task, safety, and so forth must take into consideration the effect of that change on the risk assessment, work permit, and worker safety.

(J) Incident Investigations. The electrical safety program shall include elements to investigate electrical incidents.

Informational Note: Electrical incidents include events or occurrences that result in, or could have resulted in, a fatality, an injury, or damage to health. Incidents that do not result in fatality, injury, or damage to health are commonly referred to as a "close call" or "near miss."

Incident investigations should not be limited to those situations where an employee is injured to the point where medical attention is required. Employees should be encouraged to report any potential injury situation. Any electric shock has the potential to become an electrocution under the right conditions. Each near miss presented a chance that an injury or fatality could have occurred. If it is not addressed, the hazard associated with a near miss may cause a fatality the next time the task is performed.

The investigations required by NFPA *70E* are not for the purposes of assigning blame; they are intended to improve worker safety. Employers and employees must accept their responsibilities and work together to discover the causes of incidents and near misses. The electrical safety program, work procedures, protective equipment, test instruments, and so forth might require revision to prevent another near-miss occurrence, future injury, or death.

Worker Alert

It is important for you to report all incidents, regardless of if an injury occurred. Near misses involving electricity should be viewed as near fatalities. Every electrical shock is a potential electrocution. If a thermal burn occurs, that means that all the hazards were not properly addressed. A minor injury resulting from a step missing in the work procedure could be the step that saves your life the next time the procedure is performed.

Case Study
110.5(J)

Scenario

Michael, a laborer at the subcontracting company for 1½ months, was assigned to paint a section of support steel during the construction of an automated, conveyor-based assembly plant. The structural steel had already been erected. Welders continued the fabrication on the assembly line conveyor while painters painted the installed supports. Michael was painting from a battery-powered single-man lift. Three coworkers were in lifts within 20 feet of Michael. All four were "touching-up" the same steel structure with paint brushes.

Michael told the supervisor that he was receiving shocks from the conveyor. The supervisor checked the "grounds on the welders" and both went back to work. Michael discussed getting "minor" shocks from the conveyor with coworkers several times over the next hour. All shocks were dismissed as being "minor" and probably due to "the welders." About 1 hour after those discussions, Michael and a nearby coworker descended to obtain more paint. Michael again told his coworkers that he was still receiving shocks; they were again dismissed as being insignificant.

After getting more paint, Michael and the coworker ascended in their lifts to continue painting.

Within minutes after they resumed painting, a coworker saw Michael slumped in his lift and asked Michael's son, a welder on the job, if "something was wrong with his dad." The son immediately ran to the lift and climbed to his father. He received a noticeable shock when he touched his father, but the shock decreased when he pulled Michael away from the conveyor support. Since Michael was tied-off to the conveyor rail, his son disconnected the safety belt. Once Michael was lowered to the ground and removed from the lift, coworkers immediately administered CPR. Michael was unresponsive.

Result

An emergency medical service unit arrived within 10 minutes and transported Michael to the local hospital. After 45 minutes in the emergency room, he was pronounced dead by electrocution.

Investigation

Michael's company had no safety officer, but it did have a brief, written safety program with job-specific safety and emergency response procedures. On-the-job safety training was provided to employees. Toolbox meetings were routinely held on site to discuss job-specific safety practices.

Investigators concluded that the secondary source of electrical energy responsible for the fatality was the conveyor. The conveyor is considered a secondary source in this case because it acted only as a conductive path for the primary source; the defective device which energized it. Statements from the coworkers, burns on Michael's hand, and test results substantiated this conclusion. The primary electrical source which energized the conveyor could not be determined. However, several welding machines, grinders, and other electrical tools were being used on or near the conveyor at the time of the incident. None of that equipment was available for testing by investigators.

Analysis

NFPA *70E* in its entirety is applicable to this situation since the standard does not appear to have been utilized by Michael's employer. However, this fatality illustrates three critical safety issues. The first is that electrical safety is not only for those in an electrical occupation. Most occupations require an employee to use or be near electrical equipment. 29 CFR 1910.332 lists both painters and welders as occupations being at a higher than normal risk of an electrical incident.

The second is that exposure to any electrical hazard is dangerous. No shock should be dismissed as insignificant. Michael and his coworkers reported for 2 hours that they continued to receive electrical shocks. Many employers and employees pass off such incidents as a *near miss* rather than properly considering them as a *near death* incident. Every shock has the potential to become an electrocution with minor changes to the situation. It is unlikely that the voltage varied greatly during each shock incident. It is probable that Michael's body simply completed the circuit more effectively during his electrocution than during the earlier shocks.

The third issue is that any incident involving exposure to an electrical hazard should be investigated before work continues. Any electrical shock, no matter how slight, indicates an unsafe work condition requiring immediate attention.

Many more electrocutions were possible in this scenario and work being conducted by all the trades on the conveyor should have ceased. Investigation into the cause of the early shocks would have identified and corrected the situation before this fatality occurred.

Content source: National Institute for Occupational Safety and Health (NIOSH); FACE case: 91-22.

N **(K) Electrically Safe Work Condition Policy.** An electrical safety program shall include an electrically safe work condition policy that complies with 110.3.

N **(L) Lockout/Tagout Program.** The electrical safety program shall include the information required by one of the following:

(1) A lockout/tagout program in accordance with 120.1 (A)
(2) A reference to the employer's lockout/tagout program established in accordance with 120.1(A)

(M) Auditing.

(1) Electrical Safety Program Audit. The electrical safety program shall be audited to verify that the principles and procedures of the electrical safety program are in compliance with this standard. Audits shall be performed at intervals not to exceed 3 years

Auditing and enforcement are critical parts of any electrical safety program. It is vital that the electrical safety program—as well as the auditing and enforcement actions—be documented for the benefit of the employees and of the company.

The process control points and actions (i.e., the items capable of being measured) need to be determined for effective auditing. The safety principles and procedures should be compared to the requirements in the latest adopted edition of NFPA *70E*. An audit is necessary for enforcement and to ensure that employees are following program principles and procedures.

(2) Field Work Audit. Field work shall be audited to verify that the requirements contained in the procedures of the electrical safety program are being followed. When the auditing determines that the principles and procedures of the electrical safety program are not being followed, the appropriate revisions to the training program or revisions to the procedures shall be made. Audits shall be performed at intervals not to exceed 1 year.

Auditing field work involves going into the field—wherever employees are performing their required tasks and where there is the potential of exposure to electrical hazards—to gather information. At intervals not exceeding 1 year, it is important for an employer to confirm employee compliance with the company's electrical safety regulations by watching employees perform their electrical safety-related tasks and ensuring that they are using the PPE appropriate for the task they're performing. These procedures then become the metrics used to verify the required performance.

When it has been confirmed that the electrical safety program principles or procedures are not being followed, corrective action must be taken. This corrective action should consist of either applicable modification of the training program or a revision to the procedures, such as increasing the frequency of training or adding follow-up verification of compliance. Employee involvement in creating a safer work environment should be fostered, and training employees to report near misses or incidents brought about by human error or insufficient procedures should be encouraged. However, it is also important for an enforcement program to be established for willful violations of the employer's safety regulations.

An audit should also be used to confirm that all electrical hazards are addressed, to measure program effectiveness, to develop program improvements, and to evaluate any program and physical conditions that have changed. An audit should also evaluate incidents to determine if there are any necessary changes to the electrical safety program.

(3) Lockout/Tagout Program and Procedure Audit. The lockout/tagout program and procedures required by Article 120 shall be audited by a qualified person at intervals not to exceed 1 year. The audit shall cover at least one lockout/tagout in progress. The audit shall be designed to identify and correct deficiencies in the following:

(1) The lockout/tagout program and procedures
(2) The lockout/tagout training
(3) Worker execution of the lockout/tagout procedure

The objective of this audit is to make sure that all of the requirements of the lockout or tagout procedure are properly executed and that the employees are familiar with their responsibilities. The audit must determine whether the requirements contained in the documented procedures are sufficient to ensure that the electrical energy is satisfactorily controlled. The audit should also identify and correct any deficiencies in the procedure, employee training, or enforcement of the requirements.

(4) Documentation. The audits required by 110.5(M) shall be documented.

110.6 Training Requirements.

Training can be defined as the process by which someone is taught the skills necessary for a job. Training can be seen as teaching (presenting the required information) and learning (absorbing the information and being able to perform the required skill). To be considered qualified, a person must demonstrate an understanding of the required knowledge and the ability to perform a task safely. To be competent, the person being trained should be able to show proficiency in performing a task so as to be able to do the task safely and efficiently. However, the prime goal here is safety, not efficiency.

(A) Electrical Safety Training. The training requirements contained in 110.6(A) shall apply to employees exposed to an electrical hazard when the risk associated with that hazard is not reduced to a safe level by the applicable electrical installation requirements. Such employees shall be trained to understand the specific hazards associated with electrical energy. They shall be trained in safety-related work practices and procedural requirements, as necessary, to provide protection from the electrical hazards associated with their respective job or task assignments. Employees shall be trained to identify and understand the relationship between electrical hazards and possible injury.

> Informational Note: For further information concerning installation requirements, see *NFPA 70, National Electrical Code.*

All occupations can experience electrical injuries and fatalities, including those not necessarily associated with electrical work. NFPA 70E does not deem a task to be electrical or nonelectrical work. It requires that all employees be protected from electrical hazards regardless of their occupation, job position, or title.

These training requirements are necessary at some level for all employees. The requirements are necessary when the risk of an injury from a potential electrical hazard is not reduced to an acceptable level by the pertinent installation requirements. For example, an employee using portable electrical equipment in contradiction to the manufacturer's instructions or published safety warnings must recognize the hazards. Employees interacting with electrical equipment should understand that safe operation requires proper installation and maintenance.

All employees should be trained to refrain from operating equipment when evidence of impending failure is present, such as arcing, overheating, loose equipment parts, visible damage, unusual noises or odors, or deterioration of the equipment's condition. When any of these indications exist, the risk from electrical hazards might be unacceptable.

Employees who might be exposed to an unacceptable risk of injury from the use of electricity in the work environment need to be trained. The training required depends on various factors, such as the tasks to be performed; whether the employee is a manager, supervisor, or worker; whether the employee is an unqualified person; or whether the employee is or needs to be a qualified person (for more information, see the commentary following the definition for qualified person in Article 100). Depending on their job functions and the tasks assigned to them, different groups or levels of employees might be trained in a variety of subjects.

The degree of training should be appropriate and based on the tasks that an employee will be performing. Where the risk of an electrical injury from energized electrical equipment is minimal (acceptable), such as when employees operate equipment that is properly installed, maintained, and enclosed, the electrical safety training required could be minimal.

Even though 110.6(A) stipulates the essential types of training required, the key concepts of training are the employee understanding the relevant factors and the employee demonstrating the ability to work safely. The key to working safely is to always remain vigilant and not let one's guard down, even for a second.

(1) Qualified Person. A qualified person shall be trained and knowledgeable in the construction and operation of equipment or a specific work method and be trained to identify and avoid the electrical hazards that might be present with respect to that equipment or work method.

The term *qualified person* is defined in Article 100, and by default, the person must be competent. The general definition of *competent* is having sufficient skill, knowledge, or experience for a specific purpose. A worker could be competent to install a light fixture but not qualified under NFPA *70E* to troubleshoot that fixture while it is energized.

The only place in NFPA *70E* in which the term *competent person* is used is Article 350. That definition, which uses *qualified person* as its basis, includes responsibility for all work activities or safety procedures related to custom or special equipment and is only applicable to Article 350.

In order to be considered qualified for a particular task or work assignment, an employee must have internalized the requisite knowledge regarding the electrical system involved and the required procedures. The employee must also have received the safety training identified in 110.6. Exhibit 110.4 is provided to help the employer and employees understand some of the traits necessary to be considered a minimally qualified person under NFPA *70E*, depending on the requirements of the specific tasks (e.g., responding to medical emergencies).

A person might be qualified to perform a specific task on specific equipment while being unqualified to perform another task on the same piece of equipment. Also, qualification does not necessarily carry over to a similar piece of equipment nor to an identical task on a different piece of equipment. Work practices, procedures, and hazards can vary by the task and the equipment. Qualification is not necessarily based on title, licensure, and so forth. For example, a licensed electrician might not be qualified to work on high-voltage switchgear. In order to be qualified, the person must have knowledge and demonstrated skills concerning specific hazards, work practices, and procedural requirements.

(a) Such persons shall also be familiar with the proper use of the special precautionary techniques, applicable electrical policies and procedures, PPE, insulating and shielding materials, and insulated tools and test equipment.

(b) A person can be considered qualified with respect to certain equipment and tasks but still be unqualified for others.

(c) Such persons permitted to work within the limited approach boundary shall, at a minimum, be additionally trained in all of the following:

(1) Skills and techniques necessary to distinguish exposed energized electrical conductors and circuit parts from other parts of electrical equipment
(2) Skills and techniques necessary to determine the nominal voltage of exposed energized electrical conductors and circuit parts
(3) Approach distances specified in Table 130.4(E)(a) and Table 130.4(E)(b) and the corresponding voltages to which the qualified person will be exposed
(4) Decision-making process necessary to be able to do the following:

  a. Perform the job safety planning
  b. Identify electrical hazards
  c. Assess the associated risk
  d. Select the appropriate risk control methods from the hierarchy of controls identified in 110.5(H)(3), including PPE

This section deals with limited approach boundaries, which imply shock risk. The employee performing a task should be able to identify exposed energized electrical conductors and circuit parts from those that are considered to be effectively guarded, insulated, or isolated. The employee should also be able to determine the nominal system voltage of the exposed energized components and the circuit parts concerned.

EXHIBIT 110.4

Traits of a qualified person.

Trained and knowledgeable in ...
- Construction of equipment
- Operation of systems and equipment
- Specific work procedures for assigned tasks
- Identification of electrical hazards
- Avoidance of electrical hazards
- Selection of test equipment
- Safety-related work practices
- Normal operating conditions of specific electrical equipment
- Self-awareness and self-discipline

Able to identify and understand the ...
- Specific hazards associated with electrical energy and equipment
- Relationship between electrical hazards and possible injury
- Electrical hazards regarding procedures to be used
- Approach boundary distances
- Indication of impeding equipment failure

Familiar with proper use of ...
- Required special precautionary techniques
- Personal protective equipment
- Insulating and shielding materials
- Insulated tools
- Test equipment

Has skills and techniques to ...
- Distinguish exposed energized electrical parts from other parts of electrical equipment
- Determine nominal system voltage of exposed energized electrical parts
- Inspect and test personal protective equipment
- Inspect test equipment

Has necessary decision-making process to be able to...
- Perform job safety planning
- Assess associated risk with electrical hazards
- Select appropriate risk control methods

Demonstrated ability and capability to ...
- Perform procedures necessary to safely conduct the assigned task
- Establish an electrically safe work condition

Retraining is necessary when ...
- Inspection indicates employee not peoperly complying with safety related work practices
- New equipment, including PPE, or new technology introduced into work environment
- New or revised procedures are to be used
- Scheduled for task not associated with regular job duties
- Retraining has not occurred within 3 years
- Requested by employee

Once the nominal system voltage level has been determined, the employee must be aware of the distances specified in the shock approach boundary tables in 130.4 and follow the rules applicable at each boundary point—the limited approach boundary and the restricted approach boundary.

As stated in 110.5(H), risk assessment includes identifying the hazards—electrical or otherwise—related to the task at hand, assessing the associated risk, and then selecting the appropriate safety control from the categories identified in the hierarchy of risk controls. NFPA *70E* currently addresses only two hazards directly: electric shock and arc flash burns. It is necessary to determine the need for and an appropriate method of protecting workers from all electrical hazards. The definition of *electrical hazard* in Article

100 includes any of the following: electric shock, arc flash burns, thermal burns, or arc blasts. Other known hazards include flying parts, molten metal, intense light, poisonous oxides, and generated pressure waves (blasts).

Although this standard is concerned with electrical hazards, employees need to consider all the potential hazards of the work tasks they are assigned.

(d) An employee who is undergoing on-the-job training for the purpose of obtaining the skills and knowledge necessary to be considered a qualified person, and who in the course of such training demonstrates an ability to perform specific duties safely at his or her level of training, and who is under the direct supervision of a qualified person shall be considered to be a qualified person for the performance of those specific duties.

Part of this training is learning how to select and use the personal and other protective equipment required to perform the tasks safely. Training can be completed in incremental steps. Once the instructor is sure that an employee is ready, the employee could be allowed to perform the procedure with the instructor close by to help out as necessary. Until the employee shows a level of confidence performing the task—the ability to complete the task safely with the minimum ability required in the instructor's opinion—the employee should not be allowed to perform the procedure without the instructor watching nearby. However, once this level of knowledge and ability is reached, the employee can then be considered a qualified person to perform that particular task.

(e) Employees shall be trained to select an appropriate test instrument and shall demonstrate how to use a device to verify the absence of voltage, including interpreting indications provided by the device. The training shall include information that enables the employee to understand all limitations of each test instrument that might be used.

The employee must know how to safely use the test instrument to perform the required measurement task. This requires an understanding and capability to interpret all the readings and indications of the test instrument. It also includes knowing the different settings, limitations, and operating modes of the device, as well as the proper terminals into which leads are to be installed. If the device has a duty rating or category rating, the employee needs to know how to comply with that rating. The employee must also be able to select test instruments suitable for the parameters of the system and the locations where they will be applied to the electrical distribution system. In addition, the employee must be familiar with and understand all of the required information contained in the operating and maintenance instructions provided with the test instrument.

Exhibit 110.5 shows an example of a test instrument used for measuring voltage. Note the different voltage ratings for Category III and Category IV. Understanding these ratings is critical to the safe use of the meter. For more information, see the commentary following 110.8(B) regarding meter category ratings.

(f) The employer shall determine through regular supervision or through inspections conducted on at least an annual basis that each employee is complying with the safety-related work practices required by this standard.

In order to ensure safety, compliance with the requirements of this standard and with the employer's electrical safety program must be an ongoing and continuous activity. Where there is potential exposure to electrical hazards, each employee should receive occasional observation by a mentor (such as a supervisor or senior person) or participate

EXHIBIT 110.5

*Meter for measuring voltage.
(Courtesy of Fluke Corporation)*

in checkups conducted on at least an annual basis. This might be part of the required field work audit required per 110.5(M)(2).

(2) Unqualified Persons. Unqualified persons shall be trained in, and be familiar with, any electrical safety-related practices necessary for their safety.

Employees not considered qualified persons must have the knowledge and skills necessary for their safety when interacting with electrical equipment, including during normal operation of the equipment. The following is a list of some of the situations unqualified persons might encounter and need to be aware of:

- *General potential hazards.* Understand and recognize potential hazards, including the relationship between exposure to potential electrical hazards and possible bodily injury.
- *Attachment plugs.* Understand how to properly remove an attachment plug from a receptacle.
- *Damaged equipment.* Do not use damaged electrical equipment (fixed or portable); damaged cables, cords, or connectors; or damaged receptacles.
- *Impending failure of equipment.* Be aware of what the signs of impending failure of electrical equipment are and do not remain around electrical equipment when there is evidence of impending failure.
- *Receptacle plugs/caps.* Do not remove attachment plugs (caps) from receptacles when the combination is not load-break-rated.
- *Tripped circuit breakers.* Do not reset a circuit breaker after an automatic trip. Always notify a qualified person to determine the cause.
- *Flammable materials.* Do not use flammable materials near electrical equipment that can create a spark.
- *Overhead power lines.* Be aware of the proper approach distance from overhead power lines.
- *Alerting techniques.* Be aware of alerting techniques, such as safety signs and tags, barricades, and warning attendants. Remain outside the shock protection or arc flash protection boundaries when energized work is being performed.

Worker Alert

Examples of an unqualified person interacting with electrical equipment might include a janitor responsible for turning on lights in a facility at the start of the day or a machine operator starting a machine at the beginning of a shift. Both must be trained in safety practices related to those tasks.

- *Limited approach shock boundary.* Do not cross the limited approach shock boundary unless advised and continuously escorted by a qualified person.
- *Restricted approach boundary.* Never cross the restricted approach boundary.

All employees should be given some basic, common-sense rules for avoiding electrical accidents and injuries. These rules might include the following:

- Do not overload circuits, such as by running multiple appliances from a single outlet.
- Never plug in equipment with a damaged electrical cord or use an extension cord that has damaged insulation.
- Never use electrical equipment, such as a power tool or appliance, if it is sparking, smoking, or otherwise seems to be malfunctioning.
- Keep metal objects, large and small, away from electrical equipment.

△ **(3) Additional Training and Retraining.** Additional training and retraining in safety-related work practices and applicable changes in this standard shall be performed at intervals not to exceed 3 years. An employee shall receive additional training or retraining if any of the following conditions exists:

(1) The supervision or annual inspections indicate the employee is not complying with the safety-related work practices.
(2) New technology, new types of equipment, or changes in procedures necessitate the use of safety-related work practices different from those that the employee would normally use.
(3) The employee needs to review tasks that are performed less often than once per year.
(4) The employee needs to review safety-related work practices not normally used by the employee during regular job duties.
(5) The employee's job duties change.

> **Worker Alert**
>
> You are the only one who truly knows when your skills are not up to date or sharp enough to safely perform a task. Updating and refining your skills can help prevent injury.

Electrical safety in the workplace is not a static subject. Generally, retraining is required when there are changes in situations, policies, procedures, or equipment. Because improvements in electrical safety often dictate changes to this standard, retraining employees might be necessary when a new edition is published. Employers should keep track of the tasks employees are qualified to perform and schedule retraining to make certain their qualifications do not lapse.

(4) Type of Training. The training required by 110.6(A) shall be classroom, on-the-job, or a combination of the two. The type and extent of the training provided shall be determined by the risk to the employee.

> Informational Note: Classroom training can include interactive electronic or interactive web-based training components

When developing and implementing an electrical safety training program, an employer might determine that certain parties could be helpful to develop the training material and training methods and to present the material in a clear fashion. Some, all, or a combination of the following parties can be included: consultants, engineers, a manufacturer's representative or agents, safety professionals, teachers, contract employees, and regular employees.

NFPA *70E* does not specify who is qualified to provide training. Employers must determine the qualifications of instructors. An employer must be familiar enough with the requirements in both NFPA *70E* and the applicable federal regulations to determine the suitability of an instructor. Reputation, experience, credentials, or education might be determining factors used by an employer. The instructor should have knowledge of the procedures for employees with any title or in any position. The instructor needs to be competent in teaching methods and trade practices and knowledgeable on the subjects presented. Employees will trust that a qualified person has been selected to conduct the training.

Training can be of the classroom or on-the-job type or a combination of the two. These types of training are instructor-led programs, whether in person or nontraditional classrooms. NFPA *70E* does not specify the type of classroom training necessary. The employer must determine whether the method employed conveys the necessary level of training and if it imparts the necessary knowledge for employees to safely perform their duties. If an employer needs to communicate work instructions or other workplace information to employees at a certain vocabulary level or in a language other than English, the electrical safety training needs to be provided to those employees in the same manner.

It is incumbent on the employer to verify that the employees have acquired the knowledge and skills necessary to safely perform their job tasks. Retraining needs to be provided when practices indicate that an employee has not retained or acquired the requisite understanding or skill. Employees should be tested to demonstrate their ability to perform the required tasks safely and in a timely manner. If the employer doesn't convey the training to employees in a manner they are capable of understanding, then the instruction or training has failed to meet the employer's training obligations and needs to be revised.

Although the training required by NFPA 70E and OSHA regulations is expected to be instructor-led, other forms of training can be used to augment classroom instruction. In actuality, an appropriate training mix might include some of the following methods:

- *E-book or tablet-based*. Training that uses an e-book or tablet-type computer for training.
- *Self-paced*. Training for which the pace of learning is determined by the student.
- *Web-based or online*. Training performed on the Internet, on a website, or in web-based applications.

OSHA considers classroom and on-the-job training to be the most effective types of training. These forms of training facilitate interaction between employees and trainers. For computer-based training to be as effective as classroom training, it must be interactive and participatory.

(5) Electrical Safety Training Documentation. The employer shall document that each employee has received the training required by 110.6(A). This documentation shall be in accordance with the following:

(1) Be made when the employee demonstrates proficiency in the work practices involved
(2) Be retained for the duration of the employee's employment
(3) Contain the content of the training, each employee's name, and dates of training

> Informational Note No. 1: Content of the training could include one or more of the following: course syllabus, course curriculum, outline, table of contents, or training objectives.

> Informational Note No. 2: Employment records that indicate that an employee has received the required training are an acceptable means of meeting this requirement.

Governmental rules might require safety training documentation to be retained for a longer period of time, which could exceed 7 years after an employee leaves. Where outside training is used, information about the training organization or instructor might also prove useful.

(B) Lockout/Tagout Procedure Training.

Δ **(1) Initial Training.** Employees involved in the lockout/tagout procedures required by 120.2(B) shall be trained in the following:

(1) The lockout/tagout procedures
(2) Their responsibility in the execution of the procedures

Employers, including independent contractors, must provide training for all of their employees who might be involved in the process of establishing an electrically safe work condition (ESWC) before they attempt it in the field. Training in the method to be employed for the task can help minimize the possibility of errors when implementing an unfamiliar process. Each employee associated with performing a job must be trained to understand his or her role in the lockout process and accept individual responsibility for the integrity of the process. All employees must receive additional training whenever the established procedure is changed.

Contract employer procedures might be different from host employer procedures. Contractors and facility owners must exchange information about creating an ESWC—along with any information about characteristics specific to the facility—and ensure that their respective employees understand all the issues that are important to the other employer. Employees who have been reassigned (either permanently or temporarily) must be trained to understand their new role in the lockout procedure.

(2) Retraining. Retraining in the lockout/tagout procedures shall be performed as follows:

(1) When the procedures are revised
(2) At intervals not to exceed 3 years
(3) When supervision or annual inspections indicate that the employee is not complying with the lockout/tagout procedures

(3) Lockout/Tagout Training Documentation.

(a) The employer shall document that each employee has received the training required by 110.6(B).
(b) The documentation shall be made when the employee demonstrates proficiency in the work practices involved.
(c) The documentation shall contain the content of the training, each employee's name, and the dates of the training.

Informational Note: Content of the training could include one or more of the following: course syllabus, course curriculum, outline, table of contents, or training objectives.

Training documentation can be either hard copy or electronic. Whatever format is used, the record must be retained for the duration of the worker's employment in accordance with 110.6(A)(5).

(C) Emergency Response Training.

(1) Contact Release. Employees exposed to shock hazards and those responsible for the safe release of victims from contact with energized electrical conductors or circuit parts shall be trained in methods of safe release. Refresher training shall occur annually.

Worker Alert

Although a general lockout procedure can be developed, the individual steps for establishing an electrically safe work condition on equipment will vary. You should fully understand the lockout procedures as well as the work procedures for a task before applying them in the field.

Worker Alert

You might instinctively react to another employee's predicament without considering the consequences. Proper training and your personal awareness of a situation can not only enable you to help your coworker, but it can also keep you safe. Remember that many electrocutions occur to the person responding to the initial victim.

A victim of an electrical accident might be incapable of releasing an energized electrical conductor or circuit part because muscles contract when electrical current is running through the body. Extreme caution should be a primary consideration when responding to an electrical accident. Anyone attempting to rescue a victim in contact with an energized electrical conductor or circuit part can be exposed to the same hazard and must identify and avoid the hazard and take the appropriate action. The victim's survival depends on a safe and rapid response. Before first aid can be provided, the victim has to be safely moved away from the energized electrical conductors and circuit parts.

A quick response is essential during an electrical shock incident—seconds gained or lost can decide the fate of a victim. Often, shutting off the equipment is the most efficient way to safely release an employee. However, a shock rescue kit equipped with all the necessary personal and protective equipment can help save rescue personnel vital time. The shock rescue kit could include items such as an insulated rescue stick or hook, a voltage detector, a cable cutter with insulated handles, an insulating platform or pad, insulated rubber gloves, insulated dielectric overshoes (boots), safety and first aid instructions, a roll of adhesive warning tape, and a can of talcum powder. The composition of the kit should depend on the situation in which it would be used.

(2) First Aid, Emergency Response, and Resuscitation.

(a) Employees responsible for responding to medical emergencies shall be trained in first aid and emergency procedures.

(b) Employees responsible for responding to medical emergencies shall be trained in cardiopulmonary resuscitation (CPR).

(c) Employees responsible for responding to medical emergencies shall be trained in the use of an automated external defibrillator (AED) if an employer's emergency response plan includes the use of this device.

(d) Training shall occur at a frequency that satisfies the requirements of the certifying body.

Informational Note: Employees responsible for responding to medical emergencies might not be first responders or medical professionals. Such employees could be a second person, a safety watch, or a craftsperson.

No matter how well-prepared a facility might be, where human beings are involved, accidents will occur. Employers need to have policies, procedures, and trained personnel available to deal with injuries or illnesses on the job.

Employers must determine who will be responsible for responding to an emergency or electrical incident within the facility. NFPA *70E* does not dictate that a second employee be responsible for responding to emergencies, and it does not prohibit the use of off-site response. Whoever is responsible for first aid, the person(s) must be trained to provide that response. Different levels of response might dictate different training requirements. For example, an employee might be a trained first responder for cardiopulmonary resuscitation (CPR) purposes, but the facility health care professional arriving later would have had more advanced and detailed training.

For information regarding the contents of a generic first aid kit, refer to ANSI Z308.1, *Minimum Requirements for Workplace First Aid Kits and Supplies.* Although the listed contents should be adequate for small worksites, employers at larger or more unique facilities should determine the need for other types of first aid supplies, as well as additional quantities. Employers should assess the specific needs of their worksite periodically and augment the first aid kit appropriately.

(3) Training Verification. Employers shall verify at least annually that employee training required by 110.6(C) is current.

Worker Alert

Training requirements include cardiopulmonary resuscitation (CPR) and artificial external defibrillator (AED) use, as contact with an energized conductor or circuit part can result in sudden cardiac arrest. If you are responsible for responding to medical emergencies, you must be aware of the location of the first aid supplies and AED.

OSHA Connection

29 CFR 1910.151(b)

Employers must ensure that—in the absence of medical services near the workplace—an adequately trained person is available to render first aid to an injured employee. Adequate first aid supplies must also be readily available.

OSHA Connection

OSHA Publication 3317-06N (2006), *Best Practices Guide: Fundamentals of a Workplace First-Aid Program,* identifies four essential elements for first aid programs to be effective and successful. It also includes best practices for planning and conducting safe and effective first aid training.

First aid training courses should include instruction in both general and workplace hazard-specific knowledge and skills. First aid responders might experience long intervals between learning cardiopulmonary resuscitation (CPR) and automated external defibrillator (AED) skills and putting them into practice. It can be beneficial to refresh first aid skills periodically to maintain and update knowledge and skills even if a certification for CPR or AED is valid. Instructor-led retraining for life-threatening emergencies can be done annually to keep necessary skills sharp. Retraining for non-life-threatening response can be done periodically to help employees retain the knowledge.

First aid training is offered by nationally recognized and private educational organizations, including the American Heart Association, the American Red Cross, and the National Safety Council. NFPA *70E* does not advocate for any specific first aid course. First aid courses should be customized for specific work environments. Unique conditions at specific worksites might warrant adding additional elements to a standardized first aid training program.

The training organization sets the minimum level of requirement for its first aid training program. Assessment of the successful completion of the first aid training program should include the instructor's observations of the acquired skills, as well as written performance assessments. NFPA *70E* requires that the employer verify at least annually that training for its employees who are first aid responders is current

(4) Documentation. The employer shall document that the training required by 110.6(C) has occurred.

Documentation reinforces the importance of training and training verification for an employer's first aid responders

110.7 Host and Contract Employers' Responsibilities.

Generally, the host employer is the party contracting for the premises where the work is to be performed. However, there are circumstances where one division of a company could be the host employer to another division's employees and the other division seen as the contract employer. The host employer might not always be the owner of the facility. There are also situations in which the host employer is the on-site employer (not the owner of the facility), and a contract employer is the one that is obligated to perform the work. A service contractor, such as a vending machine operator sending employees to a site, would be considered a contract employer.

The concept of a host employer and a contract employer has some flexibility, as the terms are not defined in NFPA *70E*. It might be possible to pass from the role of contract employer to host employer and from host employer to contract employer depending on the particular work agreement involved. The AHJ enforcing this standard makes the final decision regarding the terms.

(A) Host Employer Responsibilities.

(1) The host employer shall inform contract employers of the following:

(1) Known hazards that are covered by this standard, that are related to the contract employer's work, and that might not be recognized by the contract employer or its employees

(2) Information about the employer's installation that the contract employer needs to make the assessments required by Chapter 1

A host employer is responsible for safety at their facility regardless of the purpose of a person's visit. An employer should be aware of anyone's potential exposure to electrical hazards or energized electrical work being conducted within its facility, whether the task is being performed by an internal employee or a contract employee.

The information shared during the documented meeting required by 110.7(C) should be determined ahead of time. Each party should clearly communicate the information they require and the information they expect to provide, including the exchange of electrical safety programs. Where there is ambiguity, there is the potential for problems because the various parties might have different expectations.

When the justification of energized work is being proposed, the host employer should include the information necessary to complete and submit an energized electrical work permit for the host employer's management to sign. For requirements specific to energized work, see 110.4. The host employer should also provide the contract employer with the host's electrical safety-related rules that must be followed while on-site.

(2) The host employer shall report observed contract employer-related violations of this standard to the contract employer.

> Informational Note: Examples of a host employer can include owner or their designee, construction manager, general contractor, or employer.

Using a contract employee does not absolve a host employer of enforcing its own safe work practices. The host employer might be responsible for limiting access to energized electrical equipment regardless of who is conducting the work. The host employer might also be responsible for emergency response if an incident does occur.

(B) Contract Employer Responsibilities.

(1) The contract employer shall ensure that each of his or her employees is instructed in the hazards communicated to the contract employer by the host employer. This instruction shall be in addition to the basic training required by this standard.

A contract employer is often referred to as an independent contractor. The host employer is generally expected to have a greater knowledge of the special conditions and unique situations or features of equipment and the specific hazards other than electrical hazards present in its facility. The host employer must convey this information to the contract employer, and the contract employer, in turn, must provide this information to the employee performing the work at the host facility.

(2) The contract employer shall ensure that each of his or her employees follows the work practices required by this standard and safety-related work rules required by the host employer.

Contract employers must follow their own electrical safety-related practices, and they might be required to follow the host employer's electrical safety-related practices, as well. The contract employer should provide employees with training on the correct work procedures and the necessary personal and other protective equipment they need to perform a job safely. For example, the contract employer is responsible for ensuring that employees implement the host employer's lockout procedures if they are more stringent than their own. If the contract employer's lockout will be utilized, the host employer should be made aware of the steps involved in that procedure.

Worker Alert

Although the contract employer is responsible for communicating the necessary information to the contract employees, you are ultimately responsible for your own actions. As a contract employee working at an unfamiliar site, you must be aware of all the hazards associated with the job, including the work procedures involved, any special precautions, the energy source controls, and the PPE requirements. If you do not receive the information required by this section, talk to your employer.

To ensure that the host's required practices do not violate the requirements of NFPA 70E, it is important to know the requirements included in Article 120, Article 130, and, where special equipment, systems, or facilities are involved, Chapter 3. Likewise, NFPA *70E* is not an allowance to utilize practices that are less stringent than an employer's safety-related practices.

(3) The contract employer shall advise the host employer of the following:

(1) Any unique hazards presented by the contract employer's work

(2) Hazards identified during the course of work by the contract employer that were not communicated by the host employer

(3) The measures the contractor took to correct any violations reported by the host employer under 110.7(A)(2) and to prevent such violation from recurring in the future

Where conditions and situations regarding equipment or procedures need to change as a result of the work being performed by the contract employer, the contract employer must make the host employer aware of the new conditions. For example, in situations in which an additional task is necessary or the utility company has increased the size of the transformer serving a facility, the contract employer must notify the host employer. The contract employer has an obligation to inform the host employer of the resulting increase in the hazard level. Either situation could require a re-evaluation or modification of the work permit.

When a utility increases the size or efficiency of a transformer, a new risk assessment might need to be performed. When the contract employer notices that such a change might cause the newly installed equipment to be used above its ratings, the contract employer should inform the host employer of the situation. The contract employer might prefer not to perform work when the equipment, task, risk assessment, work practices, or work scope changes do not adequately protect their employees.

(C) Documentation. Where the host employer has knowledge of hazards covered by this standard that are related to the contract employer's work, there shall be a documented meeting between the host employer and the contract employer.

Informational Note to 110.7: On multi-employer work sites (in all industry sectors), more than one employer can be responsible for identifying hazardous conditions and creating safe work practices.

A documented meeting might be prudent regardless of the contract employer's prior knowledge of hazards. The host employer should be aware of all energized electrical work being conducted within its facility by a contractor. Documentation should include whether energized work by the contractor is or is not permitted. If energized diagnostic tests are necessary, the contractor must inform the host of that need. Hazards observed by the contractor and the steps taken to mitigate an injury should also be documented. The training provided to associated employees and the decision of which employer's lockout procedure to follow should be documented as well.

110.8 Test Instruments and Equipment.

Test instruments within an organization should be standardized to facilitate their use. The organization should determine the manufacturer, type, and model of the test instruments, as well as the types of systems and the locations where they can be used..

The organization should also determine if it will provide the test instruments or if it will allow employees to use their own test instruments, which could create some unique problems and situations. Each test instrument might require its own set of policies and procedures. Policies and procedures need to be developed and refined before any test instrument is used.

(A) Testing. Only qualified persons shall perform tasks such as testing, troubleshooting, and voltage measuring on electrical equipment where an electrical hazard exists.

Careful consideration should be given to circuits operating under 50 volts where conditions such as a wet environment or high available fault current exist. If it is determined that an electrical hazard does exist, only qualified persons are permitted to perform tasks such as testing, troubleshooting, voltage measuring, or similar diagnostic work.

(B) Rating. Test instruments, equipment, and their accessories shall be as follows:

(1) Rated for circuits and equipment where they are utilized

(2) Approved for the purpose

(3) Used in accordance with any instructions provided by the manufacturer

> Informational Note: See UL 61010-1, *Safety Requirements for Electrical Equipment for Measurement, Control, and Laboratory Use - Part 1: General Requirements,* for rating and design requirements for voltage measurement and test instruments intended for use on electrical systems 1000 volts and below and UL 61010-2-033, *Safety Requirements for Electrical Equipment for Measurement, Control, and Laboratory Use — Part 2-033: Particular Requirements for Hand-Held Multimeters and Other Meters, for Domestic and Professional use, Capable of Measuring Mains Voltage.*

The point on the electrical distribution system where a specific voltage test meter can be used is often indicated by a category designation. The transient overvoltage protection, fusing, and probes for these meters vary based on the location in which they can be used. For example, Category III test instruments may be rated CAT 111-600 V or CAT III-1000 V. The 600 V instrument is rated for transients up to 6000 volts, whereas the 1000 V instrument is rated for transients up to 8000 volts. However, a CAT 11-1000 V instrument is rated only for transients up to 6000 volts.

Using an inappropriate meter for a measurement location could initiate an electrocution or arc flash incident. The four categories that are typically used to indicate the location of use for test equipment are as follows:

- Category IV: Three-phase utility connections and outside
- Category III: Inside distribution (feeders and branch circuits)
- Category II: Single-phase receptacle level (30 feet from CAT III locations, 60 feet from CAT IV locations)
- Category I: Electronic equipment

Exhibit 110.6 illustrates the locations where various categories apply within an electrical system.

Worker Alert

A qualified person in this context has knowledge related to the operation of the test instruments and the electrical equipment being tested. To be a qualified person, you must have received the safety training necessary to identify and avoid the hazards related to the use of the test instruments on specific pieces of equipment. The use of the instruments on other equipment might require further qualification.

EXHIBIT 110.6

Examples of the equipment and locations suitable for Category II, Category III, and Category IV-rated test instruments. (Reproduced with Permission, Fluke Corporation

(C) Design. Test instruments, equipment, and their accessories shall be designed for the environment to which they will be exposed and for the manner in which they will be utilized.

Test instrument accessories, such as probes and leads, are part of the equipment design and should be treated with the same care as the instrument. Making or modifying accessories must be avoided. There are a variety of special accessories for test instruments available from test equipment manufacturers.

Test instruments must be selected for the conditions of use. Contacting an exposed energized electrical conductor or circuit part with a test instrument to measure voltage normally results in a small arc immediately before contact is made or when contact is broken. Therefore, such test instruments must not be used where concentrations of flammable gases, vapors, or dust occur.

(D) Visual Inspection and Repair. Test instruments and equipment and all associated test leads, cables, power cords, probes, and connectors shall be visually inspected for external defects and damage before each use. If there is a defect or evidence of damage that might expose an employee to injury, the defective or damaged item shall be removed from service. No employee shall use it until a person(s) qualified to perform the repairs and tests that are necessary to render the equipment safe has done so.

If a defect is found during the visual inspection, a tag or label should be attached to the instrument indicating that the instrument is defective and should not be used. The instrument should be removed from service until repairs have been made by a qualified person. A defective lead or probe should not be repaired; it should be destroyed and replaced with a new one.

Worker Alert

You must look for damaged insulation, cracks in the instrument or probes, exposed metal, or missing covers. You must also verify that the instrument is properly rated for the system you will be testing. You must only use probes that are identified for use with the test equipment.

(E) Operation Verification. When test instruments are used for testing the absence of voltage on conductors or circuit parts operating at voltages equal to or greater than 50 volts, the operation of the test instrument shall be verified on any known voltage source before and after an absence of voltage test is performed.

> When a test instrument is used to test for the absence of voltage, a zero reading might mean that no voltage is present during the testing or it could mean that the instrument »
> failed. Therefore, proper operation of the test instrument must be verified on a known voltage source before it can be used to test for the absence of voltage. After the voltage test has been conducted, the proper operation of the test instrument must again be verified on a known voltage source to ensure that instrument failure did not occur during the testing for the absence of voltage.
>
> Although this verification applies to conductors or circuit parts operating at 50 volts or more, under certain conditions (such as with wet contact or immersion) even circuits operating under 50 volts can pose a shock hazard. The 50-volt limit does not rely on the frequency of the circuit—it applies to all frequencies. See Exhibit 120.15 for an illustration of the procedure to test for the absence of voltage.

110.9 Portable Cord- and-Plug-Connected Electric Equipment.

This section applies to the use of cord- and plug-connected equipment, including cord- and plug-connected test instruments and cord sets (extension cords).

> Portable electrical equipment is cord- and plug-connected and is capable of being readily moved from one location to another. The requirements in this section do not include portable cordless equipment powered by battery power packs. However, the cord- and plug-connected battery charger used to recharge a battery power pack for cordless equipment is included.

(A) Handling and Storage. Portable equipment shall be handled and stored in a manner that will not cause damage. Flexible electric cords connected to equipment shall not be used for raising or lowering the equipment. Flexible cords shall not be fastened with staples or hung in such a fashion as could damage the outer jacket or insulation.

> Raising, lowering, or moving portable equipment by its flexible electric cord can damage the cord and the equipment, exposing conductors that could leave an employee vulnerable to injury. Such practices should be prohibited as part of an electrical safety plan.
>
> NEC Section 400.13 requires flexible cord to be used only in continuous lengths without splices or taps where initially installed. NEC Article 590 applies to temporary electric power and lighting installations and requires flexible cords and cables to be protected from damage when they're being used or handled. In accordance with NEC 590.4, flexible cords and cables (extension cords) should be of the hard- or extra-hard usage type, as identified in NEC Table 400.4. In accordance with NEC 590.4(J), flexible cords and cables should be supported in place at intervals that ensure they will be protected from physical damage.
>
> Extension cords are permitted to be laid on the floor or ground and to run through doorways, windows, or similar openings, provided they are protected from damage. One method of protection might be preventing doors from closing using fasteners or blocking.

Proper storage of portable equipment and the flexible electric cords connected to the equipment is just as important as proper handling. The cord listing defines indoor storage as protection from sunlight or weather or both. Cords improperly stored (such as those exposed on work trucks) without this necessary protection could suffer UV and weather damage.

(B) Grounding-Type Equipment.

(a) A flexible cord used with grounding-type utilization equipment shall contain an equipment grounding conductor

An equipment grounding conductor is an integral part of the safety system built into equipment by manufacturers, as it provides significant protection from shock or electrocution. The conductor's flexible cord must have a grounding-type attachment plug, and the receptacle supplying the equipment must be a grounding-type receptacle.

Equipment grounding conductors are not required on tools that are double insulated. Double-insulated tools have two completely separate sets of insulation and must not be connected to the equipment grounding conductor of the supply circuit.

(b) Attachment plugs and receptacles shall not be connected or altered in a manner that would interrupt continuity of the equipment grounding conductor. Additionally, these devices shall not be altered in order to allow use in a manner that was not intended by the manufacturer.

All of the components of a circuit must provide the same integrity as the equipment grounding conductor. Attachment plugs and receptacles are constructed, tested, and listed for specific uses. Altering these devices in a way the manufacturer has not approved can compromise the integrity of the equipment grounding conductor's continuity. Removing the grounding pin or twisting the blades or pins of a plug to enable the plug to mate with a receptacle of a different configuration is prohibited by this requirement.

(c) Adapters that interrupt the continuity of the equipment grounding conductor shall not be used.

Field-fabricated adapters, that use a plug of one configuration on one end and a cord cap of a different configuration on the other that interrupts the continuity of the equipment grounding conductor, are prohibited.

△ **(C) Visual Inspection and Repair of Portable Cord- and Plug-Connected Equipment and Flexible Cord Sets.**

(a) *Frequency of Inspection.* Before each use, portable cord- and plug-connected equipment shall be visually inspected for external defects (such as loose parts or deformed and missing pins) and for evidence of possible internal damage (such as a pinched or crushed outer jacket).

Exception: Stationary cord- and plug-connected equipment that remain connected once they are put in place and are installed such that the cord and plug are not subject to physical damage during normal use shall not be required to be visually inspected until they are relocated or repaired.

OSHA Connection

29 CFR 1910.304(b)(3)(ii)(C)(3)
Each cord set, attachment cap, plug, and receptacle of cord sets, and any equipment connected by cord and plug must be visually inspected before each day's use for external defects. Additional subparts of this section require documented tests before first use, before equipment is returned to service following any repairs, before equipment is used after any incident that can be reasonably suspected to have caused damage, and at intervals not to exceed 3 months.

OSHA Connection

25 CFR 1910.334(a)(2)(i)
Portable cord- and plug-connected equipment and flexible cord sets must be visually inspected before use on any shift for external defects. Inspection before each shift is not necessary if the equipment and cord sets remain connected once they are put in place and are not exposed to damage.

Damaged portable cord- and plug-connected equipment and flexible cord sets might expose employees to shock or electrocution. Visual inspections might not identify all of the possible problems, but a thorough visual inspection can provide significant assurance that equipment and cord sets are safe to use. The inspection should include a careful examination of each end of the cord or cord set and ensure that all of the pins and blades are in place and unmodified. During this inspection, it is a good practice to run a hand along the complete surface of the cord. The surface should be smooth, with no indentations, cuts, or abrasions. Any anomaly should be inspected further to ensure the integrity of the cord insulation and the conductivity of the equipment grounding conductor.

Although no additional inspection is required until equipment is moved to another location, periodic inspection of an equipment grounding conductor is recommended. The repair of the receptacle or plug end of an extension cord is covered by product listing requirements. Receptacle and plug ends are available as listed components for use with listed extension cords. Repairs must be performed in accordance with the listing requirements. Exhibit 110.7 shows a listed extension cord that has been repaired with a recognized component (receptacle), thereby maintaining the listing of the cord set.

(b) *Defective Equipment.* If there is a defect or evidence of damage that might expose an employee to injury, the defective or damaged item shall be removed from service. No employee shall use it until a person(s) qualified to perform the repairs and tests necessary to render the equipment safe has done so.

Defective or damaged portable cord- and plug-connected equipment and flexible cord sets that have been removed from service should be identified as defective by a tag or other method that will warn personnel that the item should not be used. The warning should remain with the item until repairs have been completed by a person qualified to perform the repairs and the tests necessary to render the equipment safe have been completed.

(c) *Proper Mating.* When an attachment plug is to be connected to a receptacle, the relationship of the plug and receptacle contacts shall first be checked to ensure that they are of mating configurations.

EXHIBIT 110.7

An extension cord repaired with a new receptacle. (Courtesy of Noel Williams)

Attachment plugs and receptacles are available in many configurations to ensure the proper polarity of connections and to prevent the interconnection of different electrical systems, thereby avoiding potentially dangerous conditions. It is also important to check the attachment plug to ensure the pins have not been damaged or removed.

Δ **(D) Conductive or Wet Work Locations.** Portable cord-and plug-connected electric equipment used in conductive or wet work locations shall be approved for use in those locations. In work locations where employees are likely to contact or be drenched with water or conductive liquids, ground-fault circuit-interrupter protection for personnel shall be used.

> Informational Note: The risk assessment procedure can also include identifying when the use of portable tools and equipment powered by sources other than 120 volts ac, such as batteries, air, and hydraulics, should be used to minimize the potential for injury from electrical hazards for tasks performed in conductive or wet locations.

Portable cord- and plug-connected equipment that is used in the rain can expose workers to shock or electrocution hazards. Portable electric equipment used in a wet or damp location must be suitable for that location. In such locations, it is recommended that equipment powered by sources other than 120 volts ac—such as batteries, air, and hydraulics—be used to minimize the potential for injury from electrical hazards. GFCI protection is required when employees work with portable tools in a wet or damp location.

(E) Connecting Attachment Plugs.

(a) Employees' hands shall not be wet when plugging and unplugging flexible cords and cord- and plug-connected equipment if energized equipment is involved.

(b) Energized plug and receptacle connections shall be handled only with insulating protective equipment if the condition of the connection could provide a conductive path to the employee's hand (e.g, if a cord connector is wet from being immersed in water).

(c) Locking-type connectors shall be secured after connection.

Locking-type attachment plugs and receptacles and some other portable cord-connecting devices are designed to provide a connection that is secure from accidental withdrawal. For example, the locking-type attachment plug system shown in Exhibit 110.8 must be inserted into the mating receptacle and turned to its secure position.

EXHIBIT 110.8

A locking-type attachment plug and receptacle. (Courtesy of Hubbell Inc.)

(F) Manufacturer's Instructions. Portable equipment shall be used in accordance with the manufacturer's instructions and safety warnings.

> Any instructions included with equipment must be followed to ensure safe operation. Listed equipment has been evaluated for safe use only within the context of those instructions.

Case Study

110.9

Scenario

Taylor, a 19-year-old male construction laborer, was employed by a construction company that builds docks, piers, and waterfront bulkheads for private residences. The company had no safety policy, program, or safe work procedures. Taylor, a second laborer, and a foreman were constructing a waterfront bulkhead at the edge of a lake while using a floating work platform. The bulkhead consisted of squared timbers stacked horizontally at the water's edge then secured in place with wooden posts. Galvanized rods in holes drilled through the bulkhead timbers and posts would hold them in place. Electric power was supplied from an exterior 120-volt, 20-amp, grounded receptacle located at the back porch of the residence. The workers plugged in two 100-foot electrical extension cords to reach the bulkhead to power an electric drill and a circular saw to construct the bulkhead.

Incident

Sometime during the first 2 weeks of the project, Taylor and a coworker complained to the foreman that they had received electric shocks while using a damaged extension cord. In response, the foreman removed the cord and placed it in the back of the construction truck. However, a few days before the incident, the workers resumed using the damaged cord.

The foreman told Taylor that he (the foreman) and the coworker would join him later that morning of the incident. At 9:30 a.m. Taylor arrived and placed the power tools near the bulkhead. The homeowner witnessed Taylor plugging the good extension cord into the residential receptacle. From this moment on, there were no eyewitnesses of the incident. However, evidence suggests that Taylor connected the damaged extension cord to the good extension cord. He then laid out the damaged extension cord as he walked toward the bulkhead. While he was handling the damaged extension cord, he contacted the receptacle end of the cord. This provided a path to ground for the electrical current. Taylor collapsed, fell into the lake, and sank 4½ feet to the bottom.

The coworker and foreman arrived at 10:30 a.m. They noticed Taylor's car at the site and that the tools and extension cords had been set out. The foreman saw the receptacle end of the extension cord in a water-filled hole near the bulkhead. He removed it from the water by pulling on the cord from several feet away. The foreman and coworker began working on the bulkhead, thinking that Taylor would show up later. While standing on the floating work platform, the foreman moved the platform along the edge of the bulkhead by pushing off the lake bottom with a pole. The pole contacted Taylor's body, and he floated to the surface and was taken out of the water. It is estimated that he had been submerged in the water for about 30 minutes. The coworker called the emergency number.

Result

Two police officers responded to the call and arrived in about 5 minutes. They started CPR on Taylor. Rescue squad personnel arrived about 3 minutes later and continued CPR but were unsuccessful in their attempt to revive him. The local coroner pronounced Taylor dead due to electrocution at the scene.

Investigation

One of the extension cords being used had been previously damaged. In an effort to repair the damaged cord, someone had replaced both the original equipment manufactured female receptacle and male plug with splice-on-type units. Although this damaged cord had shocked Taylor when it was initially used, it had been put into the truck. This was the extension cord used by Taylor on the day of the incident. The residence receptacle used was not equipped with a ground-fault circuit interrupter (GFCI) nor did the workers use a portable GFCI device for any of their electric work. An examination of the extension cord revealed that the noncolor-coded extension cord wires in the receptacle were cross-wired, thus establishing a reversed polarity condition. In addition, the ground wire inside the plug had pulled loose from its connection.

Analysis

Portable tools present a greater opportunity for equipment to become damaged than a fixed installation. The risk of damage increases when portable tools are transported to other sites. Any damage can expose an employee to electrical hazards when they use the equipment, so inspection just prior to use is required by 110.9(C). However, not all damage may be visible, such as the flawed repair in this case. This repair should have been addressed by 205.14(C). It is not enough to remove damaged equipment if the equipment is not discernable from undamaged equipment. Taylor's electrocution could have been avoided by preventing access to the damaged electrical cord. Any employee is put at risk without the employer properly implementing all applicable NFPA *70E* requirements. Although

Taylor's employer had no electrical safety program, there are several sections of NFPA *70E* that address safety concerns when using cord- and plug-connected electrical portable equipment.

Relevant NFPA *70E* requirements:

- Handling and storage [110.9(A)]
- Grounding-type equipment [110.9(B)]
- Visual inspection and repair [110.9(C)]
- Conductive work locations [110.9(D)]

- Connecting attachment plugs [110.9(E)]
- GFCI protection during construction [110.10(B)]
- GFCI protection outdoors [110.10(C)]
- Insulated tools [130.7(D)(1)]
- General maintenance requirements [205.3]
- Flexible cords and cables [205.14]
- Portable electric tools and equipment [Article 245]

Content source: National Institute for Occupational Safety and Health (NIOSH); FACE case: 91-05.

110.10 Ground-Fault Circuit-Interrupter (GFCI) Protection.

(A) General. Employees shall be provided with ground-fault circuit-interrupter (GFCI) protection where required by applicable state, federal, or local codes and standards. Listed cord sets or devices incorporating listed GFCI protection for personnel identified for portable use shall be permitted.

Listed GFCI protection identified for portable use incorporates open neutral protection. Open neutral protection de-energizes a load if the neutral conductor leading to the device loses its continuity. A typical Class A GFCI receptacle installed in a box with a flexible cord will not provide this additional protection.

GFCI protection is required by *NEC* Article 590 for all temporary installations involving construction, remodeling, maintenance, and repair or demolition of buildings, structures, or equipment. However, using a GFCI device wherever employees use cord- and plug-connected equipment is a best practice. Exhibits 100.8 through 100.10 show examples of ways to implement the GFCI requirements specified in *NEC* 590.6(A) for temporary installations.

(B) Maintenance and Construction. GFCI protection shall be provided where an employee is operating or using cord sets (extension cords) or cord- and plug-connected tools related to maintenance and construction activity supplied by 125-volt, 15-, 20-, or 30-ampere circuits. Where employees operate or use equipment supplied by greater than 125-volt, 15-, 20-, or 30-ampere circuits, GFCI protection or an assured equipment grounding conductor program shall be implemented.

> Informational Note: Where an assured equipment grounding conductor program is used, a special purpose ground-fault circuit interrupter may provide additional protection. See Informative Annex O.

(C) Outdoors. GFCI protection shall be provided when an employee is outdoors and operating or using cord sets (extension cords) or cord- and plug-connected equipment supplied by 125-volt, 15-, 20-, or 30-ampere circuits. Where employees working outdoors operate or use equipment supplied by greater than 125-volt, 15-, 20-, or 30-ampere circuits, GFCI protection or an assured equipment grounding conductor program shall be implemented.

> Informational Note: Where an assured equipment grounding conductor program is used, a special purpose ground-fault circuit interrupter may provide additional protection. See Informative Annex O.

The required GFCI protection can be achieved using a listed portable GFCI device or a device installed as part of the premises wiring system. Where the cord- and plug-connected equipment is supplied by a circuit rated greater than 125 volts, GFCI protection or an assured equipment grounding conductor program must be implemented.

Section 590.6(B)(2) of the 2020 *NEC* describes the requirement for an assured equipment grounding conductor program as follows:

> A written assured equipment grounding conductor program continuously enforced at the site by one or more designated persons to ensure that equipment grounding conductors for all cord sets, receptacles that are not a part of the permanent wiring of the building or structure, and equipment connected by cord and plug are installed and maintained in accordance with the applicable requirements of 250.114, 250.138, 406.4(C), and 590.4(D) [of the *NEC*],
>
> (a) The following tests shall be performed on all cord sets, receptacles that are not part of the permanent wiring of the building or structure, and cord- and plug-connected equipment required to be connected to an equipment grounding conductor:
>
> (1) All equipment grounding conductors shall be tested for continuity and shall be electrically continuous.
>
> (2) Each receptacle and attachment plug shall be tested for correct attachment of the equipment grounding conductor. The equipment grounding conductor shall be connected to its proper terminal.
>
> (3) All required tests shall be performed as follows:
>   a. Before first use on site
>   b. When there is evidence of damage
>   c. Before equipment is returned to service following any repairs
>   d. At intervals not exceeding 3 months
>
> (b) The tests required in item (a) shall be recorded and made available to the authority having jurisdiction.

OSHA Connection

29 CFR 1926.404(b)1)(iii)
The assured equipment grounding conductor program requirements for construction sites are very similar to the NEC requirements for an assured grounding program.

(D) Testing Ground-Fault Circuit-Interrupter Protection Devices. GFCI protection devices shall be tested in accordance with the manufacturer's instructions

Installation and testing instructions are provided with all listed GFCI devices. Many devices are required to be tested on a monthly basis.

110.11 Overcurrent Protection Modification.

Overcurrent protection of circuits and conductors shall not be modified, even on a temporary basis, beyond what is permitted by applicable portions of electrical codes and standards dealing with overcurrent protection.

Informational Note: For further information concerning electrical codes and standards dealing with overcurrent protection, refer to Article 240 of *NFPA 70, National Electrical Code.*

All overcurrent devices must comply with the requirements of the NEC. The protection provided could be of the overload, short-circuit, or ground-fault type, or a combination of these types, depending on the application.

Overcurrent devices are important components of a safety system to prevent conductors and equipment from exceeding their rating and ability to safely conduct current. Exceeding a conductor or equipment rating can result in overheating, which can lead to the ignition of insulation or nearby flammable material or result in device and component failure.

N **110.12 Equipment Use.**

Equipment shall be used in accordance with the manufacturer's instructions.

Establishing an Electrically Safe Work Condition

The ability of an employee to use personal protective equipment (PPE) doesn't allow an employer to permit unjustified exposure to energized electrical circuits. The main premise of providing an electrically safe work environment for employees is that equipment must be placed in an electrically safe work condition (ESWC) unless it is being used under normal operation. Both OSHA and NFPA *70E®, Standard for Electrical Safety in the Workplace®*, require this to be the default condition. Article 120 provides the steps for establishing and the method for controlling an ESWC. All of the requirements in Article 120 must be applied before an ESWC is achieved. The act of creating an ESWC requires that the appropriate PPE be worn and the work procedures be followed. Until an ESWC has been verified, it cannot be assumed that equipment is disconnected from energy sources and that it is safe to work on as de-energized.

120.1 Lockout/Tagout Program.

(A) General. Each employer shall establish, document, and implement a lockout/tagout program. The lockout/tagout program shall specify lockout/tagout procedures to safeguard workers from exposure to electrical hazards. The lockout/tagout program and procedures shall also incorporate the following:

(1) Be applicable to the experience and training of the workers and conditions in the workplace
(2) Meet the requirements of Article 120
(3) Apply to fixed, permanently installed equipment, temporarily installed equipment, and portable equipment

Since 1990, disconnect devices for electrical equipment have been required to be able to accept a lock to minimize the use of a tagout procedure. It is the employer's responsibility to establish the lockout procedures that are part of creating an electrically safe work condition (ESWC) that will protect employees from hazardous energy sources during service and maintenance. Creating a single lockout procedure might not be possible for all installed equipment. The procedures should indicate which pieces of equipment they apply to and detail the specific steps necessary to achieve an ESWC for those pieces of equipment. In order for the procedure to be effective, it must be written in a manner that qualified people tasked with establishing an ESWC can understand.

(B) Employer Responsibilities. The employer shall be responsible for the following:

(1) Providing the equipment necessary to execute lockout/tagout procedures
(2) Providing lockout/tagout training to workers in accordance with 110.6(B)
(3) Auditing the lockout/tagout program in accordance with 110.5(M)(3)
(4) Auditing execution of the lockout/tagout procedures in accordance with 110.5(M)(3)

Informational Note: For an example of a lockout/tagout program, see Informative Annex G.

Not only is the employer responsible for developing, implementing, and enforcing lockout procedures, the employer must also provide training and initiate audits. The training must ensure that each employee understands the need for an installed lockout device as part of the program. The audit must ensure that the lockout procedure is effective and is being properly implemented. The employer is also required to provide the equipment necessary to execute the procedure, such as locks, multi-lock tree, tags, PPE, and any other tools necessary to complete the lockout procedure.

120.2 Lockout/Tagout Principles.

(A) Employee Involvement. Each person who could be exposed directly or indirectly to a source of electrical energy shall be involved in the lockout/tagout procedure.

> Informational Note: An example of direct exposure is the qualified electrician who works on the motor starter control, the power circuits, or the motor. An example of indirect exposure is the person who works on the coupling between the motor and compressor.

Any employee who could be exposed to an unacceptable level of risk of an electrical hazard when executing a work task (even if the assigned task is not electrical) must be involved in the lockout process. Temporary and contract employees must also understand how the lockout procedure that is part of creating an electrically safe work condition might influence their exposure to electrical hazards, and they must participate in the process. When multiple employers are involved in the work process, such as when an independent contractor is involved, Section 110.7 requires all the employers to share information about hazards and procedures.

(B) Lockout/Tagout Procedure. A lockout/tagout procedure shall be developed on the basis of the existing electrical equipment and system and shall use suitable documentation including up-to-date drawings and diagrams. The procedure shall meet the requirements of applicable codes, standards, and regulations for lockout and tagging of electrical sources.

Because disconnect devices for electrical equipment are required to be able to use a lock, the use of a tagout procedure should be limited to equipment installed before 1990. A procedure must be developed for each lockout that is part of creating an electrically safe work condition (ESWC). Up-to-date, accurate, single-line diagrams provide essential information that is necessary when creating an ESWC. The purpose of this information is to clearly indicate all of the sources of electrical energy that are or might be available at any point in the electrical circuit. If the diagram is inaccurate, employees could be injured as a result of one or more sources of energy not being removed. See Informative Annex G for a sample lockout procedure.

(C) Control of Energy. All sources of electrical energy shall be controlled in such a way as to minimize employee exposure to electrical hazards.

All sources of energy—including stored energy and mechanical energy—must be removed by operating all of the applicable disconnecting means. After the disconnecting means have been opened, all of the employees who might be exposed to electrical hazards should be involved with the lockout procedure.

(D) Electrical Circuit Interlocks. Documentation, including up-to-date drawings and diagrams, shall be reviewed to ensure that no electrical circuit interlock operation can result in re-energizing the circuit being worked on.

Worker Alert

You must notify the other affected employees when you implement a lockout system and provide them with the reason for its implementation.

A diagrammatic drawing is commonly used to determine the possibility of a circuit being re-energized by backfeeds or the operation of a remote interlock. It is crucial that the drawing be up to date and that it accurately depict the installation. As an installed circuit or system changes, the single-line diagrams, schematic diagrams, or similar drawings that are on record should be marked to document the changes in the system.

(E) Control Devices. Locks/tags shall be installed only on circuit disconnecting means. Control devices, such as push-buttons or selector switches, shall not be used as the primary isolating device.

Some control devices are fitted with a mechanism designed to use a lock. However, these control devices are not to be used as the primary means of de-energizing circuits or equipment. Control devices do not render a circuit inoperative; therefore, installing a tag or a lock on a control device does not meet the objective of a primary isolating device. If the device being locked or tagged does not create a break in the conductors providing energy to the equipment or circuit, the device must not be used as a lockout or tagout point. Although the installation of a lock on these control devices is not prohibited, the use of an identified lockout or tagout device for that purpose is not permitted.

(F) Identification. The lockout/tagout device shall be unique and readily identifiable as a lockout/tagout device

Uniquely and readily identifiable lockout devices must be durable, substantial, and standardized. Device standardization can be achieved using specific colors, shapes, or sizes. The print and format on tagout devices should also be standardized. Employees must be able to recognize a lockout or tagout device, and there cannot be any possibility of confusing these devices with locks or tags used for other purposes, such as process control locks and information tags. See 120.3(C) and 120.3(D) for lockout and tagout device requirements.

(G) Coordination. The following items are necessary for coordinating the lockout/tagout procedure:

(1) The electrical lockout/tagout procedure shall be coordinated with all other employer's procedures for control of exposure to electrical energy sources such that all employer's procedural requirements are adequately addressed on a site basis.

Disconnect devices for electrical equipment have been required to be able to use a lock since 1990. This requirement minimizes the use of tagout procedures. A project might involve contractors and employers other than the facility owner. Because each employer is required to implement a lockout procedure, different requirements might exist. These lockout procedures must be coordinated with outside employers, such as independent contractors who service or maintain equipment that requires lockout. To make sure that the requirements of each procedure are understood and observed, each employer might need to amend one or more of its procedures. Contractors and facility owners must exchange information about creating an electrically safe work condition and ensure that their respective employees understand all the issues that are important to the other employers.

Worker Alert

You should exercise caution when working on a group of machines that work together in a coordinated manner. This type of machinery typically uses a number of electrical supplies and can have multiple sources of energy. You need to understand each machine's purpose and functionality to identify all the possible sources of hazardous energy.

When different lockout procedures for different employers must be implemented on the same worksite, the procedures must be coordinated and the employees of each employer must be instructed about any unique conditions. Training in the method to be employed for the task can help minimize the possibility of errors when implementing an unfamiliar process. The basic concerns of each employer must be addressed in the written lockout plan. In addition, employees must understand any changes and the reasons for the changes.

OSHA Connection

29 CFR 1910.147
Energy sources are defined as "any source of electrical, mechanical, hydraulic, pneumatic, chemical, thermal, or other energy."

(2) The procedure for control of exposure to electrical hazards shall be coordinated with other procedures for control of other hazardous energy based on similar or identical concepts.

All lockout procedures must clearly and specifically outline the scope, purpose, authorization, rules, and techniques to be utilized to control hazardous energy.

Other standards might require an employer to implement a procedure to control exposure to other hazardous energy sources. For instance, the general control of a hazardous energy procedure and an electrical lockout procedure that is part of creating an electrically safe work condition could have similar or identical requirements for locks and tags. The electrical lockout procedure could be integrated into an overall control of a hazardous energy procedure; however, that procedure must address all the issues identified in this standard.

(3) Electrical lockout/tagout devices shall be permitted to be similar to lockout/tagout devices for control of other hazardous energy sources, such as pneumatic, hydraulic, thermal, and mechanical, if such devices are used only for control of hazardous energy and for no other purpose.

Devices used to control hazardous energy must be easily recognizable and must be the only devices the employer uses to control hazardous energy. Electrical lockout devices should have the same physical characteristics as the devices used to control other forms of energy so that employees can easily recognize devices used to control energy sources.

(H) Forms of Control of Hazardous Electrical Energy. Two forms of hazardous electrical energy control shall be permitted; simple lockout/tagout and complex lockout/tagout [*see 120.4*], For the simple lockout/tagout, the qualified person shall be in charge. For the complex lockout/tagout, the person in charge shall have overall responsibility.

The objective of controlling exposure to electrical energy is to ensure that all the possible sources of electrical energy are disconnected and cannot be re-energized unexpectedly. The two types of controls are simple lockouts and complex lockouts, which are administrative controls (procedures) from the hierarchy of risk controls. See Informative Annex G for a sample lockout or tagout procedure.

In a simple lockout, the qualified person(s) de-energizes one source of electrical energy and is responsible for their own lockout. A written lockout plan is not required. A simple lockout does not place a limit on the number of people who can conduct work on equipment, so employees might need to apply multiple locks.

A complex lockout typically involves more than one energy source and more than one disconnecting means. It requires a single person to maintain overall responsibility and a written plan prepared in advance for each lockout application.

120.3 Lockout/Tagout Equipment.

(A) Lock Application. Energy isolation devices for machinery or equipment installed after January 2, 1990, shall be capable of accepting a lockout device.

OSHA Connection

29 CFR 1910.147(c)(2)(iii)
Whenever replacement or major repair, renovation, or modification of a machine or equipment is performed, and whenever new machines or equipment are installed, energy isolating devices must be designed to accept a lockout device.

Many *NFPA 70®, National Electrical Code® (NEC®)*, requirements for disconnecting means require that the equipment have a method built in that allows it to be locked in the open position. Any disconnecting means that cannot be locked in the open position must not be used as an energy isolation device.

(B) Lockout/Tagout Device. Each employer shall supply, and employees shall use, lockout/tagout devices and equipment necessary to execute the requirements of 120.3. Locks and tags used for control of exposure to electrical hazards shall be unique, shall be readily identifiable as lockout/tagout devices, and shall be used for no other purpose.

Each employer must provide the necessary equipment—such as locks, tags, chains, wedges, key blocks, adaptor pins, and self-locking fasteners—for employees to control their exposure to electrical hazards.

Lockout devices used to control exposure to electrical energy can be identical to lockout devices used to control the exposure to hazardous energy from other energy sources, but these devices must not be used for any other purpose. See the commentary following 120.2(F) for more information on the identification of lockout devices.

(C) Lockout Device. The lockout device shall meet the following requirements:

(1) A lockout device shall include a lock—either keyed or combination.
(2) The lockout device shall include a method of identifying the individual who installed the lockout device.
(3) A lockout device shall be permitted to be only a lock, if the lock is readily identifiable as a lockout device, in addition to having a means of identifying the person who installed the lock, provided that all of the following conditions exist:

(a) Only one circuit or piece of equipment is de-energized.
(b) The lockout period does not extend beyond the work shift.
(c) Employees exposed to the hazards associated with re-energizing the circuit or equipment are familiar with this procedure.

Even though a uniquely identified lock used as a lockout device can be used in conjunction with other components, the fundamental lockout device must be a lock. The lockout device must also include information that identifies the person who installed the lock and must be installed in a manner that prevents the operation of the energy isolation device.

(4) Lockout devices shall be attached to prevent operation of the disconnecting means without resorting to undue force or the use of tools.

The lockout device must be capable of withstanding the environment to which it is exposed for the maximum period of time that exposure is expected. It must also be substantial enough to prevent removal without the use of excessive force or unusual techniques, such as the use of bolt cutters or other metal cutting tools.

(5) Where a tag is used in conjunction with a lockout device, the tag shall contain a statement prohibiting unauthorized operation of the disconnecting means or unauthorized removal of the device.

(6) Lockout devices shall be suitable for the environment and for the duration of the lockout.

(7) Whether keyed or combination locks are used, the key or combination shall remain in the possession of the individual installing the lock or the person in charge, when provided by the established procedure.

> The method of locking (by key or combination) must prevent unauthorized removal of the lock, and the person who might be exposed to an electrical hazard must be in control of the electrical energy. To accomplish that, the key to the lock must remain in the possession of the person who installed it.

(D) Tagout Device. The tagout device shall meet the following requirements:

(1) A tagout device shall include a tag together with an attachment means.

(2) The tagout device shall be readily identifiable as a tagout device and suitable for the environment and duration of the tagout.

(3) A tagout device attachment means shall be capable of withstanding at least 224.4 N (50 lb) of force exerted at a right angle to the disconnecting means surface. The tag attachment means shall be nonreusable, attachable by hand, self-locking, nonreleasable, and equal to an all-environmental tolerant nylon cable tie.

(4) Tags shall contain a statement prohibiting unauthorized operation of the disconnecting means or removal of the tag.

> The device must be easily recognizable as a tagout device and must be securely attached to the energy isolation device to alert employees that the equipment is not to be operated until the tag is removed.

(5) A hold card tagging tool on an overhead conductor in conjunction with a hotline tool to install the tagout device safely on a disconnect that is isolated from the work(s) shall be permitted. Where a hold card is used, the tagout procedure shall include the method of accounting for personnel who are working under the protection of the hold card.

> The work environment of utility employees often leads to the disconnecting means being located several miles away from a worksite. Utility systems have successfully relied on hold cards to provide warnings when operating a disconnecting means could place employees in danger. Utility workers are trained to respect the system associated with the hold card, which generally results in a positive and effective system of energy control.
>
> When tagout is employed, at least one more safety measure, such as removing the cutout, must be used in addition to the use of the hold card. Employees of utility systems must be covered by a written policy that describes how the hold card system functions. Where contract employees perform utility maintenance or construction, the contract employer must provide a program that is at least as effective as the program of the utility authorizing the contractor's work.

120.4 Lockout/Tagout Procedures.

The employer shall maintain a copy of the procedures required by this section and shall make the procedures available to all employees.

OSHA Connection

29CFR 1910.333(b)(2)

The employer must maintain a written copy of the procedures and make it available for inspection by employees.

The use of a tagout procedure should be minimized, as disconnect devices for electrical equipment have been required to be able to use a lock since 1990. Although an employer is responsible for providing the lockout procedure, employees should be involved in gathering the information to generate the procedure. The procedure must be implemented as a step in the process of establishing an electrically safe work condition. The lockout procedure can be included in an overall lockout procedure for an employer or site or it can be a stand-alone procedure. In either instance, all the requirements of Article 120 must be addressed.

(A) Planning. The procedure shall require planning, including the requirements of 120.4(A)(1) through 120.4(B)(14).

The planner might be the person in charge, the supervisor, a person competent in establishing an electrically safe work condition, or the qualified employee performing the task themselves. Regardless of who develops the plan, the qualified persons performing the task should be involved in the development of any plan that affects their safety. The plan must identify the location, both physically and electrically, where a lockout device is necessary.

The lockout procedure must include a detailed method of achieving the objectives of 120.2(A) and (B). A complete procedure must indicate whether the plan must be in writing and whether any authorization is necessary.

(1) Locating Sources. Up-to-date single-line drawings shall be considered a primary reference source for such information. When up-to-date drawings are not available, the employer shall be responsible for ensuring that an equally effective means of locating all sources of energy is employed.

A crucial requirement in the lockout procedure is determining all the possible sources of electrical supply to specific equipment. Although applicable, up-to-date drawings must be the initial source of information, when they are not available, other sources can include manuals, panel schedules, and information tags. The system should be visually inspected so that all hazards are properly identified. Where a single-line drawing is not available, it may be appropriate to generate one as part of gathering information from other sources.

(2) Exposed Persons. The plan shall identify persons who might be exposed to an electrical hazard and the PPE required during the execution of the job or task.

The plan must identify those who might be exposed to an unacceptable level of risk of injury from an electrical hazard, either directly or indirectly. Exposed employees might not be involved with the electrical work, but could be in the vicinity of the electrical work. Exposed employees could include nonelectrical workers, such as production line workers, painters, or custodians. The act of establishing an electrically safe work condition involves performing work on an energized circuit until all of the steps in 120.5 have been completed. The plan must also identify what PPE employees must use during the implementation of a lockout and during the execution of a job or task.

(3) Person in Charge. The plan shall identify the person in charge and his or her responsibility in the lockout/tagout.

The person in charge could be the individual implementing a simple lockout procedure or the individual responsible for overseeing a complex lockout procedure. The responsibilities of the person in charge might include implementing the energy control procedures, communicating the purpose of the operation to the servicing and maintenance employees, coordinating the operation, and ensuring all the procedural steps have been properly completed.

(4) Simple Lockout/Tagout Procedure. All lockout/tagout procedures that involve only a qualified person(s) de-energizing one set of conductors or circuit part source for the sole purpose of safeguarding employees from exposure to electrical hazards shall be considered to be a simple lockout/tagout. Simple lockout/tagout procedures shall not be required to be written for each application. Each worker shall be responsible for his or her own lockout/tagout.

Exception: Lockout/tagout is not required for work on cord- and plug-connected equipment for which exposure to the hazards of unexpected energization of the equipment is controlled by the unplugging of the equipment from the energy source, provided that the plug is under the exclusive control of the employee performing the servicing and maintenance for the duration of the work.

> **Worker Alert**
>
> You must notify other affected employees when you implement a lockout system and provide them with the reason for its implementation.

A simple lockout is made up of procedures that involve a qualified person de-energizing one set of conductors or one circuit part for the sole purpose of safeguarding employees from exposure to electrical hazards. A simple lockout is not limited to a single employee or the application of a single lock. Employees are responsible for their own lockouts.

An example of a simple lockout procedure is when a single disconnect switch provides energy for equipment, such as a motor, and an employee intending to service the motor opens the disconnecting means, de-energizing the motor circuit. The only way to guarantee that the disconnecting means remains open and the motor stays de-energized is to lock the disconnecting means in the open position and affix the appropriate tag. Although no written lockout plan is needed, a simple lockout must be a planned activity. A simple lockout could involve more than a single person and might require the use of multiple locks.

(5) Complex Lockout/Tagout.

(a) A complex lockout/tagout procedure shall be permitted where one or more of the following exists:

(1) Multiple energy source
(2) Multiple crews
(3) Multiple crafts
(4) Multiple locations
(5) Multiple employers
(6) Multiple disconnecting means
(7) Particular sequences
(8) Job or task that continues for more than one work period

> **Worker Alert**
>
> If you are the person in charge, you must develop a written plan of execution and communicate that plan to all the persons involved in a job or task. You will be held accountable for the safe execution of a complex lockout plan. You must ensure that each person understands the electrical hazards to which they will be exposed and the safety-related work practices they must use.

The conditions listed in 120.4(A)(5)(a) increase the complexity and difficulty of a lockout. Multiple energy sources, as referenced in Item (1), are not limited to electric power; they could be compressed air, hydraulic, mechanical, pneumatic, natural gas, steam, thermal, or water energy. A process or machinery with multiple operations are examples of Item (7).

Exhibit 120.1 illustrates some of the basic differences between a simple lockout and a complex lockout procedure.

(b) All complex lockout/tagout procedures shall require a written plan of execution that identifies the person in charge.

If one or more of the conditions listed in 120.4(A)(5)(a) exist, the lockout is defined as complex, and a person in charge must be assigned. The primary responsibility of the person in charge is directly implementing a complex lockout procedure

(c) The complex lockout/tagout procedure shall vest primary responsibility in an authorized employee for employees working under the protection of a group lockout or tagout device, such as an operation lock or lockbox. The person in charge shall be held accountable for safe execution of the complex lockout/tagout.

EXHIBIT 120.1

An example of a simple lockout procedure and a complex lockout procedure.

The person in charge must be both a qualified person and an authorized employee. This person must coordinate personnel and ensure the continuity of lockout protection for all the employees working under the protection of a group lockout device. The person in charge is accountable for developing, implementing, and monitoring the plan.

(d) Each authorized employee shall affix a personal lockout or tagout device to the group lockout device, group lockbox, or comparable mechanism when he or she begins work and shall remove those devices when he or she stops working on the machine or equipment being serviced or maintained.

To adhere to the basic principle that each employee must be in control of hazardous energy, all persons involved in a work task must affix their own personal lockout device to the group lockout device or to each individual lockout point. The person in charge is responsible for ensuring adherence to this principle. Exhibits 120.2 and 120.3 show examples of complex lockout devices.

EXHIBIT 120.2

Lockbox.

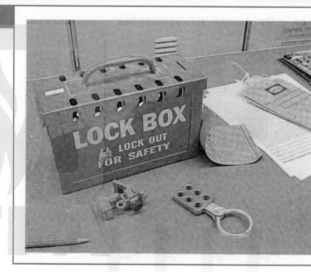

EXHIBIT 120.3

Disconnect switch with locks from more than one individual.

(e) All complex lockout/tagout plans shall identify the method to account for all persons who might be exposed to electrical hazards in the course of the lockout/tagout.

> The person in charge is responsible for ensuring that all the employees are protected by the complex lockout. This person is also responsible for the removal of the devices and the release for return to service. Each employee must understand the process by which the person in charge will do this.

(B) Elements of Control. The procedure shall identify elements of control.

(1) De-energizing Equipment (Shutdown). The procedure shall establish the person who performs the switching and where and how to de-energize the load.

(2) Stored Energy. The procedure shall include requirements for releasing stored electric or mechanical energy that might endanger personnel. All capacitors shall be discharged, and high-capacitance elements shall also be short-circuited and grounded before the associated equipment is touched or worked on. Springs shall be released or physical restraint shall be applied when necessary to immobilize mechanical equipment and pneumatic and hydraulic pressure reservoirs. Other sources of stored energy shall be blocked or otherwise relieved.

> Informational Note: For more information on methods and procedures to place capacitors in an electrically safe work condition, see 360.3, 360.5, and Informative Annex R, Working with Capacitors.

> Electrical energy can be generated electrical power, stored energy (such as in a capacitor), or static electricity. Generated electrical power can be turned off or on, whereas stored or static electricity can only be dissipated or controlled. Although the most common energy source is electrical energy, a procedure should consider all forms of energy that might be present, such as hydraulic energy (liquid under pressure), pneumatic energy (gas/air under pressure), or mechanical motion (kinetic energy/energy of motion). The procedure must indicate the steps necessary to control these sources of energy, such as by blocking springs.

(3) Disconnecting Means. The procedure shall identify how to verify that the circuit is de-energized (open).

> Creating an electrically safe work condition always includes the verification of a lack of voltage. Additional visual verification that a disconnecting means is physically open might involve looking through an observation port or opening a door and observing the position of the contacts in the disconnecting means. In other cases, such as where arc chutes are involved, the contacts are not readily visible and observation of the contacts is not possible. Employees must be instructed on how to determine if all the conductors are disconnected from the energy source.

(4) Responsibility. The procedure shall identify the person who is responsible for verifying that the lockout/tagout procedure is implemented and who is responsible for ensuring that the task is completed prior to removing locks/tags. A mechanism to accomplish lockout/tagout for multiple (complex) jobs/tasks where required, including the person responsible for coordination, shall be included.

(5) Verification. The procedure shall verify that equipment cannot be restarted. The equipment operating controls, such as push-buttons, selector switches, and electrical interlocks, shall be operated or otherwise it shall be verified that the equipment cannot be restarted.

> The operation of control devices, such as pushbuttons, might not be the only means of verifying if equipment can be restarted when creating an electrically safe work condition. Additional measures might be necessary for specific equipment.

(6) Testing. The procedure shall establish the following:

(1) Test instrument to be used, the required PPE, and the person who will use it to verify proper operation of the test instrument on a known voltage source before and after use
(2) Requirement to define the boundary of the electrically safe work condition
(3) Requirement to test before touching every exposed conductor or circuit part(s) within the defined boundary of the work area
(4) Requirement to retest for absence of voltage when circuit conditions change or when the job location has been left unattended
(5) Planning considerations that include methods of verification where there is no accessible exposed point to take voltage measurements

> The lockout procedure must include the requirements necessary to ensure that all employees know whether they might be exposed to an electrical hazard. The procedure must identify acceptable test instruments and contain requirements to ensure that the test instruments are functioning properly before and after each use. Employee training must ensure that each qualified employee is familiar with the requirements for testing voltage. See Exhibit 110.5, which shows a test instrument used for measuring voltage.
>
> Employees who use test instruments must understand the limitations of the instruments, how to use the devices, how to protect themselves from any associated hazards, and how to interpret all of the possible indications provided by the test instrument. The integrity of the test instrument must be verified before and after the voltage test. Exhibit 120.15 illustrates the correct procedure for testing for the absence of voltage.
>
> If the work task has no exposed point to measure voltage, the procedure or plan must identify the method for verifying that all the conductors and circuit parts have been de-energized.

(7) Grounding. Grounding requirements for the circuit shall be established, including whether the temporary protective grounding equipment shall be installed for the duration of the task or is temporarily established by the procedure. Grounding needs or requirements shall be permitted to be covered in other work rules and might not be part of the lockout/tagout procedure.

> Applying temporary protective grounding devices is an important part of establishing an electrically safe work condition, but it might not be necessary in all cases. Where de-energized conductors or circuit parts might come into contact with other exposed energized conductors or circuit parts, temporary protective ground devices rated for the available fault duty should be applied. The lockout procedure must define any requirements for the placement of temporary protective grounding equipment. If other work rules consider and address temporary protective grounding, the lockout procedure need not address the same issue. However, employees must be aware that the lockout procedure will be augmented by other work rules that cover the use of temporary protective

Worker Alert

There have been many incidents in which workers were injured by assuming that equipment was still in an electrically safe work condition after returning from lunch. Visually inspecting a lockout device is not enough to ensure equipment is still in a de-energized state or cannot be restarted. You must retest for the absence of voltage when a job location has been left unattended.

OSHA Connection

29 CFR 1910.334(c)(2)

Testing instruments and equipment must be visually inspected for external defects or damage before being used to determine de-energization.

grounding equipment. Establishing general rules can help employees who are attempting to determine if the use of temporary protective grounding equipment is necessary.

Some grounding and testing devices are designed to be inserted (racked) into a compartment from which a circuit breaker or disconnect has been removed. These devices can be inserted only into specific spaces. See Exhibit 120.4 for more information.

(8) Shift Change. A method shall be identified in the procedure to transfer responsibility for lockout/tagout to another person or to the person in charge when the job or task extends beyond one shift.

When work extends beyond one shift and there are personnel changes, the procedure must provide instructions for the transfer of responsibilities between off-going and incoming employees to ensure the integrity of the electrically safe work condition and the continuity of lockout protection. The process of transferring responsibility from the off-going shift's person in charge to the incoming shift's person in charge must be clearly defined. Off-going employees who installed locks and tags during their shift should remove their locks and tags, and the incoming employees should install their individual locks and tags..

(9) Coordination. The procedure shall establish how coordination is accomplished with other jobs or tasks in progress, including related jobs or tasks at remote locations as well as the person responsible for coordination.

When more than one task or job is in progress, the actions of one employee might have an impact on the actions of others. One person must be assigned responsibility for ensuring that individual work tasks—such as those performed by tradesmen or contractors—are coordinated to minimize the possibility of one person's actions adversely impacting another's.

(10) Accountability for Personnel. A method shall be identified in the procedure to account for all persons who could be exposed to hazardous energy during the lockout/tagout.

Typically, the person in charge [see 120.4(A)(3)] must account for everyone involved in a work task, including contract employees.

Worker Alert

The transfer of responsibility for a lockout is much more than just exchanging locks and tags. Be sure that you review the procedures and coordinate with the person in charge. Be aware of all the aspects of the task, including all the possible sources of energy, the placement of temporary grounding equipment, and the other employees involved in the project.

(11) Lockout/Tagout Application. The procedure shall clearly identify when and where lockout applies, in addition to when and where tagout applies, and shall address the following:

> Tagout is permitted in lieu of lockout only in cases where equipment design precludes the installation of a lock. Since 1990, disconnect devices for electrical equipment have been required to be able to accept a lock to minimize the use of tagout procedures. If tagout is permitted, the procedure must clearly define the individual responsibilities and accountability for each person that might be exposed to an electrical hazard. In addition, all employees must receive training on the limitations of tags.

(1) Lockout shall be defined as installing a lockout device on all sources of hazardous energy such that operation of the disconnecting means is prohibited, and forcible removal of the lock is required to operate the disconnecting means.

(2) Tagout shall be defined as installing a tagout device on all sources of hazardous energy, such that operation of the disconnecting means is prohibited. The tagout device shall be installed in the same position available for the lockout device.

(3) Where it is not possible to attach a lock to existing disconnecting means, the disconnecting means shall not be used as the only means to put the circuit in an electrically safe work condition.

> A disconnecting means that does not accept a lockout device must not be the only means of controlling an energy source. Tagout must be supplemented by at least one additional safety measure.

(4) The use of tagout procedures without a lock shall be permitted only in cases where equipment design precludes the installation of a lock on an energy isolation device(s). When tagout is employed, at least one additional safety measure shall be employed. In such cases, the procedure shall clearly establish responsibilities and accountability for each person who might be exposed to electrical hazards.

Informational Note: Examples of additional safety measures include the removal of an isolating circuit element such as fuses, blocking of the controlling switch, or opening an extra disconnecting device to reduce the likelihood of inadvertent energization.

> If equipment cannot be locked, tagout is permitted when an additional safety measure is employed and the employer's procedure clearly identifies the acceptable methods to be used as the additional safety measures. The informational note provides examples of additional safety measures.

(12) Removal of Lockout/Tagout Devices. The procedure shall identify the details for removing locks or tags when the installing individual is unavailable. When locks or tags are removed by someone other than the installer, the employer shall attempt to locate that person prior to removing the lock or tag. When the lock or tag is removed because the installer is unavailable, the installer shall be informed prior to returning to work.

> The procedure for the removal of a lockout device under these circumstances should include measures to ensure that the lockout device can be safely removed and that the employee who removes the lockout device documents its removal. The person who originally installed the device must be informed that it was removed before the person returns to work and should be briefed on the current status of the equipment.

(13) Release for Return to Service. The procedure shall identify steps to be taken when the job or task requiring lockout/tagout is completed. Before electric circuits or equipment are re-energized, tests and visual inspections shall be conducted to verify that all tools, mechanical restraints and electrical jumpers, short circuits, and temporary protective grounding equipment have been removed, so that the circuits and equipment are in a condition to be safely energized. When applicable, the employees responsible for operating the machines or process shall be notified when circuits and equipment are ready to be energized, and such employees shall provide assistance as necessary to safely energize the circuits and equipment. The procedure shall contain a statement requiring the area to be inspected to ensure that nonessential items have been removed. One such step shall ensure that all personnel are clear of exposure to dangerous conditions resulting from re-energizing the service and that blocked mechanical equipment or grounded equipment is cleared and prepared for return to service.

Inspection of the work area should also ensure that all the guards and covers are installed properly and that everyone in the area is notified that the lockout devices will be removed and the equipment could start. The person in charge must make sure that all employees are safely positioned or removed from the area before removing the lockout devices. The equipment should be verified as being placed back into a normal operating condition before being re-energized. See 110.4(D) for more information.

(14) Temporary Release for Testing/Positioning. The procedure shall clearly identify the steps and qualified persons' responsibilities when the job or task requiring lockout/tagout is to be interrupted temporarily for testing or positioning of equipment; then the steps shall be identical to the steps for return to service.

Informational Note: See 110.8 for requirements when using test instruments and equipment

If the equipment is not going to be returned to service after testing or repositioning, all the lockout devices should be reinstalled immediately. Temporarily restoring electrical energy to reposition equipment or to facilitate testing is very hazardous and should be avoided.

△ 120.5 Process for Establishing and Verifying an Electrically Safe Work Condition.

De-energization itself does not create an electrically safe work condition (ESWC). The process of establishing an ESWC includes turning off the power, verifying the lack of voltage, and ensuring that the equipment cannot be re-energized while work is being performed. An ESWC does not exist until all of the requirements in Article 120 have been met. The act of establishing an ESWC must be considered energized work.

When an ESWC is achieved and verified, no electrical energy is in the immediate vicinity of the work task(s). Danger of injury from an electrical hazard has been reduced to an acceptable level, PPE is not needed, and unqualified persons can perform non-electrical work, such as cleaning and painting, near electrical equipment. When the equipment is re-energized, employees must be capable of executing their task(s) in a manner that will not create an unacceptable risk of injury from electrical hazards.

Exhibit 120.5 is a summary form of the minimum required steps for establishing an ESWC. The form lists the steps in the required sequence and includes the applicable 29 CFR 1910.333 sections for cross-reference.

Worker Alert

The process of establishing and verifying an electrically safe work condition (ESWC) might be one that you complete many times, but it should not be treated as a routine task. Every time you establish an ESWC, you must carefully consider each step of the process. In most facilities, establishing an ESWC should occur more often than performing energized electrical work.

EXHIBIT 120.5

PROCEDURE TO ESTABLISH AN ELECTRICALLY SAFE WORK CONDITION

Job Number: _____ Circuit/equipment/job location: _____

	Step	Procedure	NFPA 70E section	OSHA 29 CFR section	Comments
☐	1.	Determine all the possible sources of electrical supply to the specific equipment. Check applicable up-to-date drawings, diagrams, and identification tags.	120.5(1)	1910.333(b)(2)(ii)(A)	
☐	2.	After properly interrupting the load current, open the disconnecting device(s) for each source.	120.5(2)	1910.333(b)(2)(ii)(B)	
☐	3.	Wherever possible, visually verify that all of the blades of the disconnecting devices are fully open or that the draw-out-type circuit breakers are withdrawn to the fully disconnected position.	120.5(3)		
☐	4.	Release stored electrical energy.	120.5(4)	1910.333(b)(2)(ii)(C)	
☐	5.	Release or block stored mechanical energy.	120.5(5)	1910.333(b)(2)(ii)(D)	
☐	6.	Apply lockout/tagout devices in accordance with a documented and established procedure.	120.5(6)	1910.333(b)(2)(iii)(A)	
☐	7.	Use an adequately rated portable test instrument to test each phase conductor or circuit part to verify that it is de-energized. • An adequately rated permanently mounted listed test device is permitted to be used to verify the absence of voltage of the conductors or circuit parts at the work location. • On electrical systems over 1000 volts, noncontact test instruments are permitted to be used to test each phase conductor.	120.5(7)	1910.333(b)(2)(iv)	
☐	7a.	Before and after each test, ensure that the test instrument is operating satisfactorily by verifying on any known voltage source.	120.5(7)		
☐	8.	Where the possibility of induced voltages or stored electrical energy exists, ground the phase conductors or circuit parts before touching them. Where it could be reasonably anticipated that the conductors or circuit parts being de-energized could contact other exposed energized conductors or circuit parts, apply temporary protective grounding equipment.	120.5(8)	1910.333(b)(2) 1910.333(c)(3)(ii)(C)	

NFPA 70E

Procedure to establish an electrically safe work condition.

Establishing and verifying an electrically safe work condition shall include all of the following steps, which shall be performed in the order presented, if feasible:

(1) Determine all possible sources of electrical supply to the specific equipment. Check applicable up-to-date drawings, diagrams, and identification tags.

OSHA Connection

29CFR 1910.333(b)(2)
The steps to de-energize equipment are met by the application of 120.5.

All possible sources of information must be used to identify and locate all sources of energy. These sources can include single-line diagrams, panelboard schedules, elementary or schematic diagrams, electrical plans, identification signs and tags on electrical equipment, and consultation with workers who routinely service the equipment. Although most electrical equipment is supplied by a single source, occasionally, there can be multiple sources, such as emergency or standby generators, photovoltaic or fuel cell systems, or separate control power sources. The single-line diagram in Exhibit 120.6 depicts an electrical system fed by two separate sources. Section 408.4(B) of the NEC requires marking, as shown in Exhibit 120.7, when a panelboard, switchboard, or switchgear is fed by two sources.

Usually, equipment is labeled. However, a sneak circuit (hidden path) might exist that can only be identified by reviewing diagrammatic-type drawings, which identify additional power sources. Diagrammatic-type drawings must be maintained and kept up to date, just as is required for single-line diagrams, to provide accurate information.

EXHIBIT 120.6

Single-line diagram.

Marking indicating equipment is fed by two sources. (Courtesy of Bobby Gray)

Circuits containing transformers must be checked to verify that all the links or disconnects are opened to prevent any potential backfeeds. This is especially important when connecting temporary power in situations where equipment is taken out of service for repair or maintenance.

(2) After properly interrupting the load current, open the disconnecting device(s) for each source.

Before operating any disconnecting device, it should be verified whether or not the device is capable of opening the load current. When the rating of a disconnect device is not sufficient to interrupt the load current, the load must be interrupted by another action prior to opening the device. Otherwise, the disconnecting device might be destroyed, initiating a significant failure that could escalate to an arcing fault within the equipment.

Even when the equipment is load-rated, interrupting large full-load currents can reduce the life of the disconnecting device. Motor-driven equipment should be stopped and other electrical equipment de-energized to reduce the amount of current in the circuit before the disconnecting device is operated. Exhibit 120.8 shows the interrupting of the load by stopping the equipment prior to opening the disconnecting means. Exhibit 120.9 shows the opening of the disconnect device. The equipment label in Exhibit 120.10 indicates the need to disconnect additional power sources.

Intrrupting the load. (Courtesy of Bobby Gray)

Opening of the disconnecting means. (Courtesy of Bobby Gray)

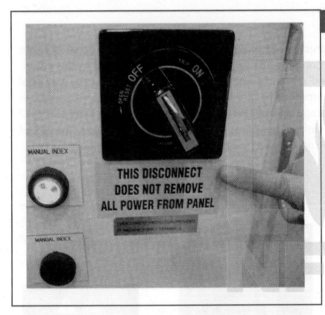

Marking of a disconnect that does not remove all power sources.

(3) Wherever possible, visually verify that all blades of the disconnecting devices are fully open or that drawout-type circuit breakers are withdrawn to the test or fully disconnected position.

Disconnecting devices occasionally malfunction and fail to open all of the phase conductors when the handle is operated. If the disconnecting mechanism does not operate freely, it should not be forced open. The circuit should be de-energized by means of an upstream device. Where possible, after operating the handle of the disconnecting device, employees should observe the physical opening of each blade of the device, such as through a viewing window. The blades in Exhibit 120.11 have been fully separated from the retention jaws. Opening a door or removing a cover to verify open contacts could expose an employee to electrical hazards. Therefore, the employee must continue to be protected from those hazards by PPE until all the steps for the verification of the electrically safe work condition have been completed.

EXHIBIT 120.11

Verifying the opening of contacts.

(4) Release stored electrical energy.

Electrical energy could be stored in batteries, capacitors, inductors, or other discrete electrical components. These components could be internal or external to the equipment being worked on. Stored electrical energy might also be present in electrical cables. Depending on the equipment or system design, it could take a considerable amount of time before the storage energy dissipates. The equipment in Exhibit 120.12 requires at least 15 minutes of discharge time and carries a reminder to verify the lack of voltage. Time itself must not be relied upon for the depletion of stored energy.

EXHIBIT 120.12

Equipment requiring dissipation of stored energy. (Courtesy of Schneider Electric)

(5) Block or relieve stored nonelectrical energy in devices to the extent the circuit parts cannot be unintentionally energized by such devices.

The procedure includes requirements for releasing mechanical energy that might endanger personnel. Springs must be released or physical restraint applied when necessary to immobilize mechanical equipment. Other sources of stored energy must be blocked or otherwise relieved. The mechanical energy in the press shown in Exhibit 120.13 has been blocked.

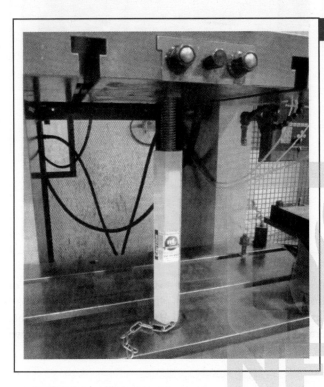

EXHIBIT 120.13

Blocked stored mechanical energy. (Courtesy of Metal Form Products Co. Ltd)

(6) Apply lockout/tagout devices in accordance with a documented and established procedure.

Only qualified persons should apply lockout devices in accordance with the employer's documented and established policy. Lockout devices are typically specifically identified padlocks that keep the disconnecting means open and isolate the equipment from all potentially hazardous energy sources. Tags identify the persons responsible for applying and removing the locks. Exhibit 120.14 shows an employee attaching a lock and tag to an open switch.

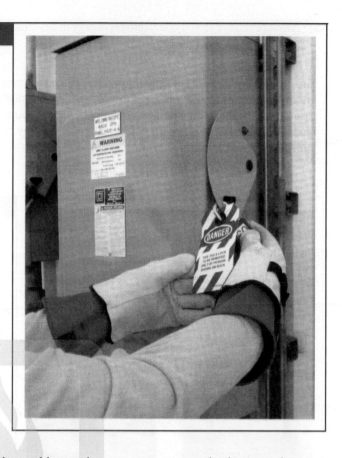

EXHIBIT 120.14

Applying a lock and tag to a switch. (Courtesy of Bobby Gray)

(7) Use an adequately rated portable test instrument to test each phase conductor or circuit part to test for the absence of voltage. Test each phase conductor or circuit part both phase-to-phase and phase-to-ground. Before and after each test, determine that the test instrument is operating satisfactorily through verification on any known voltage source.

In each instance, the qualified person must ensure the absence of voltage on each conductor to which a person could be exposed. That determination must be made by measuring the voltage to ground and the voltage between all the other conductors using a voltage detector rated for the maximum voltage available from any potential source of energy. In an abnormal situation where there is no connection to earth, the test instrument might indicate an absence of voltage to ground and thereby indicate that the equipment ground path needs to be re-established.

The test instrument should be selected on the basis of its service and duty. The rating of the device must be at least as great as the expected voltage and the transient voltage expected at the test point. Categories can also define where the instrument can be used on the electrical distribution system. See the commentary following Item (3) to 110.8(B) for test instrument ratings.

The three-step testing procedure is shown in Exhibit 120.15. First, the test instrument is used to test a known source to verify that the tester is operating properly, as shown in part (a). Then, the test instrument is used to confirm that the equipment to be de-energized has zero voltage, as shown in part (b). The tester is used again in part (c) to test a known source to confirm that the test instrument did not fail during the testing process.

EXHIBIT 120.15

(a)   (b)   (c)

Lack of voltage verification procedure.

Exception No. 1 to 7: An adequately rated permanently mounted absence of voltage tester shall be permitted to be used to test for the absence of voltage of the conductors or circuit parts at the work location, provided it meets all the following requirements: (1) It is permanently mounted and installed in accordance with the manufacturer's instructions and tests the conductors and circuit parts at the point of work; (2) It is listed and labeled for the purpose of testing for the absence of voltage; (3) It tests each phase conductor or circuit part both phase-to-phase and phase-to-ground; (4) The test device is verified as operating satisfactorily on any known voltage source before and after testing for the absence of voltage.

Typically, measurement devices indicate when voltage is present, but a lack of indicated voltage does not guarantee that equipment has been de-energized. For this reason, these mounted devices are designed to run internal diagnostics, verify the operation on a known voltage source, confirm contact with a circuit, and verify the lack of voltage. These measurement devices do not use equipment voltage to verify the operation of the device. A secondary test source is available to perform this function. The device will then actively indicate a lack of voltage. See Exhibit 120.16 for an installed absence of voltage tester indicating that equipment is de-energized. Absence of voltage testing equipment for fixed installations are listed to UL 1436, *Standard for Outlet Circuit Testers and Similar Indicating Devices.*

Exception No. 2 to 7: On electrical systems over 1000 volts, noncontact capacitive test instruments shall be permitted to be used to test each phase conductor.

Informational Note No. 1: See UL 61010-1, *Safety Requirements for Electrical Equipment for Measurement, Control, and Laboratory Use, Part 1: General Requirements,* for rating, overvoltage category, and design requirements for voltage measurement and test instruments intended for use on electrical systems 1000 volts and below.

Informational No. 2: For additional information on rating and design requirements for permanently mounted absence of voltage testers, refer to UL 1436, *Outlet Circuit Testers and Other Similar Indicating Devices.*

Informational Note No. 3: For additional information on rating and design requirements for voltage detectors, refer to IEC 61243-1, *Live Working — Voltage Detectors — Part 1: Capacitive type to be used for voltages exceeding IkV a.c.,* or IEC 61243-2, *Live Working — Voltage Detectors — Part 2: Resistive type to be used for voltages ofIkV to 36 kV a.c.,* or IEC 61243-3, *Live Working — Voltage Detectors — Part 3: Two-pole low voltage type.*

EXHIBIT 120.16

Absence of voltage tester.
(Courtesy of Panduit Corp.)

Worker Alert

Applying temporary protective grounding equipment is the last step in establishing an electrically safe work condition (ESWC). You are required to use PPE for all of these steps. Temporary grounding is not necessary for all ESWCs.

(8) Where the possibility of induced voltages or stored electrical energy exists, ground all circuit conductors and circuit parts before touching them. Where it could be reasonably anticipated that the conductors or circuit parts being de-energized could contact other exposed energized conductors or circuit parts, apply temporary protective grounding equipment in accordance with the following

The purpose of temporary grounding is to protect against electrical shock for personnel working on de-energized circuits. Temporary protective grounds are critical safety devices used to create circuit paths so that circuit overcurrent protective devices will operate if a circuit is accidentally energized. De-energized circuits could be accidentally energized due to equipment failure, mechanical failure, or static buildup. Human error, such as switching errors or inadvertently connecting a conductor, can also add a source of energy and re-energize a circuit being repaired.

Energized conductors and equipment in high-voltage installations can induce (via magnetic coupling) hazardous voltages in adjacent conductors and equipment that is de-energized. Failure of a conductor support system or conductor can result in the inadvertent re-energizing of a de-energized conductor. For instance, more than one outside overhead line might be installed on a single pole and, when a conductor supported at a higher elevation is damaged, it could fall onto a lower installed conductor and re-energize it.

a. *Placement.* Temporary protective grounding equipment shall be placed at such locations and arranged in such a manner as to prevent each employee from being exposed to a shock hazard (i.e., hazardous differences in electrical potential). The location, sizing, and application of temporary protective grounding equipment shall be identified as part of the employer's job planning.

Employees must fully understand the systems and equipment they're working on to select the appropriate temporary protective grounding device(s) and to determine their placement. A protective grounding device must be installed on a conductor at a point between a person and a source of energy. Care must be taken to properly locate conductors so that their movement by mechanical forces does not cause harm to employees. Equipment grounding conductors or equipment grounding terminals are likely points of attachment for temporary protective grounding equipment. If an unexpected source of electricity could come from both directions in an electrical circuit, temporary protective grounding equipment must be installed on both sides.

Employees who work within the area of the dc bus of a battery system must be trained to understand the unique hazards associated with ungrounded dc voltage. Normally, dc voltage is ungrounded. Although in normal settings an equipment grounding conductor decreases exposure to electrical hazards, in cell areas, any conductor that is grounded increases exposure to electrical hazards.

b. *Capacity.* Temporary protective grounding equipment shall be capable of conducting the maximum fault current that could flow at the point of grounding for the time necessary to clear the fault.

Grounding devices are available in many forms; the clamp and cable types are the most commonly used. Some equipment manufacturers provide grounding devices for switchgear, which are built on a frame to be inserted in a space or cubicle that normally holds a circuit breaker or fusible switch. Exhibit 120.17 shows a typical set of safety grounds.

Temporary safety grounding equipment must also be capable of withstanding the high mechanical stress imposed when conducting fault current. The equipment must have a rating established by the manufacturer, and it must be applied within that rating. Selecting the appropriate temporary grounding device with an established fault-duty rating for the circuit is paramount. Inadequately rated protective grounding equipment can introduce hazards that otherwise would not exist.

Worker Alert

Temporary protective grounding equipment must be capable of conducting the maximum available fault current and facilitating the operation of the protective device. You must make sure that personal protective ground equipment components, such as cables that are not properly sized or connectors that are not designed for the connection, are not used.

EXHIBIT 120.17

Two examples of temporary grounding sets. (Courtesy of Hubbell/CHANCE® Lineman Grade Tools™)

Informational Note: ASTM F855, *Standard Specification for Temporary Protective Grounds to be Used on De-energized Electric Power Lines and Equipment,* is an example of a standard that contains information on capacity of temporary protective grounding equipment.

Employers are responsible for providing equipment capable of protecting employees at risk of injury during energized work. Employers must verify that the issued temporary protective grounding equipment meets the appropriate consensus standard. For more information, see 130.7(C)(14)(b) and the associated commentary regarding equipment compliance. An employer might not be competent to determine if purchased equipment complies with the standard. Often, in order to facilitate acceptance of equipment, listed equipment is employed even when a standard, such as NFPA *70E*, does not require listing.

c. *Impedance.* Temporary protective grounding equipment and connections shall have an impedance low enough to cause immediate operation of protective devices in case of unintentional energizing of the electric conductors or circuit parts.

The objective of temporary protective grounding is to create a circuit path so that an overcurrent protective device can operate if the conductor that has been temporarily grounded is accidentally energized.

The impedance of the ground-fault current return path through the earth should be verified on a frequency determined through use. If the impedance of the ground-fault return path is high, the overcurrent device is not likely to operate or might not operate rapidly enough to protect employees and limit damage to the equipment. Therefore, creating a path for ground-fault return current other than through the earth is necessary to achieve the immediate operation of an overcurrent device if the conductors or equipment are accidentally energized.

Cable size, cable length, and proper attachment of temporary protective grounding equipment are all important factors to consider when creating a low impedance path. Cables must be of adequate length for the task but should not interfere with workers within the defined boundary of the work area. Excessive cable length could increase cable impedance and employee exposure when conducting fault current and should be avoided to reduce possible injury caused by cable whipping.

Case Study   120.5

Scenario

Nathan was employed by an electrical contractor (contract employer) and had been working at a wastewater treatment plant for 6 weeks, installing and testing high-voltage equipment. The task was to install new relays on the door of a 13,800-volt switchgear cubicle. As he prepared to install the relays on a door of the new equipment, Nathan assembled his tools and opened (disconnected) the main high-voltage switch. The procedure called for him to perform a visual inspection of the switch blades to ensure they had opened properly, but he was interrupted by Dave, the general contractor. Dave was upset that the relays hadn't already been mounted, and he instructed Nathan to finish the job as soon as possible.

Had Nathan remembered to inspect the switch, he would have discovered that one blade of the three-phase switch had failed to open. Nathan didn't have a functioning tester suitable for this level of voltage. Without it, he had no way to determine if the load side of the switch was de-energized. To mount the relays, Nathan had to drill several holes in the cabinet door. As Nathan stretched into the cabinet to plug in the drill, his right leg got close enough to the 13,800-volt bus for the electricity to jump the air gap and enter his leg. This developed into an arc flash. The extreme temperatures at the arc terminals vaporized the bus material and propagated into a huge fireball and arc blast.

Result

The arc flash event lasted only 4 milliseconds, but it ignited Nathan's clothes, resulting in third-degree burns over 40 percent of his body. Nathan was wearing a polyester shirt, which fused to his skin. He was also wearing a large metal belt buckle, a plastic watch, and his wedding ring. During the incident, the belt buckle burned a hole in his stomach, the watch melted into his wrist, and the wedding ring nearly severed his finger. He was transported to a burn unit, where he began his battle for survival. At the burn center, he underwent several months of excruciatingly painful treatments and skin grafts necessary to recover from his severe burn injuries. Nathan did not return to work as an electrician.

Analysis

Nathan's injuries could have been prevented if an electrically safe work condition (ESWC) had been established. Additionally, if barricades had been set up and the general contractor (unqualified person) was kept out of the work area, Nathan would not have been distracted from checking if the disconnecting device was fully opened and all the phases had been disconnected.

There was no indication whether Nathan wore the appropriate shock and arc-rated PPE necessary to establish an ESWC.

Although Nathan assumed that the equipment he was working on was de-energized, the fact that he was wearing conductive objects exacerbated his injuries. In accordance with 130.8(D), wearing jewelry and other conductive articles is prohibited where there is potential for contact with exposed energized conductors or circuit parts.

Likely cause of incident

There are two possible scenarios for this incident. The first requires assuming that, despite the outcome, Nathan was qualified for the task of establishing an ESWC for the specific equipment. However, if he were qualified, he would have verified the ESWC before removing the necessary PPE, if he had indeed been wearing it prior to the incident. He also would have had the proper test equipment for verification of the lack of voltage, as well as the awareness and self-discipline required by 110.5(D) to not be distracted by the general contractor.

The second and more likely scenario is that Nathan was unqualified for the task and that he considered the task routine and not worth the time to follow all the necessary procedures. A worker with this mindset will often consider the use of PPE to be a burden at the cost of suffering injuries, just as Nathan did. In either scenario, Nathan decided not to don the PPE that could have provided the protection to prevent the injury he suffered.

Article | 130 | Work Involving Electrical Hazards

There is a risk of injury to any employee conducting any task (electrical or nonelectrical) within the limited approach boundary of exposed electrical hazards. Therefore, the primary protective strategy must be establishing an electrically safe work condition (ESWC). After that strategy is executed, all electrical energy has been removed from all conductors and circuit parts to which the employee could be exposed.

While Article 120 describes the process of creating an ESWC, Article 130 defines the situations under which an ESWC must be established. Work that is performed near or on exposed energized electrical conductors or circuit parts is dangerous. NFPA *70E*® and OSHA regulations require, first and foremost, that the equipment be de-energized and in an ESWC unless it is operated under a normal condition. Section 130.2(A) explains the limited situations under which energized electrical work might be justified.

△ **130.1 General.**

Article 130 covers requirements for work involving electrical hazards such as the electrical safety-related work practices, assessments, precautions, and procedures when an electrically safe work condition cannot be established.

Safety-related work practices shall be used to safeguard employees from injury while they are exposed to electrical hazards from electrical conductors or circuit parts that are or can become energized.

When energized electrical conductors and circuit parts operating at voltages equal to or greater than 50 volts are not put into an electrically safe work condition, and work is performed as permitted in accordance with 110.4, all of the following requirements shall apply:

(1) Only qualified persons shall be permitted to work on electrical conductors or circuit parts that have not been put into an electrically safe work condition.

(2) An energized electrical work permit shall be completed as required by 130.2.

(3) A shock risk assessment shall be performed as required by 130.4.

(4) An arc flash risk assessment shall be performed as required by 130.5.

All requirements of Article 130 shall apply whether an incident energy analysis is completed or if Table 130.7(C)(15)(a), Table 130.7(C)(15)(b), and Table 130.7(C)(15)(c) are used in lieu of an incident energy analysis.

Energized electrical conductors and circuit parts must be put into an electrically safe work condition (ESWC) before an employee performs any type of work within the limited approach boundary or interacts with equipment where an increased likelihood of injury from exposure to an arc flash hazard exists. An ESWC is established when electrical conductors or circuit parts have been disconnected from energized parts, locked out or tagged out in accordance with established standards, tested to ensure the absence of voltage, and grounded if determined necessary. An ESWC is not established until all eight steps of 120.5 have been completed.

Under both NFPA *70E* and OSHA requirements, all work performed within the limited approach boundary requires that the equipment be in a verified de-energized state unless energized work can be justified. There are only three conditions in 110.4 under which energized work is permitted. Normal operation of most equipment does not meet the definition of the term working on as defined in Article 100. Normal operation [see 110.4(D)] of equipment should not place employees at an inherent risk of injury.

Worker Alert

You must fully understand the task at hand and the applicable documented safe work practices and procedures before performing justified energized work. You should not be improvising procedures in the field.

OSHA Connection

29 CFR 1910.333(a)(2)

Exposed live parts that are not de-energized for reasons of increased or additional hazards or infeasibility require the use of other safety-related work practices to protect employees against contact with energized circuit parts directly with any part of their body or indirectly through some other conductive object.

Employers are required to provide procedures to prevent injury to employees. Work that is performed near or on exposed energized electrical conductors or circuit parts is dangerous. It should be presumed that there is an unacceptable risk of injury from shock or thermal hazards—arc flashes, electrical burns, or thermal burns—from exposure to energized conductors and circuit parts unless the required risk assessments find otherwise. Both a shock risk assessment (130.4) and an arc flash risk assessment (130.5) are required before any person can approach the exposed energized electrical conductors or circuit parts.

There are two methods of conducting an arc flash risk assessment when energized electrical equipment is involved. The arc flash PPE category method uses the tables within NFPA *70E*. The incident energy analysis method consists of a variety of possible calculation approaches. Regardless of the method selected, the requirements of Article 130 apply, including the requirement that an ESWC be the primary method of establishing a safe work environment for employees.

Case Study

130

Scenario

Mark, an electrician, and John, his helper with no formal electrical training, were installing a new three-phase circuit between an existing energized 480-volt panelboard and a new piece of machinery. Mark used protective insulating gloves with leather protectors but did not use any other PPE. During the process, Mark attempted to install a missing bolt from a circuit breaker mount onto an energized busbar. He lost control of the bolt while attempting to screw it into place. Either the bolt or the mount then contacted another busbar phase, resulting in an arc flash. John was standing some distance away when the incident happened and was uninjured. John was able to find the facility owner and demonstrate what had happened. During his demonstration, a second electrical arc flash occurred at the panelboard, the cause of which is unknown. The facility owner was standing some distance away and was not hurt.

Result

Mark temporarily lost his sight and suffered first- and second-degree burns on his head, face, and forearm. John was not wearing any PPE at the time of the second incident. He received second-degree burns to his head, face, neck, arm, and hand. The nylon jacket he was wearing caught fire and melted to his skin, causing third-degree burns. John required surgery to remove destroyed skin, as well as restorative skin grafts. He did not return to work.

Analysis

An accident typically occurs due to a chain of events or mistakes that lead up to the actual event. If one of the links in the chain of events is eliminated, the accident most likely won't happen.

There are no facts to suggest that it was either infeasible or that a greater hazard or increased risk would have resulted if the power to the panelboard had been turned off to establish an electrically safe work condition (ESWC). The facts suggest that Mark and John were unqualified for the task they were assigned. If an ESWC had been established prior to the attempted replacement of the missing bolt from the circuit breaker, this incident would not have occurred.

Justifying energized work does not prevent incidents from occurring or prevent equipment damage. Even if a task is properly justified, an incident such as this can still occur, albeit with a less severe injury to Mark, who would have had the appropriate protection against all of the electrical hazards.

Relevant NFPA *70E* Requirements

If the company had followed the requirements of NFPA *70E*, Mark and John might not have been injured. The employer ignored the following primary safety principles:

- Create an electrical safety program [110.5].
- Establish an electrically safe work condition [110.3],
- Properly justify energized work [110.4].

If it could have been demonstrated that working on the energized equipment was justified, the employer should have done the following:

- Considered the possibility of human error [110.5(H)(2)]
- Conducted a shock risk assessment [130.4]
- Conducted an arc flash risk assessment [130.5]
- Obtained an energized electrical work permit [130.2]

Mark and John also hold some responsibility for the incident. As employees, they should have been aware of their responsibilities under NFPA *70E*. In addition to the requirements listed above, they should have been aware of the following:

- Their ability to meet the definition of a qualified person [100]
- Their need for awareness and self-discipline [110.5(D)]
- The training they should have received [110.6]

130.2 Energized Electrical Work Permit.

Employers are required to provide procedures to prevent injury to employees. Work conducted near or on electrical equipment that has not been placed in an electrically safe work condition leaves employees exposed to potential injury.

No matter the type or simplicity of a task, there is no such thing as routine work where electrical safety is involved. NFPA *70E* does not prohibit issuing an energized electrical work permit for simple, repetitive, or nonelectrical tasks. However, before issuing this type of open permit, due consideration must be given to the fact that no work near or on energized parts should be considered routine work. A simple task might not be routine if it is performed on different equipment. Performing a task repeatedly might not be routine after an extended work shift. Repetitive work might not be routine even if the employee is trained to understand the risks associated with exposure to the potential electrical hazards and is wearing the appropriate PPE, as situations can easily change. The electrical hazards within a limited approach boundary can vary by equipment, and employees conducting nonelectrical tasks can be exposed to different risks.

(A) When Required. When work is performed as permitted in accordance with 110.4, an energized electrical work permit shall be required and documented under any of the following conditions:

(1) When work is performed within the restricted approach boundary
(2) When the employee interacts with the equipment when conductors or circuit parts are not exposed but an increased likelihood of injury from an exposure to an arc flash hazard exists

The phrase "interacting with the equipment" might include opening or closing a disconnecting means or pushing a reset button. However, if equipment is installed in accordance with the requirements of *NFPA 70®, National Electrical Code® (NEC®)*, and the manufacturer's instructions, and it is properly maintained and operated normally, the chance of one of these actions initiating an arcing fault is remote. An arc flash hazard is more likely to exist when equipment is operated when not under normal operating conditions, such as when a circuit breaker is racked in or out of switchgear.

Once energized electrical work is properly justified, the hierarchy of risk controls has been employed, and it has been decided that justified work can be conducted safely, the basic purpose of an energized electrical work permit (EEWP) is to ensure that the people in responsible positions are involved in the decision of whether or not to accept the increased risk associated with working on energized electrical conductors or circuit parts. An additional benefit of an EEWP is that its review might initiate a decision to perform the work de-energized.

It is a good practice to consider the use of an EEWP even when one is not required. This demonstrates that proper consideration was given to all of the factors required to protect an employee when diagnostic work is being done.

(B) Elements of Work Permit. The work permit shall include, but not be limited to, the following items:

(1) Description of the circuit and equipment to be worked on and their location
(2) Description of the work to be performed
(3) Justification for why the work must be performed in an energized condition *[see 110.4]*
(4) Description of the safe work practices to be employed (*see 130.1*)

(5) Results of the shock risk assessment *[see 130.4(A)]*
   a. Voltage to which personnel will be exposed
   b. Limited approach boundary *[see 130.4(F), Table 130.4(E)(a), and Table 130.4(E)(b)]*
   c. Restricted approach boundary *[see 130.4(G), Table 130.4(E)(a), and Table 130.4(E)(b)]*
   d. Personal and other protective equipment required by this standard to safely perform the assigned task and to protect against the shock hazard *[see 130.4(F), 130.7(C)(1) through (C)(16), and 130.7(D)]*
(6) Results of the arc flash risk assessment *[see 130.5]*
   a. Available incident energy at the working distance or arc flash PPE category *(see 130.5)*
   b. Personal and other protective equipment required by this standard to protect against the arc flash hazard *[see 130.5(F), 130.7(C)(1) through (C)(16), Table 130.7(C)(15)(c), and 130.7(D)]*
   c. Arc flash boundary *[see 130.5(E)]*
(7) Means employed to restrict the access of unqualified persons from the work area *[see 130.7(E)]*
(8) Evidence of completion of a job briefing, including a discussion of any job-specific hazards *[see 110.5(1)]*
(9) Energized work approval (authorizing or responsible management, safety officer, or owner, etc.) signature(s)

> Informational Note: For an example of an acceptable energized work permit, see Figure J.1.

Employees are often reluctant to question a decision made by a supervisor that a work task must be conducted while a circuit remains energized. The employer must demonstrate that de-energizing will introduce additional hazards or increased risk. Managers and supervisors tend to be hesitant to accept an increased risk of exposure to hazards, particularly if their authorization for employees to work on energized equipment is required to be in writing. Annex J contains a flow chart in Figure J.2 to assist in determining the need for an energized electrical work permit.

Δ **(C) Exemptions to Work Permit.** Electrical work shall be permitted without an energized electrical work permit if a qualified person is provided with and uses appropriate safe work practices and PPE in accordance with Chapter 1 under any of the following conditions:

(1) Testing, troubleshooting, or voltage measuring
(2) Thermography, ultrasound, or visual inspections if the restricted approach boundary is not crossed
(3) Access to and egress from an area with energized electrical equipment if no electrical work is performed and the restricted approach boundary is not crossed
(4) General housekeeping and miscellaneous non-electrical tasks if the restricted approach boundary is not crossed

The energized electrical work permit (EEWP) exemptions require that safe work practices be followed and that appropriate PPE be worn, which includes both shock protection PPE and arc flash protection PPE as necessary. It is a good practice to use an EEWP even when it is not required. The EEWP will document the task, PPE, and work procedures that are necessary. An employee conducting voltage measurement without an EEWP might notice a loose conductor in a terminal and think that it should be tightened. The use of an EEWP will remind the employee that the only authorized task is a voltage measurement. Tightening the terminal is a separate task outside the scope of the original EEWP and could put the employee at risk of injury.

Worker Alert

Although an energized electrical work permit is not required for the conditions listed here, you are still permitted to generate one. You might want a work permit to document what is expected of you, what documented procedures you will use, and how you will be protected when conducting justified energized work when testing, troubleshooting, or voltage measuring.

OSHA Connection

29 CFR 1910.333(c)(9)
Employees must not perform housekeeping duties at such close distances to live parts that there is a possibility of contact. Adequate safeguards (such as insulating equipment or barriers) must be provided.

Note that 130.2(C)(1) limits the work to be conducted to diagnostic tasks. A work function is diagnostic when it is used to identify the condition of equipment or its parts, to verify the condition of the equipment, or to identify potential problems. This would include the verification of an electrically safe work condition. Should a planned diagnostic task change to a repair task, the work would no longer be considered diagnostic, and an additional or modified EEWP would be required. Troubleshooting does not inherently mean that energized work is justified. An alternative to energized testing might be a continuity measurement.

Note that 130.2(C)(2), (3), and (4) limit the work to be done to outside the restricted approach boundary. If the boundary is crossed for the performance of any of the tasks, then an EEWP is required.

Case Study   130.2(C)

Introduction

Section 130.2(C) permits specific electrical work to be conducted without documenting the assigned task through a completed energized electrical work permit (EEWP). The EEWP exemptions require that safe work practices be followed and that appropriate PPE be worn. Item (1) limits the work to be conducted to diagnostic tasks. Items (2), (3) and (4) are limited to staying outside the restricted approach boundary. It is good practice to use an EEWP to document the assigned employees, task, PPE, and work procedures that are necessary even when a permit is not required. The following five scenarios illustrate that testing, troubleshooting, and voltage measuring conducted on energized electrical equipment is dangerous.

Case #1

Tom, an electrician working for a small company, was relocating a 480-volt dc generator at an industrial facility. The facility engineer assisted Tom with moving the equipment and reconnecting the electrical wiring. Tom turned on the power and asked the engineer to push the start button. When the generator failed to start, Tom used his voltmeter to verify that control voltage was reaching the starter. Tom then moved to the rear of the generator to verify that he had made the electrical connections correctly and reached behind the generator to check the two fuses located in the rear.

The engineer smelled something burning and called to Tom, who did not respond. He then looked behind the generator and saw Tom slumped over. He shouted for others to call for an ambulance and to cut the power off at the power disconnect switch. Tom was then pulled from behind the generator and CPR was begun. The emergency medical service arrived approximately 15 minutes after the incident and began advanced cardiac life support. Resuscitation efforts continued but were unsuccessful. Tom was pronounced dead in the hospital emergency room due to electrocution.

Content source: National Institute for Occupational Safety and Health (NIOSH); FACE case: 87-69.

Case #2

David, a 30-year-old electrical technician, was assisting with electrical testing inside a control panel cabinet. David and a service representative were testing the voltage regulating unit on a high-temperature, steel-alloy rolling mill. The two men tested the low-voltage (15 volt) wiring and determined that the unit was not correctly regulating the voltage. The representative opened the voltage regulating control cabinet panel to trace the low-voltage wiring since it was not color-coded. Without de-energizing the system, the representative climbed onto an adjacent cabinet in order to view the wires. David kneeled in front of the opened control cabinet then positioned his head and shoulders inside the 800-volt resistor compartment to pull on the low-voltage wires. The representative tried to identify the wires from above while David pulled them.

The representative heard David making a gurgling sound and looked down to see him shaking as though he were being shocked. He jumped down from the cabinet to knock David away from the energized conductor while receiving a shock himself. CPR was administered to David approximately 10 minutes after the incident occurred. He was pronounced dead approximately 1 hour and 45 minutes after the incident as a result of his contact with an energized electrical conductor.

Content source: National Institute for Occupational Safety and Health (NIOSH); FACE case: 92-07.

Case #3

Pam, a 46-year-old electrical project supervisor, and three coworkers were installing two control cabinets and two solid-state compressor motor starters for two 400-horsepower air compressors. They were checking the operation of the unit after installation was completed. The switch on the main distribution panel was turned ON to check the starter's operation. The starter indicator light activated but the compressor motor did not start. Pam concluded that a problem existed inside the starter control panel. She opened the starter control panel door without de-energizing the unit and reached inside to trace the wiring and check the integrity of the electrical leads.

Pam contacted the 480-volt primary lead for the motor starter with her left hand. Current passed through her hand and exited through her feet. Pam yelled and the coworker immediately turned the main distribution switch to the OFF position. The coworker administered CPR after Pam collapsed to the floor. The EMS arrived within 15 minutes, continued CPR, and transported Pam to the hospital where she was pronounced dead 1 hour and 20 minutes after the incident occurred.

Content source: National Institute for Occupational Safety and Health (NIOSH); FACE case: 92-20.

Case #4

A contract company was replacing a high voltage distribution switch. This required that the electric utility coordinate a power outage. Before the utility removed power, Frank, the assistant general foreman, and Brian, the crew foreman of the electrical contractor, arrived. They debated if the switch had been de-energized. Brian was authorized to possess the cabinet lock keys so he removed the locks and opened the door of the cabinet. Frank removed the insulation barrier and, using a tic tracer, attempted to determine if the distribution system was de-energized.

Frank guided the tic tracer with his right hand to contact one phase of the 23,000-volt source. The contact allowed 13,200 volts to pass through his body. He fell forward but was still breathing. Brian felt that he was "electrified" and proceeded to run. Brian received minor flash burns to his eyes and face. Utility crew members arriving at the scene administered CPR to Frank until the rescue squad arrived. The rescue squad continued CPR during transportation to a hospital where Tom was pronounced dead more than an hour after the incident.

Content source: National Institute for Occupational Safety and Health (NIOSH); FACE case: 85-16.

Case #5

Zachary, a 38-year old employee of a process equipment manufacturer, was attempting to test the electrical power circuit for an 85-horsepower electric motor by using a multimeter rated at 600 volts. The motor was connected to a 14,400-volt, 600-amp switch box. When Zachary attempted to check the circuit fuse, an electrical arc ionized the air in the cabinet and an arc flash occurred. Zachary was transported to the hospital with burns

over 50 percent of his body. He died 18 days later from thermal burns as a consequence of the arc flash.

Content source: National Institute for Occupational Safety and Health (NIOSH); FACE case: 92CO039.

Conclusion

Not all tasks that are part of an entire work plan can be covered by a single EEWP. Diagnostic tasks are exempt from an EEWP. However, it was the diagnostic tasks being conducted that led to these fatalities. None of the reports indicated that any victim had followed proper procedures or used appropriate PPE. The allowance to omit an EEWP in 130.2(C) is predicated on both conditions being met. In each case, an EEWP would have identified the many shortcomings in the job plan. An EEWP would have required a risk assessment for every task, which would have identified the hazards and risks that led to each fatality. The following are some safety considerations an EEWP would have documented if a proper risk assessment was performed:

- Case#1 —The installation would have been a separate task from start-up.
- Case #2 — An ESWC would have been required before pulling the conductors.
- Case #3 — A continuity test would have been conducted on de-energized circuits.
- Case #4 — The coordination between the utility and contractor would have been detailed to prevent the assumption that someone else has completed a task.
- Case #5 — A properly rated voltage meter would have been specified.

What went wrong in these cases cannot be sufficiently addressed to prevent further incidents, since no one knows what the employees were authorized or trained to do. These situations make it hard to improve electrical safety. In all five cases it is unknown if procedures failed, human error occurred, training was inadequate, protective equipment was ineffective, or even if the task being performed was the task assigned. If it is not documented, then it did not happen. An EEWP in each case may have been beneficial to the point where each of these employees might still be alive.

130.4 Shock Risk Assessment.

The risk assessment procedure must determine whether any electrical part will remain energized for the duration of the task. Exhibit 110.3 illustrates various decision branches and requirement cross-references for each type of risk assessment. These risk assessments must answer many questions, including the following:

Justification
- Is energized work justified (i.e., does the alternative present a greater hazard or is it infeasible for a task to be performed de-energized)?

- What authorization is necessary to justify executing a work task when the exposed conductor(s) are energized?
- Will energized electrical work impact other work?
- What measures will be taken to minimize the impact of other work?

Hazards

- What is the potential result of equipment failure (i.e., to the employee, equipment, process, and environment)?
- What is the degree of the shock hazard?
- What is the degree of the arc flash hazard?
- Are there other electrical hazards?

Risk to employee

- Will the employee be exposed to any hazards during the work task?
- Is there a risk of injury to the employee?
- Are there situations where the risk of injury is unacceptable?
- Will other employees be exposed to an electrical hazard because of the work task?
- Is it possible to adequately protect employees from injury or death?

Employee involvement

- What employees are required to be within an approach boundary?
- Is the employee assigned to a task qualified for that specific task on that specific equipment?
- Are unqualified employees necessary?
- Are there special considerations due to a host employer/contract employer relationship?

Employee protection

- Have all the protection techniques from the hierarchy of risk controls been considered and used, if appropriate?
- What protective equipment is necessary to minimize an employee's exposure to each hazard?

(A) General. A shock risk assessment shall be performed:

(1) To identify shock hazards
(2) To estimate the likelihood of occurrence of injury or damage to health and the potential severity of injury or damage to health
(3) To determine if additional protective measures are required, including the use of PPE

Shock risk assessment is the process of identifying exposure to potential electrical shock hazards, estimating the potential severity of a shock injury, estimating the likelihood of occurrence of this injury, determining if protective measures are required, and determining the appropriate protective measures to use. The severity of the injury depends on the current flow through the body, the path it takes, and whether the heart is in a vulnerable point in the cardiac cycle. See the commentary following 340.4 for more on the effects of electricity on the human body.

As a person's distance from an exposed energized electrical conductor decreases, the risk of direct contact with the conductor increases. When conducting a shock risk assessment, employees must determine the voltage of all the conductors in their vicinity or of the tools they will use. Shock approach boundaries provide a trigger for added protection for all employees.

N **(B) Estimate of Likelihood and Severity.** The estimate of likelihood of occurrence of injury or damage to health and the potential severity of injury or damage to health shall take into consideration all of the following:

(1) The design of the electrical equipment
(2) The electrical equipment operating condition and the condition of maintenance

The severity of a shock injury, including the possibility of a fatality, depends on various factors, including whether appropriate personal and other protective equipment is used, the voltage level inflicted upon the body, the type of electrical circuit, the design of the circuit, and the body's contact points in the circuit.

(C) Additional Protective Measures. If additional protective measures are required, they shall be selected and implemented according to the hierarchy of risk control identified in 110.5(H)(3). When the additional protective measures include the use of PPE, the following shall be determined:

(1) The voltage to which personnel will be exposed
(2) The boundary requirements
(3) The personal and other protective equipment required by this standard to protect against the shock hazard

The hierarchy of risk controls must be used to address shock mitigation techniques. Arc flash mitigation techniques are addressed in 130.5(C). Some techniques can accomplish both goals.

The hierarchy in 110.5(H)(3) is listed in order of most effective to least effective and must be applied in descending order for each risk assessment. Once a shock hazard has been identified, it must first be determined if it can be eliminated. During the electrical system design stage, methods should be employed to eliminate the hazard in its entirety. In the electrical system design and equipment selection phase, it is easier to utilize the most effective controls of elimination and substitution to limit the risk associated with anticipated justified energized work. In this first context, elimination is the removal of a hazard so that it never exists. This removes the potential for human error when interacting with the equipment.

Full elimination of a hazard is often not an option for installed equipment. Although elimination can also be achieved by applying other controls, such as administration (e.g., establishing an electrically safe work condition), these other controls introduce the potential for human error. Only after all of the other risk controls have been exhausted should PPE be selected. PPE is considered the least effective and lowest level of risk control for employee protection and should not be the first or only control element used.

(D) Documentation. The results of the shock risk assessment shall be documented.

(E) Shock Protection Boundaries. The shock protection boundaries identified as limited approach boundary and restricted approach boundary shall be applicable where personnel are approaching exposed energized electrical conductors or circuit parts. Table 130.4(E)(a) shall be used for the distances associated with various ac system voltages. Table 130.4(E)(b) shall be used for the distances associated with various dc system voltages.

Worker Alert

You should be aware of other ways to protect yourself from injury. The use of PPE should be your employer's final step after all other protection schemes have been implemented. If you are not aware whether your employer has used any method other than PPE, you should determine if other ways are available to minimize injury if an incident occurs.

OSHA Connection

29 CFR 1910.132(d)(1)

The employer must assess the workplace to determine if hazards are present or are likely to be present. If hazards necessitate the use of PPE, the employer must select and have the employee use PPE that properly fits, as well as communicate selection decisions to the affected employee.

TABLE 130.4(E)(a) *Shock Protection Approach Boundaries to Exposed Energized Electrical Conductors or Circuit Parts for Alternating-Current Systems*

(1)	(2) Limited Approach Boundary[b]		(4)
Nominal System Voltage Range, Phase to Phase[a]	Exposed Movable Conductor[c]	(3) Exposed Fixed Circuit Part	Restricted Approach Boundary[b]; Includes Inadvertent Movement Adder
Less than 50 V	Not specified	Not specified	Not specified
50 V–150 V[d]	3.0 m (10 ft 0 in.)	1.0 m (3 ft 6 in.)	Avoid contact
151 V–750 V	3.0 m (10 ft 0 in.)	1.0 m (3 ft 6 in.)	0.3 m (1 ft 0 in.)
751 V–15 kV	3.0 m (10 ft 0 in.)	1.5 m (5 ft 0 in.)	0.7 m (2 ft 2 in.)
15.1 kV–36 kV	3.0 m (10 ft 0 in.)	1.8 m (6 ft 0 in.)	0.8 m (2 ft 9 in.)
36.1 kV–46 kV	3.0 m (10 ft 0 in.)	2.5 m (8 ft 0 in.)	0.8 m (2 ft 9 in.)
46.1 kV–72.5 kV	3.0 m (10 ft 0 in.)	2.5 m (8 ft 0 in.)	1.0 m (3 ft 6 in.)
72.6 kV–121 kV	3.3 m (10 ft 8 in.)	2.5 m (8 ft 0 in.)	1.0 m (3 ft 6 in.)
138 kV–145 kV	3.4 m (11 ft 0 in.)	3.0 m (10 ft 0 in.)	1.2 m (3 ft 10 in.)
161 kV–169 kV	3.6 m (11 ft 8 in.)	3.6 m (11 ft 8 in.)	1.3 m (4 ft 3 in.)
230 kV–242 kV	4.0 m (13 ft 0 in.)	4.0 m (13 ft 0 in.)	1.7 m (5 ft 8 in.)
345 kV–362 kV	4.7 m (15 ft 4 in.)	4.7 m (15 ft 4 in.)	2.8 m (9 ft 2 in.)
500 kV–550 kV	5.8 m (19 ft 0 in.)	5.8 m (19 ft 0 in.)	3.6 m (11 ft 8 in.)
765 kV–800 kV	7.2 m (23 ft 9 in.)	7.2 m (23 ft 9 in.)	4.9 m (15 ft 11 in.)

Notes:
(1) For arc flash boundary, see 130.5(E).
(2) All dimensions are distance from exposed energized electrical conductors or circuit part to employee.
[a]For single-phase systems above 250 volts, select the range that is equal to the system's maximum phase-to-ground voltage multiplied by 1.732.
[b]See definition in Article 100 and text in 130.4(D)(2) and Informative Annex C for elaboration.
[c]*Exposed movable conductors* describes a condition in which the distance between the conductor and a person is not under the control of the person. The term is normally applied to overhead line conductors supported by poles.
[d]This includes circuits where the exposure does not exceed 120 volts nominal.

TABLE 130.4(E)(b) *Shock Protection Approach Boundaries to Exposed Energized Electrical Conductors or Circuit Parts for Direct-Current Voltage Systems*

(1)	(2) Limited Approach Boundary		(4)
Nominal Potential Difference	Exposed Movable Conductor*	(3) Exposed Fixed Circuit Part	Restricted Approach Boundary; Includes Inadvertent Movement Adder
Less than 50 V	Not specified	Not specified	Not specified
50 V–300 V	3.0 m (10 ft 0 in.)	1.0 m (3 ft 6 in.)	Avoid contact
301 V–1 kV	3.0 m (10 ft 0 in.)	1.0 m (3 ft 6 in.)	0.3 m (1 ft 0 in.)
1.1 kV–5 kV	3.0 m (10 ft 0 in.)	1.5 m (5 ft 0 in.)	0.5 m (1 ft 5 in.)
5 kV–15 kV	3.0 m (10 ft 0 in.)	1.5 m (5 ft 0 in.)	0.7 m (2 ft 2 in.)
15.1 kV–45 kV	3.0 m (10 ft 0 in.)	2.5 m (8 ft 0 in.)	0.8 m (2 ft 9 in.)
45.1 kV–75 kV	3.0 m (10 ft 0 in.)	2.5 m (8 ft 0 in.)	1.0 m (3 ft 6 in.)
75.1 kV–150 kV	3.3 m (10 ft 8 in.)	3.0 m (10 ft 0 in.)	1.2 m (3 ft 10 in.)
150.1 kV–250 kV	3.6 m (11 ft 8 in.)	3.6 m (11 ft 8 in.)	1.6 m (5 ft 3 in.)
250.1 kV–500 kV	6.0 m (20 ft 0 in.)	6.0 m (20 ft 0 in.)	3.5 m (11 ft 6 in.)
500.1 kV–800 kV	8.0 m (26 ft 0 in.)	8.0 m (26 ft 0 in.)	5.0 m (16 ft 5 in.)

Note: All dimensions are distance from exposed energized electrical conductors or circuit parts to worker.
* *Exposed movable conductor describes a condition in which the distance between the conductor and a person is not under the control of the person. The term is normally applied to overhead line conductors supported by poles.*

Informational Note: In certain instances, the arc flash boundary might be a greater distance from the energized electrical conductors or circuit parts than the limited approach boundary. The shock protection boundaries and the arc flash boundary are independent of each other.

The electrical safety program must include a procedure that provides employees with guidance on the required protection when the approach distance is less than the applicable shock protection boundary. Shock approach boundaries are based on direct contact with energized electrical conductors and circuit parts and do not consider exposure to arc flashes.

There are two shock protection boundaries: the limited approach boundary and the restricted approach boundary. The limited approach boundary is the closest approach distance for an unqualified employee unless additional protective measures are used. The restricted approach boundary is the closest approach distance for a qualified employee unless additional protective measures are used. The dimensions associated with each of these boundaries depend on the maximum voltage to which employees might be exposed.

The 600-volt class motor control center (MCC) illustrated in Exhibit 130.1 shows the applicable distance for each shock protection boundary based on the operating voltage. If the conductors are placed in an electrically safe work condition, approach boundaries no longer exist and employees can approach the conductor without risk of injury.

(F) Limited Approach Boundary.

(1) Approach by Unqualified Persons. Unless permitted by 130.4(F)(3), no unqualified person shall be permitted to approach nearer than the limited approach boundary of energized conductors and circuit parts.

OSHA Connection

29CFR 1910.132(d)(2)
The employer must verify through a written certification that the required workplace risk assessment was performed. The certification must identify the workplace evaluated, the person certifying that the evaluation was performed, and the date(s) of the risk assessment.

EXHIBIT 130.1

Shock protection boundaries for a 600-volt MCC.

Unqualified persons are those who are not trained to recognize and react to a risk of injury from exposure to potential electrical shock hazards. The limited approach boundary is the approach limit for unqualified persons unless the conditions of supervision specified in 130.4(F)(3) are met. Only qualified persons should be permitted to be within the space defined by the limited approach boundary. An arc flash boundary might be a greater distance from the energized conductor or circuit part than the limited approach boundary. Arc-rated PPE is required for any employee within the arc flash boundary.

(2) Working at or Close to the Limited Approach Boundary. Where one or more unqualified persons are working at or close to the limited approach boundary, the alerting methods in 130.7(E) shall be applied to advise the unqualified person(s) of the electrical hazard and warn him or her to stay outside of the limited approach boundary.

Employees who are not associated with electrical work tasks could be exposed to electrical hazards. For instance, a painter could be working in the same room as an exposed energized electrical circuit part. If unqualified persons working near a limited approach boundary cross the shock protection boundary, they are at an elevated risk of injury from exposure to electrical shock hazards. In that case, the electrical supervisor and the painter's supervisor must communicate so that the painter is made aware of the location of the exposed energized electrical conductor, is advised to stay outside the limited approach boundary, and is informed of how to avoid exposure to any associated electrical hazard(s). Signs or barricades might be necessary.

If there are exposed energized electrical circuits, there might also be an arc flash boundary. If the arc flash boundary is outside of the limited approach boundary, unqualified persons must not cross the arc flash boundary unless they are wearing the appropriate PPE. Where alerting techniques as identified in 130.7(E) are used—such as safety signs and tags, barricades, and attendants—the unqualified persons in the area where the work is being performed also need to know what the alerting techniques mean so they stay a safe distance away.

(3) Entering the Limited Approach Boundary. Where there is a need for an unqualified person(s) to cross the limited approach boundary, a qualified person shall advise the unqualified person(s) of the possible hazards and continuously escort the unqualified person(s) while inside the limited approach boundary. Under no circumstance shall unqualified person(s) be permitted to cross the restricted approach boundary.

An unqualified person might be required to perform tasks (electrical or nonelectrical) within the limited approach boundary. If this is necessary, a qualified person must ensure that the unqualified person is advised on the location of any exposed energized electrical conductors. The unqualified person must be advised that risk of electrocution exists and a qualified person must escort the unqualified person at all times. The unqualified person must not cross the restricted approach boundary under any circumstances. The unqualified person might need to cross the arc flash boundary when within the limited approach boundary. Arc flash PPE is required for any employee within the arc flash boundary.

(G) Restricted Approach Boundary. No qualified person shall approach or take any conductive object closer to exposed energized electrical conductors or circuit parts than the restricted approach boundary set forth in Table 130.4(E)(a) and Table 130.4(E)(b), unless one of the following conditions applies:

OSHA Connection

29 CFR 1910.333(c)(9)
Employees must not perform housekeeping duties at such close distances to live parts that there is a possibility of contact. Adequate safeguards (such as insulating equipment or barriers) must be provided.

Worker Alert

The restricted approach boundary for circuit parts operating below 150 volts is that you must avoid contact with the energized parts. No uninsulated object—including your hand—should contact exposed energized parts. Many electrocutions occur at this lower voltage level. The use of insulated gloves or tools can minimize the potential of an electrocution due to human error.

(1) The qualified person is insulated or guarded from energized electrical conductors or circuit parts operating at 50 volts or more. Insulating gloves and sleeves are considered insulation only with regard to the energized parts upon which work is performed.

(2) The energized electrical conductors or circuit parts are insulated from the qualified person and from any other conductive object at a different potential

The restricted approach boundary is the closest allowable approach distance for a qualified person without the use of personal and other shock protective equipment. If it is necessary to cross the restricted approach boundary, a qualified person must take additional precautionary measures. Insulating materials with a defined voltage rating must be placed between the person and the conductor. The insulating material can take several forms; it can be installed so that the conductor is insulated from possible contact or the employee can be insulated by wearing appropriately rated PPE. In some cases, it might be necessary to use more than one protective scheme. For instance, appropriately rated rubber blankets can be installed to cover energized conductors, and employees can wear appropriate voltage-rated PPE.

This section recognizes that a tool or other object is considered an extension of a person's body. If a person is holding an object, the requirements of this section apply to both the person and the object. These requirements ensure that employees (or their extended body parts) are not exposed to any difference of potential of 50 volts or more. See 130.7(D)(1) for criteria for employees using insulated tools or handling equipment when working in the restricted approach boundary.

Exhibit 130.2 shows an employee preparing to open an enclosure. Once the enclosure is opened, the employee will be inside the shock boundary as well as the arc flash boundary. In addition, the employee is interacting with the equipment in a manner that increases their risk of potential exposure to an arc flash hazard.

The purpose of column 2 in both Table 130.4(E)(a) and Table 130.4(E)(b) is to recognize that an electrical conductor can move. If the conductor is in a fixed position, the distance between the employee and the conductor is under the control of the employee. If that distance varies because the conductor (such as a bare overhead conductor or a conductor installed on racks in a manhole) can move or because the platform on which the employee is standing (such as an articulating arm) can move, then the distance is

OSHA Connection

1926.416(a)(1)
No employee is permitted to work in proximity to any part of an electric power circuit that could be contacted in the course of work, unless the employee is protected against electric shock by de-energizing the circuit and grounding it or by guarding it effectively by insulation or other means.

Worker Alert

You should be aware that the conductive portion of an insulated tool (such as a screwdriver, wire cutters, pliers) extends the exposed, energized electrical circuit. Many electrocutions occur when a person's hand slips from the insulated portion of a tool to the energized, conductive portion of the tool.

EXHIBIT 130.2

Working on equipment inside the protection boundaries. (Courtesy of Salisbury by Honeywell)

not under the employee's control, and column 2 of both tables applies. Column 2 also applies if a conductor is being disconnected from a fixed part (such as a connection point on an equipment bus) and the disconnection could cause the conductor to swing away from the connection point.

Case Study   130.4(G)

Scenario

Don was a self-employed HVAC technician with a small company that also employed two other technicians. Don had worked in the industry for 42 years. He received a service call from a home-owner who stated that the AC unit at their townhouse would not turn on. With his other technicians already on a call, Don headed to the location himself.

The 220-volt HVAC unit was pad-mounted at the rear of the townhouse. Don proceeded directly to the unit. A separate 120-volt receptacle was available nearby for portable tools. The homeowner watched Don flip the power switch several times without the HVAC coming online. Don then proceeded to remove the access panels with a battery-operated screwdriver. When the homeowner looked out the window again about 20 minutes later, she saw Don lying on the ground. She rushed outside to check on him but received a shock when she touched his body.

The homeowner quickly called 911 and was instructed to open the breaker to the AC unit. When the EMTs arrived, Don was unresponsive. One of his hands was near an exposed con-ductor, and the other was near the AC unit's metal housing.

Results

Attempts to revive Don failed, and he was pronounced dead at the hospital. It was determined that he suffered heart failure due to electrocution.

Don's small company could only pay his two workers for the work completed that week. Without Don to run the company, no other work was scheduled, and both were unemployed for several months. Each eventually found employment at other companies.

The elderly homeowner was admitted to the hospital for observation as a result of the trauma she experienced from Don's death on her property and her discovery of his body.

Investigation

The switch on the HVAC unit was found to be in the ON position. It appeared that the exposed conductor was separated from the terminal, which might have been why the unit wasn't operating. The likely scenario is that Don was attempting to reinsert the conductor into the terminal block, and he used his left hand to brace himself on the grounded metal enclosure while using his right hand to insert the conductor into the terminal. His hand might have slipped onto the exposed (uninsulated) conductor end while he was attempting to insert the conductor.

The electrical current from one hand to the other across Don's chest was sufficient to cause entry and exit wounds on his hands. The wound pattern on his hands indicated that Don became "hung up" during the process of electrocution. Don might have been conscious but unable to respond when the homeowner first found him. It is likely that the current continued to flow through his body until the homeowner opened the branch circuit. The electrical current disrupted Don's heart's abil-ity to function.

Analysis

There was no indication that the tasks Don performed had to be done while the system was still energized. If an electrically safe work condition (ESWC) had been established, Don would not have died.

A majority of the HVAC systems maintained by Don's com-pany were household units. Interviews with Don's employees revealed that Don did not train his employees in the hazards and risks of performing energized work. Don felt confident in his ability to perform energized work at low voltages and had performed energized tasks repeatedly. Don and his employees had all experienced electric shocks in the past, but shocks were not seen as incidents. Electrical shocks were considered part of the job. As a result of this attitude, Don did not believe shock protection was necessary.

OSHA regulations requiring that employees have a safe work environment are not limited to large companies, nor is it limited to their facilities. Contract work at a dwelling is also covered by those requirements. Don's small HVAC repair company was not exempt from those regulations.

Although recent interest has focused on arc flash inci-dents, shock injuries and electrocutions still occur. The pre-vious electric shocks received by Don and his employees should have been red flags that protection from electrocu-tion was necessary. Proper incident reporting of these near deaths and subsequent improvements to the process could have saved Don's life. Regardless of the work environment, number of employees, or potential for an arc flash, the pri-mary method of preventing electrical injuries must be estab-lishing an ESWC. Don's ignorance of electrical safety require-ments and lack of understanding of the consequences of his actions directly led to his death.

130.5 Arc Flash Risk Assessment.

(A) General. An arc flash risk assessment shall be performed:

(1) To identify arc flash hazards
(2) To estimate the likelihood of occurrence of injury or damage to health and the potential severity of injury or damage to health
(3) To determine if additional protective measures are required, including the use of PPE

Whenever energized electrical conductors or circuit parts are exposed and an employee is within the limited approach boundary, a potential arc flash hazard is presumed to exist. A potential arc flash hazard can also exist when an employee interacts with energized electrical equipment when conductors or circuit parts are not exposed. However, under normal operating conditions, the potential for an arc flash hazard is greatly reduced.

Usually, an arc fault event occurs as a result of some movement, such as when a power circuit breaker is racked-out, a conductor springs loose, a tool is dropped, an animal contacts an energized circuit part, a disconnect is opened or closed, or a starter operates. Most arcing faults are caused by human interaction—such as when a person blindly reaches into a cubicle containing energized conductors or circuit parts with a conductive object.

Prior to determining the necessary PPE, an arc flash risk assessment should be re-evaluated to determine if additional use of the hierarchy of risk controls could further lower the risk or incident energy. By automatically defaulting to PPE for protection, an employer is assuming that no other hierarchy of risk control elements could lower the incident energy level or provide additional protection for employees. The employer would have decided to use the lowest level of control (PPE) for employee protection. PPE should not be the first or only control element used. Properly selected, arc-rated PPE can limit the severity of an injury, but it will not necessarily prevent an injury if an incident occurs.

(B) Estimate of Likelihood and Severity. The estimate of the likelihood of occurrence of injury or damage to health and the potential severity of injury or damage to health shall take into consideration the following:

(1) The design of the electrical equipment, including its overcurrent protective device and its operating time
(2) The electrical equipment operating condition and condition of maintenance

The severity of a potential arc flash injury depends on various factors, including whether personal and other protective equipment is used, the level of incident energy inflicted on the body, whether the enclosure is open, and, most importantly, where the person is standing in relation to the arc flash—that is, whether or not the person is within the arc flash boundary.

Δ **(C) Additional Protective Measures.** If additional protective measures are required they shall be selected and implemented according to the hierarchy of risk control identified in 110.5(H)(3). When the additional protective measures include the use of PPE, the following shall be determined:

(1) Appropriate safety-related work practices
(2) The arc flash boundary
(3) The PPE to be used within the arc flash boundary

Worker Alert

You should be aware of other methods designed to protect you from injury. The use of PPE should be your employer's last selection after all other protection schemes have been implemented. If you don't know if your employer uses any methods other than PPE, you should determine if other ways are available to minimize injury if an incident occurs.

Worker Alert

You should be aware of other methods designed to protect you from injury. The use of PPE should be your employer's last choice after all the other protection schemes have been used. If you don't know if your employer considered any methods other than PPE, you might be able to determine additional ways to minimize injury if an incident does occur.

OSHA Connection

29 CFR 1910.132(d)(1)

The employer must assess the workplace to determine if hazards are present or are likely to be present. If hazards necessitate the use of PPE, the employer must select and have the affected employee use PPE that properly fits, as well as communicate selection decisions to the affected employee.

Table 130.5(C) shall be permitted to be used to estimate the likelihood of occurrence of an arc flash event to determine if additional protective measures are required.

The hierarchy of risk controls can be used to appraise arc flash mitigation techniques. Shock mitigation techniques are addressed in 130.4(C). Some techniques can accomplish both goals.

The hierarchy in 110.5(H)(3) is listed in order of the most effective to the least effective and must be applied in descending order for each risk assessment. Once an arc flash hazard has been identified, it must be determined if it can be eliminated. During the electrical system design stage, methods should be employed to eliminate the hazard. In the electrical system design and equipment selection phases, it is easier to utilize the most effective controls of elimination and substitution to limit the risk associated with anticipated justified energized work. In this first context, elimination is the removal of a hazard so that it never exists. This removes the potential for human error when interacting with the equipment.

Full elimination of a hazard is often not an option with installed equipment. Although elimination can also be achieved by applying other controls, such as administration (establishing an electrically safe work condition), these controls introduce the potential for human error.

Only after all other risk controls have been exhausted should PPE be selected. Selection of PPE should not be the first or only risk control. PPE is considered the least effective and lowest level of risk control for employee protection and should not be the first or only control element used. An employer must also ensure that the appropriate work procedures are used by those within the arc flash boundary for the task and equipment involved.

Table 130.5(C) is applicable to both the PPE category and the incident energy analysis methods of an arc flash risk assessment. An abnormal condition exists when all the normal operating conditions have not been met. This table does not determine if arc flash PPE is necessary; it aids in determining the likelihood of an arc flash incident occurring for a specific task based on the equipment condition. Only after all other risk controls have been exhausted should PPE be selected.

Δ **TABLE 130.5(C)** *Estimate of the Likelihood of Occurrence of an Arc Flash Incident for ac and dc Systems*

Task	Equipment Condition[a]	Likelihood of Occurrence[b]
Reading a panel meter while operating a meter switch.	Any	No
Performing infrared thermography and other non-contact inspections outside the restricted approach boundary. This activity does not include opening of doors or covers.		
Working on control circuits with exposed energized electrical conductors and circuit parts, nominal 125 volts ac or dc, or below without any other exposed energized equipment over nominal 125 volts ac or dc, including opening of hinged covers to gain access.		
Examination of insulated cable with no manipulation of cable.		
For dc systems, maintenance on a single cell of a battery system or multi-cell units in an open rack.		
For ac systems, work on energized electrical conductors and circuit parts, including electrical testing.	Any	Yes
Operation of a CB or switch the first time after installation or completion of maintenance in the equipment.		
For dc systems, working on energized electrical conductors and circuit parts of series-connected battery cells, including electrical testing.		
Removal or installation of CBs or switches.		
Opening hinged door(s) or cover(s) or removal of bolted covers (to expose bare, energized electrical conductors and circuit parts). For dc systems, this includes bolted covers, such as battery terminal covers.	Any	Yes

Δ **TABLE 130.5(C)**   *(Continued)*

Task	Equipment Condition[a]	Likelihood of Occurrence[b]
Application of temporary protective grounding equipment, after voltage test.		
Working on control circuits with exposed energized electrical conductors and circuit parts, greater than 120 volts.		
Insertion or removal of individual starter buckets from motor control center (MCC).		
Insertion or removal (racking) of circuit breakers (CBs) or starters from cubicles, doors open or closed.		
Insertion or removal of plug-in devices into or from busways.		
Examination of insulated cable with manipulation of cable.		
Working on exposed energized electrical conductors and circuit parts of equipment directly supplied by a panelboard or motor control center.		
Insertion or removal of revenue meters (kW-hour, at primary voltage and current).		
Insertion or removal of covers for battery intercell connector(s).		
For dc systems, working on exposed energized electrical conductors and circuit parts of utilization equipment directly supplied by a dc source.		
Opening voltage transformer or control power transformer compartments.		
Operation of outdoor disconnect switch (hookstick operated) at 1 kV through 15 kV.		
Operation of outdoor disconnect switch (gang-operated, from grade) at 1 kV through 15 kV.		
Operation of a CB, switch, contactor, or starter.	Normal	No
Voltage testing on individual battery cells or individual multi-cell units.		
Removal or installation of covers for equipment such as wireways, junction boxes, and cable trays that does not expose bare, energized electrical conductors and circuit parts.		
Opening a panelboard hinged door or cover to access dead front overcurrent devices.		
Removal of battery nonconductive intercell connector covers.		
Maintenance and testing on individual battery cells or individual multi-cell units in an open rack	Abnormal	Yes
Insertion or removal of individual cells or multi-cell units of a battery system in an open		
Arc-resistant equipment with the DOORS CLOSED and SECURED, and where the available fault current and fault clearing time does not exceed that of the arc-resistant rating of the equipment in one of the following conditions:		
(1) Insertion or removal of individual starter buckets		
(2) Insertion or removal (racking) of CBs from cubicles		
(3) Insertion or removal (racking) of ground and test device		
(4) Insertion or removal (racking) of voltage transformers on or off the bus		

[a]Equipment is considered to be in a "normal operating condition" if all of the conditions in 110.4(D) are satisfied.

[b]As defined in this standard, the two components of risk are the likelihood of occurrence of injury or damage to health and the severity of injury or damage to health that results from a hazard. Risk assessment is an overall process that involves estimating both the likelihood of occurrence and severity to determine if additional protective measures are required. The estimate of the likelihood of occurrence contained in this table does not cover every possible condition or situation, nor does it address severity of injury or damage to health. Where this table identifies "No" as an estimate of likelihood of occurrence, it means that an arc flash incident is not likely to occur. Where this table identifies "Yes" as an estimate of likelihood of occurrence, it means an arc flash incident should be considered likely to occur. The likelihood of occurrence must be combined with the potential severity of the arcing incident to determine if additional protective measures are required to be selected and implemented according to the hierarchy of risk control identified in 110.5(H)(3).

Informational Note No. 1: An example of a standard that provides information for arc-resistant equipment referred to in Table 130.5(C) is IEEE C37.20.7, *Guide for Testing Switchgear Rated Up to 52 kV for Internal Arcing Faults.*

Informational Note No. 2: Improper or inadequate maintenance can result in increased fault clearing time of the overcurrent protective device, thus increasing the incident energy. Where equipment is not properly installed or maintained, PPE selection based on incident energy analysis or the PPE category method might not provide adequate protection from arc flash hazards.

Informational Note No. 3: Both larger and smaller available fault currents could result in higher incident energy. If the available fault current increases without a decrease in the fault clearing time of the overcurrent protective device, the incident energy will increase. If the available fault current decreases, resulting in a longer fault clearing time for the overcurrent protective device, incident energy could also increase.

Informational Note No. 4: The occurrence of an arcing fault inside an enclosure produces a variety of physical phenomena very different from a bolted fault. For example, the arc energy resulting from an arc developed in the air will cause a sudden pressure increase and localized overheating. Equipment and design practices are available to minimize the energy levels and the number of procedures that could expose an employee to high levels of incident energy. Proven designs such as arc-resistant switchgear, remote racking (insertion or removal), remote opening and closing of switching devices, high-resistance grounding of low-voltage and 5000-volt (nominal) systems, current limitation, and specification of covered bus or covered conductors within equipment are available to reduce the risk associated with an arc flash incident. See Informative Annex O for safety-related design requirements.

Informational Note No. 5: For additional direction for performing maintenance on overcurrent protective devices, see Chapter 2, Safety-Related Maintenance Requirements.

Informational Note No. 6: See IEEE 1584, *Guide for Performing Arc Flash Hazard Calculations,* for more information regarding incident energy and the arc flash boundary for three-phase systems.

Regarding Informational Note No. 2, proper maintenance of equipment does not apply only to the equipment on which an employee will be performing a task. Proper maintenance of overcurrent devices is necessary not only for the safe operation of equipment under normal operating conditions but also for establishing an electrically safe work condition or performing energized work. An employee following a safe work procedure, including the selection of PPE, for an energized task on a properly maintained piece of equipment is at a greater risk of injury if the upstream overcurrent device has not been maintained. All electrical equipment that is part of a risk assessment, including equipment that might be remotely located, must be properly maintained.

Electrical equipment is subject to both electrical and environmental stresses. Maintaining electrical equipment per the manufacturer's instructions or in accordance with consensus-based documents such as NFPA 70B, *Recommended Practice for Electrical Equipment Maintenance,* helps ensure that the equipment operates properly without posing an electrical hazard to employees who interface with the equipment to perform their tasks.

Informational Note No. 3 covers a situation in which an overcurrent protective device is operating correctly, but the parameters of the circuit in which the device is installed have changed. Under this circumstance, there could be a larger or smaller available short-circuit current, both of which can create higher available arc flash energies. Where the available short-circuit current increases without a decrease in the opening time of the overcurrent protective device, arc flash energy can increase. Where the available short-circuit current decreases—resulting in a longer clearing time for the overcurrent protective device—arc flash energies can also increase.

(D) Documentation. The results of the arc flash risk assessment shall be documented.

The use of an energized electrical work permit (EEWP), even when it is not required, is one of the best methods for documenting that the required risk assessments have been performed. See Figure J.1 in Informative Annex J for an example of an EEWP.

(E) Arc Flash Boundary.

(1) The arc flash boundary shall be the distance at which the incident energy equals 1.2 cal/cm^2 (5 J/cm^2).

Informational Note: For information on estimating the arc flash boundary, see Informative Annex D.

An arc fault incident can occur as the result of an open-air event. However, arc fault events most often occur inside electrical equipment enclosures, and an enclosure can concentrate the event. Informative Annex D provides information on various methods for estimating available incident energy and arc flash boundaries. The source documents listed in Table D.1 should be reviewed for the proper use and limitations of the techniques presented. NFPA *70E* does not limit the calculation methods to those listed, and other appropriate techniques might be available.

Public consensus is that, should an arc flash occur while an employee is performing justified work on energized electrical equipment, the employee should be able to survive without permanent physical damage. Testing has concluded that 1.2 cal/cm² is the level at which exposed skin can suffer the onset of a second-degree burn. For more information, see the commentary following the term arc flash hazard in Article 100 regarding second-degree burns.

Properly rated PPE should limit an employee's injury to a second-degree burn if an arc flash were to occur within the arc flash boundary. There is no requirement to provide the employee with arc flash protection when the incident energy is below 1.2 cal/cm², as the expected injury from such an incident is survivable and nonpermanent.

(2) The arc flash boundary shall be permitted to be determined by Table 130.7(C)(15)(a) or Table 130.7(C)(15)(b) when the requirements of these tables apply.

There are two methods that can be used in an arc flash risk assessment to determine the arc flash boundary. One is the incident energy analysis method, which results in an arc flash boundary at a distance at which the incident energy is 1.2 cal/cm². The second is the arc flash PPE category method, which results in an arc flash boundary selected directly from the tables in 130.7(0(15). The 600-volt class motor control center (MCC) illustrated in Exhibit 130.3 shows the arc flash boundary distance when the risk assessment is conducted using the PPE category method. The shock protection boundaries are also shown for this specific equipment.

(F) Arc Flash PPE. One of the following methods shall be used for the selection of arc flash PPE:

(1) The incident energy analysis method in accordance with 130.5(G)
(2) The arc flash PPE category method in accordance with 130.7(C)(15)

Either, but not both, methods shall be permitted to be used on the same piece of equipment. The results of an incident energy analysis to specify an arc flash PPE category in Table 130.7(C)(15)(c) shall not be permitted.

If an employee's body (or part of an employee's body) needs to be within the arc flash boundary to perform a task, an arc flash risk assessment must be performed to determine the amount of incident energy that might be inflicted upon the employee and to determine the necessary PPE. The employee must then select and use PPE having a rating at least as high as the predicted incident energy available from the energy source. The level of the potential arc flash hazard must be provided in calories per square centimeter (cal/cm²). There are several methods in which the arc flash risk assessment can be completed. An employer's procedure defining how to perform an arc flash risk assessment must also specify which method is preferred.

Although there are several methods for conducting an arc flash risk assessment, in NFPA *70E*, there are only two methods for selecting the required arc flash PPE. Either the

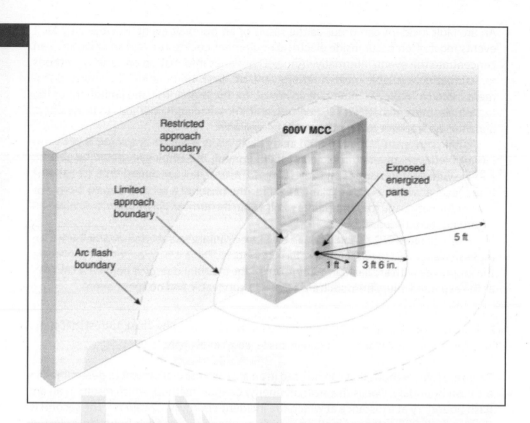

incident energy analysis method or the arc flash PPE category method must be used. NFPA *70E* does not recommend one method over the other, but there are differences in their uses and benefits. Exhibit 130.4 illustrates the steps required for each method.

Both methods ensure a level of safety for employees when energized work is justified. Both require that the hierarchy of risk controls be used, and both require that the available short-circuit current and fault-clearing time be determined. From there, the methods diverge. To use the PPE category method, the equipment must be listed in the table and the specific parameters for that piece of equipment cannot be exceeded. The incident energy analysis method can be used on any piece of electrical equipment, but it requires the selection of the most appropriate calculation method for each type of circuit.

Each method has its merits and its limitations. Regardless of the method selected, the reason for selecting one method over the other, or other issues associated with a particular method, the main concern is protecting the employee. NFPA *70E* allows both methods to be used. Both can be used in the same facility, but they must not be used on the same piece of equipment.

The availability of arc flash PPE must not be used to justify authorization to conduct energized work. PPE does not prevent an incident from occurring, nor does it necessarily prevent an injury if an incident occurs. Properly selected arc flash PPE can minimize the severity of an injury, but the employee might still suffer some level of injury. Also, arc flash and shock-protection PPE might not provide protection from an arc blast if the pressure wave is strong enough, for example, to knock an employee off a ladder or into a wall or to eject shrapnel at a velocity high enough to penetrate the body.

(G) Incident Energy Analysis Method. The incident energy exposure level shall be based on the working distance of the employee's face and chest areas from a prospective arc source for the specific task to be performed. Arc-rated clothing and other PPE shall be used by the employee based on the incident energy exposure associated with the specific task. Recognizing

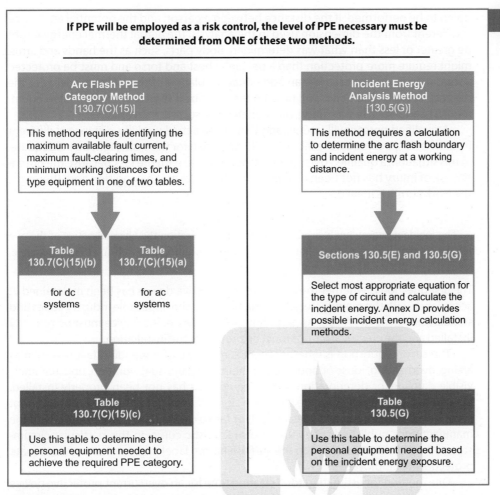

If PPE will be employed as a risk control, the level of PPE necessary must be determined from ONE of these two methods.

Arc Flash PPE Category Method [130.7(C)(15)]

This method requires identifying the maximum available fault current, maximum fault-clearing times, and minimum working distances for the type equipment in one of two tables.

Table 130.7(C)(15)(b)

for dc systems

Table 130.7(C)(15)(a)

for ac systems

Table 130.7(C)(15)(c)

Use this table to determine the personal equipment needed to achieve the required PPE category.

Incident Energy Analysis Method [130.5(G)]

This method requires a calculation to determine the arc flash boundary and incident energy at a working distance.

Sections 130.5(E) and 130.5(G)

Select most appropriate equation for the type of circuit and calculate the incident energy. Annex D provides possible incident energy calculation methods.

Table 130.5(G)

Use this table to determine the personal equipment needed based on the incident energy exposure.

EXHIBIT 130.4

Two methods for selecting the required arc flash PPE.

that incident energy increases as the distance from the arc flash decreases, additional PPE shall be used for any parts of the body that are closer than the working distance at which the incident energy was determined.

The incident energy analysis method is permitted for any arc flash risk assessment and can be used in lieu of the PPE category method for the specified equipment. Incident energy analysis allows for a more precise determination of the level of PPE necessary for a given distance from a specific electrical system or equipment. This method requires extensive calculation. The incident energy analysis method requires the selection of the most appropriate calculation method for the type of circuit. Although there are several methods listed in Informative Annex D, NFPA 70E does not advocate for any specific method of incident energy calculation.

One equation is not necessarily applicable to all equipment, and different equations might be necessary for different equipment. The owner/employer must ensure that the appropriate equation for the electrical system and the equipment is used for the calculation. The use of consultants or computer software does not absolve the owner/employer from determining the source of the equations and their applicability to the equipment. Employees' lives are at risk if the incident energy analysis is conducted incorrectly. Regardless of the calculation method selected, a threshold of 1.2 cal/cm² is the limit for the arc flash boundary.

The incident energy analysis predicts the amount of incident energy that might be available from the energy source at the point in the circuit where the work task is going to be performed. If the distance between a person and the potential arc source is different from the dimension used in the analysis, the actual thermal energy might be greater or less than what was determined. Body parts, such as the hands and arms, might require more protection than a person's chest and torso and must be protected accordingly. This might require an additional calculation of the incident energy at the distance at which the hands will be from the energized source. Where arc-rated equipment is used at less than its rating, the probability of success increases.

A qualified person will understand that, if the actual working distance is different from what is specified on the label, the PPE specified for the task might be inadequate. In this situation, a qualified person should not proceed with the task because the potential risk of injury has not been evaluated for this unforeseen condition and, therefore, the work permit is invalid.

The incident energy analysis shall take into consideration the characteristics of the overcurrent protective device and its fault clearing time, including its condition of maintenance.

The first question is whether the overcurrent protective device has been maintained in accordance with the manufacturer's instructions and the applicable industry codes and standards, such as NFPA 70B. As part of this maintenance, the device must be properly installed and the electrical ratings must be proper for the installation.

The second question is whether there is evidence of impending failure—such as arcing, overheating, loose or bound equipment parts, unusual vibration, unusual smell, visible damage, or deterioration. Where equipment has not been properly installed, maintained, and rated, or where there are signs of impending failure, an overcurrent protective device might fail to clear a fault or fail to clear a fault in accordance with the manufacturer's published time-current characteristic curve. In this particular circumstance, the PPE selected based on the arc flash hazard label might not provide adequate protection for employees.

One method for estimating total clearing time for an overcurrent protective device where arcing currents are involved is determining the estimated arcing current and then plotting that arcing current on the protective device's time-current characteristic curve, thereby determining its tripping time. Where power circuit breakers are involved, the device opening time needs to be added to the tripping time for the device to obtain the total fault clearing time. Manufacturers of overcurrent devices can provide the time-current curves for their devices. See Exhibit 130.5 for a representative time-current curve of a circuit breaker with overload protection, short-time delay, and instantaneous trip override.

The incident energy analysis shall be updated when changes occur in the electrical distribution system that could affect the results of the analysis. The incident energy analysis shall also be reviewed for accuracy at intervals not to exceed 5 years.

NFPA 70E does not define what is meant by a change to an electrical distribution system. Where there is exposure to a possible arc flash hazard, a change could be interpreted to mean that the data on the arc flash hazard equipment label is no longer applicable or that new equipment has been added that requires an arc flash label.

In some facilities, the electrical distribution system changes infrequently, while in others, it changes constantly. A modification that necessitates a new risk assessment does not have to be a change to the conditions on the premises itself. It could result from changes made by the utility company to its electrical distribution system supplying the premises, which can result in a change to the available fault current to the facility.

The 5-year review applies to all equipment that has been evaluated. The employer is responsible for being aware of changes in the electrical system and for conducting

EXHIBIT 130.5

Circuit breaker time-current curve. (Courtesy of IAEI)

a review whenever such changes add or increase electrical hazards. The review must be conducted within 5 years of the last review if no known changes to the electrical system have occurred. This requires the knowledge that equipment is being properly maintained and that actions, such as replacing a fuse, have not altered the electrical parameters of a system.

Reviewing the arc flash risk assessment does not require an entire study. If there are no changes to a system, such as a circuit breaker, a conductor, or a utility transformer, and the installed equipment has been properly maintained, the review might just be verifying the facts that led to the original assessment result.

Table 130.5(G) identifies the arc-rated clothing and other PPE requirements of Article 130 and shall be permitted to be used with the incident energy analysis method of selecting arc flash PPE.

Informational Note: For information on estimating the incident energy, see Informative Annex D. For information on selection of arc-rated clothing and other PPE, see Informative Annex H.

There is no requirement to provide employees with arc flash protection when an incident energy is below 1.2 cal/cm², as the expected injury from such an incident is survivable and nonpermanent. However, providing protection for employees from incident energies below this survivable limit might be prudent.

Heavy-duty leather gloves or leather protectors worn over rubber gloves are considered additional arc flash protection. Leather materials are typically not arc flash rated.

However, heavy-duty leather gloves made entirely of leather with a minimum thickness of 0.03 inches (0.7 mm) that are unlined or lined with nonflammable, nonmelting fabrics have been shown to have arc thermal performance values (ATPV) in excess of 10 cal/cm². Leather protectors worn over rubber insulated gloves provide additional arc flash protection for the hands. Before opting for leather gloves instead of leather protectors or arc-rated gloves, it is necessary to determine if the leather gloves will provide adequate protection from the anticipated incident energy. When using the incident energy analysis method, the selection of PPE must also comply with the requirements of 130.7(C).

Δ **TABLE 130.5(G)** *Selection of Arc-Rated Clothing and Other PPE When the Incident Energy Analysis Method Is Used*

Incident energy exposures equal to 1.2 cal/cm² up to and including 12 cal/cm²

Arc-rated clothing with an arc rating equal to or greater than the estimated incident energy[a]

Arc-rated long-sleeve shirt and pants or arc-rated coverall or arc flash suit (SR)

Arc-rated face shield and arc-rated balaclava or arc flash suit hood (SR)[b]

Arc-rated outerwear (e.g., jacket, parka, rainwear, hard hat liner, high-visibility apparel) (AN)[e]
Heavy-duty leather gloves, arc-rated gloves, or rubber insulating gloves with leather protectors (SR)[c]
Hard hat

Safety glasses or safety goggles (SR)
Hearing protection

Leather footwear4*

Incident energy exposures greater than 12 cal/cm²

Arc-rated clothing with an arc rating equal to or greater than the estimated incident energy[a]

Arc-rated long-sleeve shirt and pants or arc-rated coverall or arc flash suit (SR)

Arc-rated arc flash suit hood

Arc-rated outerwear (e.g., jacket, parka, rainwear, hard hat liner, high-visibility apparel) (AN)[e]
Arc-rated gloves or rubber insulating gloves with leather protectors (SR)[c]

Hard hat

Safety glasses or safety goggles (SR)

Hearing protection

Leather footwear[d]

SR: Selection of one in group is required.

AN: As needed.

[a]Arc ratings can be for a single layer, such as an arc-rated shirt and pants or a coverall, or for an arc flash suit or a multi-layer system if tested as a combination consisting of an arc-rated shirt and pants, coverall, and arc flash suit.

[b]Face shields with a wrap-around guarding to protect the face, chin, forehead, ears, and neck area are required by 130.7(C)(10)(c). Where the back of the head is inside the arc flash boundary, a balaclava or an arc flash hood shall be required for full head and neck protection.

[c]Rubber insulating gloves with leather protectors provide arc flash protection in addition to shock protection. Higher class rubber insulating gloves with leather protectors, due to their increased material thickness, provide increased arc flash protection.

[d]Footwear other than leather or dielectric shall be permitted to be used provided it has been tested to demonstrate no ignition, melting, or dripping at the estimated incident energy exposure.

[e]The arc rating of outer layers worn over arc-rated clothing as protection from the elements or for other safety purposes, and that are not used as part of a layered system, shall not be required to be equal to or greater than the estimated incident energy exposure.

(H) Equipment Labeling. Electrical equipment such as switchboards, panelboards, industrial control panels, meter socket enclosures, and motor control centers that are in other than dwelling units and that are likely to require examination, adjustment, servicing, or maintenance while energized shall be marked with a label containing all the following information:

(1) Nominal system voltage

(2) Arc flash boundary

(3) At least one of the following:

    a. Available incident energy and the corresponding working distance, or the arc flash PPE category in Table 130.7(C)(15)(a) or Table 130.7(C)(15)(b) for the equipment, but not both

    b. Minimum arc rating of clothing

    c. Site-specific level of PPE

> **Worker Alert**
>
> You should be aware that equipment labeled with an incident energy should not also be labeled with a PPE category. A misunderstanding of these protection requirements can potentially put you at a greater risk of injury. If you see both an incident energy and PPE category on a label, you might not be sufficiently protected from arc flash hazards.

Equipment that will be the point of verification of an electrically safe work condition (ESWC) or equipment that can be justifiably worked on while energized should carry this label. The information on the label is vital for employees performing tasks where exposure to electrical hazards is possible. The label examples in Exhibit 130.6 illustrate two possible configurations. The example on the left is for equipment evaluated using the incident energy analysis method, and the example on the right is for equipment evaluated using the PPE category method. The information on the label should primarily be used to establish an ESWC. Energized work must be justified regardless of the presence of the label, and equipment labeling cannot be used to justify energized work.

It is the employer's responsibility to provide employees with the information they need to work safely. An employee should not be expected to calculate an incident energy value or determine whether a job complies with the arc flash PPE category method. However, the employee should be capable of reading and interpreting the information included on an arc flash hazard label. The employer must ensure that arc flash hazard labels are in place and that the employee has the information necessary to select the appropriate PPE.

Without proper equipment maintenance, an affixed label could be invalid. Qualified persons should understand the maintenance program for the energized equipment they are working on as well as that of the protective devices that were used to determine the label parameters. Without proper maintenance, unexpected hazards could be present in the equipment, or the chosen PPE might not provide protection for the actual inciden

EXHIBIT 130.6

⚠ **WARNING**

ARC FLASH HAZARD

Nominal system voltage _____

Arc flash boundary _____

Available incident energy _____

Working distance _____

Minimum arc rating of clothing _____

⚠ **WARNING**

ARC FLASH HAZARD

Nominal system voltage _____

Arc flash boundary _____

Working distance _____

PPE category _____

Representative warning labels.

energy exposure due to, for example, an inoperable circuit breaker. Utilizing label information without a maintenance program places employees at risk of injury.

NFPA *70E* does not require that homeowners install field-marked arc flash hazard labels on the equipment installed on their premises. However, any employee (contractor) performing energized work in dwelling units where electrical conductors and circuits are exposed is subject to possible injury. The lack of a labeling requirement for dwellings is not permission for energized work to be performed at these locations. Employees within dwellings and their employers are not exempt from the requirements of NFPA *70E* or OSHA. A shock risk assessment and an arc flash risk assessment must be performed to establish the required ESWC or to perform properly justified energized work within a dwelling.

Exception No. 1: Unless changes in electrical distribution system(s) render the label inaccurate, labels applied prior to the effective date of this edition of the standard shall be acceptable if they complied with the requirements for equipment labeling in the standard in effect at the time the labels were applied.

This exception applies to the information on an existing label. If nothing else has changed in an electrical system, the labels do not need to be replaced when electrical safety is not affected. The exception assumes that the applied label complies with a previous edition of the standard. Depending on how a facility handles electrical safety, there might be reasons to change a label to match the current labeling method for consistency or due to written safety procedures. Notice that the exception is applicable upon adoption of the current standard; it is not based on a 5-year review.

Exception No. 2: In supervised industrial installations where conditions of maintenance and engineering supervision ensure that only qualified persons monitor and service the system, the information required in 130.5(H)(1) through 130.5(H)(3) shall be permitted to be documented in a manner that is readily available to persons likely to perform examination, servicing, maintenance, and operation of the equipment while energized.

All equipment labels must include the nominal system voltage, the arc flash boundary, and at least one of the items listed in 130.5(H)(3). Section 130.5(H)(3)(a) permits including either the incident energy or the PPE category. An incident energy and a PPE category are not permitted to be on the label for the same piece of equipment, as only one method of risk assessment can be applied to a piece of equipment.

By providing the calculated incident energy on a label, employees can select equipment rated for at least the same energy level. Using the PPE category method, PPE can be selected from Table 130.7(0(15)(c). Alternately, 130.5(H)(3)(b) permits equipment to be labeled with a minimum arc rating for the required PPE. This arc rating can be at any level above that required by the arc flash risk assessment. Another alternative in 130.5(H)(3)(c) permits using site-specific PPE, which is any PPE designated by a facility. For example, HRC2 or BLUE could be a site-specific designation for 6 cal/crrP-rated equipment.

It is advantageous to specify or select arc-rated equipment that will be exposed to less than its rating during an incident. The testing of arc-rated clothing is based on a 50 percent probability of success at a specific energy level. Exceeding the minimum NFPA *70E* requirements for PPE can substantially increase the probability of success.

The method of calculating and the data to support the information for the label shall be documented. The data shall be reviewed for accuracy at intervals not to exceed 5 years. Where the review of the data identifies a change that renders the label inaccurate, the label shall be updated.

The owner of the electrical equipment shall be responsible for the documentation, installation, and maintenance of the marked label.

130.7 Personal and Other Protective Equipment.

The requirements of 130.7 apply regardless of the risk assessment method used to determine the required PPE rating.

Even when energized work is justified, the decision to default to PPE as the primary protection method for safe work practices means that the employer has assumed that no other risk control from the hierarchy could be utilized to lower the incident energy level or to provide additional protection for the employee. The most effective level of control is elimination of the hazard.

PPE does not prevent an injury if an incident occurs. Using arc-rated PPE at its rating provides only a 50 percent probability of protection from a second-degree burn. Properly selected arc flash PPE can minimize the severity of an injury to one that is recoverable, but employees might still suffer some level of injury.

PPE does not have an arc blast rating; it is typically only rated for arc flash protection. PPE also does not protect from blunt force trauma. Arc flash and shock protection PPE might not provide protection from an arc blast where, for example, the pressure wave is strong enough to knock an employee off a ladder or into a wall, to project a door or panel into the employee, or to eject shrapnel at a high velocity.

(A) General. Employees exposed to electrical hazards when the risk associated with that hazard is not adequately reduced by the applicable electrical installation requirements shall be provided with, and shall use, protective equipment that is designed and constructed for the specific part of the body to be protected and for the work to be performed.

Personal and other protective equipment is normally designed to provide protection from a particular electrical hazard for a particular body part, but it can also provide protection from other electrical hazards. An example is the use of rubber insulated gloves and leather protectors that provide shock protection for the hands and forearms, and that also provide some degree of arc flash protection.

A proper analysis includes identifying each electrical hazard involved, the body parts that are within a specific protection boundary, and the severity of the hazard, as well as comparing the hazard level to the protection offered by the selected PPE. Where an employee's face (but not the back of the head) is going to be within the arc flash boundary, a hard hat and face shield combination that is rated for the anticipated available incident energy level is required. Where the employee's whole head is going to be within the arc flash boundary, a properly rated arc flash hood or hard hat and face shield combination with arc-rated balaclava is required.

Employees are to be provided with the appropriate PPE. Since employers are typically responsible for the enforcement of NFPA 70E, supplying appropriate PPE not only means providing properly rated PPE for the planned task, it also means verifying that the supplied PPE is in compliance with the applicable protective equipment standards listed in Informational Tables 130.7(0(14) and 130.7(G). Verification that issued PPE complies with industry consensus standards is paramount to providing protection for employees in the event of shock or arc flash incidents. Equipment that has not been adequately tested might not provide the expected protection, and in some cases, it could increase the severity of an injury inflicted on an employee during an incident.

A garment label might not be sufficient to confirm that the required tests have been conducted on equipment. Some standards evaluate only the fabric, not the final product (i.e., shirt and pants) that is made with the fabric. A separate standard might be necessary to address the testing of the final product. It is the employer's responsibility to confirm that the correct standard has been used to determine the protective rating of purchased PPE. For more information, see 130.7(C)(14).

> Informational Note: The PPE requirements of 130.7 are intended to protect a person from arc flash and shock hazards. While some situations could result in burns to the skin, even with the protection selected, burn injury should be reduced and survivable. Due to the explosive effect of some arc events, physical trauma injuries could occur. The PPE requirements of 130.7 do not address protection against physical trauma other than exposure to the thermal effects of an arc flash.

The primary method required to protect employees is placing equipment in an electrically safe work condition. Although NFPA 70E does not specify a limit to the level of incident energy a protected employee can be subjected to, the employer should understand that other injuries not addressed by the standard are also possible. The PPE required by NFPA *70E* is designed to protect against shock and thermal injuries. However, this PPE might not be capable of protecting employees against other injuries. An employer who authorizes energized work must determine the method of protection the employee will use to prevent these other potential injuries.

During an arcing fault, electrical energy is converted into various forms of energy. Electrical energy can vaporize metal, which can change from a solid state to gas vapor in an expanding plasma ball with explosive, concussive force. When copper vaporizes, it expands 67,000 times in volume and can create a superheated plasma. Arc temperatures can reach as high as 19,500°C (35,000°F) and create molten metal, aluminum, or copper vapor or superheated air. The threshold for a second-degree burn is 80°C (175°F) for 0.1 seconds, and the threshold for a third-degree burn is 96°C (205°F) for 0.1 seconds. Also, eye damage can result from the radiation associated with intense light.

The level of a pressure wave is relative to the amount of arcing current that is generated. Pressure levels from an incident can be over 2000 lb/ft2. Lung damage occurs at a threshold of 82,737 to 103,421 Pa (1728 to 2160 lb/ft2). Unprotected eardrums can rupture at a threshold as low as 34,475 Pa (720 lb/ft2) or from a pressure differential of as low as 5 psi across the eardrum. Sound levels can exceed 160 dB during an arc flash. Short-term exposure to 140 dB can cause permanent hearing damage. There is an equation identified in the commentary on Informative Annex K pertaining to the level of a pressure wave relative to the amount of arcing current generated, but it has not been generally adopted. Therefore, the strength of a pressure wave, and the possible results of it, are not considered to be predictable with reasonable reliability.

In addition to the thermal energy generated from an arc flash event, an arcing fault can generate an arc blast. Shrapnel can be ejected at speeds in excess of 1100 kph (700 mph). Objects and personnel can be flung across a room, from a ladder, or out of the bucket of a bucket truck.

(B) Care of Equipment. Protective equipment shall be maintained in a safe, clean, and reliable condition and in accordance with manufacturers' instructions. The protective equipment shall be visually inspected before each use. Protective equipment shall be stored in a manner to prevent damage from physically damaging conditions and from moisture, dust, or other deteriorating agents.

> Informational Note: Specific requirements for periodic testing of electrical protective equipment are given in 130.7(C)(14) and 130.7(G).

Personal and other protective equipment has a lifespan that can include many use cycles, such as donning and doffing, cleaning, and laundering. To ensure that protective equipment is maintained in a reliable condition and that it is ready for use and will be effective when needed, it must be cared for and inspected at regular intervals and prior to use. Specialized gear, like an arc-rated suit, might be purchased and maintained by the employer. Everyday arc-rated shirts and pants might be the employee's responsibility to purchase and maintain. Rips and tears must be properly repaired.

Contaminated gear can be prone to catastrophic failure. Laundering must be done in the correct cycle and at the correct temperature, as well as with the appropriate detergent. If anything is done incorrectly, the resultant level of protection might not be sufficient.

Employers are responsible for protecting employees; therefore, employers need policies and procedures for maintaining equipment regardless of who is maintaining the protective gear. Adherence to the manufacturer's instructions as well as the guidance and requirements contained in consensus standards ensures that personal and other protective equipment is kept in a suitable condition and is ready for use when needed. Specific guidance regarding the care and laundering of some protective equipment can be found in the national consensus standards listed in Informative Annex A.3.2.

Guidance on commercial and home laundering can be found in ASTM FI 449, *Standard Guide for Industrial Laundering of Flame, Thermal, and Arc Resistant Clothing*, and ASTM F2757, *Standard Guide for Home Laundering Care and Maintenance of Flame, Thermal and Arc Resistant Clothing*. These standards can help determine the types of cleaning agents that can be used, whether bleach-type additives can be used, and which cleaning processes and procedures can be used, as well as the water temperature that can be used. Employers also need to determine whether to use commercial or home laundering. If arc-rated PPE is to be shared, sanitary considerations need to be addressed, such as cleaning the equipment between each use.

(C) Personal Protective Equipment (PPE).

(1) General. When an employee is working within the restricted approach boundary, the worker shall wear PPE in accordance with 130.4. When an employee is working within the arc flash boundary, he or she shall wear protective clothing and other PPE in accordance with 130.5. All parts of the body inside the arc flash boundary shall be protected.

Informational Note: Where the estimated incident energy exposure is greater than the arc rating of commercially available arc-rated PPE. then for the purpose of testing for the absence of voltage, the following examples of risk reduction methods could be used to reduce the likelihood of occurrence of an arcing event or the severity of exposure:

(1) Use noncontact proximity test instrument(s) or measurement of voltage on the secondary side of a low-voltage transformer (VT) mounted in the equipment before using a contact test instrument to test for the absence of voltage below 1000 volts.

(2) If equipment design allows, observe visible gaps between the equipment conductors and circuit parts and the electrical source(s) of supply.

(3) Increase the working distance.

(4) Consider system design options to reduce the incident energy level.

Nothing in this informational note should be taken as permission to violate the requirements in NFPA *70E* or the OSHA regulations. All employees must be properly protected from all exposed electrical hazards. Until an electrically safe work condition is established, employees are at risk of injury should an incident occur. These four items should not be the only considerations when employees must be protected. Considering a

Worker Alert

You should confirm that the equipment provided by your employer will protect all your body parts that might be subjected to injury during an assigned task. You must be provided with the necessary protection before beginning the task.

OSHA Connection

29CFR 1910.335(a)(l)(i)

Employees must be provided with, and must use, protective equipment that is appropriate for the specific parts of the body to be protected and for the work to be performed.

shutdown via the utility might be beneficial, as it has policies, practices, and procedures to deal with electrical hazards beyond what is typically present on the load side of the service point. Another possibility is voltage verification via remote control or special probes. Remember, the goal of an electrical safety program is to prevent employee injury or death, not to avoid inconvenience.

Items (1) and (2) can provide increased assurance that a circuit has been de-energized. Item (3) relies on the fact that incident energy is inversely proportional to distance from a hazard. Increasing the working distance necessitates calculating the incident energy at the new working distance to determine the appropriate PPE.

Item (4) is the most important suggestion in the informational note and might involve installation modification. The ideal time to use the hierarchy of risk controls to mitigate the dangerous situation in the future is when equipment is de-energized. Steps should be taken to better protect the next employee who conducts the same task. At the very least, the voltage and incident energy values should be lowered to the level for which protection is available. At best, the levels should be lowered as far as practicably possible.

Consideration should be given to the potential outcome of exposing an employee to dangerous hazards if increasing safety for the next employee performing a task is overlooked. If an inadequately protected employee is injured or killed the third time a dangerous task is performed, it will be difficult to justify not addressing it the first time the equipment was de-energized.

(2) Movement and Visibility. When arc-rated clothing is worn to protect an employee, it shall cover all ignitible clothing and shall allow for movement and visibility.

Rehearsing a work task on similar equipment in an electrically safe work condition while wearing PPE is one way to determine if PPE is restricting.

(3) Head, Face, Neck, and Chin (Head Area) Protection. Employees shall wear nonconductive head protection wherever there is a danger of head injury from electric shock or burns due to contact with energized electrical conductors or circuit parts or from flying objects resulting from electrical explosion. Employees shall wear nonconductive protective equipment for the face, neck, and chin whenever there is a danger of injury from exposure to electric arcs or flashes or from flying objects resulting from electrical explosion. If employees use hairnets or beard nets, or both, these items shall be arc rated.

Informational Note: See 130.7(C)(10)(b) and (C)(10(c) for arc flash protective requirements.

(4) Eye Protection. Employees shall wear protective equipment for the eyes whenever there is danger of injury from electric arcs, flashes, or from flying objects resulting from electrical explosion.

Safety glasses or goggles protect the eyes from any impact that exceeds the protection offered by face shields and hoods. Face shields or hoods in accordance with ANSI/ISEA Z87.1-2015, *American National Standard for Occupational and Educational Personal Eye and Face Protection Devices,* are considered as a "secondary eye protective device" that must be used with a "primary eye protective device" (spectacle or goggle) underneath.

(5) Hearing Protection. Employees shall wear hearing protection whenever working within the arc flash boundary.

Worker Alert

Ear canal inserts are the preferred hearing protection for your ears.

Ear canal inserts are the form of hearing protection recognized by NFPA *70E*, as they interfere the least with the proper fit and application of other PPE that is intended to protect the head and face. Hearing protection should not adversely impact the performance of other items of PPE. For example, earmuffs worn over a balaclava not only present additional flammable material, but they might not provide the necessary hearing protection. Likewise, earmuffs worn under a balaclava could stretch the fabric beyond its ability to withstand an incident exposure or could affect the snug fit necessary to provide adequate protection.

(6) Body Protection. Employees shall wear arc-rated clothing wherever there is possible exposure to an electric arc flash above the threshold incident energy level for a second degree burn [1.2 cal/cm^2 (5 J/cm^2)].

> **Worker Alert**
>
> Although protection from a burn is not required below 1.2 cal/cm^2, you can opt to protect yourself from an injury that, while not life-threatening, could be painful.

The arc flash boundary is the approach limit from an arc source at which incident energy equals 1.2 cal/cm^2. Based on research, this level of thermal energy can result in a second-degree burn. Employees exposed to incident energy greater than 1.2 cal/cm^2 need to wear arc-rated clothing for protection from the thermal effects of an arcing event..

Although protection from an arc flash incident is not specified when the incident energy is less than 1.2 cal/cm^2, this does not mean that a survivable burn should be considered acceptable. This standard covers the minimum protection that is necessary to enable an employee involved in an arc flash incident to go home at the end of the day. The primary method used to protect employees is placing equipment in an electrically safe work condition regardless of the amount of incident energy present.

An employer defaulting to PPE as a safe work practice has assumed that no other risk controls from the hierarchy could be employed to lower the incident energy level or to provide additional protection for employees. The most effective method of control is the elimination of a hazard. Under no circumstance should the ability to wear PPE be used to justify energized work. An arc flash incident cannot be prevented using PPE.

(7) Hand and Arm Protection. Hand and arm protection shall be provided in accordance with 130.7(C)(7)(a), (C)(7)(b), and (C)(7)(c).

(a) *Shock Protection.* Employees shall wear rubber insulating gloves with leather protectors where there is a danger of hand injury from electric shock due to contact with exposed energized electrical conductors or circuit parts. Employees shall wear rubber insulating gloves with leather protectors and rubber insulating sleeves where there is a danger of hand and arm injury from electric shock due to contact with exposed energized electrical conductors or circuit parts. Rubber insulating gloves shall be rated for the voltage for which the gloves will be exposed. Rubber insulating gloves shall be permitted to be used without leather protectors, under the following conditions:

(1) There shall be no activity performed that risks cutting or damaging the glove.

(2) The rubber insulating gloves shall be electrically retested before reuse.

(3) The voltage rating of the rubber insulating gloves shall be reduced by 50 percent for class 00 and by one whole class for classes 0 through 4.

(b) *Arc Flash Protection.* Hand and arm protection shall be worn where there is possible exposure to arc flash burn. The apparel described in 130.7(C)(10)(d) shall be required for protection of hands from burns. Arm protection shall be accomplished by the apparel described in 130.7(C)(6).

Where an employee's hands and arms are closer to equipment than the specified working distance, a greater level of protection is required when using the incident energy analysis method. This might require an additional determination of the incident energy at the hands' positions during the task or of the arc rating of PPE for the body parts nearer to the energized parts. Sleeves must not be shortened or rolled up, as that would expose skin or flammable undergarments. Voltage-rated gloves with heavy-duty leather gloves have been shown to provide arc flash protection up to 10 cal/cm².

OSHA Connection

29 CFR 1910.137(c)(2)(xii)

The employer must certify that protective equipment has been tested. The certification must identify the equipment that passed the test and the date it was tested.

(c) *Maintenance and Use.* Electrical protective equipment shall be maintained in a safe, reliable condition. Insulating equipment shall be inspected for damage before each day's use and immediately following any incident that can reasonably be suspected of having caused damage. Insulating gloves shall be given an air test, along with the inspection. Maximum use voltages for rubber insulating gloves shall not exceed that specified in Table 130.7(C)(7)(a). The top of the cuff of the protector glove shall be shorter than the rolled top of the cuff of the insulating glove by at least the distance specified in Table 130.7(C)(7)(a).

Manufacturers of arc-rated clothing and other arc-rated protective equipment provide instructions for the cleaning and care of their products. The electrical safety program must describe the maintenance and cleaning processes that ensure the integrity of the apparel. Employees should inspect their arc-rated clothing and ensure that the apparel is not soiled with a flammable contaminant. Company logos and patches attached to arc-rated clothing must also be made of arc-rated material.

(d) *Periodic Electrical Tests.* Rubber insulating equipment shall be subjected to periodic electrical tests. Test voltages shall be in accordance with applicable state, federal, or local codes and standards. The maximum intervals between tests shall not exceed that specified in Table 130.7(C)(7)(b).

Informational Note: See OSHA 29 CFR 1910.137; ASTM F478, *Standard Specification for In-Service Care of Insulating Line Hose and Covers',* ASTM F479, *Standard Specification for In-Service Care of Insulating* Blankets', and ASTM F496, *Standard Specification for In-Service Care of Insulating Gloves and Sleeves,* which contain information related to in-service and testing requirements for rubber insulating equipment.

N *TABLE 130.7(C)(7)(a) Maximum Use Voltage for Rubber Insulating Gloves*

Class Designation of Glove or Sleeve	Maximum ac Use Voltage rms, volts	Maximum dc Use Voltage avg, volts	Distances Between Gauntlet and Cuff, minimum
00	500	750	13 mm (0.5 in.)
0	1,000	1,500	13 mm (0.5 in.)
1	7,500	11,250	25 mm (1 in.)
2	17,000	25,500	51 mm (2 in.)
3	26,500	39,750	76 mm (3 in.)
4	36,000	54,000	102 mm (4 in.)

TABLE 130.7(C)(7)(b) *Rubber Insulating Equipment, Maximum Test Intervals*

Rubber Insulating Equipment	When to Test
Blankets	Before first issue; every 12 months thereafter*
Covers	If insulating value is suspect
Gloves	Before first issue; every 6 months thereafter*
Line hose	If insulating value is suspect
Sleeves	Before first issue; every 12 months thereafter*

*New insulating equipment is not permitted to be placed into service unless it has been electrically tested within the previous 12 months. Insulating equipment that has been issued for service is not new and is required to be retested in accordance with the intervals in this table.

(8) Foot Protection. Where insulated footwear is used as protection against step and touch potential, dielectric footwear shall be required. Insulated soles shall not be used as primary electrical protection.

> Informational Note: Electrical Hazard footwear meeting ASTM F2413, *Standard Specification for Performance Requirements for Protective (Safety) Toe Cap Footwear,* can provide a secondary source of electric shock protection under dry conditions.

The integrity of the insulating quality of footwear with insulated soles cannot be easily determined after they have been worn in a work environment. Electrical hazard (EH)-rated footwear with insulated soles must not serve as the primary form of protection from touch and step potential hazards

(9) Factors in Selection of Protective Clothing. Clothing and equipment that provide worker protection from shock and arc flash hazards shall be used. If arc-rated clothing is required, it shall cover associated parts of the body as well as all flammable apparel while allowing movement and visibility.

Clothing and equipment required for the degree of exposure shall be permitted to be worn alone or integrated with flammable, nonmelting apparel. Garments that are not arc rated shall not be permitted to be used to increase the arc rating of a garment or of a clothing system.

> Informational Note: Protective clothing includes shirts, pants, coveralls, jackets, and parkas worn routinely by workers who, under normal working conditions, are exposed to momentary electric arc and related thermal hazards. Arc-rated rainwear worn in inclement weather is included in this category of clothing.

OSHA Connection

29 CFR 1910.132(d)(1)
The employer must assess the workplace to determine if hazards are present or are likely to be present. If hazards necessitate the use of PPE, the employer must select and have the affected employee use PPE that properly fits, as well as communicate selection decisions to the affected employee.

For equipment to provide protection for an employee conducting justified energized electrical work, it must be capable of withstanding the conditions presented by an incident. Shock protection PPE is typically used to insulate an employee from exposure to a specific maximum voltage level. Arc flash PPE is typically used to limit the probability and severity of a thermal injury when an employee is exposed to a specific maximum incident energy arc flash. The employer is responsible for providing equipment capable of protecting an employee who is put at risk of injury during energized work. Verification via test is generally the only reliable method of determining if a material is capable of functioning as expected. The employer must verify that the issued PPE meets the applicable consensus standard. For more information, see the Informational Note Table in 130.7(C)(14).

(a) *Layering.* Nonmelting, flammable fiber garments shall be permitted to be used as underlayers in conjunction with arc-rated garments in a layered system. If nonmelting, flammable fiber garments are used as underlayers, the system arc rating shall be sufficient to prevent breakopen of the innermost arc-rated layer at the expected arc exposure incident energy level to prevent ignition of flammable underlayers. Garments that are not arc rated shall not be permitted to be used to increase the arc rating of a garment or of a clothing system.

Informational Note: A typical layering system might include cotton underwear, a cotton shirt and trouser, and an arc-rated coverall. Specific tasks might call for additional arc-rated layers to achieve the required protection level.

This is not only the layering of arc-rated PPE to increase the arc rating of a system but also the layering of clothing worn under arc-rated PPE. Layering can increase the overall protective characteristics of arc-rated clothing. Air is a good thermal insulator; wearing multiple layers of clothing can trap air in between clothing layers. Layering tends to improve the thermal insulating efficiency of a protective system. However, this increase in efficiency does not necessarily increase the arc rating of the protective clothing system.

The combined rating of two arc-rated garments is not linear. Combination systems must be tested, and the rating of those systems cannot be determined by simply adding the arc rating of two garments together.

(b) *Outer Layers.* Garments worn as outer layers over arc-rated clothing, such as jackets, high-visibility safety apparel, or rainwear, shall also be made from arc-rated material. The arc rating of outer layers worn over arc-rated clothing as protection from the elements or for other safety purposes, and that are not used as part of a layered system, shall not be required to be equal to or greater than the estimated incident energy exposure.

Flammable garments such as jackets; rainwear; and protective gear, such as a harness worn over arc-rated clothing, can act as flame sources themselves. This can serve as a heat source for the arc-rated clothing underneath, which might exceed its insulating capacity, exposing the user to sufficient thermal energy to cause a burn injury. An arc-rated fall protection harness is shown in Exhibit 130.7.

Although arc-rated PPE worn over other arc-rated PPE cannot be directly added together to get a higher arc rating, it will not lower the arc rating of either piece of PPE. There is no concern for continued exposure to a thermal hazard because all arc-rated PPE is flame-resistant. An outer layer with any arc rating is permitted over appropriately rated PPE.

(c) *Underlayers.* Meltable fibers such as acetate, nylon, polyester, polypropylene, and spandex shall not be permitted in fabric underlayers.

Exception: An incidental amount of elastic used on nonmelting fabric underwear or socks shall be permitted.

Informational Note No. 1: Arc-rated garments (e.g., shirts, trousers, and coveralls) worn as underlayers that neither ignite nor melt and drip in the course of an exposure to electric arc and related thermal hazards generally provide a higher system arc rating than nonmelting, flammable fiber underlayers.

Informational Note No. 2: Arc-rated underwear or undergarments used as underlayers generally provide a higher system arc rating than nonmelting, flammable fiber underwear or undergarments used as underlayers.

EXHIBIT 130.7

Arc-rated harness. (Courtesy of Salisbury by Honeywell)

Significant injuries can occur when fabrics melt onto an employee's skin. Arc-rated PPE does not necessarily prevent the passage of thermal energy to the employee. However, properly rated PPE should limit the thermal energy level inflicted on the employee's body to one that does not cause worse than second-degree burns. This energy level might be sufficient to melt undergarments onto an employee's skin. Therefore, undergarments must be made of nonmelting material. However, an incidental quantity of these fabrics, such as those used in the elastic bands in underwear, is permitted. There might be some additional benefits to wearing arc-rated undergarments.

(d) *Coverage.* Clothing shall cover potentially exposed areas as completely as possible. Shirt and coverall sleeves shall be fastened at the wrists, shirts shall be tucked into pants, and shirts, coveralls, and jackets shall be closed at the neck.

Arc-rated clothing must completely cover all the body areas within the arc flash boundary. Shirt sleeves must be fastened at the wrists, and the top buttons of shirts and jackets must be fastened to minimize the chance that heated air could reach below the arc-rated clothing. Shirt sleeves should fit under the gauntlet of the protective gloves to minimize the chance that thermal energy could enter under the shirt sleeves.

(e) *Fit.* Tight-fitting clothing shall be avoided. Loose-fitting clothing provides additional thermal insulation because of air spaces. Arc-rated apparel shall fit properly such that it does not interfere with the work task.

The fit of arc-rated clothing is important for the safety of employees. Heat is conducted through the material when the surface of arc-rated clothing is heated. This conducted heat energy could result in a burn if the arc-rated clothing is touching skin. Arc-rated clothing must fit loosely to provide additional thermal insulation. However, arc-rated clothing must not be so loose that it interferes with an employee's movements. Men's and women's PPE is available.

Worker Alert

You are ultimately responsible for assuring that you have donned all the protective gear correctly and have properly closed it off to prevent flames from entering it during an incident.

Worker Alert

You must make sure the PPE you wear is the proper size. Men's and women's PPE is available. Tight clothing can increase the severity of an injury during an incident even if the PPE functions as intended.

(f) *Interference.* The garment selected shall result in the least interference with the task but still provide the necessary protection. The work method, location, and task could influence the protective equipment selected.

> The plan for the work task must define the protective garments to be worn by the employee. As the plan is developed, the location and position of an employee must be considered to provide the best chance that the PPE will not interfere with the employee's movements during the work task. Doing a dry run of the task while wearing PPE can help identify whether the task has PPE restrictions.

(10) Arc Flash Protective Equipment.

(a) *Arc Flash Suits.* Arc flash suit design shall permit easy and rapid removal by the wearer. The entire arc flash suit, including the hood's face shield, shall have an arc rating that is suitable for the arc flash exposure. When exterior air is supplied into the hood, the air hoses and pump housing shall be either covered by arc-rated materials or constructed of nonmelting and nonflammable materials.

> The protection provided by an arc flash suit is comprised of more than the arc rating of the fabric or the fabric system. The design and construction of the suit are of great importance. A poorly or improperly designed suit can enable the passage of energy through the holes or ports in the garment, bypassing the protection offered by the fabric.
>
> Care must be taken with older arc flash suits. In the past, suits were rated to the greater protection offered by the double layers of fabric on the chest—not by the lesser rating of the single layer of fabric on the arms and back. Protection adequate for the incident energy must be provided for all the body parts within the arc flash boundary.
>
> An arc flash suit must be evaluated as a complete system. A suit is not a combination of individual components; they must be evaluated together. Exhibit 130.8 shows an employee in a 40 cal/cm² arc flash suit with other necessary PPE for the assigned task. An arc flash suit does not provide protection for an employee's hands and feet, which must also be covered by adequate arc-rated protective equipment, as shown in the exhibit.

(b) *Head Protection.*

> **Worker Alert**
>
> You must understand the working distances and arc flash boundaries on labels. You should be aware of the proximity of your head to these boundaries. There is a greater risk of injury during the performance of an assigned task if your head is closer to the equipment than was planned.

(1) An arc-rated hood or an arc-rated balaclava with an arc-rated face shield shall be used when the back of the head is within the arc flash boundary.
(2) An arc-rated hood shall be used when the anticipated incident energy exposure exceeds 12 cal/cm² (50.2 J/cm²).

> Complete protection for the head is required when it is within the arc flash boundary. The combination of an arc-rated face shield and balaclava is different from a full arc-rated hood as shown in Exhibit 130.9.

(c) *Face Protection.* Face shields shall have an arc rating suitable for the arc flash exposure. Face shields with a wrap-around guarding to protect the face, chin, forehead, ears, and neck area shall be used. Face shields without an arc rating shall not be used. Eye protection (safety glasses or goggles) shall always be worn under face shields or hoods.

> Informational Note: Face shields made with energy-absorbing formulations that can provide higher levels of protection from the radiant energy of an arc flash are available, but these shields are tinted and can reduce visual acuity and color perception. Additional illumination of the task area might be necessary when these types of arc-protective face shields are used.

It is critical that the face and head be protected from the potential thermal energy exposure determined by the risk assessment. ASTM F2178, *Standard Test Method for Determining the Arc Rating and Standard Specification for Eye or Face Protective Products,*

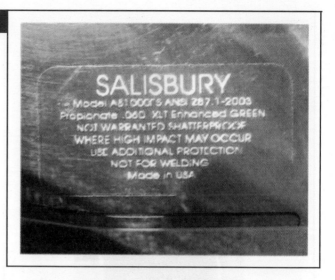

EXHIBIT 130.10

Face shield indicating the need for additional impact protection for the eyes.

requires that the arc rating of an arc flash face shield or hood must not be the lesser rating of the window and the fabric. It mandates that a manufacturer must conduct testing on its product as it is sold to the marketplace because the shape and design of the hood and face shield often have more to do with the performance of the product than its fabric and plastic qualities.

The light transmission and clarity of colors visible through arc flash face shields and hood windows have dramatically improved. However, additional illumination might be required to enhance an employee's ability to see while performing a task.

Face shields or hoods in accordance with ANSI/ISEA Z87.1, *American National Standard for Occupational and Educational Personal Eye and Face Protection Devices,* are considered secondary eye protective devices that must be used with primary eye protective devices (spectacles or goggles) underneath. The markings on the face shield in Exhibit 130.10 indicate that the shield itself is not shatterproof and additional protection is necessary.

Worker Alert

Heavy-duty leather gloves have not been found to limit injury when subjected to incident energies above 10 cal/cm². You should be provided with arc-rated gloves if the ability of leather gloves to provide protection is questionable. Note that equipment marked with an incident energy below 10 cal/cm² at a working distance might have a higher incident energy where your hands are positioned.

(d) *Hand Protection.*

(1) Heavy-duty leather gloves or arc-rated gloves shall be worn where required for arc flash protection.

Informational Note: Heavy-duty leather gloves are made entirely of leather with minimum thickness of 0.03 in. (0.7 mm) and are unlined or lined with nonflammable, nonmelting fabrics. Heavy-duty leather gloves meeting this requirement have been shown to have ATPV values in excess of 10 cal/cm² (41.9 J/cm²).

(2) Where insulating rubber gloves are used for shock protection, leather protectors shall be worn over the rubber gloves.

Informational Note: The leather protectors worn over rubber insulating gloves provide additional arc flash protection for the hands for arc flash protection exposure.

Generally, an arc flash risk assessment is based on an exposure distance of 18 or 36 inches. Thermal exposure to the hands will likely be much greater since they are often closer to the hazard than the body. Additional thermal protection for the hands is necessary in this case, which might also include equipment labeled at or below an incident energy level of 1.2 cal/cm². This might require an additional determination of

EXHIBIT 130.11

Leather protectors over insulated gloves. (Courtesy of Salisbury by Honeywell)

the incident energy at the hand position during the task or of the arc rating of PPE for the body parts that will be closer to the energized parts.

Leather materials are typically not arc flash rated. However, heavy-duty leather gloves made entirely of leather with a minimum thickness of 0.03 inches that is unlined or lined with nonflammable, nonmelting fabrics have been shown to have arc thermal performance values (ATPV) in excess of 10 cal/cm². Care should be taken when evaluating the arc rating of rubber gloves in conjunction with leather protectors. Because of the wide variation in the thickness of leather, correlation of the test value could prove difficult. Before opting for leather gloves rather than arc-rated gloves, it is necessary to determine if they will provide adequate protection from the anticipated incident energy. Leather protectors are an option when the incident energy exceeds 12 cal/cm². Exhibit 130.11 shows heavy-duty leather protectors over insulated gloves.

Rehearsal of the work task while wearing layers of hand protection can help determine if the dexterity for the task is sufficient. If the hands are being protected against only exposure to an arc flash, then heavy-duty leather gloves or arc-rated gloves can be used without voltage-rated rubber gloves.

(e) *Foot Protection.* Leather footwear or dielectric footwear or both provide some arc flash protection to the feet and shall be used in all exposures greater than 4 cal/cm² (16.75 J/cm²). Footwear other than leather or dielectric shall be permitted to be used provided it has been tested to demonstrate no ignition, melting, or dripping at the estimated incident energy exposure or the minimum arc rating for the respective arc flash PPE category.

Footwear with an arc rating is not available. Normally, an employee's feet are less exposed than the hands or head due to the proximity of most tasks. However, employees should not wear footwear made from lightweight materials or from materials that

EXHIBIT 130.12

Dielectric overshoes. (Courtesy of Salisbury by Honeywell)

are flammable or can melt and drip. In most cases, heavy-duty leather work shoes are satisfactory.

Dielectric overshoes, as shown in Exhibit 130.12, can be used over heavy-duty footwear.

(11) Clothing Material Characteristics. Arc-rated clothing shall meet the requirements described in 130.7(C)(12) and 130.7(C)(14).

Informational Note No. 1: Arc-rated materials, such as flame-retardant-treated cotton, meta-aramid, para-aramid, and poly-benzimidazole (PBI) fibers, provide thermal protection. These materials can ignite but will not continue to bum after the ignition source is removed. Arc-rated fabrics can reduce bum injuries during an arc flash exposure by providing a thermal barrier between the arc flash and the wearer.

Informational Note No. 2: Non-arc-rated cotton, polyester-cotton blends, nylon, nylon-cotton blends, silk, rayon, and wool fabrics are flammable. Fabrics, zipper tapes, and findings made of these materials can ignite and continue to bum on the body, resulting in serious bum injuries.

Informational Note No. 3: Rayon is a cellulose-based (wood pulp) synthetic fiber that is a flammable but nonmelting material.

Clothing consisting of fabrics, zipper tapes, and findings made from flammable synthetic materials that melt at temperatures below 315°C (600°F), such as acetate, acrylic, nylon, polyester, polyethylene, polypropylene, and spandex, either alone or in blends, shall not be used.

Informational Note: These materials melt as a result of arc flash exposure conditions, form intimate contact with the skin, and aggravate the bum injury.

Exception: Fiber blends that contain materials that melt, such as acetate, acrylic, nylon, polyester, polyethylene, polypropylene, and spandex, shall be permitted if such blends in fabrics are arc rated and do not exhibit evidence of melting and dripping during arc testing.

Informational Note: ASTM F1959/F1959M, *Standard Test Method for Determining the Arc Rating of Materials for Clothing*, and ASTM F1506, *Standard Performance Specification for Flame Resistant and Electric Arc Rated Protective Clothing Worn by Workers Exposed to Flames and Electric Arcs*, contain information on test methods used to determine the arc rating of fabrics.

(12) Clothing and Other Apparel Not Permitted. Clothing and other apparel (such as hard hat liners and hair nets) made from materials that do not meet the requirements of 130.7(C)(11) regarding melting or made from materials that do not meet the flammability requirements shall not be permitted to be worn.

> Informational Note: Some flame-resistant fabrics, such as non-flame-resistant modacrylic and non-durable flame-retardant treatments of cotton, are not recommended for industrial electrical or utility applications.

Apparel made from materials that are not arc rated must not be worn. For instance, hair nets, ear warmers, or head covers could melt onto an employee's hair and head unless they are made of arc-rated material.

Exception No. 1: Nonmelting, flammable (non-arc-rated) materials shall be permitted to be used as underlayers to arc-rated clothing, as described in 130.7(C)(11).

Exception No. 2: Where the work to be performed inside the arc flash boundary exposes the worker to multiple hazards, such as airborne contaminants, and the risk assessment identifies that the level of protection is adequate to address the arc flash hazard, non-arc-rated PPE shall be permitted.

Δ **(13) Care and Maintenance of Arc-Rated Clothing and Arc-Rated Arc Flash Suits.**

(a) *Inspection.* Arc-rated apparel shall be inspected before each use. Work clothing or arc flash suits that are contaminated or damaged to the extent that their protective qualities are impaired shall not be used. Protective items that become contaminated with grease, oil, or flammable liquids or combustible materials shall not be used.

Any flammable soiling or contamination on the surface of arc-rated clothing can reduce or even void the apparel's arc rating. The clothing must also be free from tears, cuts, or rips. Garments that are not suitable for use must be removed from service. If corrections can be made, such as laundering or repair using the appropriate techniques, a garment can be returned to service; otherwise, the garment should be disposed of.

(b) *Manufacturer's Instructions.* The garment manufacturer's instructions for care and maintenance of arc-rated apparel shall be followed.

The manufacturer's laundry care instructions are a required element on the label of any arc flash garment per ASTM F1506, *Standard Performance Specification for Flame Resistant and Electric Arc Rated Protective Clothing Worn by Workers Exposed to Flames and Electric Arcs.* Improper laundering or failure to follow the instruction provided by the manufacturer can diminish the longevity of a product's useful life and reduce the product's protective qualities.

(c) *Storage.* Arc-rated apparel shall be stored in a manner that prevents physical damage; damage from moisture, dust, or other deteriorating agents; or contamination from flammable or combustible materials.

For protective clothing to perform as intended, it must be protected when in use and storage. Contaminants such as grease and oil must be avoided, as contamination

Worker Alert

PPE is the last line of defense to prevent a permanent injury or death. You should take great care in inspecting, maintaining, and storing the PPE that is intended to save your life if an incident occurs.

reduces the thermal protection provided by clothing. Exposure to flammable materials must also be avoided.

(d) *Cleaning, Repairing, and Affixing Items.* When arc-rated clothing is cleaned, manufacturer's instructions shall be followed. When arc-rated clothing is repaired, the same arc-rated materials used to manufacture the arc-rated clothing shall be used to provide repairs.

> Informational Note No. I: The purpose of following manufacturer's instructions is to avoid the loss of protection and to remove contaminants such as hydrocarbons and metallic and disease-causing contaminants that could compromise safety.

> Informational Note No. 2: Additional guidance is provided in ASTMF1506, *Standard Performance Specification for Flame Resistant and Electric Arc Rated Protective Clothing Worn by Workers Exposed to Flames and Electric Arcs,* when trim, name tags, logos, or any combination thereof are affixed to arc-rated clothing.

> Informational Note No. 3: Additional guidance is provided in ASTM FI449, *Standard Guide for Industrial Laundering of Flame, Thermal, and Arc Resistant Clothing,* and ASTM F2757, *Standard Guide for Home Laundering Care and Maintenance of Flame, Thermal, and Arc Resistant Clothing.*

Manufacturers provide cleaning instructions for their thermal protection products. These instructions should be followed closely to ensure that the performance of a garment is not compromised. Company logos, replacement zippers, and the sewing thread used to attach them can affect the arc rating of PPE. There should be a policy in place for arc-rated clothing that will be laundered or repaired by the employee to ensure continued protection.

△ **(14) Standards for PPE.**

(a) *General.* PPE shall conform to applicable state, federal, or local codes and standards.

> Informational Note No. 1: The standards listed in Table 130.7(C)(14), which is part of this Informational Note, are examples of standards that contain information on the care, inspection, testing, and manufacturing of PPE.

> Informational Note No. 2: Non-arc-rated or flammable fabrics are not covered by any of the standards in Table 130.7(C)(14), Informational Note. See 130.7(C)(11) and 130.7(C)(12).

Informational Table 130.7(C)(14) encompasses only protective equipment that is normally considered PPE. Employers are required by 130.7(A) to provide the appropriate PPE to employees. The PPE is required by this section to conform to the appropriate standard. Therefore, it is the employer's responsibility to ensure that PPE supplied to employees complies with the applicable standard.

(b) *Conformity Assessment.* All suppliers or manufacturers of PPE shall demonstrate conformity with an appropriate product standard by one of the following methods:

(1) Self-declaration with a Supplier's Declaration of Conformity
(2) Self-declaration under a registered quality management system and product testing by an accredited laboratory and a Supplier's Declaration of Conformity
(3) Certification by an accredited independent third-party certification organization

△ **TABLE 130.7(C)(14)** *Informational Note: Standards for PPE*

Subject	Document Title	Document Number
Clothing — Arc Rated	Standard Performance Specification for Flame Resistant and Electric Arc Rated Protective Clothing Worn by Workers Exposed to Flames and Electric Arc	ASTM F1506
	Standard Guide for Industrial Laundering of Flame, Thermal, and Arc Resistant Clothing	ASTM F1449
	Standard Guide for Home Laundering Care and Maintenance of Flame, Thermal and Arc Resistant Clothing	ASTM F2757
	Live working — Protective clothing against the thermal hazards of an electric arc — Part 1-1: Test methods — Method 1: Determination of the arc rating (ELIM, ATPV, and/or EBT) of clothing materials and of protective clothing using an open arc	IEC 61482–1–1
	Live working — Protective clothing against the thermal hazards of an electric arc — Part 2: Requirements	IEC 61482–2
Aprons — Insulating	Standard Specification for Electrically Insulating Aprons	ASTM F2677
Eye and Face Protection — General	American National Standard for Occupational and Educational Professional Eye and Face Protection	ANSI/ISEA Z87.1
Face — Arc Rated	Standard Test Method for Determining the Arc Rating and Standard Specification for Personal Eye or Face Protective Products	ASTM F2178
Fall Protection	Standard Specification for Personal Climbing Equipment	ASTM F887
Footwear — Dielectric Specification	Standard Specification for Dielectric Footwear	ASTM F1117
Footwear — Dielectric Test Method	Standard Test Method for Determining Dielectric Strength of Dielectric Footwear	ASTM F1116
Footwear — Standard Performance Specification	Standard Specification for Performance Requirements for Protective (Safety) Toe Cap Footwear	ASTM F2413
Footwear — Standard Test Method	Standard Test Methods for Foot Protections	ASTM F2412
Gloves — Arc Rated	Standard Test Method for Determining Arc Ratings of Hand Protective Products Developed and Used for Electrical Arc Flash Protection	ASTM F2675/ F2675M
Gloves — Leather Protectors	Standard Specification for Leather Protectors for Rubber Insulating Gloves and Mittens	ASTM F696
Gloves — Rubber Insulating	Standard Specification for Rubber Insulating Gloves	ASTM D120
Gloves and Sleeves — In-Service Care	Standard Specification for In-Service Care of Insulating Gloves and Sleeves	ASTM F496
Head Protection — Hard Hats	American National Standard for Head Protection	ANSI/ISEA Z89.1
Rainwear — Arc Rated	Standard Specification for Arc and Flame Resistant Rainwear	ASTM F1891
Rubber Protective Products — Visual Inspection	Standard Guide for Visual Inspection of Electrical Protective Rubber Products	ASTM F1236
Sleeves — Insulating	Standard Specification for Rubber Insulating Sleeves	ASTM D1051

Informational Note No. 1: Examples of a process for conformity assessment to an appropriate product standard can be found in ANSI/ISEA 125, *American National Standard for Conformity Assessment of Safety and Personal Protective Equipment.* See H.4

Informational Note No. 2: An example of a process to accredit independent third-party certification organizations is ISO 17065, *Conformity assessment — Requirements for bodies certifying products, processes, and services.*

Section 130.7(0(14)(b) is not a requirement that the manufacturer of PPE must have its equipment evaluated for conformance to any standard. The requirement states only that the manufacturer be able to provide such a claim. The effectiveness of protective equipment might not be evident until that equipment is called upon to perform its safety function. An employer must not supply their employees with substandard, counterfeit, or inappropriate PPE. Such gear might increase the severity of an injury to an employee when an incident occurs.

The responsibility of determining compliance with the appropriate standard lies with the employer, purchaser, or person providing PPE to employees. Delivery of one of these conformity methods to the PPE purchaser does not absolve them from determining the validity of the claim. The employer must be competent to determine the standard applicable to the purchased equipment, the correctness of the claim, and the validity of the test results. It might be necessary for the purchaser to specify exactly which standard the purchased equipment must meet.

Within the European Union (EU) and in some other locations, a Declaration of Conformity (DoC) is a legal document declaring that equipment complies with the specific laws of the governing country. The individual signing the DoC must reside within the EU. The signatory of the DoC is liable if the equipment leads to or is involved in an incident, and their residence within the EU allows for them to be formally charged.

In contrast, the supplier's DoC in 130.7(C)(14)(b)(1) is a variation of the system used in the EU. However, this DoC is not tied to a legal system and has no external oversight. It is the employer's responsibility to determine the validity of the declaration.

The accredited laboratory mentioned in 130.7(C)(14)(b)(2) does not necessarily have to be an independent testing laboratory. Many companies are registered under the ISO 9000 series of standards for management systems. These companies might have on-site laboratories in which their employees conduct evaluation and testing of products. The quality management accreditation does not recognize laboratories to conduct product testing. Accreditation only verifies that the procedures for operating a laboratory are documented.

Section 130.7(C)(14)(b)(3) covers testing to the applicable standards by independent organizations. Within the United States, OSHA has a process for accrediting organizations to perform evaluations using specific standards. Within NFPA *70E,* equipment evaluated under this system is considered to be listed.

An employer might not be competent to determine if purchased equipment complies with the applicable standards or if the information provided demonstrates proper compliance. Often, to facilitate the acceptance of equipment, listed equipment is employed even when the standard, such as NFPA *70E,* does not require listing.

(c) *Marking.* All suppliers or manufacturers of PPE shall provide the following information on the PPE, on the smallest unit container, or contained within the manufacturer's instructions:

(1) Name of manufacturer
(2) Product performance standards to which the product conforms
(3) Arc rating where appropriate for the equipment
(4) One or more identifiers such as model, serial number, lot number, or traceability code
(5) Care instructions

PPE labels are often the first indication of compliance with the appropriate standard. Employers must understand the markings required by a specific standard and the differences between similar standards. For example, one standard might apply to the general flame- or arc-resistance testing of a fabric. When the fabric is used to manufacture an arc-rated suit, however, compliance might not rely on the fabric testing but on the testing addressed in the standard for the entire suit, including the zipper, buttons, logos, thread, face shield, and so forth. The correct standard must be referenced on the label.

Employers must also be able to identify markings that indicate equipment has not been properly evaluated. For example, no PPE should be labeled as "NFPA approved" or as complying with NFPA *70E*.

Case Study

130.7(C)(14)

Scenario

Ian was an electrician for an electrical contracting firm. Fie arrived at a worksite to conduct tasks assigned by the host employer. A documented meeting was held between the two. The host employer provided information on the electrical hazards within the equipment and the documentation regarding the risk assessments for the equipment and tasks.

Ian's initial task was a voltage measurement in a 600-volt motor control center. The risk assessment provided by the host employer and the equipment label indicated an incident energy of 5.1 cal/cm² at a distance of 18 inches Ian donned the 8 cal/cm² PPE that was provided by his employer. During the act of measuring the terminal voltage, an arc flash occurred. Ian was nonresponsive when the plant supervisor found him, and his PPE was severely damaged. Ian was rushed to the hospital.

Results

Ian sustained third-degree burns over nearly 60 percent of his body. The injury was so severe that he died 3 weeks later.

Investigation

It was not determined what initiated the incident. Investigation after the incident determined that both the risk assessment provided to Ian and the information on the equipment label were appropriate for the task. Inspection of the label on his arc-rated PPE indicated a rating of 8 cal/cm², presumably based on the specified testing standards. The work procedure was deemed to be sufficient.

From the label information and manufacturer's documentation, it was determined that the PPE was counterfeit, the arc rating of the PPE had not been properly evaluated, and the PPE was not capable of withstanding the marked incident energy exposure. It is unclear if the inappropriate PPE exacerbated Ian's injury.

Analysis

Ian's employer failed in its responsibility to protect him from the electrical hazards present for his assigned tasks. Ian's employer might not have had the qualifications necessary to determine if the PPE issued to him was appropriate or capable of providing the protection necessary to save his life.

Relevant NFPA *70E* Requirements

If Ian's employer had followed the requirements of NFPA *70E*, Ian might not have been killed. Some of the requirements his employer failed to meet include the following:

- Provide employees with PPE [130.7(A)].
- The PPE used must provide protection for the employee [130.7(C)(9)],
- PPE must conform to the applicable standards [130.7(0(14)(a)].

Δ **(15) Arc Flash PPE Category Method.** The requirements of 130.7(C)(15) shall apply when the arc flash PPE category method is used for the selection of arc flash PPE.

If the arc flash risk assessment is conducted using the incident energy calculation method, the tables referenced in 130.7(C)(15)(a) and (C)(15)(b) are not permitted to be used to determine the required PPE.

When conducting the arc flash risk assessment using the PPE category method, the tables must be used in the following sequence:

1. Considering site-specific factors, it must be determined if an arc flash is likely for the tasks specified in Table 130.5(C).
2. If an arc flash is likely, the hierarchy of risk controls in 110.5(H)(3) must be exhausted before determining the necessary PPE.

3. When PPE will be employed as a risk control, the level of PPE necessary must be determined using eitherTable 130.7(C(15)(a) for ac systems orTable 130.7(C(15)(b) for open-air dc systems.
4. Table 130.7(C(15)(c) must then be used to determine the personal equipment necessary to achieve the required PPE category.

It cannot be overstated that the use of the arc flash PPE category method requires strict adherence to the tables. This not only includes the specific equipment listed, but also the electrical parameters in the tables. This method does not require that extensive calculations be conducted; it provides a simple method for determining PPE for the equipment listed in the tables. The method does not allow for lower PPE categories to be selected for electrical circuit parameters that are lower than the table values. The tables cannot be interpolated. The application of the tables is either a"go"or"no go."

The arc flash PPE category method cannot be used if the proposed task or equipment type is not listed in the tables. Also, the arc flash PPE category method cannot be used if the electrical equipment is in the table but has electrical parameters that exceed a specified value. These cases would require that the incident energy analysis method be used.

As with any standard, the requirements included in the arc flash PPE category method tables are minimum requirements only. The user of this standard might determine that arc flash PPE is required for a task even when the table indicates that it is not. It is permissible to require arc flash PPE rated above the values specified in this minimum standard. When arc-rated equipment is exposed to an incident energy less than its rating, the probability of injury is reduced.

It is inappropriate to utilize the PPE category method as justification to authorize energized work.The tables are devised to protect employees when establishing an electrically safe work condition (ESWC) or in the limited instances when an ESWC is either infeasible or creates a greater hazard. Justifying energized work under the assumption that it is safe to do so because of the use of the PPE category tables can expose employees to undue hazards and an unnecessary risk of injury.

(a) *Alternating Current (ac) Equipment.* When the arc flash risk assessment performed in accordance with 130.5 indicates that arc flash PPE is required and the arc flash PPE category method is used for the selection of PPE for ac systems in lieu of the incident energy analysis of 130.5(G), Table 130.7(C)(15)(a) shall be used to determine the arc flash PPE category. The estimated maximum available fault current, maximum fault-clearing times, and minimum working distances for various ac equipment types or classifications are listed in Table 130.7(C)(15)(a). An incident energy analysis shall be required in accordance with 130.5(G) for the following:

(1) Power systems with greater than the estimated maximum available fault current
(2) Power systems with longer than the maximum fault clearing times
(3) Less than the minimum working distance

The arc flash PPE category tables are only applicable when using the arc flash PPE category method. They do not apply to evaluations conducted using the incident energy analysis method.

Determining whether the arc flash PPE category method is applicable involves deciding whether or not the available fault current and total fault clearing time fall within the maximum available short-circuit current and fault clearing time parameters. These parameters are defined in the applicable equipment classification category in Table 130.7(C)(15)(a) for ac systems. If the task is not listed in Table 130.5(C), then an incident energy analysis is required. If the equipment type is not listed or if the determined values for the working distance, available fault current, or total fault clearing time are outside of the parameters defined in Table 130.7(C)(15)(a), then an incident energy analysis is required. These tables cannot be interpolated. The application of the tables is either a "go" or "no go."

(b) *Direct Current (dc) Equipment.* When the arc flash risk assessment performed in accordance with 130.5(G) indicates that arc flash PPE is required and the arc flash PPE category method is used for the selection of PPE for dc systems in lieu of the incident energy analysis of 130.5(G), Table 130.7(C)(15)(b) shall be used to determine the arc flash PPE category. The estimated maximum available fault current, maximum arc duration, and working distances for dc equipment are listed in 130.7(C)(15)(b). An incident energy analysis shall be required in accordance with 130.5(G) for the following:

(1) Power systems with greater than the estimated maximum available fault current
(2) Power systems with longer than the maximum arc duration
(3) Less than the minimum working distance

> Informational Note No.1: The arc flash PPE category of the protective clothing and equipment is generally based on determination of the estimated exposure level.

> Informational Note No.2: In most cases, closed doors do not provide enough protection to eliminate the need for PPE in situations in which the state of the equipment is known to readily change (e.g., doors open or closed, rack in or rack out).

The arc flash PPE category tables are only applicable when using the arc flash PPE category method. They do not apply to evaluations conducted using the incident energy analysis method.

Determining whether the arc flash PPE category method is applicable involves deciding whether or not the available fault current and arc duration fall within the maximum available short-circuit current and arc duration parameters. These parameters are defined in the applicable equipment classification category in Table 130.7(C)(15)(b) for dc systems. If the task is not listed in Table 130.5(C), then an incident energy analysis is required. If the equipment type is not listed or if the determined values for the working distance, available fault current, or arc duration are outside of the parameters defined in Table 130.7(C)(15)(b), then an incident energy analysis is required. These tables cannot be interpolated. The application of the tables is either a "go" or "no go."

(c) *Protective Clothing and Personal Protective Equipment (PPE).* Once the arc flash PPE category has been identified from Table 130.7(C)(15)(a) or Table 130.7(C)(15)(b), Table 130.7(C)(15)(c) shall be used to determine the required PPE. Table 130.7(C)(15)(c) lists the requirements for PPE based on arc flash PPE categories 1 through 4. This clothing and equipment shall be used when working within the arc flash boundary. The use of PPE other than or in addition to that listed shall be permitted provided it meets 130.7(C)(7).

> Informational Note No. 1: See Informative Annex H for a suggested simplified approach to ensure adequate PPE for electrical workers within facilities with large and diverse electrical system

An employer can implement a procedure that includes a general requirement for employees to wear a minimum level of protective clothing. The procedure could also define a secondary level of protection that is easily recognizable and a third level of protection that is required in special situations. Two key factors for this type of requirement

OSHA Connection

29 CFR 1910.132(d)(1)

The employer must assess the workplace to determine if hazards are present or are likely to be present. If hazards necessitate the use of PPE, the employer must select and have each affected employee use PPE that properly fits, as well as communicate selection decisions to the affected employee.

are that the protection must be adequate for the greatest exposure of each level of protective clothing and that each employee must be able to recognize when a higher level of protection is necessary.

Informational Note No. 2: The PPE requirements of this section are intended to protect a person from arc flash hazards. While some situations could result in burns to the skin even with the protection described in Table 130.7(C)(15)(c), bum injury should be reduced and survivable. Due to the explosive effect of some arc events, physical trauma injuries could occur. The PPE requirements of this section do not address protection against physical trauma other than exposure to the thermal effects of an arc flash.

Wearing arc-rated clothing and protective equipment reduces the chance of thermal injury from an arc flash event. However, because of the nature of an arcing fault, determining the degree of each hazard associated with an arcing fault can be difficult. There is currently no consensus method for determining the strength of the pressure wave associated with an arc blast from an arc flash event.

Informational Note No. 3: The arc rating for a particular clothing system can be obtained from the arc-rated clothing manufacturer

The combined rating of arc-rated garments is not linear and can only be determined through testing. To have a combined rating, both garments must be arc-rated. Combination systems must be tested, and the overall rating of the system cannot be determined by simply adding the arc ratings of the garments together.

Δ **TABLE 130.7(C)(15)(a)** *Arc Flash PPE Categories for Alternating Current (ac) Systems*

Equipment	Arc Flash PPE Category	Arc Flash Boundary
Panelboards or other equipment rated 240 volts and below	1	485 mm
Parameters: Maximum of 25 kA available fault current; maximum of 0.03 sec (2 cycles) fault clearing time; minimum working distance 455 mm (18 in.)		(19 in.)
Panelboards or other equipment rated greater than 240 volts and up to 600 volts	2	900 mm
Parameters: Maximum of 25 kA available fault current; maximum of 0.03 sec (2 cycles) fault clearing time; minimum working distance 455 mm (18 in.)		(3 ft)
600-volt class motor control centers (MCCs)	2	1.5 m
Parameters: Maximum of 65 kA available fault current; maximum of 0.03 sec (2 cycles) fault clearing time; minimum working distance 455 mm (18 in.)		(5 ft)
600-volt class motor control centers (MCCs)	4	4.3 m
Parameters: Maximum of 42 kA available fault current; maximum of 0.33 sec (20 cycles) fault clearing time; minimum working distance 455 mm (18 in.)		(14 ft)
600-volt class switchgear (with power circuit breakers or fused switches) and 600-volt class switchboards	4	6 m
Parameters: Maximum of 35 kA available fault current; maximum of up to 0.5 sec (30 cycles) fault clearing time; minimum working distance 455 mm (18 in.)		(20 ft)
Other 600-volt class (277 volts through 600 volts, nominal) equipment	2	1.5 m
Parameters: Maximum of 65 kA available fault current; maximum of 0.03 sec (2 cycles) fault clearing time; minimum working distance 455 mm (18 in.)		(5 ft)

△ **TABLE 130.7(C)(15)(a)** *(Continued)*

Equipment	Arc Flash PPE Category	Arc Flash Boundary
NEMA E2 (fused contactor) motor starters, 2.3 kV through 7.2 kV	4	12 m
Parameters: Maximum of 35 kA available fault current; maximum of up to 0.24 sec (15 cycles) fault clearing time; minimum working distance 910 mm (36 in.)		(40 ft)
Metal-clad switchgear, 1 kV through 15 kV	4	12 m
Parameters: Maximum of 35 kA available fault current; maximum of up to 0.24 sec (15 cycles) fault clearing time; minimum working distance 910 mm (36 in.)		(40 ft)
Metal enclosed interrupter switchgear, fused or unfused type construction, 1 kV through 15 kV	4	12 m
Parameters: Maximum of 35 kA available fault current; maximum of 0.24 sec (15 cycles) fault clearing time; minimum working distance 910 mm (36 in.)		(40 ft)
Other equipment 1 kV through 15 kV	4	12 m
Parameters: Maximum of 35 kA available fault current; maximum of up to 0.24 sec (15 cycles) fault clearing time; minimum working distance 910 mm (36 in.)		(40 ft)
Arc-resistant equipment up to 600-volt class	N/A	N/A
Parameters: DOORS CLOSED and SECURED; with an available fault current and a fault clearing time that does not exceed the arc-resistant rating of the equipment*		
Arc-resistant equipment 1 kV through 15 kV	N/A	N/A
Parameters: DOORS CLOSED and SECURED; with an available fault current and a fault clearing time that does not exceed the arc-resistant rating of the equipment*		

N/A: Not applicable

Note:

For equipment rated 600 volts and below and protected by upstream current-limiting fuses or current-limiting molded case circuit breakers sized at 200 amperes or less, the arc flash PPE category can be reduced by one number but not below arc flash PPE category 1.

*For DOORS OPEN refer to the corresponding non-arc-resistant equipment section of this table.

Informational Note No. 1 to Table 130.7(C)(15)(a): The following are typical fault clearing times of overcurrent protective devices:

(1) 0.5 cycle fault clearing time is typical for current-limiting fuses and current-limiting molded case circuit breakers when the fault current is within the current limiting range.

(2) 1.5 cycle fault clearing time is typical for molded case circuit breakers rated less than 1000 volts with an instantaneous integral trip.

(3) 3.0 cycle fault clearing time is typical for insulated case circuit breakers rated less than 1000 volts with an instantaneous integral trip or relay operated trip.

(4) 5.0 cycle fault clearing time is typical for relay operated circuit breakers rated 1 kV to 35 kV when the relay operates in the instantaneous range (i.e., "no intentional delay").

(5) 20 cycle fault clearing time is typical for low-voltage power and insulated case circuit breakers with a short time fault clearing delay for motor inrush.

(6) 30 cycle fault clearing time is typical for low-voltage power and insulated case circuit breakers with a short time fault clearing delay without instantaneous trip.

Informational Note No. 2 to Table 130.7(C)(15)(a): See Table 1 of IEEE 1584, Guide for Performing Arc Flash Hazard Calculations, for further information regarding list items (2) through (4) in Informational Note No. 1.

Informational Note No. 3 to Table 130.7(C)(15)(a): An example of a standard that provides information for arc-resistant equipment referred to in Table 130.7(C)(15)(a) is IEEE C37.20.7, *Guide for Testing Switchgear Rated Up to 52 kV for Internal Arcing Faults.*

Informational Note No. 4 to Table 130.7(C)(15)(a): See 0.2.4(9) for information on arc-resistant equipment.

△ **TABLE 130.7(C)(15)(b)** *Arc Flash PPE Categories for dc Systems*

Equipment	Arc Flash PPE Category	Arc Flash Boundary
Storage batteries, dc switchboards, and other dc supply sources		
Parameters: Greater than or equal to 100 volts and less than or equal to 250 volts		
Maximum arc duration and minimum working distance: 2 sec @ 455 mm (18 in.)		
Available fault current less than 4 kA	2	900 mm (3 ft)
Available fault current greater than or equal to 4 kA and less than 7 kA	2	1.2 m (4 ft)
Available fault current greater than or equal to 7 kA and less than 15 kA	3	1.8 m (6 ft)
Storage batteries, dc switchboards, and other dc supply sources		
Parameters: Greater than 250 volts and less than or equal to 600 volts		
Maximum arc duration and minimum working distance: 2 sec @ 455 mm (18 in.)		
Available fault current less than 1.5 kA	2	900 mm (3 ft)
Available fault current greater than or equal to 1.5 kA and less than 3 kA	2	1.2 m (4 ft)
Available fault current greater than or equal to 3 kA and less than 7 kA	3	1.8 m (6 ft.)
Available fault current greater than or equal to 7 kA and less than 10 kA	4	2.5 m (8 ft)

Notes:

(1) Apparel that can be expected to be exposed to electrolyte must meet both of the following conditions:
  (a) Be evaluated for electrolyte protection

  Informational Note: ASTM FI 296, Standard Guide for Evaluating Chemical Protective Clothing, contains information on evaluating apparel for protection from electrolyte.

  (b) Be arc rated

  Informational Note: ASTM F1891, Standard Specification for Arc and Flame Resistant Rainwear, contains information on evaluating arc-rated apparel.

(2) A two-second arc duration is assumed if there is no overcurrent protective device (OCPD) or if the fault clearing time is not known. If the fault clearing time is known and is less than 2 seconds, an incident energy analysis could provide a more representative result.

Informational Note No. 1: When determining available fault current, the effects of cables and any other impedances in the circuit should be included. Power system modeling is the best method to determine the available short-circuit current at the point of the arc. Battery cell short-circuit current can be obtained from the battery manufacturer. See D.5 for the basis for table values and alternative methods to determine dc incident energy. Methods should be used with good engineering judgment.

Informational Note No. 2: The methods for estimating the dc arc flash incident energy that were used to determine the categories for this table are based on open-air incident energy calculations. Open-air calculations were used because many battery systems and other dc process systems are in open areas or rooms. If the specific task is within an enclosure, it would be prudent to consider additional PPE protection beyond the value shown in this table.

The arc flash PPE category method is only suitable for use where open-air arcs are involved, such as those found in many battery systems and other dc process systems that are in open areas or rooms. The arc flash PPE category method does not cover arc-in-a-box type setups where the incident energy is focused and a multiplier effect is involved.

The arc-rated clothing and protective equipment shown in Table 130.7(C)(15)(c) are only to be used with Table 130.7(C)(15)(a) for ac systems and Table 130.7(C)(15)(b) for dc systems. Table 130.7(C)(15)(c) is not to be used to select PPE as a result of an incident energy calculation. The PPE listed in these tables only protects against an arc flash hazard. Arc-rated clothing is available in many forms, and arc flash PPE rated in cal/cm² is suitable for that incident energy level. Table 130.7(C)(15)(c) suggests acceptable combinations of clothing items to achieve a desired arc flash PPE category. Other combinations are also possible.

Δ **TABLE 130.7(C)(15)(c)** *Personal Protective Equipment (PPE)*

Arc-Flash PPE Category	PPE
1	**Arc-Rated Clothing, Minimum Arc Rating of 4 cal/cm^2 (16.75 J/cm^2)^a** Arc-rated long-sleeve shirt and pants or arc-rated coverall Arc-rated face shield^b or arc flash suit hood Arc-rated jacket, parka, high-visibility apparel, rainwear, or hard hat liner (AN)^f **Protective Equipment** Hard hat Safety glasses or safety goggles (SR) Hearing protection (ear canal inserts)^c Heavy-duty leather gloves, arc-rated gloves, or rubber insulating gloves with leather protectors (SR)^d Leather footwear^e (AN)
2	**Arc-Rated Clothing, Minimum Arc Rating of 8 cal/cm^2 (33.5 J/cm^2)^a** Arc-rated long-sleeve shirt and pants or arc-rated coverall Arc-rated flash suit hood or arc-rated face shield^b and arc-rated balaclava Arc-rated jacket, parka, high-visibility apparel, rainwear, or hard hat liner (AN)^f **Protective Equipment** Hard hat Safety glasses or safety goggles (SR) Hearing protection (ear canal inserts)^c Heavy-duty leather gloves, arc-rated gloves, or rubber insulating gloves with leather protectors (SR)^d Leather footwear^e
3	**Arc-Rated Clothing Selected so That the System Arc Rating Meets the Required Minimum Arc Rating of 25 cal/cm^2 (104.7 J/cm^2)^a** Arc-rated long-sleeve shirt (AR) Arc-rated pants (AR) Arc-rated coverall (AR) Arc-rated arc flash suit jacket (AR) Arc-rated arc flash suit pants (AR) Arc-rated arc flash suit bood Arc-rated gloves or rubber insulating gloves with leather protectors (SR)^d Arc-rated jacket, parka, high-visibility apparel, rainwear, or hard hat liner (AN)^f **Protective Equipment** Hard hat Safety glasses or safety goggles (SR) Hearing protection (ear canal inserts)^c Leather footwear^e
4	**Arc-Rated Clothing Selected so That the System Arc Rating Meets the Required Minimum Arc Rating of 40 cal/cm^2 (167.5 J/cm^2)^a** Arc-rated long-sleeve shirt (AR) Arc-rated pants (AR) Arc-rated coverall (AR) Arc-rated arc flash suit jacket (AR) Arc-rated arc flash suit pants (AR) Arc-rated arc flash suit hood Arc-rated gloves or rubber insulating gloves with leather protectors (SR)^d Arc-rated jacket, parka, high-visibility apparel, rainwear, or hard hat liner (AN)^f

(continues)

Δ **TABLE 130.7(C)(15)(c)** *(Continued)*

Arc-Flash PPE Category	PPE
4	**Protective Equipment**
	Hard hat
	Safety glasses or safety goggles (SR)
	Hearing protection (ear canal inserts)[c]
	Leather footwear[c]

AN: As needed (optional). AR: As required. SR: Selection required.

[a]Arc rating is defined in Article 100.

[b]Face shields are to have wrap-around guarding to protect not only the face but also the forehead, ears, and neck, or, alternatively, an arc-rated arc flash suit hood is required to be worn.

[d]Other types of hearing protection are permitted to be used in lieu of or in addition to ear canal inserts provided they are worn under an arc-rated arc flash suit hood.

[e]Rubber insulating gloves with leather protectors provide arc flash protection in addition to shock protection. Higher class rubber insulating gloves with leather protectors, due to their increased material thickness, provide increased arc flash protection.

[e]Footwear other than leather or dielectric shall be permitted to be used provided it has been tested to demonstrate no ignition, melting or dripping at the minimum arc rating for the respective arc flash PPE category.

[f]The arc rating of outer layers worn over arc-rated clothing as protection from the elements or for other safety purposes, and that are not used as part of a layered system, shall not be required to be equal to or greater than the estimated incident energy exposure.

Table 130.7(C)(15)(c) is not applicable to evaluations conducted using the incident energy analysis method. For arc flash PPE clothing requirements for the incident energy analysis method, see 130.5(G) and 130.7(C)(1) through (C)(14).

Table 130.7(C)(15)(c) provides general information that can help employees understand the process of selecting clothing based on an arc flash PPE category designation, but it does not describe any of the required combinations or the construction of protective systems. The manufactured system can differ from what is described in the table; the clothing manufacturer needs to be consulted.

Δ **(D) Other Protective Equipment.**

Δ **(1) Insulated Tools and Equipment.** Tools and handling equipment used within the restricted approach boundary shall be insulated. Insulated tools shall be protected from damage to the insulating material.

Informational Note: See 130.4(E), Shock Protection Boundaries.

(a) *Requirements for Insulated Tools.* The following requirements shall apply to insulated tools:

(1) Insulated tools shall be rated for the voltages on which they are used.
(2) Insulated tools shall be designed and constructed for the environment to which they are exposed and the manner in which they are used.
(3) Insulated tools and equipment shall be inspected prior to each use. The inspection shall look for damage to the insulation or damage that can limit the tool from performing its intended function or could increase the potential for an incident (e.g., damaged tip on a screwdriver).

When working inside the restricted approach boundary, employees must select and follow the work procedures, which can include the use of insulated tools. The term *insulated* means that the tool manufacturer has assigned a voltage rating to the insulating material. Qualified persons are expected to be competent to inspect insulated tools for potential damage. Qualified persons must also be able to determine whether the voltage rating remains intact.

Exhibit 130.13 shows marked insulated tools. Only tools with a defined voltage rating are considered insulated. It is important for employees to look for the markings on a tool before using it. Tools with unmarked rubber grips and plastic handles must not be used in lieu of properly rated tools.

(b) *Fuse or Fuseholder Handling Equipment.* Fuse or fuseholder handling equipment, insulated for the circuit voltage, shall be used to remove or install a fuse if the fuse terminals are energized.

Replacing fuses live is energized work and, as such, must be justified.

(c) *Ropes and Handlines.* Ropes and handlines used within the limited approach boundary shall be nonconductive

Where ropes and handlines are used around energized conductors and circuit parts, they must be made of nonconductive materials to protect employees from potential shock hazards.

(d) *Fiberglass-Reinforced Plastic Rods.* Fiberglass-reinforced plastic rod and tube used for live-line tools shall meet the requirements of applicable portions of electrical codes and standards dealing with electrical installation requirements.

Informational Note: For further information concerning electrical codes and standards dealing with installation requirements, refer to ASTM F711, *Standard Specification for Fiberglass-Reinforced Plastic (FRP) Rod and Tube Used in Live Line Tools*

(e) *Portable Ladders.* Portable ladders shall have nonconductive side rails when used within the limited approach boundary or where the employee or ladder could contact exposed energized electrical conductors or circuit parts. Nonconductive ladders shall meet the requirements of applicable state, federal, or local codes and standards.

Informational Note: The standards listed in Table 130.7(G), Informational Note are examples of standards that contain information on portable ladders.

The use of ladders with conductive side rails in the vicinity of exposed energized conductors or circuit parts poses an unacceptable risk of injury from an electric shock. It can also pose an unacceptable risk of injury from a potential arc flash hazard, depending on the circumstances.

N **(2) Barriers.** Exposed energized electrical conductors or circuit parts operating at 50 volts or more shall be guarded by a barrier in accordance with 130.7(D)(2)(a) through 130.7(D)(2)(c) to prevent unintentional contact while an employee is working within the restricted approach boundary of those conductors or circuit parts. Barriers shall be supported to remain in place and shall prevent unintentional contact by a person, tool, or equipment.

(a) *Rubber Insulating Equipment.* Rubber insulating equipment used for protection from unintentional contact with energized conductors or circuit parts shall be rated for the voltage and shall meet the requirements of applicable state, federal, or local codes and standards.

Informational Note: The standards listed in Table 130.7(G), Informational Note are examples of standards that contain information on rubber insulating equipment.

(b) *Voltage-Rated Plastic Guard Equipment.* Plastic guard equipment for protection of employees from unintentional contact with energized conductors or circuit parts, or for protection of employees or energized equipment or material from contact with ground, shall be rated for the voltage and shall meet the requirements of applicable state, federal, or local codes and standards.

Informational Note: The standards listed in Table 130.7(G), Informational Note are examples of standards that contain information on voltage-rated plastic guard equipment.

(c) *Physical or Mechanical Barriers.* Physical or mechanical (field-fabricated) barriers shall be installed no closer than the restricted approach boundary distance given in Table 130.4(E)(a) and Table 130.4(E)(b). While the barrier is being installed, the restricted approach boundary distance specified in Table 130.4(E)(a) and Table 130.4(E)(b) shall be maintained, or the energized conductors or circuit parts shall be placed in an electrically safe work condition.

Worker Alert

The placement of barriers and barricades will often be your duty when performing a task. You typically won't find the limited approach boundary distance on an equipment label—it should be on the energized electrical work permit. If the task does not require a work permit, you must be capable of determining the limited approach distance from the appropriate table.

The use of these techniques is necessary to protect employees from injuries from potential exposure to electrical hazards. Generally, plastic guards, protective barriers, and insulating materials are not considered full protection against an arc flash event. Anyone within the arc flash boundary must use the appropriate arc flash personal and other protective equipment to be effectively protected from a potential arc flash event.

When qualified persons are performing tasks within the restricted approach boundary and unqualified persons are allowed within the limited approach boundary, the energized conductors and circuit parts must be guarded to protect the unqualified persons from contacting them and initiating an event. For equipment to be considered guarded, the unqualified person must be isolated from, kept away from, or protected from the energized conductors or circuit parts.

(E) Alerting Techniques.

Employees who are not involved in a work task might be exposed to an electrical hazard when the work task is being executed. They must be provided with a warning that an electrical hazard exists to avoid unnecessary exposure.

(1) Safety Signs and Tags. Safety signs, safety symbols, or tags shall be used where necessary to warn employees about electrical hazards that might endanger them. Such signs and tags shall meet the requirements of applicable state, federal, or local codes and standards.

> Informational Note No. 1: Safety signs, tags, and barricades used to identify energized "look-alike" equipment can be employed as an additional preventive measure.

> Informational Note No. 2: The standards listed in Table 130.7(G), Informational Note are examples of standards that contain information on safety signs and tags.

(2) Barricades. Barricades shall be used in conjunction with safety signs where it is necessary to prevent or limit employee access to work areas containing energized conductors or circuit parts. Conductive barricades shall not be used where it might increase the likelihood of exposure to an electrical hazard. Barricades shall be placed no closer than the limited approach boundary given in Table 130.4(E)(a) and Table 130.4(E)(b). Where the arc flash boundary is greater than the limited approach boundary, barricades shall not be placed closer than the arc flash boundary.

Barricades are not intended to prevent someone's approach to an area. Instead, a barricade is intended to act as a warning. When installed, the barricade should enclose the area containing the electrical hazard. The barricade must not be closer to the exposed energized electrical part than the limited approach boundary. The barricade should be placed so as not to impede the exit of employees within the boundary. See Exhibit 130.14 for an example of a barricade.

EXHIBIT 130.14

A barricade used to keep unqualified persons out of a hazardous area. (Courtesy of The T-CAP/www.TheTCap.com)

(3) Attendants. If signs and barricades do not provide sufficient warning and protection from electrical hazards, an attendant shall be stationed to warn and protect employees. The primary duty and responsibility of an attendant providing manual signaling and alerting shall be to keep unqualified employees outside a work area where the unqualified employee might be exposed to electrical hazards. An attendant shall remain in the area as long as there is a potential for employees to be exposed to the electrical hazards.

> The attendant should have no other duty than to deliver the warning.

(F) Look-Alike Equipment. Where work performed on equipment that is de-energized and placed in an electrically safe condition exists in a work area with other energized equipment that is similar in size, shape, and construction, one of the alerting methods in 130.7(E)(1), (2), or (3) shall be employed to prevent the employee from entering look-alike equipment.

> Similar electrical equipment is likely to exist in the same physical area when an installation involves multiple similar processes. Often, the only visible difference is the equipment labels. Employees must be aware that equipment similar to the equipment being maintained exists. Employees should install some temporary identifying mark to reduce the chances of interacting with the wrong equipment.

Case Study

130.7(F)

Scenario

A team of five technicians was performing preventative maintenance of switchgear in a rail car maintenance shop. The switchgear had two compartments, each with its own door. The upper compartment contained three knife switches used to disengage the incoming power by operating a lever. The lower compartment was de-energized when the three knife switches were opened. The lower compartment contained circuitry for transferring power to other areas of the maintenance shop. The lead technician placed the equipment in a maintenance mode by opening the primary switch (20 kV interrupter switch), which disconnected power to the ac switchgear. The team members then simultaneously performed maintenance on various pieces of the equipment. Mario, an electronic technician, was assigned the task of cleaning the lower compartment of the switchgear.

Mario proceeded to clean the upper compartment area by spraying cleaning fluid from an aerosol can onto the circuitry. When the aerosol spray contacted the line side of the switch, it provided a conductive plasma for the electric current. The current passed through the spray to Mario's right hand, went across his chest, and exited from his left upper arm, which was in contact with the center switch blade. This caused a flash of light and a loud explosion. The other technicians found Mario leaning into the upper switch compartment with his clothes on fire.

Result

One technician used a fire extinguisher to extinguish the fire on Mario. Another technician used the plastic hose of a vacuum cleaner to pull him from the compartment. Emergency medical service personnel responded within 5 minutes and treated him at the scene before transporting him to a hospital. There was evidence of darkening of his right thumb, a melted spray can finger actuator, and an exit wound on the inside of his left upper arm. Particles removed from one open switch blade were identified as human skin by a testing laboratory. At the time of the incident, the electric current exceeded 3,000 amperes of phase current and 1,200 amperes of neutral current as registered on power company equipment prior to the breakers tripping. Mario died in the hospital 24 hours later from electrical burns.

Analysis

Mario's employer was a large municipal transportation company that had an extensive safety program with a full-time safety manager and a safety board with representatives from each of the company's operating divisions. Each division had a safety committee that conducted monthly safety discussions. Classroom safety training was provided to employees. Mario received 41.5 hours of Maintenance-of-Way Electronic Technician Training. This training addressed the theory of operation for traction power substations and gap breakers and included safety considerations.

Assuming that the company's electrical safety program (ESP) specifically addressed this task on this equipment, it would be easy to include human error as the primary cause of this fatality. However, there is no indication that a procedure to properly establish an electrically safe work condition (ESWC) existed, that job planning included all employees impacted by a lockout procedure, or that the shock protection boundaries were defined. Additionally, a well-developed ESP would have addressed look-alike equipment. NFPA 70E requires that, when equipment in an ESWC is in an area with similar energized equipment, alerting techniques be used to prevent entrance into the energized equipment. Additionally, a company rule stated "for equipment normally energized between 2,500 and 50,000 volts, a distance of 3 feet should be maintained when working about the equipment." With the top 20-kV cabinet open, the 3-foot distance addressed the restricted approach boundary, but the limited approach boundary was 10 feet. Mario, an unescorted, unqualified person, was within both boundaries when he was working on the equipment.

Relevant NFPA 70E Requirements

Although Mario's fatality could have been prevented if an ESWC was properly established, neither Mario nor his company followed several requirements in NFPA 70E. An employee is typically trained only to the ESP established by the employer. It is not uncommon for an ESP to miss addressing all the requirements in NFPA 70E or those additionally necessary for specific tasks and equipment. It is difficult to properly train both qualified and unqualified persons without a well-developed ESP. In this case, the employer's ESP appears to

have missed several relevant NFPA 70E requirements that may have prevented Mario's death, including the following:

- Applicability of NFPA 70E to the maintenance shop [90.2(A) and 90.2(B)(2)]
- Install awareness and self-discipline in employees through training [110.5(D)]
- Elements of a risk assessment procedure [110.5(H)(1)]
- Address the potential for human error [110.5(H)(2)]
- Require job safety planning and job briefing [110.5(1)]
- Train unqualified persons [110.6(A)(2)]
- Train employees on safe release techniques [110.6(C)(1)]
- Require all affected employees to be involved with lockout process [120.2(B)]
- Identify all persons exposed to an electrical hazard [120.4(A)(2)]
- Use an energized electrical work permit [130.2(B)]
- Determine applicable shock protection boundaries [130.4(E)]
- Enforce shock protection boundaries [130.4(F) and (G)]
- Other precautions for personnel activities, including the use of flammable materials [130.8]
- Available alerting techniques [130.7(E)]
- Look-alike equipment [130.7(F)]

Content source: National Institute for Occupational Safety and Health (NIOSH); FACE case: 87-31

(G) Standards for Other Protective Equipment. Other protective equipment required in 130.7(D) shall conform to the applicable state, federal, or local codes and standards.

Informational Note: The standards listed in Table 130.7(G), which is part of this Informational Note, are examples of standards that contain information on other protective equipment.

Informational Table 130.7(G) identifies the standards that define the requirements for specific protective equipment. All the equipment listed in the table can impact the safe work procedures that a qualified person might implement. To provide protection for an employee conducting justified energized electrical work, the equipment must be capable of withstanding the conditions of an incident. Shock protection PPE is typically used to insulate employees from exposure to a specific maximum voltage level. Arc flash PPE is typically used to limit the probability and severity of a thermal injury when employees are exposed to a specific maximum incident energy arc flash. Verification testing is generally the only reliable method to determine if a material is capable of functioning as expected during an incident.

Per 130.7(A), an employer is required to provide the appropriate PPE to employees, and the protective equipment must conform to the appropriate standard. The employer, who is often the authority having jurisdiction (AHJ) within the scope of this standard, is responsible for providing equipment capable of protecting employees who are put at risk of injury during energized work. The employer must verify that the equipment issued meets the applicable consensus standard. Section 130.7(0(14)(b) provide three methods that can assist the employer when determining compliance with the appropriate standard. The employer is responsible for determining the validity of any stated compliance by a PPE manufacturer. However, the employer might not be competent to determine if purchased equipment complies with an applicable standard or if the information provided demonstrates compliance. Often, to facilitate the acceptance of equipment, listed equipment is employed even when a standard, such as NFPA *70E,* does not require listing.

Informational Table 130.7(G) covers only protective equipment that is normally considered PPE. For instance, voltmeters provide information that enables employees to protect themselves from electrical shock, but because they are not generally considered PPE, voltmeters are not covered in the table.

Δ **TABLE 130.7(G)** *Informational Note: Standards on Other Protective Equipment*

Subject	Document	Document Number
Arc Protective Blankets	Standard Test Method for Determining the Protective Performance of an Arc Protective Blanket for Electric Arc Hazards	ASTM F2676
Arc Protective Blankets — Selection, Care, and Use	Standard Guide for Selection, Care, and Use of Arc Protective Blankets	ASTM F3272
Blankets	Standard Specification for Rubber Insulating Blankets	ASTM D1048
Blankets — In-service Care	Standard Specification for In-Service Care of Insulating Blankets	ASTM F479
Covers	Standard Specification for Rubber Insulating Covers	ASTM D1049
Fiberglass Rods — Live Line Tools	Standard Specification for Fiberglass-Reinforced Plastic (FRP) Rod and Tube Used in Live Line Tools	ASTM F711
Insulated Hand Tools	Standard Specification for Insulated and Insulating Hand Tools	ASTM F1505
Ladders	American National Standard for Ladders — Wood — Safety Requirements	ANSI/ ASC A14.1
	American National Standard for Ladders — Fixed — Safety Requirements	ANSI /ASC A14.3
	American National Standard Safety Requirements for Job Made Wooden Ladders	ANSI ASC A14.4
	American National Standard for Ladders — Portable Reinforced Plastic — Safety Requirements	ANSI ASC A14.5
Line Hose	Standard Specification for Rubber Insulating Line Hoses	ASTM D1050
Line Hose and Covers — In-service Care	Standard Specification for In-Service Care of Insulating Line Hose and Covers	ASTM F478
Plastic Guard	Standard Test Methods and Specifications for Electrically Insulating Plastic Guard Equipment for Protection of Workers	ASTM F712
Sheeting	Standard Specification for PVC Insulating Sheeting	ASTM F1742
	Standard Specification for Rubber Insulating Sheeting	ASTM F2320
Safety Signs and Tags	Series of Standards for Safety Signs and Tags	ANSI Z535
Shield Performance on Live Line Tool	Standard Test Method for Determining the Protective Performance of a Shield Attached on Live Line Tools or on Racking Rods for Electric Arc Hazards	ASTM F2522
Temporary Protective Grounds — In-service Testing	Standard Specification for In-Service Test Methods for Temporary Grounding Jumper Assemblies Used on De-energized Electric Power Lines and Equipment	ASTM F2249
Temporary Protective Grounds — Test Specification	Standard Specification for Temporary Protective Grounds to Be Used on De-energized Electric Power Lines and Equipment	ASTM F855

130.8 Other Precautions for Personnel Activities.

(A) Alertness.

(1) Where Electrical Hazards Might Exist. Employees shall be instructed to be alert at all times where electrical hazards might exist.

> Human factors are generally recognized as one of the leading causes of injury from electrical hazards. An employee conducting work is typically solely responsible for their actions. After employees have gone through training, been qualified for a task, and been given the procedures, it is their personal actions or lack thereof that will impact their safety. Alertness, as used in this section, is attentiveness to the self, others, and the situation.

△ **(2) When Impaired.** Employees shall not be permitted to work where electrical hazards exist while their alertness is recognizably impaired due to illness, fatigue, or other reasons.

> Human factors are generally recognized as one of the leading causes of injuries from electrical hazards. An impaired employee might be unable to safely perform a task. Employers and employees must realize that an illness or fatigue from extended hours can put employees at risk. The employer has a duty to observe the physical and mental condition of the employees. At the time of a job briefing, the person in charge must evaluate whether any employee is impaired for any reason. It might be advantageous to reschedule work rather than put an employee at undue risk. No employee should be compelled to rush to complete a task or to work when impaired. Doing so can expose the qualified person to a risk that was not considered in the energized electrical work permit.

(3) Changes in Scope. Employees shall be instructed to be alert for changes in the job or task that could lead the person outside of the electrically safe work condition or expose the person to additional hazards that were not part of the original plan.

> When a job briefing is given, employees must be instructed on the details and limits of the expected work task. A change in the condition or work environment that was not part of the original plan might result in unanticipated exposure to an electrical hazard. A seemingly minor deviation from the work plan could drastically alter the shock assessment or arc flash assessment, or it could require the employee to perform a task for which they are not qualified. For example, closing a switch rather than conducting the planned voltage measurements might introduce an unanticipated hazard. Employees should be trained to stop work when there is any deviation from the planned task. Work should not proceed until a new job plan or work permit has been provided. A new risk assessment might be necessary prior to performing the new task.

(B) Blind Reaching. Employees shall be instructed not to reach blindly into areas that might contain exposed energized electrical conductors or circuit parts where an electrical hazard exists

> The employee must be able to see the location where a task will be conducted. There is no way to assume that the task can be safely performed if the employee is unable to see what they are doing. The use of a mirror to see behind an obstruction is also considered blind reaching.

Worker Alert

It is solely your responsibility to remain alert and attentive when conducting an energized task. You should not be distracted by your cellphone, other persons, or other tasks being performed around you.

Worker Alert

You are uniquely qualified to determine impairments that might prevent you from safely performing an assigned task. You must recognize when you feel ill or are fatigued and acknowledge that continuing in your condition could put you or others around you at risk.

Worker Alert

You might not realize until you reach the equipment that an assigned task was incorrectly documented in the energized electrical work permit. You might also be approached during the assigned task to perform another undocumented task. In either case, changes to the original plan can put you at an increased risk of injury.

Worker Alert

You should not attempt to pick up a nut, bolt, or tool that has fallen into equipment—even if it is visible. Retrieving a dropped item inches away from the assigned task location might present additional hazards and greater risk of injury. You need to address all the hazards and associated risks before deviating from the issued work permit.

Δ **(C) Illumination.**

(1) General. Employees shall not enter spaces where electrical hazards exist unless illumination is provided that enables the employees to perform the work safely.

> The employer should ensure that adequate lighting is provided to perform the work safely. Adequate lighting should also be included in the risk assessment procedure. Additional illumination could be required due to the darkness of a face shield. Prior to starting work, the work area should be viewed wearing the face shield to determine if additional illumination is necessary.
>
> The work permit should specify the type of additional lighting necessary to safely perform a task. For example, if the required fixed temporary lighting necessary to perform the task is not available, work should not begin until it is in place. The improvised use of a flashlight would alter the work plan and could introduce unanticipated risks to employees. Work should not be performed until appropriate and sufficient lighting as specified in the work permit is available.

Δ **(2) Obstructed View of Work Area.** Where lack of illumination or an obstruction precludes observation of the work to be performed, employees shall not perform any task where an electrical hazard exists.

> The primary objective is for employees to be able to see what they are working on. An obstruction could be a barrier installed by the equipment manufacturer to protect specific points within the equipment or a barrier that has been installed to isolate an energized component. The view of the work area could also be obstructed by the installation location of the equipment or by equipment that was not installed with the required working space.

(D) Conductive Articles Being Worn. Conductive articles of jewelry and clothing (such as watchbands, bracelets, rings, key chains, necklaces, metalized aprons, cloth with conductive thread, metal headgear, or metal frame glasses) shall not be worn within the restricted approach boundary or where they present an electrical contact hazard with exposed energized electrical conductors or circuit parts.

(E) Conductive Materials, Tools, and Equipment Being Handled.

(1) General. Conductive materials, tools, and equipment that are in contact with any part of an employee's body shall be handled in a manner that prevents unintentional contact with energized electrical conductors or circuit parts. Such materials and equipment shall include, but are not limited to, long conductive objects, such as ducts, pipes and tubes, conductive hose and rope, metal-lined rules and scales, steel tapes, pulling lines, metal scaffold parts, structural members, bull floats, and chains.

> Long objects that are difficult to control, such as ladders, should be handled by assigning an employee to each end of the object. This work practice enables the object to be handled safely without crossing the limited approach boundary. Conductive fish tapes should not be used for a work task associated with an exposed energized electrical conductor or circuit part.

(2) Approach to Energized Electrical Conductors and Circuit Parts. Means shall be employed to ensure that conductive materials approach exposed energized electrical conductors or circuit parts no closer than that permitted by 130.4(F).

Δ **(F) Confined or Enclosed Work Spaces.** When an employee works in a confined or enclosed space (such as a manhole or vault) where an electrical hazard exists, the employer shall provide, and the employee shall use, protective shields, protective barriers, or insulating materials as necessary to protect against electrical hazards.

> Confined spaces are areas that are not necessarily designed for people, but that are large enough for employees to enter to perform certain tasks. Another characteristic of a confined space is a limited or restricted means for entry or exit. A large equipment housing is an example of a confined space that could contain exposed energized electrical conductors or circuit parts.
>
> A confined space might contain a hazardous atmosphere—due to toxic gases, low oxygen, flammability, or excessive heat—that could be life-threatening. Ventilation, emergency evacuation, and atmospheric testing should be included in the risk assessment procedure. All the hazards identified in the risk assessment procedure should be mitigated.

Δ **(G) Doors and Hinged Panels.** Doors, hinged panels, and the like shall be secured to prevent their swinging into an employee and causing the employee to contact exposed energized electrical conductors or circuit parts where an electrical hazard exists if movement of the door, hinged panel, and the like is likely to create a hazard.

(H) Clear Spaces. Working space required by other codes and standards shall not be used for storage. This space shall be kept clear to permit safe operation and maintenance of electrical equipment.

> The space must not be used for the storage of any items, including portable equipment on rollers, hand carts, and other easily movable items.

(I) Housekeeping Duties. Employees shall not perform housekeeping duties inside the limited approach boundary where there is a possibility of contact with energized electrical conductors or circuit parts, unless adequate safeguards (such as insulating equipment or barriers) are provided to prevent contact. Electrically conductive cleaning materials (including conductive solids such as steel wool, metalized cloth, and silicone carbide, as well as conductive liquid solutions) shall not be used inside the limited approach boundary unless procedures to prevent electrical contact are followed.

> It is important to understand that the limited approach boundary only exists where there are exposed energized electrical conductors and circuit parts. This requirement does not apply where mitigation strategies have been implemented to prevent employees from accidentally contacting exposed electrical conductors and circuit parts. However, arc-rated PPE is necessary if housekeeping duties are being performed within the arc flash boundary.

(J) Occasional Use of Flammable Materials. Where flammable materials are present only occasionally, electric equipment capable of igniting them shall not be permitted to be used, unless measures are taken to prevent hazardous conditions from developing. Such materials shall include, but are not limited to, flammable gases, vapors, or liquids, combustible dust, and ignitible fibers or flyings.

Informational Note: Electrical installation requirements for locations where flammable materials are present on a regular basis are contained in *NFPA 70, National Electrical Code*

Many cleaning materials and the propellant used in some spray cans are flammable. Liquids sometimes vaporize readily and flow into the recesses and crevices of electrical equipment. An electrical arc caused by the operation of equipment could ignite any vapor that remains. See the case study in 130.7(F) for such an incident.

(K) Anticipating Failure. When there is evidence that electric equipment could fail and injure employees, the electric equipment shall be de-energized, unless the employer can demonstrate that de-energizing introduces additional hazards or increased risk or is infeasible because of equipment design or operational limitation. Until the equipment is de-energized or repaired, employees shall be protected from hazards associated with the impending failure of the equipment by suitable barricades and other alerting techniques necessary for safety of the employees.

Informational Note: See 130.7(E) for alerting techniques.

Electrical equipment frequently offers indications when failure is impending, and employees should be trained to recognize these indications. Indications of impending failure include hot enclosures, unusual noises or sounds, warning lights, and unfamiliar smells. If any of these indications is observed, normal operation of the equipment should not be permitted or attempted. The equipment in failure mode must be isolated using barricades or similar protective measures to protect employees from accidental contact with the equipment. After the equipment has been isolated, it should be de-energized from a remote location. The disconnecting means located in the equipment should not be operated unless the person operating it is protected from the effects of equipment failure.

(L) Routine Opening and Closing of Circuits. Load-rated switches, circuit breakers, or other devices specifically designed as disconnecting means shall be used for the opening, reversing, or closing of circuits under load conditions. Cable connectors not of the load-break type, fuses, terminal lugs, and cable splice connections shall not be permitted to be used for such purposes, except in an emergency.

When non-load-break-rated devices are used to break electrical load currents in an emergency, the party breaking the load needs to be aware of the risk of injury from exposure to potential electrical hazards.

(M) Reclosing Circuits After Protective Device Operation. After a circuit is de-energized by the automatic operation of a circuit protective device, the circuit shall not be manually re-energized until it has been determined that the equipment and circuit can be safely energized. The repetitive manual reclosing of circuit breakers or re-energizing circuits through replaced fuses shall be prohibited. When it is determined from the design of the circuit and the overcurrent devices involved that the automatic operation of a device was caused by an overload rather than a fault condition, examination of the circuit or connected equipment shall not be required before the circuit is re-energized.

If an overcurrent device (such as a fuse or circuit breaker) operates, it can be assumed that the rated current has been exceeded or that a short circuit or ground-fault condition exists. Reclosing a circuit into a short circuit or ground fault could have a disastrous effect and must be avoided. The cause of the device's operation must be determined before the circuit can be reclosed.

(N) Safety Interlocks. Only qualified persons following the requirements for working inside the restricted approach boundary as covered by 130.4(G) shall be permitted to defeat or bypass an electrical safety interlock over which the person has sole control, and then only temporarily while the qualified person is working on the equipment. The safety interlock system shall be returned to its operable condition when the work is completed.

130.9 Work Within the Limited Approach Boundary or Arc Flash Boundary of Overhead Lines.

In most cases, overhead conductors are guarded by being elevated so that they are not subject to incidental contact. When working near or on an overhead conductor, employees are likely to be supported by an elevated or articulating platform or by a permanently installed platform or deck. When using such support methods, employees might have difficulty escaping from an arc flash or avoiding direct contact with energized conductors. These factors must be considered in the risk assessment. They also emphasize the need for an emergency recovery plan.

(A) Uninsulated and Energized. Where work is performed in locations containing uninsulated energized overhead lines that are not guarded or isolated, precautions shall be taken to prevent employees from contacting such lines directly with any unguarded parts of their body or indirectly through conductive materials, tools, or equipment. Where the work to be performed is such that contact with uninsulated energized overhead lines is possible, the lines shall be de-energized and visibly grounded at the point of work or suitably guarded.

Electrical conductors that are not insulated for their circuit voltage have the same potential for shock and electrocution as the conductors that are completely bare. Some overhead conductors have a covering for protection from environmental degradation, but the covering has no insulation rating.

Exhibit 130.15(a) illustrates the operation of equipment in proximity to overhead power lines. Equipment such as a crane, with the capability of reaching overhead power lines, presents a shock hazard to the equipment operator and to employees who are working in the vicinity of the equipment. Qualified persons must observe and comply with the approach boundaries identified in Table 130.4(E)(a) for ac systems or Table 130.4(E)(b) for dc systems. While the employee is at ground level, the overhead bare conductors are adequately isolated from contact. When the bucket approaches the conductors, the possibility of contact with the bare conductors greatly increases, so the conductors need to be de-energized and visibly grounded. Exhibit 130.15(b) shows signage indicating that equipment booms should be kept a safe distance away from overhead power lines. For more information, see 130.9(F) regarding elevated equipment.

Employees should not work near overhead conductors unless they are protected from unintentional contact with the conductors. Personnel carrying conduits, pipes, ladders, and other long objects must exercise caution to avoid entering the space defined by the limited approach boundary. When long objects are moved, employees should be assigned to each end of the object to maintain control of both ends.

(B) Determination of Insulation Rating. A qualified person shall determine if the overhead electrical lines are insulated for the lines' operating voltage.

(C) De-energizing or Guarding. If the lines are to be de-energized, arrangements shall be made with the person or organization that operates or controls the lines to de-energize them and visibly ground them at the point of work. If arrangements are made to use protective measures, such as guarding, isolating, or insulation, these precautions shall prevent each employee

EXHIBIT 130.15

(a) A crane operating near energized overhead power lines. (Courtesy of FEMA, photo by George Armstrong); (b) Signage warning against contact with overhead power lines.

from contacting such lines directly with any part of his or her body or indirectly through conductive materials, tools, or equipment.

> The operation and maintenance of transmission and distribution lines are often the responsibility of a utility. The person responsible for the operation and maintenance of the affected conductors must be consulted and directly involved in de-energizing and grounding the overhead conductors.
>
> Suitable guards should be installed to prevent accidental contact with the overhead lines. However, to eliminate the chance of unintentional contact, the guards must be of sufficient strength to control the approach or any possible movement of a person or object. In most instances, line hose is not satisfactory to prevent unintentional contact.
>
> Safety grounds, as shown in Exhibit 120.17, must be installed in a manner that provides an equipotential zone for the work area. An equipotential zone is an area in which no (or unperceivable) voltage differences exist between exposed conductive surfaces that an employee might come into contact with while performing the task. Other conductors in the immediate vicinity of the work area must be guarded against potential contact.

(D) Employer and Employee Responsibility. The employer and employee shall be responsible for ensuring that guards or protective measures are satisfactory for the conditions. Employees shall comply with established work methods and the use of protective equipment.

Employers are responsible for providing the electrical safety program, and employees are responsible for implementing the requirements of the program. Both employers and employees are responsible for ensuring that any installed guards are adequate for the conditions. The employer and employee must work together to make sure that effective procedures exist and that they are stringently applied and frequently reviewed

(E) Approach Distances for Unqualified Persons. When unqualified persons are working on the ground or in an elevated position near overhead lines, the location shall be such that the employee and the longest conductive object the employee might contact do not come closer to any unguarded, energized overhead power line than the limited approach boundary in Table 130.4(E)(a), column 2 or Table 130.4(E)(b), column 2

The approach distance for unqualified persons remains the same, regardless of the installation method for the conductors. The limited approach distance depends on whether the distance between the conductor and the employee is under the employee's control.

If the supporting platform can move, as would be the case for an articulating platform, column 2 of both Table 130.4(E)(a) and Table 130.4(E)(b) applies. If the conductor is supported by a messenger or a similar support method, it can move as the wind blows, and, therefore, the distance between the employee and the conductor is not under the employee's control and column 2 still applies. If the overhead conductor is fixed into position, as is the case with solid bus conductors, and the employee is standing on a fixed platform or scaffolding, the employee has control over the distance between them and the conductor and column 3 applies.

> Informational Note: Objects that are not insulated for the voltage involved should be considered to be conductive.

Some conductors have coverings that are intended to serve as protection from the effects of the environment. These coverings are often not insulating and generally have no established voltage rating. Weatherproof conductors must be considered uninsulated.

(F) Vehicular and Mechanical Equipment.

(1) Elevated Equipment. Where any vehicle or mechanical equipment structure will be elevated near energized overhead lines, it shall be operated so that the limited approach boundary distance of Table 130.4(E)(a), column 2 or Table 130.4(E)(b), column 2, is maintained. However, under any of the following conditions, the clearances shall be permitted to be reduced:

The limited approach boundary in column 2 of both Table 130.4(E)(a) and Table 130.4(E)(b) defines the closest that any vehicle or mechanical equipment structure can be to an exposed energized overhead conductor unless the conditions defined in this section permit closer approach. Distances can be difficult to estimate when standing on the ground or sitting in the seat of a crane or other mobile equipment..

(1) If the vehicle is in transit with its structure lowered, the limited approach boundary to overhead lines in Table 130.4(E)(a), column 2 or Table 130.4(E)(b), column 2, shall be permitted to be reduced by 1.83 m (6 ft). If insulated barriers, rated for the voltages involved, are installed and they are not part of an attachment to the vehicle, the clearance shall be permitted to be reduced to the design working dimensions of the insulating barrier.

Any elevating structure on a vehicle, such as a boom or a dump truck bed, must be in the resting position. The limited approach boundary cannot be reduced if such structures are not in the resting position.

(2) If the equipment is an aerial lift insulated for the voltage involved, and if the work is performed by a qualified person, the clearance (between the uninsulated portion of the aerial lift and the power line) shall be permitted to be reduced to the restricted approach boundary given in Table 130.4(E)(a), column 4 or Table 130.4(E)(b), column 4.

When qualified persons are supported by an aerial lifting device, such as a truck boom that is fully insulated from contact with the earth, the minimum approach distance is defined as the restricted approach boundary given in column 4 of both Table 130.4(E)(a) and Table 130.4(E)(b). The qualified persons should have received training in the operation of the aerial lifting device in addition to all the other required training.

(2) Equipment Contact. Employees standing on the ground shall not contact the vehicle or mechanical equipment or any of its attachments unless either of the following conditions apply:

(1) The employee is using protective equipment rated for the voltage.

(2) The equipment is located so that no uninsulated part of its structure (that portion of the structure that provides a conductive path to employees on the ground) can come closer to the line than permitted in 130.9(F)(1).

Although equipment contact with overhead conductors could be several feet away, an employee on the ground might provide the conductive path to the earth when touching the equipment with unprotected hands or another body part. Handlines and tag lines sometimes serve as the point of contact.

Employees who are outside of equipment that is in contact with an energized conductor can have greater exposure to electrocution than those who are inside the equipment cab. Employees could be exposed to electrocution via step potential if they are standing on the ground near equipment that makes contact with an overhead line.

A barricade should be erected around the physical area to surround equipment that could contact an overhead line and should not permit approach closer than the limited approach boundary. Signs should be installed to warn people to stay out of the area.

(3) Equipment Grounding. If any vehicle or mechanical equipment is capable of having parts of its structure elevated within the limited approach boundary of exposed movable conductors of energized overhead lines and is intentionally grounded, employees working on the ground near the point of grounding shall not stand at the grounding location whenever there is a possibility of overhead line contact. Additional precautions, such as the use of barricades, dielectric overshoe footwear, or insulation, shall be taken to protect employees from hazardous ground potentials (step and touch potential).

Informational Note: Upon contact of the elevated structure with the energized lines, hazardous ground potentials can develop within a few feet or more outward from the grounded point.

Some safety programs require mobile equipment to be grounded with a temporary grounding conductor connected to an existing earth ground or a temporary ground rod. The grounding conductor expands the touch and step potential hazard to include the grounding conductor and the ground rod (or other earth ground connection point). If such a grounding conductor is installed, employees must not be within the limited approach boundary of any portion of the temporary grounding circuit.

Scenario

Two well drillers had been assigned the task of repairing a submersible pump and other electrical-related equipment for an existing water well at a private residence. Derek had been performing this type of work for 15 years. The well was inside a fenced pasture intersected by three separate and parallel overhead power lines, one of which is a three-phase, 12,000-volt power line that crosses directly above the well head, 31 feet 6 inches above the ground. The well company had no safety program and no written safety policy or procedures.

On the day before the incident, Derek and a coworker worked on the well for about 2 hours. They returned the following morning and continued the repair work for about 30 minutes. At that time, they decided they needed a truck-mounted crane to pull the submersible pump out of the well. They drove to the company office then returned to the site in a 5-ton hydraulic derrick crane truck. Derek positioned the crane truck near the well and lowered the outriggers to stabilize the truck. He stood near the side of the truck and operated the crane with a hand-held remote-control pendant while the coworker stood near the back of the truck. Derek fully extended the end of the boom 36 feet above the ground. The coworker attached the cable and hook to the end of the galvanized pipe protruding from the well head.

With the pendant control in his left hand, Derek began hoisting the pipe out of the well. As he raised the pipe it contacted the power line phase directly above the well. The coworker stated that Derek yelled for him to "get out of the way." The coworker began running away from the crane and did not see the galvanized pipe contact the overhead power line. However, a solidified molten drip at the end of the galvanized pipe suggests contact at that point. When contact occurred, the truck-mounted crane, the remote-control cable, and the hand-held pendant became energized. While running, the coworker heard a loud noise "like a shotgun going off." A motorist driving along the highway reported later that he saw a ball of fire rising from the well enclosure. The electric current entered Derek's left hand (holding the pendant) and exited his feet to the ground. The power line phase melted into two at the point where the galvanized pipe made contact. This caused the non-energized end (load end) of the power line phase to fall to the ground. The energized end (line end) of the phase dangled about 12 feet above the ground from a utility pole 17 feet from the well.

Result

After hearing the noise, the coworker looked back and saw Derek lying face down about 10 feet from the well enclosure. The coworker ran to him and noted that he was still conscious. The hand-held pendant was lying on the ground nearby. The coworker called the office from inside the crane truck, and the secretary called the emergency medical service on 911. The coworker returned to Derek, who was now unconscious, and

attempted cardiopulmonary resuscitation (CPR) but was unsuccessful in reviving him. A police officer and an emergency rescue squad from the local fire department arrived at the scene in 2 and 8 minutes, respectively, after the 911 emergency call was received. The police officer and rescue squad personnel continued CPR on him, including advanced cardiac life support. Derek was transported to a local hospital where he was pronounced dead on arrival by the attending physician.

Analysis

Employers not involved in the electrical industry often believe that electrical safety and the requirements of NFPA *70E* do not apply to them. Electrical injuries and fatalities are not limited to those in an electrical occupation. Federal law mandates that an employer furnish a place of employment that is free from recognized hazards that are causing or are likely to cause death or serious physical harm to employees. It is foreseeable that Derek would be exposed to known electrical hazards given that fields, yards, and lots were parts of his work environment. However, his employer had no documented electrical safety program, policies, or procedures.

NFPA *70E, Standard for Electrical Safety in the Workplace,* as its title suggests, is for all employees who might be exposed to electrical hazards while performing their assigned tasks. It requires that all employees be protected from electrical hazards. NFPA *70E* uses the terms *qualified person* and *unqualified person* rather than an employee's title or designating a task as electrical or non-electrical. There are specific requirements for who is permitted to cross a specific boundary and what should occur upon doing so. Section 130.8 specifically addresses any employee working within the approach boundaries of overhead lines.

Fatalities occur in trades that are mistaken in the belief that an electrical safety program does not apply to them. This may be one reason for so many overhead power line and transformer fatalities occurring even though NFPA *70E* has requirements specifically covering this scenario. Groundskeepers, roofers, painters, tree trimmers, well drillers, dump and cement truck drivers, and boom truck operators are common victims. Since 1992, there have been 3,529 electrical contact fatalities attributed to overhead power lines and transformers, according to the Bureau of Labor Statistics. This accounts for more than half (57%) of workplace electrocutions.

Derek may not have become a fatality if his employer had applied NFPA *70E*. The assigned task exposed Derek to foreseeable electrical hazards at the work location. Requirements ranging from documenting an electrical safety program to performing risk assessments for assigned tasks to operating elevated equipment near overhead lines might have saved Derek's life.

Content source: National Institute for Occupational Safety and Health (NIOSH); FACE case: 90-38.

130.10 Underground Electrical Lines and Equipment.

Before excavation starts where there exists a reasonable possibility of contacting electrical lines or equipment, the employer shall take the necessary steps to contact the appropriate owners or authorities to identify and mark the location of the electrical lines or equipment. When it has been determined that a reasonable possibility of contacting electrical lines or equipment exists, appropriate safe work practices and PPE shall be used during the excavation.

Marking the location of underground conductors and equipment can help to minimize the possibility of accidental contact with buried electrical conductors during excavation. Safe work practices commensurate with the hazard must be implemented during the excavation.

All underground utilities, including gas, electricity, telephone, and cableTV companies, are members of 811. The call center notifies utility companies of excavation work near their underground installations and directs them to mark the approximate location of underground lines, pipes, and cables. There is a legal obligation in some states for a call to be made to 811 prior to any excavation work. Exhibit 130.16 shows a public service bulletin for the 811 system.

The NEC requires that a warning ribbon be placed 12 inches above underground service conductors that are not encased in concrete.

EXHIBIT 130.6

Public service bulletin for the Call 811 program. (Courtesy of Common Ground Alliance)

Always Call Before You Dig.

811

One easy call gets your utility lines marked and helps protect you from injury and expense.

Safe Digging Is No Accident: Always Call 811 Before You Dig

Visit call811.com for more information.

811
Know what's below.
Call before you dig.

130.11 Cutting or Drilling.

Before cutting or drilling into equipment, floors, walls, or structural elements where a likelihood of contacting energized electrical lines or parts exists, the employer shall perform a risk assessment to:

(1) Identify and mark the location of conductors, cables, raceways, or equipment
(2) Create an electrically safe work condition
(3) Identify safe work practices and PPE to be used

Δ **130.12 Cutting, Removing, or Rerouting of Conductors.**

Where conductors are de-energized in order to cut, remove, or reroute them and the conductor terminations are not within sight from the point of work, such as where they are the conductors are remote from the source of supply in a junction or pull box, additional steps to verify absence of voltage or identify the conductors shall be taken prior to cutting, removing, or rerouting the conductors.

> Informational Note: Additional steps to be taken where conductors are de-energized in order to cut, remove, or reroute them include, but are not limited to, remotely spiking the conductors, pulling conductors to visually verify movement, remotely cutting the conductors, or other approved methods. Nonshielded conductors could be additionally verified with a noncontact test instrument, and shielded conductors could be verified with devices that identify the conductors.

Safety-Related Maintenance Requirements

ARTICLE 200 Introduction

ARTICLE 205 General Maintenance Requirements

ARTICLE 210 Substations, Switchgear Assemblies, Switchboards, Panelboards, Motor Control Centers, and Disconnect Switches

ARTICLE 215 Premises Wiring

ARTICLE 220 Controller Equipment

ARTICLE 225 Fuses and Circuit Breakers

ARTICLE 230 Rotating Equipment

ARTICLE 235 Hazardous (Classified) Locations

ARTICLE 240 Batteries and Battery Rooms

ARTICLE 245 Portable Electric Tools and Equipment

ARTICLE 250 Personal Safety and Protective Equipment

An electrical work environment consists of three interrelated components: installation, maintenance, and safe work practices. Safe work practices are most effective when the installation is code-compliant and the equipment is maintained appropriately. The NFPA documents that address each aspect are *NFPA 70®, National Electrical Code® (NEC®)*; NFPA 70B, *Recommended Practice for Electrical Equipment Maintenance*; and NFPA *70E®, Standard for Electrical Safety in the Workplace®*. The exhibit on the next page illustrates how these documents are interrelated.

NFPA *70E* considers equipment to be safe for operation if the equipment is installed according to the *NEC* and the manufacturer's instructions and, in the absence of specific manufacturer instructions, maintained in accordance with NFPA 70B. A deficiency in the installation or maintenance of a system has the potential to adversely impact the electrical safety of employees, as well as safe work practices.

Properly maintained electrical equipment has proven to be reliable. General maintenance dictates that equipment be maintained in accordance with the manufacturer's instructions and often addresses the continued operation of the equipment. Chapter 2 is not a comprehensive maintenance program, but it does address safety-related maintenance of electrical equipment. A good maintenance program can provide the predictability and reliability necessary for safe operation.

A companion document for NFPA *70E* is NFPA 70B. The purpose of this recommended practice is to reduce hazards to life and property that can result from the failure or malfunction of industrial-type electrical systems and equipment. It provides guidance on maintenance practices and setting up preventive maintenance programs. NFPA 70B applies to preventive maintenance for electrical, electronic, and communication systems and equipment, and it is not intended to duplicate or supersede instructions that manufacturers normally provide. NFPA *70E* addresses the work practices that should be used during maintenance work.

NFPA 70®
National Electrical Code®
Stipulates the **installation rules** necessary to assure that an electrical installation is safe to operate.

NFPA 70B
Recommended Practice for Electrical Equipment Maintenance
Provides **preventive maintenance** recommendations for electrical systems and equipment

NFPA 70E®
Standard for Electrical Safety in the Workplace®
Provides the requirements to establish a **practical safe working area** for employees relative to the hazards arising from the use of electricity.

Introduction

Inadequate maintenance can have a negative impact on personal safety. Normal operation of inadequately maintained equipment increases the risk of injury to the equipment operator as well as the employee performing maintenance. The risk of equipment failure is reduced when equipment is properly and adequately maintained. A comprehensive electrical equipment maintenance program can increase the reliability of electrical systems, helping to prevent electrical outages and malfunctions and decrease the exposure of employees to electrical hazards.

Table 130.5(C) requires that the equipment condition, including its maintenance, be taken into consideration when determining the likelihood of an arc flash, as a poorly maintained piece of equipment is more prone to failure. Section 130.5(G) requires that an arc flash risk assessment take into consideration the maintenance condition of overcurrent protective devices. The maintenance condition of an overcurrent protective device can affect it's clearing time, thus increasing the incident energy.

Δ **200.1 Scope.**

Chapter 2 addresses the requirements that follow.

(1) Chapter 2 covers practical safety-related maintenance requirements for electrical equipment and installations in workplaces as included in 90.2. These requirements identify only that maintenance directly associated with employee safety.

(2) Chapter 2 does not prescribe specific maintenance methods or testing procedures. It is left to the employer to choose from the various maintenance methods available to satisfy the requirements of Chapter 2.

Employers must establish maintenance strategies and then implement the necessary components. Maintenance is necessary to support electrical safety programs. For information on preventive maintenance programs, see NFPA 70B.

(3) For the purpose of Chapter 2, maintenance shall be defined as preserving or restoring the condition of electrical equipment and installations, or parts of either, for the safety of employees who work where exposed to electrical hazards. Repair or replacement of individual portions or parts of equipment shall be permitted without requiring modification or replacement of other portions or parts that are in a safe condition.

Informational Note: Refer to NFPA 70B, *Recommended Practice for Electrical Equipment Maintenance,* ANSI/NETA MTS, *Standard for Maintenance Testing Specifications for Electrical Power Distribution Equipment and Systems',* and IEEE 3007.2, *Recommended Practice for the Maintenance of Industrial and Commercial Power* Systems, for guidance on maintenance frequency, methods, and tests.

Maintenance is often the most neglected component of a strategy to provide a safe work environment. NFPA 70B provides solutions, techniques, and testing intervals for adequate maintenance to maximize the reliability of electrical equipment and systems. It describes electrical maintenance subjects and the issues surrounding the maintenance of electrical equipment.

NFPA 70B provides information on commissioning and effective preventive maintenance programs. Commissioning, or acceptance testing, verifies that equipment is functioning as intended by the design specifications. Acceptance testing generates baseline results that can help to identify equipment deterioration or a change in reliability or safety. Future trend analysis is useful in predicting when equipment failure or an out-of-tolerance condition might occur and can enable convenient scheduling of outages.

Most electrical equipment has a predictable life cycle, and knowing the service life of equipment can be crucial in predicting its reliability and its safe operation. Routine maintenance and maintenance tests can be performed at regular intervals over the service life of equipment or when condition indicators warrant it. Maintenance tests can help identify changes in overcurrent protective device characteristics and potential failures before they occur. A shutdown can then be scheduled and repairs can be performed before equipment is damaged and with minimum exposure to employees. An alternative method is utilizing reliability-centered maintenance (RCM) techniques. See Chapter 30 of NFPA 70B for further information on RCM.

General Maintenance Requirements

New equipment is expected to be in order and operating correctly. Through its use, equipment slowly begins to show signs of wear and tear. Proper maintenance is not just the act of fixing, adjusting, or filling fluids. There is a time aspect that is just as important. Maintenance of a piece of equipment might only be necessary every year or two in one installation. However, that same piece of equipment in another installation might require monthly maintenance to be considered properly maintained.

205.1 Qualified Persons.

Employees who perform maintenance on electrical equipment and installations shall be qualified persons as required in Chapter 1 and shall be trained in, and familiar with, the specific maintenance procedures and tests required.

205.2 Single-Line Diagram.

A single-line diagram, where provided for the electrical system, shall be maintained in a legible condition and shall be kept current.

Single-line diagrams are among the best sources of information for locating electrical hazards at a worksite. Therefore, qualified employees must have the ability to read and understand the single-line diagrams of the systems they work on.

Single-line diagrams are created for different purposes and might display different information. Some single-line diagrams can be supplemented with equipment schedules that might be included in the diagram. Some power sources, such as control power for a motor control center, might not be detailed on a single-line diagram. These sources might be detailed on a schematic, elementary diagram, or panelboard schedule. Exhibit 205.1 shows a simple single-line diagram.

To be useful, the diagrams must be updated and verified. Legible, up-to-date single-line diagrams, along with any necessary supplemental documentation, can help with the implementation of an electrically safe work condition. Maintaining these drawings can provide valuable information, including the following:

- The sources of power to a specific piece of equipment
- The interrupting capacity of devices at each point in the system
- The possible paths of potential backfeed
- The correct rating for overcurrent devices

205.3 General Maintenance Requirements.

Electrical equipment shall be maintained in accordance with manufacturers' instructions or industry consensus standards to reduce the risk associated with failure. The equipment owner or the owner's designated representative shall be responsible for maintenance of the electrical equipment and documentation.

Informational Note No. 1: Common industry practice is to apply test or calibration decals to equipment to indicate the test or calibration date and overall condition of equipment that has been tested and maintained in the field. These decals provide the employee immediate indication of last maintenance date and if the tested device or system was found acceptable on the date of test. This local information can assist the employee in the assessment of overall electrical equipment maintenance status.

Worker Alert

You must be qualified to perform maintenance on a specific piece of equipment. Your knowledge of similar equipment or identical tasks does not equate to the ability to correctly or safely perform maintenance on another piece of equipment.

EXHIBIT 205.1

Simple single-line diagram.

Informational Note No. 2: Noncontact diagnostic methods in addition to scheduled maintenance activities of electrical equipment can assist in the identification of electrical anomalies.

Not maintaining or overly maintaining equipment not only decreases the reliability of equipment, but it also poses an increased risk to employees. A well-established maintenance program must include scheduled maintenance. Chapters 4, 5, and 6 of NFPA 70B contain recommendations for an effective electrical preventive maintenance program. (See Supplement 2 for excerpts from these NFPA 70B chapters.) The chapters provide a better understanding of the benefits that can be derived from a well-administered electrical preventive maintenance program. Deterioration of equipment is normal, and effective electrical preventive maintenance can delay and even predict equipment failure.

On-site conditions can also affect the required maintenance of equipment. The equipment owner might need to alter the maintenance schedule to address concerns specific to the installation. The equipment manufacturer should be consulted when the recommended maintenance is modified.

205.4 Overcurrent Protective Devices.

Overcurrent protective devices shall be maintained in accordance with the manufacturers' instructions or industry consensus standards. Maintenance, tests, and inspections shall be documented.

The automatic operation of an overcurrent device should not be assumed to be the result of a false condition. The system should be investigated to determine the cause of the device's operation before resetting it.

Following the maintenance schedule defined by the manufacturer or by a consensus standard reduces the risk of failure and the subsequent exposure of employees to electrical hazards such as shock, arc flash, or arc blast. Documents such as NFPA 70B and ANSI/NETA MTS, *Standard for Maintenance Testing Specifications for Electrical Power Equipment and Systems,* provide testing and maintenance instructions for some overcurrent devices. ANSI/NEMA AB 4, *Guidelines for Inspection and Preventive Maintenance of Molded Case Circuit Breakers Used in Commercial and Industrial Applications,* provides useful information on the type of maintenance, testing, and inspections that should be documented. See Exhibit 205.2 for an example of an adjustable-trip circuit breaker.

An overcurrent protective device is a critical component for reducing the risk of injury to employees. Whether an employer's policy is always establishing an electrically safe work condition or justifying some energized electrical work, an overcurrent device is used to determine the required arc flash PPE. Although all maintenance should be documented, the need is specifically stated for overcurrent devices. Any action without documentation is generally considered to have not occurred. This is especially true in the event of an incident.

Worker Alert

If the maintenance of overcurrent devices can't be proven with documentation, relying on the questionable maintenance of those devices places you at greater risk of injury. If you are operating equipment, establishing an electrically safe work condition, or performing justified energized work, you might not be adequately protected from severe injury.

EXHIBIT 205.2

An adjustable-trip circuit breaker with a transparent, removable, and sealable cover. (Courtesy of Square D by Schneider Electric)

205.5 Spaces About Electrical Equipment.

All working space and clearances required by electrical codes and standards shall be maintained.

Informational Note: For further information concerning spaces about electrical equipment, see Article 110, Parts II and III, of *NFPA 70, National Electrical Code.*

Worker Alert

You should recognize when there is insufficient space for you to safely perform an assigned task. You should not conduct the task unless adequate room is provided.

Adequate working space enables employees to perform tasks without jeopardizing their safety. Sufficient clearance permits the proper use of tools and equipment while preventing inadvertent contact, which could result in an electrical incident and injury. Exhibit 205.3 shows the working space in front of electrical equipment required by the *NEC*®. Working spaces must be kept clear. Obstructions—even if temporary, such as with stored equipment—restrict access to and egress from the working space.

The *NEC* general rule for working space is that all equipment be provided with enough space for safe operation and maintenance. The specific working space in the *NEC* is for equipment that warrants justified energized work. This working space should be applied to equipment that will always be in an electrically safe work condition when work is performed. The design layout must consider the possibility that an expected task might require more working space than that specified in the *NEC*.

205.6 Grounding and Bonding.

Equipment, raceway, cable tray, and enclosure bonding and grounding shall be maintained to ensure electrical continuity.

The electrical continuity achieved with grounding and bonding enables the fault current to return to the source. During a short-circuit condition, an overcurrent device relies on an effective grounding path to operate as designed. Without effective grounding and bonding, the clearing time might be extended, thus increasing the amount of incident energy to which an employee could be exposed.

205.7 Guarding of Energized Conductors and Circuit Parts.

Enclosures shall be maintained to guard against unintentional contact with exposed energized conductors and circuit parts and other electrical hazards. Covers and doors shall be in place with all associated fasteners and latches secured.

Worker Alert

In order to recognize when a guard is missing, you must first be able to identify equipment that is in a normal operating condition.

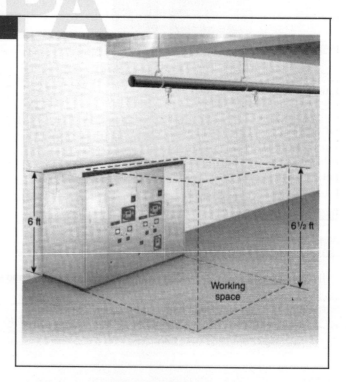

EXHIBIT 205.3

Working space in front of electrical equipment.

Preventing access to energized conductors and circuits is a core concept of employee safety. Energized electrical conductors are required to be guarded against accidental contact, which can be achieved by covering, shielding, enclosing, elevating, or otherwise preventing contact by unauthorized persons or objects. Access to exposed energized electrical components guarded by a locked fence or door can be restricted to only authorized and qualified personnel who have a key. Energized parts should not be exposed to any employee unless safety measures are put in place.

205.8 Safety Equipment.

Locks, interlocks, and other safety equipment shall be maintained in proper working condition to accomplish the control purpose.

Locks and interlocks provide safety for employees by ensuring that only authorized and qualified persons have access to areas that contain exposed energized electrical conductors or circuit parts. They can also be used to establish an electrically safe work condition with a lockout or tagout program. An interlocking system can be used to control the flow of electrical power through some systems and to control the sequence of switch operations. Maintaining these locks and interlocks in good working condition can help to minimize exposure to electrical hazards.

205.9 Clear Spaces.

Access to working space and escape passages shall be kept clear and unobstructed.

Good housekeeping is an important aspect of a safe work environment. Maintaining adequate access is essential for employees to operate the equipment in a safe and efficient manner. Storage that blocks access or egress or that prevents safe work practices must be avoided at all times. The area must not be used for storage, including the storage of movable items, such as pushcarts or trash bins. The primary intent of providing egress from an area is so that, in the event of an emergency, such as an arc flash incident, employees can escape.

Worker Alert

Clear space is necessary to enable you to quickly leave an area in the event of an incident. Items including toolboxes, shipping containers, and hand carts must not be placed in your path of egress.

205.10 Identification of Components.

Identification of components, where required, and safety-related instructions (operating or maintenance), if posted, shall be securely attached and maintained in legible condition

It is crucial for electrical safety that the component identification on the single-line diagram is up to date and that it matches the identification on the installed equipment. Up-to-date operating or maintenance instructions and necessary warnings are vital for ensuring employee safety.

205.11 Warning Signs.

Warning signs, where required, shall be visible, securely attached, and maintained in legible condition.

Warning signs inform both qualified and unqualified employees of potential hazards they might encounter. Exhibit 205.4 shows an example of the warning label required by 130.5(H), which must be visible and legible before any task can be performed on the equipment. Other warning signs might be required by installation standards and OSHA regulations.

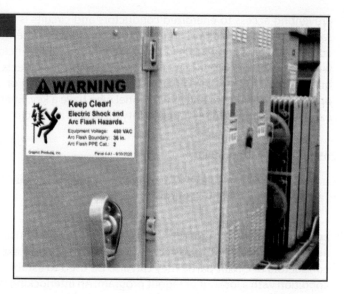

EXHIBIT 205.4

Example of warning label clearly visible, securely attached, and in legible condition. (Courtesy of Graphic Products, Inc.)

205.12 Identification of Circuits.

Circuit or voltage identification shall be securely affixed and maintained in updated and legible condition

Several sections of the NEC require that circuit identification be securely affixed to equipment. *NEC* Section 110.22(A) requires that the purpose of each disconnecting means be indicated unless the purpose is obvious based on the arrangement. Section 230.70(B) requires the identification of the service disconnecting means. Where a structure is supplied by more than one service, 230.2(E) requires that each service disconnecting means location must have a permanent plaque indicating the location of the other disconnecting means.

NEC Section 408.4 details the circuit identification information required for switchgear, switchboards, and panelboards. Circuit identification must be up to date, accurate, and legible. Mislabeled equipment can endanger employees who might assume that they have de-energized the circuit feeding the equipment. However, circuit identification does not change the employee's responsibility to verify the absence of voltage when establishing an electrically safe work condition. Regardless of the presence of labels or warnings, a risk assessment must still be performed.

205.13 Single and Multiple Conductors and Cables.

Electrical cables and single and multiple conductors shall be maintained free of damage, shorts, and ground that would expose employees to an electrical hazard.

Cables might be exposed after installation. Single and multiple conductors are often installed in raceways or cable trays. When cables or conductors are installed in an open cable tray, they should be protected from falling objects that could cause damage. Temporary protection should be provided when working around exposed cable and conductors so as not to damage them.

205.14 Flexible Cords and Cables.

Flexible cords and cables shall be maintained to preserve insulation integrity.

Worker Alert

You will usually be the last one to inspect cords and cables after they have been brought to a worksite. Your inspection should occur before a tool or extension cord is plugged into a receptacle. Typically, you will also be responsible for routing and protecting cords during the performance of a task.

(1) Damaged Cords and Cables. Cords and cables shall not have worn, frayed, or damaged areas that would expose employees to an electrical hazard.

(2) Strain Relief. Strain relief of cords and cables shall be maintained to prevent pull from being transmitted directly to joints or terminals.

(3) Repair and Replacement. Cords and cord caps for portable electrical equipment shall be repaired and replaced by qualified personnel and checked for proper polarity, grounding, and continuity prior to returning to service.

The transient use of flexible cords and cables increases the possibility of cord and plug damage or interruption of the equipment grounding conductor. Before each use, extension cords must be inspected to ensure that they are not damaged [see 110.9(C)]. Damaged ground prongs are a common problem with extension cords and cord caps for portable equipment. A ground prong provides the grounding path necessary to mitigate electrical shock or electrocution. Incorrect termination of flexible cords and cables at an enclosure is another common problem. In addition, tension placed on a cable can expose conductors and subject employees to hazards.

NEC Section 400.13 requires that flexible cord only be used in continuous lengths without splices or taps where initially installed. The repair of hard-service cord and junior hard-service cord 14 AWG and larger is permitted if the conductors are spliced and the completed splice retains the insulation, outer sheath properties, and usage characteristics of the cord being spliced. In-line repair is not permitted if the cord is reused or reinstalled.

NEC Section 590.6(B)(2) has criteria for an assured equipment grounding conductor program for the temporary use of flexible cords. This written program must be continuously enforced at the site by designated persons to ensure that equipment grounding conductors are installed and maintained for all the cord sets and equipment connected by cord and plug. The following tests must be performed before the cord's first use on-site, when there is evidence of damage, before equipment is returned to service following any repairs, and at intervals not exceeding 3 months:

1. Test all the equipment grounding conductors for electrical continuity.
2. Test the attachment of each receptacle and attachment plug to the equipment grounding conductor.
3. Verify that the equipment grounding conductor is connected to its proper terminal.

Case Study 205.14

Scenario

Julia, a 38-year-old welder, worked for a metal fabricating company. A safety officer at the company devoted up to 25 percent of his time to safety issues. Safety rules and procedures covered the work being performed by Julia. On the job, classroom, and written safety manuals were used in safety training. Julia was scheduled to work on a roller metal bending machine, which required connection to electrical power through an extension cord. The system was powered by 440 volts. Julia was standing on a dry surface while connecting the twist lock male plug of the roll machine to the twist lock female receptacle of an energized extension cord. Julia received a shock that knocked her unconscious, and a rescue squad was called.

Result

Despite emergency care and transport to a hospital, Julia was pronounced dead 1 hour after the incident. Burns were found on her chest, and her left-hand palm had three small burned areas.

Investigation

The same extension cord had been used earlier in the day on another machine without incident. The roll machine had also been used earlier in the day but had been plugged into a different extension cord. The employee who had last used the roll machine inspected the machine's male plug and noticed broken insulation but used it anyway. That employee unplugged it at

(continues)

the end of the shift and reported the defective plug to the maintenance foreman. A work order was started to replace the plug, but the roll machine was not taken out of service.

Julia and a coworker decided to use the roll machine with the defective plug since they knew it had been used earlier in the day without incident. They also located and used an energized extension cord that was not normally coupled with this roll machine. Both the female and male metal plugs that Julia was attempting to connect were defective. The combination of the two damaged plugs allowed the grounding conductor of the plug to be inserted into an energized phase conductor of the receptacle.

Analysis

This case illustrates two important issues. The first is the safety training necessary for unqualified persons. The first employee using the roll machine noticed the damaged plug yet still risked injury by using it anyway. The report indicates that Julia most likely noticed the damaged plug prior to attempting to connect it to the extension cord. Unqualified persons need the training and awareness to avoid electrical hazards associated with their assigned tasks. They should be trained in the correct use of plugs and receptacles. Physical abuse and stress on flexible cords and connectors should be avoided through care in storage, handling, and use. Employees should be aware that immediate corrective action is required when damaged equipment or safety hazards are encountered. A starting point for this is recognizing the normal operating condition of electrical equipment that they interact with and the risk of using it when it is in an abnormal condition.

The second important issue is that proper maintenance is necessary to prevent exposure to electrical hazards that can lead to this type of fatality. Unqualified persons do not expect to be injured while performing their assigned tasks. Safe normal operation of equipment is dependent on the condition of maintenance, and the equipment owner is responsible for its maintenance. However, the owner is typically not aware of the day-to-day condition of a piece of equipment. The unqualified person using the equipment should be trained to inspect and recognize an abnormal operation condition before each use. The electrical safety program should identify who is responsible for corrective action, and supervisors should immediately enforce safety policies when a hazard has been identified. Damaged electrical cords and plugs should be removed from service. Damaged equipment should be locked or tagged as out of service to prevent unsafe use. Lastly, persons must be qualified to conduct the necessary repairs and to verify the equipment is safe for use before it is put back into service.

Content source: National Institute for Occupational Safety and Health (NIOSH); FACE case: 92WI10601.

205.15 Overhead Line Clearances.

For overhead electric lines under the employer's control, grade elevation shall be maintained to preserve no less than the minimum designed vertical and horizontal clearances necessary to minimize risk of unintentional contact.

Substations, Switchgear Assemblies, Switchboards, Panelboards, Motor Control Centers, and Disconnect Switches

Article | **210**

210.1 Enclosures.

Enclosures shall be kept free of material that would expose employees to an electrical hazard.

> Housekeeping is critical, and it must be performed before a work task is completed. Materials or tools left in enclosures commonly cause faults and can initiate arc flash events. Employees must remove all extraneous materials and tools within and around enclosures to ensure electrical safety.

210.2 Area Enclosures.

Fences, physical protection, enclosures, or other protective means, where required to guard against unauthorized access or unintentional contact with exposed energized conductors and circuit parts, shall be maintained.

> Fences and other enclosures should be inspected regularly to ensure that they continue to guard against the entry of unauthorized personnel or animals. Gates and doors, especially if they are equipped with panic hardware, should be checked regularly for security and proper operation. Any defect or damage must be repaired promptly and sufficiently to afford equivalent protection to the initial installation.

210.3 Conductors.

Current-carrying conductors (buses, switches, disconnects, joints, and terminations) and bracing shall be maintained to perform as follows:

(1) Conduct rated current without overheating

> The bundling of conductors can affect the ability of those conductors to carry current without overheating. Conductors bundled in wiring methods such as raceways, cable trays, and gutters are calculated for the proper ampacity based on the number of conductors present at the time of installation. Additional conductors placed into these routing methods can affect the safety of all the conductors. Re-evaluation of the ampacity of new and existing conductors should be conducted prior to the installation of additional conductors to determine their capacity to dissipate heat.
>
> Discoloration of conductors or terminals is evidence of overheating. Infrared thermography performed while equipment is operating is one way to investigate overheating. However, thermography might be considered hazardous depending on how it is performed. The use of properly installed infrared windows in enclosures is one way to lower the risk associated with infrared scanning. If evidence of overheating is found, the equipment should be de-energized and the problem investigated and repaired in accordance with the manufacturer's specifications.

(2) Withstand available fault current

Short circuits or fault currents present a significant amount of destructive energy that can cause serious damage to electrical equipment and create the potential for serious injury to personnel. The short-circuit current rating of electrical equipment is the amount of current that it can carry safely for a specific period of time before it is damaged. For example, a bus duct might have a short-circuit current rating of 22,000 rms symmetrical amperes for three cycles. The duct can be damaged if 30,000 amperes were to flow through the bus for three cycles or if 22,000 amperes were to flow for six cycles.

210.4 Insulation Integrity.

Insulation integrity shall be maintained to support the voltage impressed.

Temperature extremes, chemical contamination, operating conditions, and aging can all degrade insulation performance, and they can jeopardize the safety of personnel. Insulation testing performed on a regular basis can indicate if insulation is deteriorating over time. If the insulation resistance falls below an acceptable level or is declining rapidly, corrective measures should be taken to prevent damage to equipment and injury to personnel. Degradation of insulation below an acceptable level is a sign of impending failure, and normal operation of the equipment might no longer be safe.

210.5 Protective Devices.

Protective devices shall be maintained to adequately withstand or interrupt available fault current.

Informational Note: Improper or inadequate maintenance can result in increased opening time of the overcurrent protective device, thus increasing the incident energy.

Protective devices are designed to operate within a prescribed range and to disconnect the power to equipment in a timely manner to minimize damage and decrease the risk of injury to personnel. If the amount of available fault current increases for any reason—due to a change in upstream components, for example—each protective device must be analyzed to determine if it is adequate to interrupt the new fault current.

When a protective device fails to operate as intended, employees performing normal operation of equipment can be exposed to injury from a shock or an arcing fault. If the employee is conducting justified energized work and the clearing time of the protective device is delayed, an incident energy level greater than anticipated can occur, which can render the PPE the employee selected based on the labeled incident energy level inadequate.

See Article 225 for further information regarding the maintenance of fuses and circuit breakers.

Worker Alert

Whether you are operating equipment, establishing an electrically safe work condition, or performing justified energized work, you are at a greater risk of injury if the protective devices have not been maintained.

Premises Wiring

215.1 Covers for Wiring System Components.

Covers for wiring system components shall be in place with all associated hardware, and there shall be no unprotected openings.

> To protect employees from contact with energized electrical components, all covers and doors must be closed and latched using all of the fasteners provided with the equipment. All unused openings other than those that are intended for the operation of equipment or are part of the equipment design must be closed to afford protection equivalent to the walls of the equipment.
>
> Some panelboards are equipped with dead-front covers and outer trim. The trim has a hinged door that provides access to circuit breakers without exposing any live parts. Removing the trim will expose the gutter space. Although the breaker terminals are not visible with the trim removed, they are capable of being inadvertently touched and are considered exposed.

215.2 Open Wiring Protection.

Open wiring protection, such as location or barriers, shall be maintained to prevent unintentional contact.

> A barrier that has been damaged or moved will not provide the same level of protection. The protection provided by elevating equipment can be breached if a new means of access, such as a mezzanine, is installed. Installing open wiring in a room accessible only to qualified persons is another option, as shown in Exhibit 215.1.

215.3 Raceways and Cable Trays.

Raceways and cable trays shall be maintained to provide physical protection and support for conductors.

EXHIBIT 215.1

Open wiring in a restricted access battery room. (Courtesy of International Association of Electrical Inspectors)

Periodic inspection of raceway and cable tray systems can help ensure that the systems function as intended, which is not limited to providing physical protection and support for conductors. Metal raceway and metal cable tray systems are recognized by the NEC® as equipment grounding conductors. When these systems are used as equipment grounding conductors, electrical continuity must be maintained to ensure that they can safely conduct any fault current likely to be imposed. The systems must also have sufficiently low impedance to ground to cause the circuit protective device to operate.

Controller Equipment

220.1 Scope.

This article shall apply to controllers, including electrical equipment that governs the starting, stopping, direction of motion, acceleration, speed, and protection of rotating equipment and other power utilization apparatus in the workplace.

> A controller can be a remote-controlled magnetic contactor, variable frequency drive, switch, circuit breaker, or device that is normally used to start and stop motors and other apparatus. Stop-and-start stations and similar control circuit components that do not open the power conductors to the motor are not considered controllers.

220.2 Protection and Control Circuitry.

Protection and control circuitry used to guard against unintentional contact with exposed energized conductors and circuit parts and to prevent other electrical or mechanical hazards shall be maintained

> Some controller equipment is designed with removable protective components that can be used to prevent or minimize employee exposure to an electrical hazard. If these protective components are removed for equipment repairs or maintenance, they must be reinstalled after the task is complete to ensure the continued integrity of the installed components.

Article | 225 | Fuses and Circuit Breakers

Overcurrent devices play an important role in electrical safety. They protect not only conductors and equipment but also employees. To do this, fuses and circuit breakers must operate within their published time-current characteristic curves safely and correctly. Section 130.5(B) requires that the condition of overcurrent protective devices be taken into consideration when determining the severity of a potential injury to an employee. Section 130.5(G) requires considering the device's condition for an arc flash risk assessment because its condition can have an effect on the device's clearing time. Improper maintenance of these devices can place employees performing normal equipment operations, establishing electrically safe work environments, or performing justified energized work at an increased risk of injury. Therefore, adequate maintenance is essential to maintaining a safe work environment

225.1 Fuses.

Fuses shall be maintained free of breaks or cracks in fuse cases, ferrules, and insulators. Fuse clips shall be maintained to provide adequate contact with fuses. Fuseholders for current-limiting fuses shall not be modified to allow the insertion of fuses that are not current-limiting. Non-current limiting fuses shall not be modified to allow their insertion into current-limiting fuseholders.

Discoloration of fuse terminals and fuse clips could be caused by heat from poor contact or corrosion. Fuseholders with rejection features need to be maintained so that they only accept current-limiting fuses. A fuseholder should never be altered or forced to accept a fuse for which it is not designed. A damaged fuse should promptly be replaced with an identical fuse. Exhibit 225.1 shows examples of fuses that include a rejection feature to prohibit the installation of non-current-limiting fuses.

Different types of fuses are used in electrical systems, and fuses from different manufacturers differ by performance, characteristics, and physical size. Although many fuses might have the same ampere rating, their operating characteristics can differ, making coordination unlikely. Replacement fuses must conform to all the requirements detailed in the electrical hazards risk assessment. For further information on the electrical maintenance of fuses, see Chapter 18 of NFPA 70B.

EXHIBIT 225.1

Fuses with a rejection feature. (Courtesy of Eaton, Bussmann Division)

225.2 Molded-Case Circuit Breakers.

Molded-case circuit breakers shall be maintained free of cracks in cases and cracked or broken operating handles

Although molded-case circuit breakers can be in service for years and never be called upon to perform their overload- or short-circuit-tripping functions, they are not maintenance-free devices. They require both mechanical and electrical maintenance. Mechanical maintenance consists of inspecting and adjusting mechanical mounting and electrical connections and manual operation of the circuit breaker as needed. Electrical maintenance verifies that a circuit breaker will trip at its desired set point.

Excessive heat in a circuit breaker can cause tripping and eventual failure. Molded-case circuit breakers should be kept free of external contamination so the internal heat can dissipate normally. A clean circuit breaker enclosure also reduces the potential for arcing between energized conductors and between energized conductors and the ground. Loose connections are a common cause of excessive heat; maintenance should include checking for loose connections or evidence of overheating. All the connections should be maintained in accordance with manufacturers' instructions.

The structural strength of a molded case is important for withstanding the stresses imposed during fault current operation. Therefore, an inspection of the molded case should check for cracks, and a replacement should be installed if necessary.

Different types of circuit breakers are used in electrical systems. Circuit breakers from different manufacturers or those from a different series from the same manufacturer differ by performance and characteristics. Although many circuit breakers might have the same ampere rating, their operating characteristics can differ, making coordination unlikely. Replacement circuit breakers must conform to all the requirements detailed in the electrical hazards risk assessment.

Although the manual operation of a circuit breaker will not move the mechanical linkages in the tripping mechanisms, it can assist in keeping the contacts clean and the lubrication operating properly, which can help ensure that the circuit breaker will operate as intended. Some circuit breakers have push-to-trip buttons that should be operated periodically to exercise the tripping mechanical linkages. See Chapter 17 of NFPA 70B and ANSI/NEMA AB 4, *Guidelines for Inspection and Preventive Maintenance of Molded Case Circuit Breakers Used in Commercial and Industrial Applications,* for more information on the electrical maintenance of molded-case circuit breakers

225.3 Circuit Breaker Testing After Electrical Faults.

Circuit breakers that interrupt faults approaching their interrupting ratings shall be inspected and tested in accordance with the manufacturer's instructions

Circuit breakers are tested for thousands of manual operations, but a trip due to a fault is different. Testing of circuit breakers includes higher currents and overloads, which typically involves a few automatic trips. The type of fault, the energy level of the fault, and the duration of the fault can all impact the operation of the circuit breaker. A single incident might damage a circuit breaker if it's pushed beyond its specifications. The manufacturer should be consulted for information regarding the capabilities of specific circuit breakers.

A high-level fault current can cause damage even when catastrophic failure does not occur. Testing should be performed to ensure circuit breakers are not damaged and will operate at their set point if called upon again. Circuit breakers that encounter high short-circuit currents should receive a thorough inspection and be replaced as necessary.

The results of a circuit breaker not operating within its designed parameters can be disastrous. If the circuit breaker does not trip within its set clearing time, the incident energy can increase. For example, an employee 18 inches from a 20-kA short circuit with a 5-cycle tripping time has a potential incident energy exposure of 6.5 cal/cm². If the tripping time is increased to 30 cycles due to improper maintenance or the circuit breaker being out of calibration, the incident energy is increased to 38.7 cal/cm². An employee wearing 8 cal/cm² arc flash PPE for the task as specified in the work permit will not be adequately protected and might suffer substantial injury or death.

Circuit breakers should have an initial acceptance test and subsequent maintenance testing at recommended intervals. Following the maintenance schedule defined by the manufacturer or by a consensus standard can reduce the risk of failure and the subsequent exposure of employees to electrical hazards. NFPA 70B, ANSI/NEMA AB 4, and ANSI/NETA MTS, *Standard for Maintenance Testing Specifications for Electrical Power Equipment and Systems,* are documents that can help an employer understand the specific tests and testing intervals required to ensure the reliability and safety of circuit breakers.

Rotating Equipment

230.1 Terminal Boxes.

Terminal chambers, enclosures, and terminal boxes shall be maintained to guard against unintentional contact with exposed energized conductors and circuit parts and other electrical hazards

The vibration and movement of a motor terminal box could exert pressure on the conductors that are terminated or spliced within it. The terminal box must be securely mounted in place by the complete set of hardware supplied by the manufacturer

230.2 Guards, Barriers, and Access Plates.

Guards, barriers, and access plates shall be maintained to prevent employees from contacting moving or energized parts

The inspection and maintenance of rotating equipment and motor guards are necessary to prevent an employee from contacting or becoming entangled in the moving part. Should any guard, barrier, or access plate be removed for repair or maintenance, it must be properly restored.

Article | 235 | Hazardous (Classified) Locations

Confined spaces, toxic chemicals, and radiation exposure are often associated with the term *hazardous location*. While each of these might exist in a location, they do not necessarily make a location hazardous as defined by the *NEC®*. A flammable or combustible concentration of a material must exist for a location to be considered hazardous within the scope of the *NEC*.

235.1 Scope.

This article covers maintenance requirements in those areas identified as hazardous (classified) locations.

Informational Note No. 1: These locations need special types of equipment and installation to ensure safe performance under conditions of proper use and maintenance. It is important that inspection authorities and users exercise more than ordinary care with regard to installation and maintenance. The maintenance for specific equipment and materials is covered elsewhere in Chapter 2 and is applicable to hazardous (classified) locations. Other maintenance will ensure that the form of construction and of installation that makes the equipment and materials suitable for the particular location are not compromised.

Informational Note No. 2: The maintenance needed for specific hazardous (classified) locations depends on the classification of the specific location. The design principles and equipment characteristics, for example, use of positive pressure ventilation, explosionproof, nonincendive, intrinsically safe, and purged and pressurized equipment, that were applied in the installation to meet the requirements of the area classification must also be known. With this information, the employer and the inspection authority are able to determine whether the installation as maintained has retained the condition necessary for a safe workplace.

Worker Alert

You should not carry flashlights, radios, cellphones, computers, multimeters, or other devices into a hazardous location unless the devices have been evaluated for use in that specific hazardous location.

Hazardous locations are required by the NEC to be documented. This documentation often includes the source of a material, the process parameters (e.g., the temperature, flow, and pressure); the hazardous location boundaries; and any other pertinent information. Personnel responsible for the design, installation, inspection, operation, and maintenance of electrical equipment must have access to this document.

Maintenance personnel must be trained to understand the explosive nature of a material, the type of protection employed, and how equipment maintenance is important to a safe environment. There are 15 different types of protection recognized by the NEC, and each prevents ignition of the atmosphere in a different manner. Misunderstanding a protection technique or applying inappropriate maintenance methods can be catastrophic.

Troubleshooting equipment in a hazardous location represents a special challenge. Most equipment cannot be opened while it is energized in the presence of explosive or combustible material. Most portable troubleshooting instruments are powered by a battery; however, battery-operated instruments are not necessarily safe to use in hazardous locations. When a testing device contacts a conductor, a spark can occur, and an explosion is possible if an explosive atmosphere exists. The energy in a single battery is capable of igniting some explosive atmospheres. Before conducting any troubleshooting or maintenance in a hazardous area, it should be determined if an explosive atmosphere exists.

235.2 Maintenance Requirements for Hazardous (Classified) Locations.

Equipment and installations in these locations shall be maintained such that the following criteria are met:

(1) No energized parts are exposed.

Exception to (1): Intrinsically safe and nonincendive circuits.

(2) There are no breaks in conduit systems, fittings, or enclosures from damage, corrosion, or other causes.

(3) All bonding jumpers are securely fastened and intact.

(4) All fittings, boxes, and enclosures with bolted covers have all bolts installed and bolted tight.

(5) All threaded conduit are wrenchtight and enclosure covers are tightened in accordance with the manufacturer's instructions.

(6) There are no open entries into fittings, boxes, or enclosures that would compromise the protection characteristics.

(7) All close-up plugs, breathers, seals, and drains are securely in place.

(8) Marking of luminaires (lighting fixtures) for maximum lamp wattage and temperature rating is legible and not exceeded.

(9) Required markings are secure and legible.

> Equipment maintenance in hazardous locations should only be performed by personnel trained to maintain that electrical equipment. Employees must be trained to identify and eliminate ignition sources such as high surface temperatures, stored electrical energy, and the buildup of static charges, and to identify the need for special tools, equipment, and tests. These individuals should be familiar with the requirements of the equipment's electrical installation and the applicable protection techniques. Employees should understand that, for example, a joint compound or tape might weaken an explosionproof fitting during ignition or interrupt the required ground path.
>
> Maintenance personnel should be trained to look for cracked viewing windows, missing fasteners, and damaged threads that might affect the integrity of the protection systems. All bolts, screws, fittings, and covers must be properly installed. Every missing or damaged fastener must be replaced with those specified by the manufacturer to provide sufficient strength to withstand internal ignition.
>
> After equipment maintenance is performed, the integrity of the protective scheme that prevents an explosion must be restored. Re-establishing the required airflow for a purged system or sealing a cable within a conduit fitting of an explosionproof system are two examples of restoring protective schemes.

Worker Alert

You should be aware that fasteners for hazardous location equipment are evaluated for the locations, atmospheres, and chemicals they are designed to be subjected to. These cover bolts, screws, nuts, and fittings are often a very specific grade of metal selected to withstand internal explosions. To prevent the occurrence of a larger explosion, you should not substitute these fasteners with any other than those specified by the manufacturer.

Article | 240 | Batteries and Battery Rooms

Article 480 of the NEC® applies to the installation of stationary storage batteries. The standards that follow also cover the installation of stationary batteries:

- NFPA 855, *Standard for the Installation of Stationary Energy Storage Systems*
- IEEE 484, *Recommended Practice for Installation Design and Installation of Vented Lead-Acid Batteries for Stationary Applications*
- IEEE 485, *Recommended Practice for Sizing Lead-Acid Batteries for Stationary Applications*
- IEEE 1145, *Recommended Practice for the Installation and Maintenance of Nickel-Cadmium Batteries for Photovoltaic (PV) Systems*
- IEEE 1187, *Recommended Practice for Installation Design and Installation of Valve-Regulated Lead-Acid Batteries for Stationary Applications*
- IEEE 1375, *Guide for the Protection of Stationary Battery Systems*
- IEEE 1578, *Recommended Practice for Stationary Battery Electrolyte Spill Containment and Management*
- IEEE 1635/ASHRAE 21, *Guide for the Ventilation and Thermal Management of Batteries for Stationary Applications*

240.1 Ventilation.

When forced or natural ventilation systems are required by the battery system design and are present, they shall be examined and maintained to prevent buildup of explosive mixtures. This maintenance shall include a functional test of any associated detection and alarm systems.

> Informational Note: "Natural ventilation" implies there are no mechanical mechanisms. Maintenance includes activities such as inspection and removal of any obstructions to natural air flow.

Depending on a battery's construction and chemistry, ventilation of a battery room might not be required. A ventilation system is designed to provide sufficient diffusion and ventilation of gases to prevent the accumulation of an explosive mixture. However, mechanical ventilation might not be mandated for all systems, and ventilation might be achieved by other means. Maintenance of ventilation systems not only includes any electrical systems but also the associated mechanical systems, such as ductwork, screens, louvers, and exhaust ports. Where necessary, NFPA 1, Fire Code, requires ventilation in accordance with the mechanical code and either limits the maximum concentration of hydrogen to 1.0 percent of the total volume of the room or requires ventilation at a rate of not less than 1 ft³/min/ft² (5.1 L/sec/m²) of floor area.

240.2 Eye and Body Wash Apparatus.

Eye and body wash apparatus shall be maintained in operable condition.

Proper maintenance of eye and body wash apparatus ensures that they supply clean, potable water and that they are in proper working order. A maintenance program should define guidelines for inspection, testing, and maintenance of these systems and include procedures for flushing and flow rate testing.

Portable Electric Tools and Equipment

Fixed equipment is typically included in a maintenance program, but portable tools are commonly omitted. The intermittent use of a portable tool for a multitude of tasks in various locations by different users often subjects the tool to damage. Electrical shock and electrocution from portable tool use are often the results of improper handling or storage of tools. A facility's electrical safety program must include the maintenance and inspection of portable tools and equipment.

245.1 Maintenance Requirements for Portable Electric Tools and Equipment.

Attachment plugs, receptacles, cover plates, and cord connectors shall be maintained such that the following criteria are met:

(1) There are no breaks, damage, or cracks exposing energized conductors and circuit parts.
(2) There are no missing cover plates.
(3) Terminations have no stray strands or loose terminals.
(4) There are no missing, loose, altered, or damaged blades, pins, or contacts.
(5) Polarity is correct.

A visual inspection should be conducted both when a tool is issued and when the tool is returned to the storage area after each use. Employees should be trained to recognize visible defects such as cut, frayed, spliced, or broken cords; cracked or broken attachment plugs; and missing or deformed grounding prongs. Employees should also look for damaged housings, broken switches, and missing parts during a visual inspection. Any defect should be reported immediately, and the tool should be removed from service and tagged Do Not Use until it is repaired.

Employees should report all shocks immediately, no matter how minor, and cease using the tools that caused them. A tool that causes a shock must be immediately removed from service, tagged Do Not Use, examined, and repaired before further use. Tools that trip GFCI devices must also be removed from service until the cause of the trip has been determined and corrected. Also, the record of the GFCI tripping should be given to the next work shift.

Periodic electrical testing of portable electric tools can uncover operating defects. Nonfunctioning and malfunctioning equipment should be repaired before further use. Immediate correction of a defect ensures safe operation, prevents breakdowns, and limits more costly repairs.

Worker Alert

Equipment inspected prior to arriving at a worksite could suffer damage in transit. You should always inspect portable tools and flexible cords prior to plugging the equipment into a receptacle. Periodic inspection of portable equipment is also important to help uncover damage or defects from its use.

Article 250 Personal Safety and Protective Equipment

The use of PPE is the last protective measure an employer can use after exhausting all the other hierarchy of risk control methods to minimize the risk of employee injury. Because PPE is an employee's final opportunity to avoid severe injury in the event of an incident, they must have a vested interest in maintaining PPE. The condition of PPE can have a direct impact on employees' well-being; therefore, they should actively inspect and maintain this special equipment. See 130.7 for additional information and requirements for the selection of PPE

250.1 Maintenance Requirements for Personal Safety and Protective Equipment.

Personal safety and protective equipment such as the following shall be maintained in a safe working condition:

(1) Grounding equipment
(2) Hot sticks
(3) Rubber gloves, sleeves, and leather protectors
(4) Test instruments
(5) Blanket and similar insulating equipment
(6) Insulating mats and similar insulating equipment
(7) Protective barriers
(8) External circuit breaker rack-out devices
(9) Portable lighting units
(10) Temporary protective grounding equipment
(11) Dielectric footwear
(12) Protective clothing
(13) Bypass jumpers
(14) Insulated and insulating hand tools

> This is not an all-inclusive list of the PPE that employees can use. To ensure reliability, all equipment must be maintained in accordance with manufacturers' instructions and listings.

250.2 Inspection and Testing of Protective Equipment and Protective Tools.

(A) Visual. Safety and protective equipment and protective tools shall be visually inspected for damage and defects before initial use and at intervals thereafter, as service conditions require, but in no case shall the interval exceed 1 year, unless specified otherwise by the applicable state, federal, or local codes and standards.

> Although PPE inspection can be conducted at regular intervals, employees should visually inspect each component of PPE immediately before using it to verify that no visual defects exist. The employee is the last person who will inspect the equipment before it might be called upon to prevent a serious injury. See Informational Table 130.7(0(14) for the specific ASTM standards that describe what aspects of the equipment should be included in the visual inspection.

Worker Alert

You should take a personal interest in any PPE, including tools, that you use. This equipment is your last line of defense to prevent serious injury or death. Poorly maintained gear can not only initiate an incident, but it can also increase the severity of your injury.

Worker Alert

Regardless of your employer's inspection program, you should visually inspect all gear prior to use. This serves as a final check of the equipment's ability to prevent a serious injury.

In some instances, such as with rubber insulating equipment, PPE should have a date stamp or some other means of identification that indicates when the equipment must be retested. The visual inspection must verify that the equipment has not passed the date at which retesting is required. See Table 130.7(C)(7) for test intervals and the Informational Note in 130.7(C)(7)(d) for the specific ASTM standards applicable to rubber insulating equipment.

(B) Testing. The insulation of protective equipment and protective tools, such as items specified in 250.1(1) through 250.1(14), that is used as primary protection from shock hazards and requires an insulation system to ensure protection of personnel, shall be verified by the appropriate test and visual inspection to ascertain that insulating capability has been retained before initial use, and at intervals thereafter, as service conditions and applicable standards and instructions require, but in no case shall the interval exceed 3 years.

See Informational Note Table 130.7(C)(14) for the ASTM standards that describe the testing requirements.

250.3 Safety Grounding Equipment.

Temporary protective grounding equipment, safety grounds, and ground sets are all terms used to refer to personal protective grounding equipment. Temporary protective grounding equipment is normally constructed with insulated conductors terminated at devices intended for connection to a bare conductor or part. See 120.5(8) for further information regarding the use of this equipment.

Temporary protective grounding equipment should be assigned an identifying mark for record keeping. The identifying mark can be recorded when the equipment is installed on a circuit. After a task has been performed, the equipment can be removed and the identifying mark logged. This will confirm that all the temporary protective grounding equipment has been removed prior to re-energizing the circuit.

Some grounding and testing devices are designed to be inserted (racked) into a compartment from which a circuit breaker or disconnect has been removed. These devices can only be inserted into specific locations. See Exhibit 250.1.

EXHIBIT 250.1

A ground and test device for rack systems. (Courtesy of Schneider Electric)

Access door key interlock
Temporary ground cables
Circuit breaker compartment key interlock
Hook stick
Primary grounding bars
Spare interlock key

(A) Inspection. Personal protective ground cable sets shall be inspected for cuts in the protective sheath and damage to the conductors. Clamps and connector strain relief devices shall be checked for tightness. These inspections shall be made at intervals thereafter as service conditions require, but in no case shall the interval exceed 1 year.

> Temporary protective grounding equipment should be visually inspected before each use.

(B) Testing. Prior to being returned to service, temporary protective grounding equipment that has been repaired or modified shall be tested. Temporary protective grounding equipment shall be tested as service conditions require.

> Informational Note: Guidance for inspecting and testing safety grounds is provided in ASTM F2249, *Standard Specification for In-Service Test Methods for Temporary Grounding Jumper Assemblies Used on De-energized Electric Power Lines and Equipment.*

> Temporary protective grounding equipment must be capable of conducting any available fault current long enough for the overcurrent protection to clear the fault. A destructive test is normally performed when a manufacturer determines the rating of specific devices. However, destructive testing is not an option for equipment that will be used again. For maintenance testing of temporary protective grounding equipment, see ASTM F2249, *Standard Specification for In-Service Test Methods for Temporary Grounding Jumper Assemblies Used on De-Energized Electric Power Lines and Equipment.*

(C) Grounding and Testing Devices. Grounding and testing devices shall be stored in a clean and dry area. Grounding and testing devices shall be properly inspected and tested before each use.

> Informational Note: Guidance for testing of grounding and testing devices is provided in Section 9.5 of IEEE C37.20.6, *Standard for 4.76 kV to 38 kV Rated Ground and Test Devices Used in Enclosures.*

> Grounding and testing devices must be visually inspected for defects and tested before each use. IEEE C37.20.6, *Standard for 4.76 kV to 38 kV Rated Ground and Test Devices Used in Enclosures,* provides information on integrity tests for grounding and testing devices.

Worker Alert

You should inspect all your equipment, including the lead, prior to use. Test leads that are not specifically designed for a piece of equipment must be avoided, as they can expose you to the risk of electrocution or an arc flash injury.

Δ **250.4 Test Instruments.**

Test instruments and associated test leads used to verify the absence or presence of voltage shall be maintained to assure functional integrity. The maintenance program shall include functional verification as described in 110.8(E).

> Test instruments used in the verification of the absence or presence of voltage are critical to worker safety. The maintenance program for these instruments must include the operation of the test instrument on a known voltage source to verify its proper operation, as well as any calibration that is required in the manufacturer's instructions.

CHAPTER 3

Safety Requirements for Special Equipment

ARTICLE 300 Introduction

ARTICLE 310 Safety-Related Work Practices for Electrolytic Cells

ARTICLE 320 Safety Requirements Related to Batteries and Battery Rooms

ARTICLE 330 Safety-Related Work Practices: Lasers

ARTICLE 340 Safety-Related Work Practices: Power Electronic Equipment

ARTICLE 350 Safety-Related Work Requirements: Research and Development Laboratories

ARTICLE 360 Safety-Related Requirements for Capacitors

Some facilities use electrical energy in different ways than most general industries. In some cases, electrical energy is an integral part of the manufacturing process. In others, electrical energy is converted in such a way that it presents unique hazards. When electrical energy is used as a process variable, the general safe work practices defined in Chapter 1 can become unsafe or can produce unsafe conditions. Chapter 3 modifies the requirements of Chapter 1 as necessary for use in special situations.

Some workplaces require unique equipment. For example, research and development facilities frequently use equipment that exposes employees to unique hazards. General safe work practices might not mitigate that exposure adequately. Chapter 3 permits employers to comply with the appropriate requirements in Chapter 1 by amending the requirements that are not appropriate for specific conditions. Chapter 3 supplements or modifies the safety-related work practices of Chapter 1 with safety requirements for special equipment.

Article | 300   Introduction

300.1 Scope.

Chapter 3 covers special electrical equipment in the workplace and modifies the general requirements of Chapter 1.

> Chapter 3 covers the additional safety-related work practices necessary to practically safeguard employees against the electrical hazards associated with the special equipment and processes that have not been excluded by 90.2(B).

300.2 Responsibility.

The employer shall provide safety-related work practices and employee training. The employee shall follow those work practices.

> Employers must define their electrical safety programs, and employees must implement the requirements defined in the programs. Electrical safety programs are most effective when employers and employees work together to accomplish both objectives. Employers are required to provide safety-related work practices and training to employees. They must teach employees to be aware of the actions they take and of the hazards around them. Employers should also instill a sense of self-discipline in their employees. They must train employees to perform tasks, recognize hazards, understand the potential for injury from those hazards, and protect themselves against those hazards.
>
> Employees are responsible for implementing each of these work practices. Although it is the employers that train, audit, and retrain employees, it is the employees who will make decisions and take actions that could result in injury. Employees have a responsibility to know their limitations. Only employees can determine if they are truly qualified to safely perform tasks.

300.3 Organization.

Chapter 3 of this standard is divided into articles. Article 300 applies generally. Article 310 applies to electrolytic cells. Article 320 applies to batteries and battery rooms. Article 330 applies to lasers. Article 340 applies to power electronic equipment. Article 350 applies to research and development (R&D) laboratories. Article 360 applies to safety-related requirements for capacitors.

> Each article in Chapter 3 addresses a single unique equipment type or work area, and each article stands alone. Requirements defined in one article apply only to that special equipment type or work area and amend the requirements of Chapter 1 only for that purpose. However, more than one article might apply, such as Article 340 and Article 360, which both cover power conversion equipment.

Safety-Related Work Practices for Electrolytic Cells

Article 310 identifies safe work practices for electrolytic cell line working zones and the special hazards of working with these ungrounded direct current (dc) systems. A cell line is a series of individual cells that are connected electrically. Generally, this process requires a significant amount of direct current and is ungrounded. See Exhibit 310.1.

Working on an electrolytic cell line is always considered energized electrical work. Each individual cell of an electrolytic cell line is a battery and cannot be de-energized without removing the electrolyte in the vessel. Therefore, establishing an electrically safe work condition is not, by itself, a viable method of avoiding injury in this scenario.

EXHIBIT 310.1

An electrolytic cell line. (Photo by David Pace and Michael Petry, Courtesy of 01 in Corporation, McIntosh, AL)

310.1 Scope.

The requirements of this article shall apply to the electrical safety-related work practices used in the types of electrolytic cell areas.

> Informational Note No. 1: See Informative Annex L for a typical application of safeguards in the cell line working zone.

> Informational Note No. 2: For further information about electrolytic cells, see *NFPA 70, National Electrical Code,* Article 668.

> Informational Note No. 3: For further information about electrical safety-related work practices in electrolytic cell lines, see IEEE 463, *Electrical Safety Practices in Electrolytic Cell Line Working Zones.*

310.2 Definitions.

For the purposes of this article, the definitions that follow shall apply.

Battery Effect. A voltage that exists on the cell line after the power supply is disconnected.

> Informational Note: Electrolytic cells can exhibit characteristics similar to an electrical storage battery and a shock hazard could exist after the power supply is disconnected from the cell line.

Safeguarding. Safeguards for personnel include the consistent administrative enforcement of safe work practices. Safeguards include training in safe work practices, cell line design, safety equipment, PPE, operating procedures, and work checklists.

310.3 Safety Training.

(A) General. The training requirements of this chapter shall apply to employees exposed to electrical hazards in the cell line working zone defined in 110.6 and shall supplement or modify the requirements of 110.3, 120.5, 130.1, and 130.9.

(B) Training Requirements. Employees shall be trained to understand the specific electrical hazards associated with electrical energy on the cell line. Employees shall be trained in safety-related work practices and procedural requirements to provide protection from the electrical hazards associated with their respective job or task assignment.

Employees who work in the vicinity of cells and an interconnecting bus must be trained to understand the hazards associated with an unintentional grounded condition of either an individual cell or the interconnecting bus. Employees must also understand that the significant magnetic field generated by the current flowing in the interconnecting bus might interfere with certain medical devices.

310.4 Employee Training.

(A) Qualified Persons.

(1) Training. Qualified persons shall be trained and knowledgeable in the operation of cell line working zone equipment and specific work methods and shall be trained to avoid the electrical hazards that are present. Such persons shall be familiar with the proper use of precautionary techniques and PPE. Training for a qualified person shall include the following:

(1) Skills and techniques to avoid a shock hazard:
    a. Between exposed energized surfaces, which might include temporarily insulating or guarding parts to permit the employee to work on exposed energized parts
    b. Between exposed energized surfaces and grounded equipment, other grounded objects, or the earth itself, that might include temporarily insulating or guarding parts to permit the employee to work on exposed energized parts

The employee training and qualifications specified in Article 110 are also applicable to cell line work. Employees who work near a dc bus must be trained to understand the unique hazards associated with ungrounded dc voltage. Hand tools that might contact the ungrounded dc bus must not be grounded.

(2) Method of determining the cell line working zone area boundaries

(2) Qualified Persons. Qualified persons shall be permitted to work within the cell line working zone.

(B) Unqualified Persons.

(1) Training. Unqualified persons shall be trained to identify electrical hazards to which they could be exposed and the proper methods of avoiding the hazards.

(2) In Cell Line Working Zone. When there is a need for an unqualified person to enter the cell line working zone to perform a specific task, that person shall be advised of the electrical hazards by the designated qualified person in charge to ensure that the unqualified person is safeguarded.

310.5 Safeguarding of Employees in the Cell Line Working Zone.

(A) General. Operation and maintenance of electrolytic cell lines might require contact by employees with exposed energized surfaces such as buses, electrolytic cells, and their attachments. The approach distances referred to in Table 130.4(E)(a) and Table 130.4(E)(b) shall not apply to work performed by qualified persons in the cell line working zone. Safeguards such as safety-related work practices and other safeguards shall be used to protect employees from injury while working in the cell line working zone. These safeguards shall be consistent with the nature and extent of the related electrical hazards. Safeguards might be different for energized cell lines and de-energized cell lines. Hazardous battery effect voltages shall be dissipated to consider a cell line de-energized.

> Informational Note No. 1: Exposed energized surfaces might not present an electrical hazard. Shock hazards are related to current through the body, producing possible injury or damage to health. Shock severity is a function of many factors, including skin and body resistance, current path through the body, paths in parallel with the body, and system voltage. Arc flash burns and arc blasts are a function of the arcing current and the duration of arc exposure.

> Informational Note No. 2: A cell line or group of cell lines operated as a unit for the production of a particular metal, gas, or chemical compound might differ from other cell lines producing the same product because of variations in the particular raw materials used, output capacity, use of proprietary methods or process practices, or other modifying factors. Detailed standard electrical safety-related work practice requirements could become overly restrictive without accomplishing the stated purpose of Chapter 1.

The limited and restricted approach boundaries do not apply to cell line work zones. However, a cell line work zone must be defined. This is the limit of approach for unqualified persons, and only unqualified persons with a need to cross into this zone are permitted. Employees might cross the arc flash boundary before entering the cell line work zone.

Employers must institute electrical safety programs that address the issues identified in Chapter 1. However, the work practices can be modified as necessary to recognize the different types of exposure to electrical hazards. For instance, because each cell acts like a battery, the employer must define the actions necessary if an employee needs to contact a dc bus structure. Those procedures must be consistent with the risk associated with the work task. See Informative Annex L for more information on applying safeguards in the cell line working zone.

(B) Signs. Permanent signs shall clearly designate electrolytic cell areas.

(C) Arc Flash Risk Assessment. The requirements of 130.5, Arc Flash Risk Assessment, shall not be required for electrolytic cell line working zones.

Although the arc flash risk assessment in Article 130 does not apply to cell line work, an arc flash risk assessment is still required. The procedure for conducting an arc flash risk assessment must be specified in the employer's electrical safety program. The risk assessment must include the use of the hierarchy of risk controls. See 110.5(H) regarding the required risk assessment procedure.

Worker Alert
When performing tasks in cell line working zones, you have a greater responsibility to maintain safety. The inability to establish an electrically safe work condition and the reliance on work procedures to provide for your safety emphasize the need for human-error-free work.

Informative Annex D provides information on the various methods of estimating the available incident energy and the arc flash boundary. The source documents listed in Table D.1 should be reviewed for the proper use and limitations of the techniques. NFPA *70E®* does not limit the calculation methods to those listed, and other appropriate techniques might be available.

(1) General. Each task performed in the electrolytic cell line working zone shall be analyzed for the likelihood of arc flash injury. If there is a likelihood of personal injury, appropriate measures shall be taken to protect persons exposed to the arc flash hazards, including one or more of the following:

(1) Providing appropriate PPE *[see 310.5(D)(2)]* to prevent injury from the arc flash hazard
(2) Altering work procedures to reduce the likelihood of occurrence of an arc flash incident
(3) Scheduling the task so that work can be performed when the cell line is de-energized

An arc flash risk assessment must include the use of the hierarchy of risk controls. The hierarchy is listed in order of the most effective to the least effective and must be applied in this descending order for each risk assessment. The result of each risk assessment should be evaluated to determine if additional controls could further lower the risk or reduce the hazard. Only after all other risk controls have been exhausted should PPE be selected. PPE is considered the least effective and lowest level safety of control for employee protection; it should not be the first or only control element used. See 110.5(H) for more information regarding the necessary elements of a risk assessment.

(2) Routine Tasks. Arc flash risk assessment shall be done for all routine tasks performed in the cell line work zone. The results of the arc flash risk assessment shall be used in training employees in job procedures that minimize the possibility of arc flash hazards. The training shall be included in the requirements of 310.3.

(3) Nonroutine Tasks. Before a nonroutine task is performed in the cell line working zone, an arc flash risk assessment shall be done. If an arc flash hazard is a possibility during nonroutine work, appropriate instructions shall be given to employees involved on how to minimize the risk associated with arc flash.

(4) Arc Flash Hazards. If the likelihood of occurrence of an arc flash hazard exists for either routine or nonroutine tasks, employees shall use appropriate safeguards.

(D) Safeguards. Safeguards shall include one or a combination of the following means.

(1) Insulation. Insulation shall be suitable for the specific conditions, and its components shall be permitted to include glass, porcelain, epoxy coating, rubber, fiberglass, and plastic and, when dry, such materials as concrete, tile, brick, and wood. Insulation shall be permitted to be applied to energized or grounded surfaces.

(2) Personal Protective Equipment (PPE). PPE shall provide protection from electrical hazards. PPE shall include one or more of the following, as determined by authorized management:

(1) Footwear for wet service
(2) Gloves for wet service
(3) Sleeves for wet service

(4) Footwear for dry service

(5) Gloves for dry service

(6) Sleeves for dry service

(7) Electrically insulated head protection

(8) Protective clothing

(9) Eye protection with nonconductive frames

(10) Face shield (polycarbonate or similar nonmelting type

> The employer is responsible for determining the parts of the body that must be protected. The employer is also responsible for determining the appropriate type of PPE necessary to protect employees from all the identified electrical hazards, including protection against shocks and arc flashes.

    (a) *PPE.* Personal and other protective equipment shall be appropriate for conditions, as determined by authorized management.

    (b) *Testing of PPE.* PPE shall be verified with regularity and by methods that are consistent with the exposure of employees to electrical hazards.

> All PPE used in cell line work is required to be tested, and its ability to provide the necessary protection must be verified on a regular basis. NFPA *70E* does not specify the testing necessary to determine the continued acceptance of issued PPE. Employers must determine the method used to confirm that PPE can protect workers. Product testing standards, such as those in Informational Note Table 130.7(G), can provide guidance on determining the necessary testing. PPE can be routinely tested by an organization other than the employer. However, the employer must determine the qualifications of the external testing organization.

(3) Barriers. Barriers shall be devices that prevent contact with energized or grounded surfaces that could present an electrical hazard.

(4) Voltage Equalization. Voltage equalization shall be permitted by bonding a conductive surface to an exposed energized surface, either directly or through a resistance, so that there is insufficient voltage to create an electrical hazard.

(5) Isolation. Isolation shall be established by placing equipment or other items in locations such that employees are unable to simultaneously contact exposed conductive surfaces that could present an electrical hazard.

(6) Safe Work Practices. Employees shall be trained in safe work practices. The training shall include why the work practices in a cell line working zone are different from similar work situations in other areas of the plant. Employees shall comply with established safe work practices and the safe use of protective equipment.

    (a) *Attitude Awareness.* Safe work practice training shall include attitude awareness instruction. Simultaneous contact with energized parts and ground can cause serious electrical shock. Of special importance is the need to be aware of body position where contact may be made with energized parts of the electrolytic cell line and grounded surfaces.

    (b) *Bypassing of Safety Equipment.* Safe work practice training shall include techniques to prevent bypassing the protection of safety equipment. Clothing may bypass protective equipment if the clothing is wet. Trouser legs should be kept at appropriate length, and shirt sleeves should be a good fit so as not to drape while reaching. Jewelry and other metal accessories that may bypass protective equipment shall not be worn while working in the cell line working zone.

Worker Alert

Your personal actions in a cell line work zone can greatly affect your safety. Human-error-free work is particularly important when you are not able to establish an electrically safe work condition and you rely on work procedures.

(7) Tools. Tools and other devices used in the energized cell line work zone shall be selected to prevent bridging between surfaces at hazardous potential difference.

> Informational Note: Tools and other devices of magnetic material could be difficult to handle in the area of energized cells due to their strong dc magnetic fields.

(8) Portable Cutout-Type Switches. Portable cell cutout switches that are connected shall be considered as energized and as an extension of the cell line working zone. Appropriate procedures shall be used to ensure proper cutout switch connection and operation.

(9) Cranes and Hoists. Cranes and hoists shall meet the requirements of applicable codes and standards to safeguard employees. Insulation required for safeguarding employees, such as insulated crane hooks, shall be periodically tested.

(10) Attachments. Attachments that extend the cell line electrical hazards beyond the cell line working zone shall use one or more of the following:

(1) Temporary or permanent extension of the cell line working zone
(2) Barriers
(3) Insulating breaks
(4) Isolation

(11) Pacemakers and Metallic Implants. Employees with implanted pacemakers, ferromagnetic medical devices, or other electronic devices vital to life shall not be permitted in cell areas unless written permission is obtained from the employee's physician.

> Informational Note: The American Conference of Governmental Industrial Hygienists (ACGIH) and IEEE 463, *Electrical Safety Practices in Electrolytic Cell Line Working Zones*, recommend that persons with implanted pacemakers should not be exposed to magnetic flux densities above 5 gauss.

Employers must take steps to ensure that employees who wear pacemakers and similar electro-medical devices are not exposed to the magnetic fields that normally exist in a cell area.

(12) Testing. Equipment safeguards for employee protection shall be tested to ensure they are in a safe working condition.

310.6 Portable Tools and Equipment.

> Informational Note: The order of preference for the energy source for portable hand-held equipment is considered to be as follows:

(1) Battery power
(2) Pneumatic power
(3) Portable generator
(4) Nongrounded-type receptacle connected to an ungrounded source

Grounded portable tools and equipment must not be used in areas containing cells or interconnecting buses. Although an equipment grounding conductor decreases exposure to electrical hazards in normal settings, in cell areas, any conductor that is grounded increases the risk of exposure to an electrical hazard. Equipment and tools, including pneumatic tools, must be free from any grounding circuit. Pneumatic tools must be fitted with nonconductive hoses.

(A) Portable Electrical Equipment. The grounding requirements of 110.9(B) shall not be permitted within an energized cell line working zone. Portable electrical equipment and associated power supplies shall meet the requirements of applicable codes and standards.

(B) Auxiliary Nonelectric Connections. Auxiliary nonelectric connections such as air, water, and gas hoses shall meet the requirements of applicable codes and standards. Pneumatic-powered tools and equipment shall be supplied with nonconductive air hoses in the cell line working zone.

(C) Welding Machines. Welding machine frames shall be considered at cell potential when within the cell line working zone. Safety-related work practices shall require that the cell line not be grounded through the welding machine or its power supply. Welding machines located outside the cell line working zone shall be barricaded to prevent employees from touching the welding machine and ground simultaneously where the welding cables are in the cell line working zone.

(D) Portable Test Equipment. Test equipment in the cell line working zone shall be suitable for use in areas of large magnetic fields and orientation.

Informational Note: Test equipment that is not suitable for use in such magnetic fields could result in an incorrect response. When such test equipment is removed from the cell line working zone, its performance might return to normal, giving the false impression that the results were correct.

Safety Requirements Related to Batteries and Battery Rooms

Article 320 identifies the work practices associated with the installation and maintenance of batteries containing many cells, such as those used with uninterruptible power supplies (UPS), telecommunications systems, and unit substation dc power supplies.

Working with batteries can expose employees to both potential shock and arc flash hazards. A person's body might react to contact with dc voltage differently than from contact with ac voltage (see Commentary Table 340.1). Batteries can also expose employees to the hazards associated with the chemical electrolyte used in batteries. Battery charging can sometimes generate flammable gases, so it is important for employees to avoid anything that could cause open flames or sparks. Employees must consider exposure to these hazards when selecting work practices and PPE.

320.1 Scope.

This article covers electrical safety requirements for the practical safeguarding of employees while working with exposed stationary storage batteries that exceed 50 volts, nominal.

> Informational Note: For additional information on best practices for safely working on stationary batteries, see the following documents:
>
> (1) NFPA 1, *Fire Code.* Chapter 52, Stationary Storage Battery Systems, 2015
>
> (2) *NFPA 70, National Electrical Code,* Article 480, Storage Batteries, 2014
>
> (3) IEEE 450, *IEEE Recommended Practice for Maintenance, Testing, and Replacement of Vented Lead-Acid Batteries for Stationary Applications,* 2010
>
> (4) IEEE 937, *Recommended Practice for Installation and Maintenance of Lead-Acid Batteries for Photovoltaic Systems,* 2007
>
> (5) IEEE 1106, *IEEE Recommended Practice for Installation, Maintenance, Testing, and Replacement of Vented Nickel-Cadmium Batteries for Stationary Applications,* 2005 (R 2011)
>
> (6) IEEE 1184, IEEE *Guide for Batteries for Uninterruptible Power Supply Systems, 2006* (R 2011)
>
> (7) IEEE 1188, *IEEE Recommended Practice for Maintenance, Testing, and Replacement of Valve-Regulated Lead-Acid (VRLA) Batteries for Stationary Applications,* 1188a-2014
>
> (8) IEEE 1657, *Recommended Practice for Personnel Qualifications for Installation and Maintenance of Stationary Batteries,* 2009
>
> (9) OSHA 29 CFR 1910.305(j)(7), "Storage batteries"
>
> (10) OSHA 29 CFR 1926.441, "Batteries and battery charging"
>
> (11) DHHS (NIOSH) Publication No. 94-110, *Applications Manual for the Revised NIOSH Lifting Equation,* 1994
>
> (12) IEEE/ASHRAE 1635, *Guide for the Ventilation and Thermal Management of Batteries for Stationary Applications,* 2012

320.2 Definitions.

For the purposes of this article definitions that follow shall apply.

Authorized Personnel. The person in charge of the premises, or other persons appointed or selected by the person in charge of the premises who performs certain duties associated with stationary storage batteries.

Battery. A system consisting of two or more electrochemical cells connected in series or parallel and capable of storing electrical energy received and that can give it back by reconversion.

Battery Room. A room specifically intended for the installation of batteries that have no other protective enclosure.

Cell. The basic electrochemical unit, characterized by an anode and a cathode used to receive, store, and deliver electrical energy.

Electrolyte. A solid, liquid, or aqueous immobilized liquid medium that provides the ion transport mechanism between the positive and negative electrodes of a cell.

Nominal Voltage. The value assigned to a cell or battery of a given voltage class for the purpose of convenient designation; the operating voltage of the cell or system may vary above or below this value.

Pilot Cell. One or more cells chosen to represent the operating parameters of the entire battery (sometimes called "temperature reference" cell).

Prospective Short-Circuit Current. The highest level of fault current that could theoretically occur at a point on a circuit. This is the fault current that can flow in the event of a zero impedance short circuit and if no protection devices operate.

> Informational Note: Some batteries have built-in management devices to limit maximum short-circuit current. The determination of the prospective short-circuit current for these batteries assumes that the internal battery management system protection devices are operable.

Valve-Regulated Lead Acid (VRLA) Cell. A lead-acid cell that is sealed with the exception of a valve that opens to the atmosphere when the internal pressure in the cell exceeds atmospheric pressure by a pre-selected amount, and that provides a means for recombination of internally generated oxygen and the suppression of hydrogen gas evolution to limit water consumption.

Vented Cell. A type of cell in which the products of electrolysis and evaporation are allowed to escape freely into the atmosphere as they are generated. (Also called "flooded cell.")

320.3 Safety Procedures.

(A) General Safety Hazards.

(1) Energy Thresholds. Energy exposure levels shall not exceed those identified in the following list unless appropriate controls are implemented:

(1) AC: 50 volts and 5 milliamperes
(2) DC: 100 volts

> Informational Note: This information is extracted from the Department of Energy (DOE) Electrical Safety Handbook, DOE-HDBK-1092.

Although the dc threshold for the potential for an electrical shock is 50 volts according to Article 130, Article 320 allows an increase of this threshold to 100 volts. Employers

OSHA Connection

29 CFR 1910.333(a)(1)
Live parts that operate at 50 volts or above must be de-energized. Compliance with this regulation might not be met where 100 volts dc is used as the energy exposure limit.

must implement the hierarchy of risk controls and define the safe work practices for each scheduled task when 100 volts dc or greater is present.

Environmental conditions, such as wet environments, might warrant a lower dc threshold. In addition, cuts on human skin can decrease the voltage level necessary to injure someone.

(2) Battery Risk Assessment. Prior to any work on a battery system, a risk assessment shall be performed to identify the chemical, electrical shock, and arc flash hazards and assess the risks associated with the type of tasks to be performed.

> Informational Note: For an example of a risk assessment method for work on batteries, see F.7 and Figure F.7 in Informative Annex F.

Batteries are sources of energy; therefore, isolating the source of voltage from a cell is not possible. Working on a battery system is always considered energized electrical work.

Unlike Article 310, Article 320 does not waive the risk assessments outlined in Article 130. The procedure for conducting an arc flash risk assessment must be specified in an employer's electrical safety program. The risk assessment must include the use of the hierarchy of risk controls. The hierarchy is listed in order of the most effective to the least effective and must be applied in this descending order for each risk assessment. The result of each risk assessment should be evaluated to determine if the hierarchy of controls could be further employed to lower the risk or reduce the hazard. Only after all other risk controls have been exhausted should PPE be selected. PPE is considered the least effective and lowest level of safety control for employee protection and should not be the first or only control element used. For more information, see 110.5(H) regarding the necessary elements of a risk assessment.

The risk associated with batteries can be mitigated starting with the system design. For example, a battery system could be designed to allow the battery to be partitioned into low-voltage segments before work is conducted on it. Other system design mitigation methods might include widely separating the positive and negative conductors and installing insulated covers on battery intercell connector busbars or terminals.

Either the PPE category or the incident energy analysis method can be used for the arc flash risk assessment. Informative Annex D provides information on the various methods that can be used to estimate the available incident energy and the arc flash boundary. The source documents listed in Table D.1 should be reviewed for the proper use and limitations of the techniques presented. NFPA *70E®* does not limit the calculation methods to those listed, and other appropriate techniques might be available.

Exhibit 320.1 illustrates how a risk assessment of a battery system for the various types of hazards (shock, chemical, arc flash, and thermal) might be conducted. It also illustrates how the likely exposure (risk) depends on the type of task being performed. The same process could be applied to other types of systems. The figure is for illustrative purposes and might not apply to all installations or electrical safety programs. The illustration does not serve to absolve the user of their responsibility to read, understand, and properly apply the requirements.

EXHIBIT 320.1

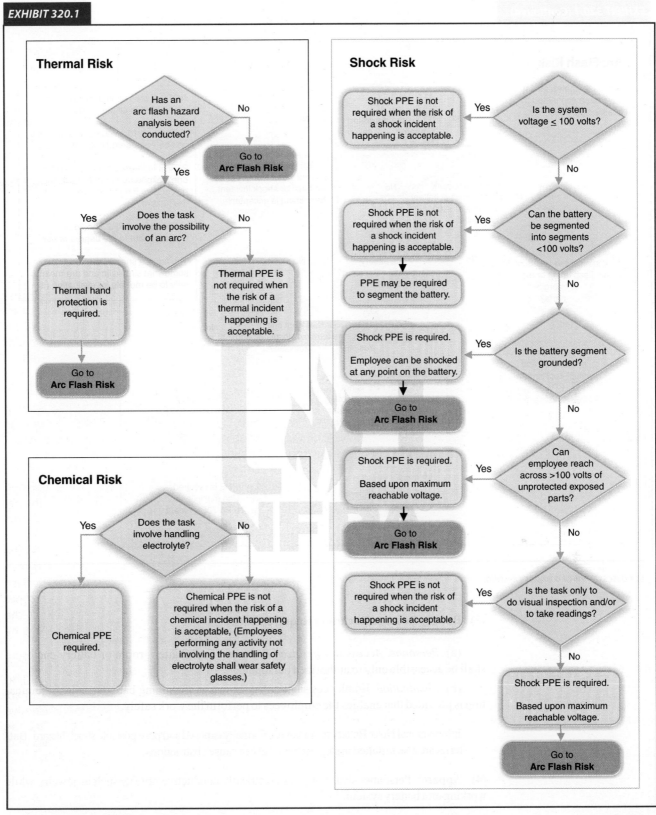

Risk assessment of a battery system.

(continues)

EXHIBIT 320.1 (Continued)

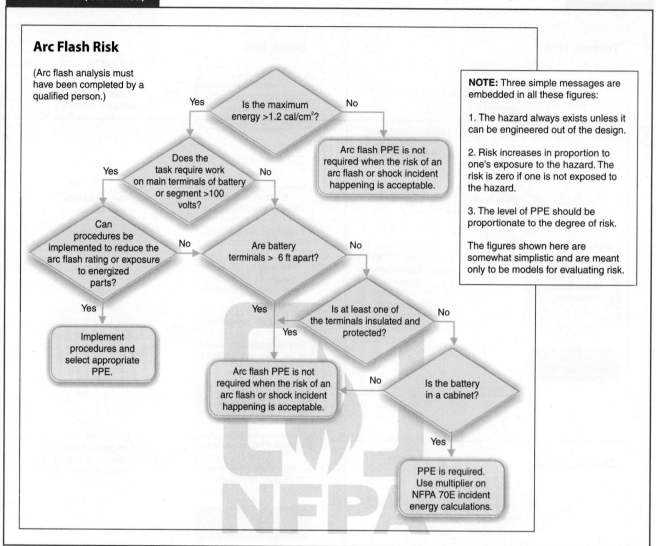

Arc Flash Risk

(Arc flash analysis must have been completed by a qualified person.)

Is the maximum energy >1.2 cal/cm²?

Yes → Does the task require work on main terminals of battery or segment >100 volts?

No → Arc flash PPE is not required when the risk of an arc flash or shock incident happening is acceptable.

Yes → Can procedures be implemented to reduce the arc flash rating or exposure to energized parts?

No → Are battery terminals > 6 ft apart?

No → Is at least one of the terminals insulated and protected?

Yes → Implement procedures and select appropriate PPE.

Yes → Arc flash PPE is not required when the risk of an arc flash or shock incident happening is acceptable.

No → Is the battery in a cabinet?

Yes → PPE is required. Use multiplier on NFPA 70E incident energy calculations.

NOTE: Three simple messages are embedded in all these figures:

1. The hazard always exists unless it can be engineered out of the design.

2. Risk increases in proportion to one's exposure to the hazard. The risk is zero if one is not exposed to the hazard.

3. The level of PPE should be proportionate to the degree of risk.

The figures shown here are somewhat simplistic and are meant only to be models for evaluating risk.

Risk assessment of a battery system.

(3) Battery Room or Enclosure Requirements.

(a) *Personnel Access to Energized Batteries.* Each battery room or battery enclosure shall be accessible only to authorized personnel.

(b) *Illumination.* Employees shall not enter spaces containing batteries unless illumination is provided that enables the employees to perform the work safely.

Informational Note: Battery terminals are normally exposed and pose possible shock hazard. Batteries are also installed in steps or tiers that can cause obstructions.

(4) Apparel. Personnel shall not wear electrically conductive objects such as jewelry while working on a battery system.

(5) Abnormal Battery Conditions. Instrumentation that provides alarms for early warning of abnormal conditions of battery operation, if present, shall be tested annually.

Informational Note: Battery monitoring systems typically include alarms for such conditions as overvoltage, undervoltage, overcurrent, ground fault, and overtemperature. The type of conditions monitored will vary depending upon the battery technology. One source of guidance on monitoring battery systems is IEEE 1491, *Guide for the Selection and Use of Battery Monitoring Equipment in Stationary Applications.*

(6) Warning Signs. The following warning signs or labels shall be posted in appropriate locations:

(1) Electrical hazard warnings indicating the shock hazard due to the battery voltage and the arc flash hazard due to the prospective short-circuit current, and the thermal hazard.

Informational Note No.1: Because internal resistance, prospective short-circuit current, or both are not always provided on battery container labels or data sheets, and because many variables can be introduced into a battery layout, the battery manufacturer should be consulted for accurate data. Variables can include, but are not limited to, the following:

    (1) Series connections

    (2) Parallel connections

    (3) Charging methodology

    (4) Temperature

    (5) Charge status

    (6) Dc distribution cable size and length

Informational Note No. 2: See 130.5(D) for requirements for equipment labeling.

(2) Chemical hazard warnings, applicable to the worst case when multiple battery types are installed in the same space, indicating the following:

    a. Potential presence of explosive gas (when applicable to the battery type)

    b. Prohibition of open flame and smoking

    c. Danger of chemical burns from the electrolyte (when applicable to the battery type)

(3) Notice for personnel to use and wear protective equipment and apparel appropriate to the hazard for the battery

(4) Notice prohibiting access to unauthorized personnel

(B) Electrolyte Hazards.

> Batteries are somewhat unique in that they present chemical hazards as well as electrical hazards. Electrolyte (chemical) hazards vary depending on the type of battery, so the risks are product-specific and activity-specific. For example, nickel-cadmium (NiCd) and vented lead-acid (VLA) batteries allow access to liquid electrolyte, thereby potentially exposing employees to chemical hazards when performing certain tasks. By contrast, valve-regulated lead-acid (VRLA) and certain lithium batteries are designed with solid or immobilized electrolyte so that employees are only exposed to electrolyte under failure conditions.

(1) Battery Activities That Include Handling of Liquid Electrolyte. The following protective equipment shall be available to employees performing any type of service on a battery with liquid electrolyte:

(1) Goggles and face shield appropriate for the electrical hazard and the chemical hazard

(2) Gloves and aprons appropriate for the chemical hazards

(3) Portable or stationary eye wash facilities and equipment within the work area that are capable of drenching or flushing of the eyes and body for the duration necessary to mitigate injury from the electrolyte hazard.

Informational Note: Guidelines for the use and maintenance of eye wash facilities for vented batteries in nontelecom environments can be found in ANSI/ISEA Z358.1, *American National Standard for Emergency Eye Wash and Shower Equipment*.

These requirements only apply if electrolyte is being handled, which is possible only with batteries utilizing free-flowing liquid electrolyte. Activities in which electrolyte is being handled include acid adjustment, removal of excess electrolyte, or cleanup of an electrolyte leak or spill. Most battery maintenance activities do not involve handling electrolyte, so the requirement for safety glasses in 320.3(B)(2) would apply.

(2) Activities That Do Not Include Handling of Electrolyte. Employees performing any activity not involving the handling of electrolyte shall wear safety glasses.

Informational Note: Battery maintenance activities usually do not involve handling electrolyte. Batteries that are hermetically sealed (such as most lithium batteries) or immobilized electrolyte (such as valve-regulated lead acid batteries) present little or no electrolyte hazard. Most modern density meters expose a worker to a quantity of electrolyte too minute to be considered hazardous, if at all. Such work would not be considered handling electrolyte. However, if specific gravity readings are taken using a bulb hydrometer, the risk of exposure is higher — this could be considered to be handling electrolyte, and the requirements of 320.3(B)(1) would apply.

(C) Tools and Equipment.

N **(1) Handles.** Tools and equipment for work on batteries shall be equipped with handles listed as insulated for the maximum working voltage.

N **(2) Contact.** Battery terminals and all electrical conductors shall be kept clear of unintended contact with tools, test equipment, liquid containers, and other foreign objects.

N **(3) Nonsparking Tools.** Nonsparking tools shall be required when the risk assessment required by 110.5(H) justifies their use.

(D) Cell Flame Arresters and Cell Ventilation. When present, battery cell ventilation openings shall be unobstructed. Cell flame arresters shall be inspected for proper installation and unobstructed ventilation and shall be replaced when necessary in accordance with the manufacturer's instructions.

Safety-Related Work Practices: Lasers

330.1 Scope.

This article applies to safety-related work practices for maintaining lasers and their associated equipment.

> Informational Note No. 1: For recommendations on laser safety requirements for laser use, see ANSIZ136.1, *Standard for Safe Use of Lasers.*

> Informational Note No. 2: For laser product requirements for laser manufacturers, see 21 CFR Part 1040, "Performance Standards for Light-Emitting Products," Sections 1040.10 "Laser products" and 1040.11, "Specific purpose laser products."

Article 330 is limited to the tasks necessary to maintain a laser system in a laboratory or workshop. It does not cover the general application and use of lasers in the workplace. Employees who work with lasers might be exposed to the hazards associated with laser output in addition to the electrical hazards associated with the equipment.

330.2 Definitions.

For the purposes of this article, the following definitions shall apply.

Field Evaluated. A thorough evaluation of nonlisted or modified equipment in the field that is performed by persons or parties acceptable to the authority having jurisdiction.

> Informational Note: The evaluation approval ensures that the equipment meets appropriate codes and standards or is similarly found suitable for a specified purpose.

Laser. A device that produces radiant energy at wavelengths between 180 nm (nanometer) and 1 mm (millimeter) predominantly by controlled stimulated emission. Laser radiation can be highly coherent temporally, spatially, or both.

Laser Energy Source. Any device intended for use in conjunction with a laser to supply energy for the excitation of electrons, ions, or molecules.

Laser Radiation. All electromagnetic radiation emitted by a laser or laser system between 180 nm (nanometers) and 1 mm (millimeters) that is produced as a result of a controlled stimulated emission.

Laser System. A laser in combination with an appropriate laser energy source with or without additional incorporated components.

There are two classification systems for lasers, the FDA laser regulations and the international standard, IEC 60825-1, *Safety of Laser Products*. The FDA and IEC 60825-1 laser classification systems are not fully harmonized. Laser systems are classified by output power and wavelength. The classifications described by their physical hazard levels are as follows:

- *Class I laser system* — Incapable of producing damaging radiation levels during operation. Class 1 systems might contain laser sources of a higher class but are intrinsically safe when used as intended. Examples can be found in DVD players and laser printers.

- *Class 1M laser system* — Incapable of producing hazardous exposure conditions during normal operation unless the beam is viewed with an optical instrument.
- *Class 2 laser system (Class 2 and 2M)* — Emits in the visible portion of the spectrum (0.4 pm to 0.7 pm) and eye protection is normally afforded by the aversion response (blinking reflex). Examples of Class 2 systems can be found in laser pointers and some point-of-sale scanners.
- *Class 3 laser system (Class 3R and Class 3B)* — Hazardous if viewed directly but is considered safe if handled carefully and with restricted beam viewing. Examples of Class 3 lasers can be found inside DVD writers.
- *Class 4 laser system* — Can burn the skin or cause permanent eye damage as a result of direct, diffuse, or indirect beam viewing. These systems can ignite combustible materials. Class 4 lasers are typically limited to industrial, scientific, military, and medical use.

Protective Barrier. Prevents user access to a hazardous voltage, current, or stored energy area.

330.3 Hazardous Energy.

(A) Voltage and Current. For the purpose of this section, hazardous voltage and current for ac systems is considered greater than or equal to 50 volts ac and 5 mA. For dc systems, hazardous voltage or current is considered greater than or equal to 100 volts dc and 40 mA.

Although the dc threshold for the potential for electrical shock is 50 volts in Article 130, Article 330 allows for an increase of the threshold to 100 volts. However, unlike other NFPA *70E®* articles addressing dc systems, Article 330 also limits the current to 40 mA. Employers must implement the hierarchy of risk controls and define the safe work practices for each scheduled task when 100 volts dc or greater is present.

Environmental conditions, such as wet environments, might warrant a lower dc threshold. In addition, cuts to human skin can decrease the voltage level necessary to injure a worker.

(B) Stored Energy. For the purpose of this article, hazardous stored energy is considered greater than or equal to 0.25 joules at 400 volts or greater, or 1 joule at greater than 100 volts up to 400 volts.

These energy levels are not incident energy levels. These are the levels of energy that a system can store without being considered a hazard. This is independent of the hazardous voltage and current levels in 330.3(A).

330.4 Electrical Safety Training.

(A) Personnel to Be Trained. Employers shall provide training for all personnel who work on or are near lasers or laser systems with user-accessible hazardous voltage, current, or stored energy (e.g., flashlamp-pumped lasers).

Although NFPA *70E* addresses the electrical hazards associated with maintaining laser systems, understanding the laser class is essential to addressing the safety issues. Although any class of laser might be found in a laboratory or workshop, many are not considered to be hazardous under normal operation. For more information, see the commentary following the definition of *laser system* in 330.2 above.

The ANSI Z136 series addresses hazards and their associated regulatory information in detail. The hazards are also addressed by the IEC 60825 series. The ANSI series contains nine ANSI standards for lasers. The following documents are applicable to the facilities addressed by Article 330:

- ANSI Z136.1-2014, *American National Standard for Safe Use of Lasers*
- ANSI Z136.4-2010, *Recommended Practice for Laser Safety Measurements for Hazard Evaluation*
- ANSI Z136.5-2000, *American National Standard for Safe Use of Lasers in Educational Institutions*
- ANSI Z136.6-2005, *American National Standard for Safe Use of Lasers Outdoors*
- ANSf Z136.8-2012, *American National Standard for Safe Use of Lasers in Research, Development, or Testing*

(B) Electrical Safety Training for Work on or with Lasers. Training in electrical safe work practices shall include, but is not limited to, the following:

(1) Chapter 1 electrical safe work practices
(2) Electrical hazards associated with laser equipment
(3) Stored energy hazards, including capacitor bank explosion potential
(4) Ionizing radiation
(5) X-ray hazards from high-voltage equipment (>5 kV)
(6) Assessing the listing status of electrical equipment and the need for field evaluation of nonlisted equipment

Great care is necessary when working with the various types of laser systems, and electrical safety training is paramount. Lasers that are electrically powered can be hazardous due to their radiation as well as their power sources. High-energy density batteries, generators, ultracapacitors, and the associated power distribution panels present potential shock, arc flash, and fire hazards. Some source batteries are megajoule systems. A typical welding laser will have a prime power source of 50 kVA to 100 kVA, with larger systems approaching 500 kVA. Large systems are often water-cooled, so wet environments might be present as well. These units could be mobile units powered by diesel generators.

330.5 Safeguarding of Persons from Electrical Hazards Associated with Lasers and Laser Systems.

(A) Temporary Guarding. Temporary guarding (e.g., covers, protective insulating barriers) shall be used to limit exposure to any electrical hazard when the permanent laser enclosure covers are removed for maintenance and testing.

(B) Work Requiring an Electrically Safe Work Condition. Work that might expose employees to electrical hazards shall be performed with the equipment in an electrically safe work condition in accordance with 120.1, 120.2, and 110.3

Work that is performed on exposed energized electrical conductors or circuit parts is dangerous. The requirements in NFPA *70E* and the OSHA regulations state that, first and foremost, employees must work with equipment that is de-energized and in an electrically safe work condition (ESWC) unless it is operated in a normal condition. The primary protective strategy must be establishing an ESWC. Once this is complete, all the electrical energy will have been removed from all the conductors and circuit parts to which the employee could be exposed.

Although Chapter 1 addresses shock hazards, arc flash hazards, and the limited conditions that permit justified energized work, Article 330 includes additional hazard limits in 330.3. If the laser system exceeds the specified voltage, current, or energy levels, the primary safe work practice must be establishing an ESWC.

(C) Energized Electrical Testing. Energized electrical testing, troubleshooting, and voltage testing shall not require an energized work permit in accordance with 130.2(C).

(D) Warning Signs and Labels. Electrical safety warning signs and labels shall be posted as applicable on electrical equipment doors, covers, and protective barriers. The warning signs and labels shall adequately warn of the hazard using effective words, colors, and symbols. These signs and labels shall be permanently affixed to the equipment and shall be of sufficient durability to withstand the environment involved.

(E) Listing. Laser system electrical equipment shall be listed or field evaluated prior to use.

330.6 Responsibility for Electrical Safety.

All persons with access to hazardous voltage, current, or stored energy shall be responsible for the following:

(1) Obtaining authorization for work with or on hazardous electrical equipment in lasers and laser systems

(2) Use of Chapter 1 safety-related work practices

(3) Reporting laser equipment failures, accidents, inadequate barriers, and inadequate signage to the employer

OSHA Connection

29 CFR 1926.54(d)

Areas in which lasers are used must be posted with standard laser warning placards. The warning signs should comply with ANSI Z535, *Series of Standards for Safety Signs and Tags.*

Safety-Related Work Practices: Power Electronic Equipment

Chapter 1 applies to electrical equipment that operates at frequencies normally supplied for consumer use. The reaction of the human body to current flow changes as the frequency increases or decreases. When a frequency reaches the microwave band, joule heating can result in internal burns.

Employees who work on or with equipment within the scope of Article 340 must be qualified to perform tasks using the specific electronic equipment. They must be trained to understand the unique hazards associated with specific equipment and how to avoid exposure to those hazards.

340.1 Scope.

This article shall apply to safety-related work practices around power electronic equipment, including the following:

(1) Electric arc welding equipment
(2) High-power radio, radar, and television transmitting towers and antennas
(3) Industrial dielectric and radio frequency (RF) induction heaters
(4) Shortwave or RF diathermy devices
(5) Process equipment that includes rectifiers and inverters such as the following:
   a. Motor drives
   b. Uninterruptible power supply systems
   c. Fighting controllers

Informational Note: The following standards provide specific guidance for safety-related work practices around power electronic equipment: International Electrotechnical Commission IEC 60479-1, *Effects of Current on Human Beings and Livestock, Part 1: General Aspects,* and the International Commission on Radiological Protection (ICRP) Publication 33, *Protection Against Ionizing Radiation from External Sources Used in Medicine.*

Article 340 includes some common types of equipment that can be found on construction sites or at industrial or commercial facilities. It also includes some types of equipment that are not as common. This list is not all-inclusive. For example, photovoltaic, fuel cell, and wind systems used for the generation of electricity generally incorporate power electronic devices (power converters).

340.2 Definition.

For the purposes of this article, the definition that follows shall apply.

Radiation Worker. A person who is required to work in electromagnetic fields, the radiation levels of which exceed those specified for nonoccupational exposure.

340.3 Application.

The purpose of this article is to provide guidance for safety personnel in preparing specific safety-related work practices within their industry.

340.4 Hazards Associated with Power Electronic Equipment.

The employer and employees shall be aware of the hazards associated with the following:

(1) High voltages within the power supplies
(2) Radio frequency energy-induced high voltages
(3) Effects of RF fields in the vicinity of antennas and antenna transmission lines, which can introduce electrical shock and burns
(4) Ionizing (X-radiation) hazards from magnetrons, klystrons, thyratrons, cathode-ray tubes, and similar devices
(5) Nonionizing RF radiation hazards from the following:
   a. Radar equipment
   b. Radio communication equipment, including broadcast transmitters
   c. Satellite-earth-transmitters
   d. Industrial scientific and medical equipment
   e. RF induction heaters and dielectric heaters
   f. Industrial microwave heaters and diathermy radiators

Commentary Table 340.1 (see next page) contains quantitative data on the physiological effects of current on the human body.

Power electronic equipment commonly holds stored electrical energy. Filter boards and power boards in equipment contain capacitors that could store energy in addition to the stored energy in the bus capacitors. Electromagnetic interference (EMI) filters must be discharged prior to servicing equipment to prevent electric shock or arc flash hazards. The equipment in Exhibit 340.1 requires a 15-minute waiting period before the enclosure can be opened to allow time for stored energy to discharge, and it carries a reminder to verify the lack of voltage. The depletion of stored energy should not be based on time alone. Before accessing the interior of an uninterruptible power

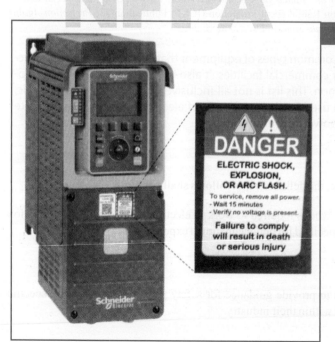

EXHIBIT 340.1

Equipment requiring dissipation of stored energy. (Courtesy of Schneider Electric)

supply (UPS) unit, care must be exercised to ensure that each source of input and output power has been electrically or physically isolated. Batteries or capacitors located within the UPS unit might still be charged even after all the apparent voltage sources have been isolated or confirmed to be de-energized.

COMMENTARY TABLE 340.1 *Quantitative Effects of Electric Current on Humans (Average Data)*

	Current (mA)					
	Direct Current (mA)		Alternating Current (mA)			
	DC		60 Hz		10 kHz	
Effects	150 lbs	115 lbs	150 lbs	115 lbs	150 lbs	115 lbs
Slight sensation on hand	1	0.6	0.4	0.3	7	5
Perception threshold, median	5.2	3.5	1.1	0.7	12	8
Shock —not painful and no loss of muscular control	9	6	1.8	1.2	17	11
Painful shock — muscular control lost by 0.5%	62	41	9	6	55	37
Painful shock —let-go threshold, median	76	51	16	10.5	75	50
Painful and severe shock — breathing difficult, muscular control lost by 99.5%	90	60	23	15	94	63
Possible ventricular fibrillation:						
Three-second shocks	500	500	100	100		
Short shocks (T in seconds)			165($\sqrt{T}$)	165($\sqrt{T}$)		
High-voltage surges (Energy in joules, i.e., watt-seconds)	50 J	50 J	13.6 J	13.6 J		

Notes:
Derived from "Deleterious Effects of Electric Shock,"Charles F. Dalziel, p. 24. Refer to the study for definitions and details.

The data in Commentary Table 340.1 are based on limited experiments conducted on human subjects and animals in 1961. These figures might not be fully dependable due to a lack of additional information and normal physiological differences between individuals. Electric current should probably be considered fatal at current values lower than is indicated. According to the LBNL Health and Safety Manual (PUB-3000) from the Environmental, Health, and Safety (EH&S) Division of Lawrence Berkley National Laboratory, which is operated by the University of California for the US Department of Energy, from experimental data derived from 115 subjects, the thresholds are as follows:

- The average threshold of perception of dc current in a 150 lb person (average healthy young male) is 5 mA.
- The threshold varies considerably from 2 mA to 10 mA dc.
- The average threshold for 60 Hz ac current in a 150 lb person is 1 mA.
- The threshold of perception increases with frequency, so that at 100 kHz, it is 150 mA.
- The threshold for a 115 lb person (average healthy young female) is around two-thirds of that for a 150 lb person (average healthy young male).

340.5 Specific Measures for Personnel Safety.

(A) Employer Responsibility. The employer shall be responsible for the following:

(1) Proper training and supervision by properly qualified personnel, including the following:
   a. Identification of associated hazards
   b. Strategies to reduce the risk associated with the hazards

    c. Methods of avoiding or protecting against the hazard

    d. Necessity of reporting any incident that resulted in, or could have resulted in, injury or damage to health

(2) Properly installed equipment

(3) Proper access to the equipment

(4) Availability of the correct tools for operation and maintenance

(5) Proper identification and guarding of dangerous equipment

(6) Provision of complete and accurate circuit diagrams and other published information to the employee prior to the employee starting work (The circuit diagrams should be marked to indicate the components that present an electrical hazard.)

(7) Maintenance of clear and clean work areas around the equipment to be worked on

(8) Provision of adequate and proper illumination of the work area

Servicing damaged equipment can present additional hazards not associated with servicing properly functioning equipment. For example, stored energy in damaged equipment might not discharge as intended. High earth leakage currents to an equipment chassis or enclosure can occur if the equipment grounding system is damaged or improperly installed. Testing for the presence of voltage is necessary even after waiting the prescribed time.

(B) Employee Responsibility. The employee shall be responsible for the following:

(1) Understanding the hazards associated with the work

(2) Being continuously alert and aware of the possible hazards

(3) Using the proper tools and procedures for the work

(4) Informing the employer of malfunctioning protective measures, such as faulty or inoperable enclosures and locking schemes

(5) Examining all documents provided by the employer relevant to the work to identify the location of components that present an electrical hazard

(6) Maintaining good housekeeping around the equipment and work space

(7) Reporting any incident that resulted in, or could have resulted in, injury or damage to health

(8) Using and appropriately maintaining the PPE and tools required to perform the work safely

Safety-Related Work Requirements: Research and Development Laboratories

Article 350 addresses unique conditions that might exist in laboratory and research areas. Electrical installations in laboratory or research areas often contain custom or specially designed electrical equipment that might have unique electrical safety-related requirements.

350.1 Scope

The requirements of this article shall apply to the electrical installations in those areas, with custom or special electrical equipment, designated by the facility management for research and development (R&D) or as laboratories.

This article covers all laboratory facilities, including those in educational institutions. Research and development facilities, including those associated with institutions of higher learning, are also covered.

350.2 Definitions.

For the purposes of this article, the definitions that follow shall apply.

Competent Person. A person who meets all the requirements of *qualified person,* as defined in Article 100 in Chapter 1 of this standard and who, in addition, is responsible for all work activities or safety procedures related to custom or special equipment and has detailed knowledge regarding the exposure to electrical hazards, the appropriate control methods to reduce the risk associated with those hazards, and the implementation of those methods.

Field Evaluated. A thorough evaluation of nonlisted or modified equipment in the field that is performed by persons or parties acceptable to the authority having jurisdiction. The evaluation approval ensures that the equipment meets appropriate codes and standards, or is similarly found suitable for a specified purpose.

Informational Note: For additional information on recommended practices and procedures for the field evaluation of nonlisted equipment, see NFPA 791, *Recommended Practice and Procedures for Unlabeled Electrical Equipment Evaluation.* For help in evaluating whether third-party entities are acceptable to an authority having jurisdiction, see NFPA 790, *Standard for Competency of Third-Party, Field Evaluation Bodies.*

Equipment in laboratory or research areas is often custom-designed. A consensus product standard covering this special equipment might not exist. Also, submitting a one-off piece of equipment for formal listing might not be necessary, as the equipment is usually not available for sale or use outside of the company for which it was designed. Field evaluation of custom equipment ensures that it is suitable for employee use within its intended application

Laboratory. A building, space, room, or group of rooms intended to serve activities involving procedures for investigation, diagnostics, product testing, or use of custom or special electrical components, systems, or equipment.

Research and Development (R&D). An activity in an installation specifically designated for research or development conducted with custom or special electrical equipment.

350.3 Applications of Other Articles.

The electrical system for R&D and laboratory applications shall meet the requirements of the remainder of this document, except as amended by Article 350.

> Informational Note: Examples of these applications include low-voltage-high-current power systems; high-voltage-low-current power systems; dc power supplies; capacitors; cable trays for signal cables and other systems, such as steam, water, air, gas, or drainage; and custom-made electronic equipment.

350.4 Electrical Safety Authority (ESA).

Each laboratory or R&D system application shall be permitted to assign an ESA to ensure the use of appropriate electrical safety-related work practices and controls. The ESA shall be permitted to be an electrical safety committee, engineer, or equivalent qualified individual. The ESA shall be permitted to delegate authority to an individual or organization within their control.

(A) Responsibility. The ESA shall act in a manner similar to an authority having jurisdiction for R&D electrical systems and electrical safe work practices.

(B) Qualifications. The ESA shall be competent in the following:

(1) The requirements of this standard
(2) Electrical system requirements applicable to the R&D laboratories

350.5 Specific Measures and Controls for Personnel Safety.

Each laboratory or R&D system application shall designate a competent person as defined in this article to ensure the use of appropriate electrical safety-related work practices and controls.

> As required in Chapter 1, employers must provide written procedures or other instructions in their electrical safety programs for the unique conditions encountered in laboratory and research areas. A competent person—not just a qualified person—is required to oversee the laboratory to ensure that employees follow the correct procedures.

(A) Job Briefings. Job briefings shall be performed in accordance with 110.5(1).

Exception: Prior to starting work, a brief discussion shall be permitted if the task and hazards are documented and the employee has reviewed applicable documentation and is qualified for the task.

(B) Personnel Protection. Safety-related work practices shall be used to safeguard employees from injury while they are exposed to electrical hazards from exposed electrical conductors or circuit parts that are or can become energized. The specific safety-related work practices shall be consistent with the electrical hazard(s) and the associated risk. For calibration and adjustment of equipment as it pertains to sensors, motor controllers, control hardware, and other devices that need to be installed inside equipment or control cabinet, surrounded by electrical hazards, the ESA shall define the required PPE based on the risk and exposure.

Use of electrical insulating blankets, covers, or barriers shall be permitted to prevent inadvertent contact to exposed terminals and conductors. Insulated/nonconductive adjustment and alignment tools shall be used where feasible.

350.6 Approval Requirements.

The equipment or systems used in the R&D area or in the laboratory shall be listed or field evaluated prior to use.

> Informational Note: Laboratory and R&D equipment or systems can pose unique electrical hazards that might require mitigation. Such hazards include ac and dc, low voltage and high amperage, high voltage and low current, large electromagnetic fields, induced voltages, pulsed power, multiple frequencies, and similar exposures.

This requirement is not intended for equipment that is under development. Unique equipment is often necessary to conduct research or to evaluate items under development, and listing of that equipment is often not possible. This equipment is permitted to be field evaluated (see the definition of *field evaluated* in 350.2) by a party acceptable to the authority having jurisdiction. The use of custom-made equipment does not change the employer's responsibility for providing electrical safety-related work practices.

350.7 Custom Built, Non-Listed Research Equipment, 1000 Volts or less AC or DC.

(A) Equipment Marking and Documentation.

(1) Marking. Marking of equipment shall be required for, but not limited to, equipment fabricated, designed, or developed for research testing and evaluation of electrical systems. Marking shall sufficiently list all voltages entering and leaving control cabinets, enclosures, and equipment.

Caution, Warning, or Danger labels shall be affixed to the exterior describing specific hazards and safety concerns.

> Informational Note: Refer to ANSI Z535, *Series of Standards for Safety Signs and Tags,* for more information on precautionary marking of electrical systems or equipment.

(2) Documentation. Sufficient documentation shall be provided and readily available to personnel that install, operate, and maintain equipment that describes operation, shutdown, safety concerns, and nonstandard installations.

Schematics, drawings, and bill of materials describing power feeds, voltages, currents, and parts used for construction, maintenance, and operation of the equipment shall be provided.

(3) Shutdown Procedures. Safety requirements and emergency shutdown procedures of equipment shall include lockout/tagout (LOTO) requirements. If equipment-specific LOTO is required, then documentation outlining this procedure and PPE requirements shall be made readily available.

(4) Specific Hazards. Specific hazards, other than electrical, associated with research equipment shall be documented and readily available.

(5) Approvals. Drawings, standard operational procedures, and equipment shall be approved by the ESA on site before initial startup. Assembly of equipment shall comply with national standards where applicable unless research application requires exceptions. Equipment that does not meet the applicable standards shall be required to be approved by the ESA. Proper safety shutdown procedures and PPE requirements shall be considered in the absence of grounding and/or bonding.

(B) Tools. Training, and Maintenance. Documentation shall be provided if special tools, unusual PPE, or other equipment is necessary for proper maintenance and operation of equipment. The ESA shall make the determination of appropriate training and qualifications required to perform specific tasks.

350.8 Custom Built, Unlisted Research Equipment, >1000 V AC or DC.

Installations shall comply with all requirements of 350.7.

In the event that research equipment requires PPE beyond what is commercially available, the ESA shall determine safe work practices and PPE to be used.

△ **350.9 Energy Thresholds.**

Energy exposure levels shall not exceed those identified in the following list unless appropriate controls are implemented as approved by the ESA:

(1) AC: 50 volts and 5 milliamperes

(2) DC: 100 volts and 40 milliamperes

> Informational Note No. 1: This information is extracted from the Department of Energy, *DOE Electrical Safety Handbook*, DOE-HDBK-1092.

> Informational Note No. 2: See 360.3 and Informative Annex R for information on capacitor hazards and controls.

Although the dc threshold for the potential for an electrical shock is 50 volts in Article 130, Article 350 allows for an increase in the threshold to 100 volts. However, unlike other NFPA *70E*® articles addressing dc systems, Article 350 limits the current to 40 mA.

350.10 Establishing an Electrically Safe Work Condition.

Energized electrical conductors and circuit parts shall be put into an electrically safe work condition before an employee performs work.

Exception: At the discretion of the ESA, alternative methods of ensuring worker safety shall be permitted to be employed for the following conditions:

(1) Minor tool changes and adjustments, and other normal production operations that are routine, repetitive, or sequential and integral to the use of the equipment for production

(2) Minor changes to the unit under test and other minor servicing activities, to include the activities listed under 350.10 Exception condition (1), that take place during research and development

(3) Work on cord-and-plug-connected equipment for which exposure to the hazards of unexpected energization or start up is controlled by the following:

a. Unplugging the equipment from the energy source

b. The employee performing the work maintaining exclusive control of the plug

OSHA Connection

29 CFR 1910.333(a)(1)

Live parts that operate at 50 volts or above must be de-energized. Compliance with this regulation might not be met where 100 volts dc is used as the energy exposure limit.

Work that is performed on exposed energized electrical conductors or circuit parts is dangerous. The requirements in NFPA *70E* and the OSHA regulations state that, first and foremost, employees must work with equipment that is de-energized and in an electrically safe work condition (ESWC) unless it is operated in a normal condition. Therefore, the primary protective strategy must be establishing an ESWC. After this strategy is executed, all electrical energy will have been removed from all the conductors and circuit parts to which the employee could be exposed.

The requirements of Chapter 3 can modify the requirements of Chapter 1. Although Chapter 1 addresses shock hazards, arc flash hazards, and the limited conditions that permit justified energized work, Article 350 includes additional hazard limits in 350.9. If the system exceeds specified voltage or current levels, the primary safe work practice must be establishing an ESWC. The explicit exception to establishing an ESWC is the sole allowance for justified energized work in a research and development laboratory. The exceptions in 110.4(A) do not apply.

Safety-Related Requirements for Capacitors

> Capacitors are used in many ways, including in several of the specific Chapter 3 locations. The requirements of Article 360 apply to capacitors in all applications. For example, if capacitors are used in power electronic equipment covered by Article 340, both articles must be used to determine the appropriate electrical safety procedures and practices. Refer to Annex R for information regarding the hazards associated with capacitive systems.

N 360.1 Scope.

This article covers the electrical safety-related requirements for the practical safeguarding of employees while working with capacitors that present an electrical hazard.

> Informational Note: For more information on working safely with capacitors, see Informative Annex R, Working with Capacitors.

N 360.2 Definitions.

N Arc Blast Hazard. A source of possible injury or damage to health from the energy deposited into acoustical shock-wave and high-velocity shrapnel.

N Bleed Resistor. A resistor network connected in parallel with a capacitor's terminals that drains the charge after power has been disconnected.

N Charge Transfer. Improper discharging of capacitor networks that results in transferring from one capacitor to another charge instead of fully discharging the stored energy.

N Dielectric Absorption. The property of certain capacitors to recharge after being discharged.

> Informational Note: A voltage recharge of up to 10 percent can occur a few minutes after the grounding or shorting device has been removed.

N Discharge Time. The time required to discharge a capacitor to below a stored energy hazard threshold.

N Ground Stick. A device that is used to ensure that the capacitor is discharged by applying it to all terminals of the capacitor element.

> Informational Note: This is also called a ground hook and could incorporate power-rated discharge resistors for high-energy applications.

N Hard Grounding (Low-Z). The practice of discharging a capacitor through a low impedance, also called Low-Z (impedance) grounding.

N Hearing Protection Boundary. Worker distance at which a 1 percent probability of ear damage exists from a 20 kPa (3.0 psi) shock wave.

N **Lung Protection Boundary.** Worker distance at which a 1 percent probability of lung damage exists from a 70 kPa (10 psi) shock wave.

N **Soft Grounding (High-Z).** The practice of connecting a capacitor to ground through a power resistor to avoid the hazards related with hard grounding.

N **Time Constant.** The time it takes for voltage to drop by ~63 percent (1/e) during discharge.

N **360.3 Stored Energy Hazard Thresholds.**

Appropriate controls shall be applied where any of the following hazard thresholds are exceeded:

(1) Less than 100 volts and greater than 100 joules of stored energy
(2) Greater than or equal to 100 volts and greater than 1.0 joule of stored energy
(3) Greater than or equal to 400 volts and greater than 0.25 joules of stored energy

> These stored energy thresholds are solely for capacitive installations in the application of Article 360. The energy levels are not incident energy levels. These levels are the limit of the energy that a capacitive system can have without being considered a hazard. A capacitive system must meet the conditions in (1), (2), or (3). For example, a system with 150 volts and 1.2 joules would fall under item (2), but a system with 150 volts and 0.7 joules would not. Note that the dc threshold for the potential for an electrical shock is 50 volts in Article 130 and is independent of the current or energy level.

OSHA Connection

29CFR 1910.333(a)(1)
Live parts that operate at 50 volts or above must be de-energized. Compliance with this regulation might not be met where 100 volts dc is used as the energy exposure limit.

N **360.4 Specific Measures for Personnel Safety.**

N **(A) Qualification and Training.**

The following qualifications and training shall be required for personnel safety:

(1) Employees who perform work on electrical equipment with capacitors that exceed the energy thresholds in 360.3 shall be qualified and shall be trained in. and familiar with, the specific hazards and controls required for safe work.
(2) Unqualified persons who perform work on electrical equipment with capacitors shall be trained in, and familiar with, any electrical safety-related work practices necessary for their safety.

N **(B) Performing a Risk Assessment for Capacitors.** The risk assessment process for capacitors shall follow the overall risk assessment procedures in Chapter 1. If additional protective measures are required, they shall be selected and implemented according to the hierarchy of risk control identified in 110.5(H)(3). When the additional protective measures include the use of PPE. the following shall be determined:

(1) Capacitor voltage and stored energy for the worker exposure. An exposure shall be considered to exist when a conductor or circuit part that could potentially remain energized with hazardous stored energy is exposed.
(2) Thermal hazard. The appropriate thermal PPE shall be selected and used if the stored energy of the exposed part is greater 100 joules.
(3) Shock hazard. The appropriate shock PPE in accordance with 130.7 shall be selected and used if the voltage is greater than or equal to 100 volts.

(4) Arc flash and arc blast hazard at the appropriate working distance. The appropriate protection for the arc flash and arc blast hazard shall be selected, as follows:

(a) Arc flash PPE in accordance with 130.7 shall be selected and used if the incident energy exceeds 1.2 cal/cm^2 (5 J/cm^2) at the working distance.

(b) Hearing protection shall be required where the stored energy exceeds 100 joules.

(c) The lung protection boundary shall be determined if stored energy is above 122 kJ. Employees shall not enter the lung protection boundary.

(d) Alerting techniques in accordance with 130.7(E) shall be used to warn employees of the hazards.

(5) Required test and grounding method. Soft grounding shall be used for stored energy greater than 1000 joules. If capacitors are equipped with bleed resistors, or if using a soft grounding system, the required discharge wait time shall be determined where applicable.

(6) Develop a written procedure that captures all of the required steps to place the equipment in an electrically safe work condition. Include information about the amount of stored energy available, how long to wait after de-energization before opening the enclosure, how to test for absence of voltage, and what to do if there is still stored energy present.

Informational Note No. 1: For more information on calculating capacitor stored energy, arc flash, and arc blast boundaries, see Informative Annex R, Working Safely with Capacitors.

Informational Note No. 2: Heavy duty leather with a minimum thickness of 0.03 in. (0.7 mm) provides protection from thermal hazards.

N **360.5 Establishing an Electrically Safe Work Condition for a Capacitor(s).**

N **(A) Written Procedure.** Where a conductor or circuit part is connected to a capacitor(s) operating at or above the thresholds in 360.3, a written procedure shall be used to document the necessary steps and sequence to discharge the capacitor(s) and place the equipment into an electrically safe work condition. The written procedure shall incorporate the results of the risk assessment performed in 360.5(B) and specify the following at a minimum:

N **(B) Safe Work Practices.** In order to place the capacitor(s) into an electrically safe work condition, a qualified person shall use the appropriate safe work practices and PPE and shall apply the following process for establishing and verifying an electrically safe work condition:

(1) Determine all possible sources of electrical supply to the specific equipment. Check applicable up-to-date drawings, diagrams, and identification tags.

(2) After properly interrupting the load current, open the disconnecting device(s) for each source.

(2) Wherever possible, visually verify that all blades of the disconnecting devices are fully open or that drawout-type circuit breakers are withdrawn to the fully disconnected position.

(4) Apply lockout/tagout devices in accordance with a documented and established policy.

(5) If bleed resistors or automatic discharge systems are applicable, wait the prescribed time for the. capacitors to discharge to less than the thresholds in 360.3 and proceed to step (6). For systems without bleed resistors or automatic discharge systems, discharge the capacitors with an adequately rated grounding device (e.g., ground stick). Soft grounding shall be performed above 1000 joules, and remote soft grounding shall be performed above 100 kJ.

(6) Verify that the capacitors are discharged. For capacitors less than 1000 joules, verification shall be permitted to be done either by testing or by grounding. For capacitors between 1000 joules and less than 100 kJ, verification shall be done using testing or soft grounding, then hard grounding. Above 100 kJ, an engineered and redundant system shall be

used for remote testing and grounding. An adequately rated portable test instrument shall be used to test between each capacitor terminal and from each terminal to ground to assure that the capacitor is de-energized.

(7) Before and after each verification, determine that the test instrument is operating satisfactorily through verification on a known dc voltage source. If voltage remains, determine and correct the cause, and repeat step (5) to discharge the capacitors. Where recharging can occur due to dielectric absorption or induced voltages, all the capacitor terminals shall be connected together and grounded with a bare or transparent-insulated wire.

(2) For series capacitors the shorting wires shall be attached across each individual capacitor, and to case.

For single capacitors or for a parallel capacitor bank, the grounding device shall be permitted to be left attached to the capacitor terminals for the duration of the work (e.g., a ground stick).

Exception: Lockout/tagout shall not be required for work on cord- and plug-connected equipment for which exposure to the hazards of unexpected energization of the equipment is controlled by the unplugging of the equipment from the energy source, provided that the plug is under the exclusive control of the employee performing the servicing and maintenance for the duration of the work.

N 360.6 Grounding Sticks.

Grounding sticks shall be provided for qualified persons to safely discharge any residual stored energy contained in capacitors or to hold the capacitor potential at 0 volts. The grounding sticks shall be designed, constructed, installed, and periodically inspected so that the full energy and voltage of the capacitors can be safely discharged.

N (A) Visual Inspection.
The ground stick shall be visually inspected for defects before each use. All mechanical connections shall be examined for loose connections. Resistors shall be visually inspected for cracks or other defects and electrically tested for proper resistance. The following shall occur if defects or contamination are found:

(1) If any defect or contamination that could adversely affect the insulating qualities or mechanical integrity of the ground stick is present, the tool shall be removed from service.

(2) If the defect or contamination exists on the grounding stick, then it shall be replaced or repaired and tested before returning to service.

(3) If the defect or contamination exists on the cable, then it shall be replaced or repaired and tested before returning to service.

N (B) Electrical Testing.
All ground sticks shall be electrically tested as follows:

(1) The ground stick cable shall be tested to verify that the impedance is less than 0.1 ohms to ground every 2 years.

(2) The testing shall be documented.

Exception: The test shall be performed annually if the ground stick is utilized outdoors or in other adverse conditions.

(3) Soft grounding (High-Z) ground sticks with resistors shall be measured and compared to the specified value before each use.

N **(C) Storage and Disposal.** Any residual charge from capacitors shall be removed by discharging before servicing or removal.

(1) All uninstalled capacitors capable of storing 10 joules or greater at their rated voltage shall be short-circuited with a conductor of appropriate size.

(2) When an uninstalled capacitor is discovered without the shorting conductor attached to the terminals, it shall be treated as energized and charged to its full rated voltage until determined safe by a qualified person.

Informational Note: A capacitor that develops an internal open circuit could retain substantial charge internally even though the terminals are short-circuited. Such a capacitor can be hazardous to transport, because the damaged internal wiring could reconnect and discharge the capacitor through the short-circuiting conductor. Any capacitor that shows a significant change in capacitance after a fault could have this problem. Action should be taken to reduce the risk associated with this hazard when it is discovered.

Informative Publications

Informative Annex A identifies important publications that provide additional information to assist users in understanding and applying the requirements of NFPA *70E*®. This informative annex provides further information about the publishers and editions of the documents referenced in the Informational Notes. These documents are for informational purposes only.

The state of electrical safety is constantly moving forward. Existing documents are often either deleted or revised periodically, while new documents continue to be issued. Users of NFPA *70E* are encouraged to verify that the referenced documents are the latest published editions, as the documents' issue cycle might be different from that of NFPA *70E*.

A.1 General.

The following documents or portions thereof are referenced within this standard for informational purposes only and are thus not part of the requirements of this document.

Δ A.2 NFPA Publications.

National Fire Protection Association, 1 Batterymarch Park. Quincy, MA 02169-7471.

NFPA 70®, *National Electrical Code*®, 2020 edition.

NFPA 1, *Fire Code,* 2018 edition.

NFPA 70B, *Recommended Practice for Electrical Equipment Maintenance,* 2019 edition.

NFPA 790, *Standard for Competency of Third-Party Field Evaluation Bodies,* 2021 edition.

NFPA 791, *Recommended Practice and Procedures for Unlabeled Electrical Equipment Evaluation,* 2021 edition.

A.3 Other Publications.

Δ A.3.1 ANSI Publications. American National Standards Institute, Inc., 25 West 43rd Street, 4th Floor, New York, NY 10036.

ANSI/ASC A14.1, *American National Standard for Ladders — Wood — Safety Requirements,* 2007.

ANSI/ASC A14.3, *American National Standard for Ladders — Fixed — Safety Requirements,* 2008.

ANSI/ASC A14.4, *American National Standard Safety Requirements for Job Made Wooden Ladders,* 2009.

ANSI/ASC A14.5, *American National Standard for Ladders — Portable Reinforced Plastic — Safety Requirements,* 2007.

ANSI C84.1, *Electric Power Systems and Equipment — Voltage Ratings (60 Hz),* 2011.

ANSI/AIHA Z10, *American National Standard for Occupational Health and Safety Management Systems,* 2012.

ANSI Z136.1, *Standard for Safe Use of Lasers,* 2014.

ANSI/ASSE Z244.1, *Control of Hazardous Energy — Lockout/Tagout and Alternative Methods,* 2003 (R 2008).

ANSI Z535, *Series of Standards for Safety Signs and Tags,* 2011.

ANSI Z535.4, *Product Safety Signs and Tags Labels,* 2011.

ANSI/NETA MTS, *Standard for Maintenance Testing Specifications for Electrical Power Distribution Equipment and Systems,* 2011.

A.3.2 ASTM Publications. ASTM International, 100 Barr Harbor Drive, P.0 Box C700, West Conshohocken, PA 19428-2959.

ASTM D120, *Standard Specification for Rubber Insulating Gloves,* 2014a.

ASTM D1048, *Standard Specification for Rubber Insulating Blankets,* 2014.

ASTM D1049, *Standard Specification for Rubber Insulating Covers,* 1998 (R 2017).

ASTM D1050, *Standard Specification for Rubber Insulating Line Hoses,* 2005 (R 2017).

ASTM D1051, *Standard Specification for Rubber Insulating Sleeves,* 2014a.

ASTM F478, *Standard Specification for In-Service Care of Insulating Line Hose and Covers,* 2014a.

ASTM F479, *Standard Specification for In-Service Care of Insulating Blankets,* 2006 (R 2017).

ASTM F496, *Standard Specification for In-Service Care of Insulating Gloves and Sleeves,* 2014a.

ASTM F696, *Standard Specification for Leather Protectors for Rubber Insulating Gloves and Mittens,* 2006 (R 2011).

ASTM F711, *Standard Specification for Fiberglass-Reinforced Plastic (FRP) Rod and Tube Used in Live Line Tools,* 2017.

ASTM F712, *Standard Test Methods and Specifications for Electrically Insulating Plastic Guard Equipment for Protection of Workers,* 2006 (R 2011).

ASTM F855, *Standard Specification for Temporary Protective Grounds to Be Used on De-energized Electric Power Lines and Equipment,* 2017.

ASTM F887, *Standard Specification for Personal Climbing Equipment,* 2016.

ASTM FI 116, *Standard Test Method for Determining Dielectric Strength of Dielectric Footwear,* 2014a.

ASTM FI 117, *Standard Specification for Dielectric Footwear,* 2003 (R 2013).

ASTM FI 236, *Standard Guide for Visual Inspection of Electrical Protective Rubber Products,* 2016.

ASTM F1296, *Standard Guide for Evaluating Chemical Protective Clothing,* 2015.

ASTM F1449, *Standard Guide for Industrial Laundering of Flame, Thermal, and Arc Resistant Clothing,* 2015.

ASTM F1505, *Standard Specification for Insulated and Insulating Hand Tools,* 2016.

ASTM F1506, *Standard Performance Specification for Flame Resistant and Electric Arc Rated Protective Clothing Worn by Workers Exposed to Flames and Electric Arcs,* 2018.

ASTM F1742, *Standard Specification for PVC Insulating Sheeting,* 2003 (R 2011).

ASTM FI 891, *Standard Specification for Arc and Flame Resistant Rainwear,* 2012.

ASTM F1959/F1959M, *Standard Test Method for Determining the Arc Rating of Materials for Clothing,* 2014.

ASTM F2178, *Standard Test Method for Determining the Arc Rating and Standard Specification for Eye or Face Protective Products,* 2017b.

ASTM F2249, *Standard Specification for In-Service Test Methods for Temporary Grounding Jumper Assemblies Used on De-energized Electric Power Lines and Equipment,* 2003 (R 2015).

ASTM F2320, *Standard Specification for Rubber Insulating Sheeting,* 2011.

ASTM F2412, *Standard Test Methods for Foot Protections,* 2018.

ASTM F2413, *Standard Specification for Performance Requirements for Protective (Safety) Toe Cap Footwear,* 2017.

ASTM F2522, *Standard Test Method for Determining the Protective Performance of a Shield Attached on Live Line Tools or on Racking Rods for Electric Arc Hazards,* 2017.

ASTM F2675/F2675M, *Standard Test Method for Determining Arc Ratings of Hand Protective Products Developed and Used for Electrical Arc Flash Protection,* 2013.

ASTM F2676, *Standard Test Method for Determining the Protective Performance of an Arc Protective Blanket for Electric Arc Hazards,* 2016.

ASTM F2677, *Standard Specification for Electrically Insulating Aprons,* (R 2013).

ASTM F2757, *Standard Guide for Home Laundering Care and Maintenance of Flame, Thermal, and Arc Resistant Clothing,* 2016.

ASTM F3272, *Standard Guide for Selection, Care, and Use of Arc Protective Blankets,* 2018.

A.3.3 British Standards Institute, Occupational Health and Safety Assessment Series (OHSAS) Project Group Publications. British Standards Institute, American Headquarters, 12110 Sunset Hills Road, Suite 200, Reston VA 20190-5902.

BS OSHAS 18001, *Occupational Health and Safety Management Systems,* 2007.

A.3.4 CSA Publications. Canadian Standards Association, 5060 Spectrum Way, Mississauga, ON L4W 5N6, Canada.

CAN/CSA Z1000, *Occupational Health and Safety Management,* 2006 (R 2011).

A.3.5 ICRP Publications. International Commission on Radiological Protection, SE-171 16 Stockholm, Sweden.

ICRP Publication 33, *Protection Against Ionizing Radiation from External Sources Used in Medicine,* March 1982.

A.3.6 IEC Publications. International Electrotechnical Commission, 3, rue de Varembe, P.O. Box 131, CH-1211 Geneva 20, Switzerland.

IEC TS 60479-1, *Effects of Current on Human Beings and Livestock Part 1: General Aspects,* 2016.

IECTS 60479-2, *Effects of Current on Humans and Livestock,* Part 2, Special Aspects, 2017.

IEC 61243-1. *Live Working — Voltage Detectors — Part 1: Capacitive type to be used for voltages exceeding 1kV a.c.,* 2009.

IEC 61243-2, *Live Working — Voltage Detectors — Part 2: Resistive type to be used for voltages of 1kV to 36 kV a.c.,* 2002.

IEC 61243.3, *Live Working — Voltage Detectors — Part 3: Two-pole low voltage type,* 2014.

A.3.7 IEEE Publications. Institute of Electrical and Electronics Engineers, IEEE Operations Center, 445 Hoes Lane, P. O. Box 1331, Piscataway, NJ 08855-1331.

IEEE C37.20.7, *Guide for Testing Switchgear Rated up to 52 kV for Internal Arcing Faults,* 2007/Corrigendum 1, 2010.

ANSI/IEEE C2, *National Electrical Safety Code,* 2012, 2017.

IEEE 4, *Standard Techniques for High Voltage Testing,* 2013.

IEEE 450, *IEEE Recommended Practice for Maintenance, Testing, and Replacement of Vented Lead-Acid Batteries for Stationary Applications,* 2010.

IEEE 463, *Electrical Safety Practices in Electrolytic Cell Line Working Zones,* 2013.

IEEE 516, *Guide for Maintenance Methods on Energized Power Lines,* 2009.

IEEE 937, *Recommended Practice for Installation and Maintenance of Lead-Acid Batteries for Photovoltaic Systems,* 2007.

IEEE 946, *Recommended Practice for the Design of DC Auxiliary Power Systems for Generating Systems,* 2004.

IEEE 1106, *Recommended Practice for Installation, Maintenance, Testing, and Replacement of Vented Nickel-Cadmium Batteries for Stationary Applications,* 2010.

IEEE 1184, *Guide for Batteries for Uninterruptible Power Supply Systems,* 2006.

IEEE 1188, *Recommended Practice for Maintenance, Testing, and Replacement of Valve - Regulated Lead-Acid (VRLA) Batteries for Stationary Applications,* 2005 (R 2010).

IEEE 1491, *Guide for Selection and Use of Battery Monitoring Equipment in Stationary Applications,* 2012.

IEEE 1584™, *Guide for Performing Arc Flash Hazard Calculations,* 2018.

IEEE/ASHRAE 1635, *Guide for the Ventilation and Thermal Management of Batteries for Stationary Applications,* 2018.

IEEE 1657, *Recommended Practice for Personnel Qualifications for Installation and Maintenance of Stationary Batteries,* 2009.

IEEE 3007.1, *Recommended Practice for the Operation and Management of Industrial and Commercial Power Systems,* 2010.

IEEE 3007.2, *Recommended Practice for the Maintenance of Industrial and Commercial Power Systems,* 2010.

IEEE 3007.3, *Recommended Practice for Electrical Safety in Industrial and Commercial Power Systems,* 2012.

Ammerman, R. F., Gammon, T., Sen, R K., and Nelson, J. R, "DC-Arc Models and Incident-Energy Calculations," *IEEE Transactions on Industry Applications,* Vol. 46, No. 5, 2010.

Doan, D. R, "Arc Flash Calculations for Exposures to DC Systems," *IEEE Transactions on Industry Applications,* Vol 46, No. 6, 2010.

Doughty, R. L., T. E. Neal, and H. L. Floyd II, "Predicting Incident Energy to Better Manage the Electric Arc Hazard on 600 V Power Distribution Systems," Record of Conference Papers IEEE IAS 45th Annual Petroleum and Chemical Industry Conference, September 28-30, 1998.

Lee, R., "The Other Electrical Hazard: Electrical Arc Flash Bums," *IEEE Trans. Applications,* Vol. 1A-18, No. 3, May/June 1982.

A.3.8 ISEA Publications. International Safety Equipment Association, 1901 North Moore Street, Arlington, VA 22209-1762.

ANSI/ISEA 125, *American National Standard for Conformity Assessment of Safety and Personal Protective Equipment,* 2014.

ANSI/ISEA Z87.1, *American National Standard for Occupational and Educational Eye and Face Protection,* 2015.

ANSI/ISEA Z89.1, *American National Standard for Head Protection,* 2014.

ANSI/ISEA Z358.1, *American National Standard for Emergency Eye Wash and Shower Equipment,* 2009.

A.3.9 ISO Publications. International Organization for Standardization, 1, Ch. de la Voie-Creuse, Case postale 56, CH-1211 Geneva 20, Switzerland.

ISO 9001, *Quality management systems,* 2015.

ISO 14001, *Environmental Management Systems — Requirements with Guidance for Use,* 2004.

ISO 17025, *General requirements for the competence of testing and calibration laboratories,* 2017.

ISO 17065, *Conformity assessment — Requirements for bodies certifying products, processes and services,* 2012.

ISO 31000, *Risk management,* 2018.
ISO 31010, *Risk management — Risk assessment techniques.*

A.3.10 NIOSH Publications. National Institute for Occupational Safety and Health, Centers for Disease Control and Prevention, 1600 Clifton Road, Atlanta, GA 30333.

DHHS (NIOSH) Publication No. 94-110, *Applications Manual for the Revised NIOSH Lifting Equation,* 1994.

A.3.11 UL Publications. Underwriters Laboratories Inc., 333 Pfingsten Road, Northbrook, IL 60062-2096.

ANSI/UL 943, *Standard for Ground-Fault Circuit Interrupters,* 2006 ® 2012)
UL 943C, *Outline of Investigation for Special Purpose Ground-Fault Circuit-Interrupters,* 2012.
UL 1436, *Outlet Circuit Testers and Other Similar Indicating Devices,* 2016.
UL 61010-1, *Safety Requirements for Electrical Equipment for Measurement, Control, and Laboratory Use, Part 1: General Requirements,* 2012.
UL 61010-2-033, *Safety Requirements for Electrical Equipment for Measurement, Control, and Laboratory Use — Part 2-033: Particular Requirements for Hand-Held Multimeters and Other Meters, for Domestic and Professional use, Capable of Measuring Mains Voltage,* 2014.

Δ **A.3.12 Government Publications.** U.S. Government Publishing Office, 732 North Capitol Street, NW, Washington, DC 20401-0001.

Department of Energy, *DOE Electrical Safety Handbook,* DOE-HDBK-1092-2013.
Title 21, Code of Federal Regulations, Part 1040, "Performance Standards for Light-Emitting Products," Sections 1040.10, "Laser products" and 1040.11, "Specific purpose laser products."
Title 29, Code of Federal Regulations, Part 1910, "Occupational Safety and Health Standards," Subpart S, "Electrical."
Title 29, Code of Federal Regulations, Part 1910.137, "Personal Protective Equipment."
Title 29, Code of Federal Regulations, Part 1910.305(j)(7), "Storage Batteries."
Title 29, Code of Federal Regulations, Part 1926, "Safety and Health Regulations for Construction," Subpart K, "Electrical."
Title 29, Code of Federal Regulations, Part 1926.441, "Batteries and Battery Charging."

A.3.13 Other Publications. Charles R. Hummer, Richard J. Pearson, and Donald H. Porschet, *"Safe Distances From a High-Energy Capacitor Bank for Ear and Lung Protection,"* Army Research Laboratory Report, ANL-TN-608, July 2014.

"DC Arc Hazard Assessment Phase II," Copyright Material, Kinectrics Inc., Report No. K-012623-RA-0002-R00.
Occupational Injuries From Electrical Shock and Arc Flash Events Final Report, Richard Campbell and David Dini, Fire Protection Research Foundation, Quincy, MA.
Occupational Electrical Injuries in the US, 2003-2009, James Cawley and Brett C. Banner, ESFI.
Rasmussen, J., "Skills, rules, and knowledge; signals, signs, and symbols, and other distinctions in human performance models," *IEEE Transactions on Systems, Man, and Cybernetics,* (3), 257-266, 1983.
Reason, J., *Human Error.* Cambridge, UK: Cambridge University Press, 1990.
Technical paper ESW 2012-24 presented at IEEE ESW conference, *Arc Flash Hazards, Incident Energy, PPE Ratings and Thermal Burn Injury — A Deeper Look,* Tammy Gammon, Wei-Jen Lee, and Ben Johnson.
Technical Paper ESW 2015-17 presented at IEEE ESW conference, OSHA Subpart V, *Electric Power and Distribution,* April 11, 2014.

Reserved B

In the 2021 edition of NFPA *70E®, Standard for Electrical Safety in the Workplace®,* Informative Annex B is reserved for future use.

INFORMATIVE ANNEX B

Reserved

In the 2021 edition of NFPA 70E®, Standard for Electrical Safety in the Workplace®, Informative Annex B is reserved for future use.

INFORMATIVE ANNEX

Limits of Approach

This informative annex is not a part of the requirements of this NFPA document but is included for informational purposes only.

Informative Annex C provides information on approach boundaries. The information is intended to provide suggestions for workers' safety near each limit. The approach limits trigger the need for greater control over the work performed inside that approach limit.

C.1 Preparation for Approach.

Observing a safe approach distance from exposed energized electrical conductors or circuit parts is an effective means of maintaining electrical safety. As the distance between a person and the exposed energized conductors or circuit parts decreases, the potential for electrical incident increases.

C.1.1 Unqualified Persons, Safe Approach Distance. Unqualified persons are safe when they maintain a distance from the exposed energized conductors or circuit parts, including the longest conductive object being handled, so that they cannot contact or enter a specified air insulation distance to the exposed energized electrical conductors or circuit parts. This safe approach distance is the limited approach boundary. Further, persons must not cross the arc flash boundary unless they are wearing appropriate personal protective clothing and are under the close supervision of a qualified person. Only when continuously escorted by a qualified person should an unqualified person cross the limited approach boundary. Under no circumstance should an unqualified person cross the restricted approach boundary, where special shock protection techniques and equipment are required.

According to 130.1, safety-related work practices must be used to safeguard employees from injury when the risk of exposure to electrical hazards or potential electrical hazards is unacceptable, and the work practices must be consistent with the nature and extent of the hazard. These work practices can help protect employees from the risks associated with the four conditions of electrical hazards: arc flashes, arc blasts, thermal burns, and electrical shock.

The restricted and limited approach boundaries only address the potential for electric shock and electrocution. An unqualified worker within the limited approach boundary might be at risk of an arc flash injury even when under the close supervision of, or while continuously escorted by, a qualified person. Employees must not be allowed to cross the arc flash boundary without first receiving the specific safety-related training necessary to understand the hazards involved and the appropriate use of the necessary PPE.

257

C.1.2 Qualified Persons, Safe Approach Distance.

C. 1.2.1 Determine the arc flash boundary and, if the boundary is to be crossed, appropriate arc-rated protective equipment must be utilized.

C.1.2.2 For a person to cross the limited approach boundary and enter the limited space, a person should meet the following criteria:

(1) Be qualified to perform the job/task
(2) Be able to identify the hazards and associated risks with the tasks to be performed

C.1.2.3 To cross the restricted approach boundary and enter the restricted space, qualified persons should meet the following criteria:

(1) As applicable, have an energized electrical work permit authorized by management.
(2) Use personal protective equipment (PPE) that is rated for the voltage and energy level involved.
(3) Minimize the likelihood of bodily contact with exposed energized conductors and circuit parts from inadvertent movement by keeping as much of the body out of the restricted space as possible and using only protected body parts in the space as necessary to accomplish the work.
(4) Use insulated tools and equipment.

(See Figure C. 1.2.3.)

FIGURE C.1.2.3 *Limits of Approach.*

Exhibit C.1 illustrates the three approach boundary distances for a 600-volt motor control center (MCC) when the risk assessment is conducted using the PPE category method.

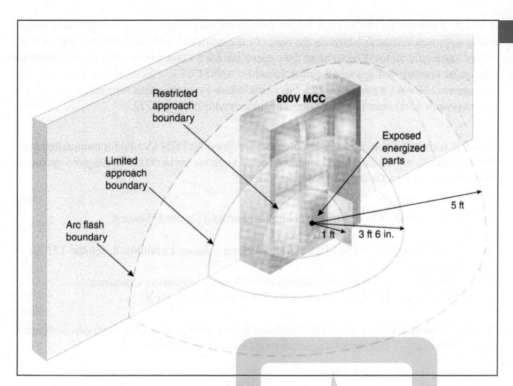

C.2 Basis for Distance Values in Tables 130.4(E)(a) and 130.4(E)(b).

The information contained in Tables 130.4(E)(a) and 130.4(E)(b) is derived from various sources. Section C.2 explains how the distances in the tables were selected.

C.2.1 General Statement. Columns 2 through 5 of Table 130.4(E)(a) and Table 130.4(E)(b) show various distances from the exposed energized electrical conductors or circuit parts. They include dimensions that are added to a basic minimum air insulation distance. Those basic minimum air insulation distances for voltages 72.5 kV and under are based on IEEE 4, *Standard Techniques for High Voltage Testing,* Appendix 2B; and voltages over 72.5 kV are based on IEEE 516, *Guide for Maintenance Methods on Energized Power Lines.* The minimum air insulation distances that are required to avoid flashover are as follows:

(1) ≤300 V: 1 mm (0 ft 0.03 in.)
(2) >300 V to ≤750 V: 2 mm (0 ft 0.07 in.)
(3) >750 V to ≤2 kV: 5 mm (0 ft 0.19 in.)
(4) >2 kV to ≤15 kV: 39 mm (0 ft 1.5 in.)
(5) >15 kV to ≤36 kV: 161 mm (0 ft 6.3 in.)
(6) >36 kV to ≤48.3 kV: 254 mm (0 ft 10.0 in.)
(7) >48.3 kV to ≤72.5 kV: 381 mm (1 ft 3.0 in.)
(8) >72.5 kV to ≤121 kV: 640 mm (2 ft 1.2 in.)
(9) >138 kV to ≤145 kV: 778 mm (2 ft 6.6 in.)
(10) >161 kV to ≤169 kV: 915 mm (3 ft 0.0 in.)
(11) >230 kV to ≤242 kV: 1.281 m (4 ft 2.4 in.)
(12) >345 kV to ≤362 kV: 2.282 m (7 ft 5.8 in.)
(13) >500 kV to ≤550 kV: 3.112 m (10 ft 2.5 in.)
(14) >765 kV to ≤800 kV: 4.225 m (13 ft 10.3 in.)

C.2.1.1 Column 1. The voltage ranges have been selected to group voltages that require similar approach distances based on the sum of the electrical withstand distance and an inadvertent movement factor. The value of the upper limit for a range is the maximum voltage for the highest nominal voltage in the range, based on ANSI C84.1, *Electric Power Systems and Equipment — Voltage Ratings (60 Hz).* For single-phase systems, select the range that is equal to the system's maximum phase-to-ground voltage multiplied by 1.732.

C.2.1.2 Column 2. The distances in column 2 are based on OSHA's rule for unqualified persons to maintain a 3.05 m (10 ft) clearance for all voltages up to 50 kV (voltage-to-ground), plus 100 mm (4.0 in.) for each 10 kV over 50 kV.

C.2.1.3 Column 3. The distances in column 3 are based on the following:

(1) ≤750 V: Use *NEC* Table 110.26(A)(1), Working Spaces, Condition 2, for the 151 V to 600 V range.
(2) >750 V to ≤145 kV: Use *NEC* Table 110.34(A), Working Space, Condition 2.
(3) >145 kV: Use OSHA's 3.05 m (10 ft) rules as used in Column 2.

C.2.1.4 Column 4. The distances in column 4 are based on adding to the flashover dimensions shown in C.2.1 the following inadvertent movement distance:

≤300 V: Avoid contact.

Based on experience and precautions for household 120/240-V systems:

>300 V to ≤750 V: Add 304.8 mm (1 ft 0 in.) for inadvertent movement.

These values have been found to be adequate over years of use in ANSI/IEEE C2, *National Electrical Safety Code,* in the approach distances for communication workers.

>72.5 kV: Add 304.8 mm (1 ft 0 in.) for inadvertent movement.

These values have been found to be adequate over years of use in ANSI/IEEE C2, National Electrical Safety Code, in the approach distances for supply workers.

Incident Energy and Arc Flash Boundary Calculation Methods

This informative annex is not a part of the requirements of this NFPA document but is included for informational purposes only.

Informative Annex D illustrates how the arc flash boundary and incident energy can be calculated. These examples are not intended to limit the choice of calculation methods; the method chosen should be applicable to the situation. All the publicly known methods of calculating the arc flash incident energy and arc flash boundary produce results that are estimates of the actual values. The thermal hazard associated with an arcing fault is very complex, with many variable attributes having an impact on the calculation.

NFPA and the Institute of Electrical and Electronics Engineers (IEEE) have issued the "IEEE/NFPA Collaboration on Arc Flash Phenomena Research Project" report. This report collected data to further understand arc flash phenomena, as well as data on the non-thermal effects of arc blasts.

Arc flash hazards are not limited to three-phase systems. Single-phase systems can also present arc flash hazards and must be considered. The calculation examples in Annex D do not specifically address single-phase systems. For example, the IEEE 1584, *Guide for Performing Arc-Flash Hazard Calculations,* theoretically derived model is intended for use with applications where faults escalate to three-phase faults.

NFPA *70E®* does not place an upper limit on the level of incident energy an employee can be exposed to during a justified energized task. Employees that could be exposed to arcing faults must wear appropriately arc-rated clothing or use other equipment to avoid severe thermal injuries. The incident energy limit is predicated on the currently available protective gear. However, protecting employees from the thermal effects of arcing faults does not necessarily protect them from injury.

An arcing fault can exhibit the characteristics of other hazards. For instance, the arc can generate a significant pressure wave. The calculations in this informative annex do not determine the pressure wave value. An employee could also be injured by the pressure differential between the outside and inside of the body. Currently, there are no standards available that address worker protection from the effects of any pressure wave, shrapnel, etc.

D.1 Introduction.

Informative Annex D summarizes calculation methods available for calculating arc flash boundary and incident energy. It is important to investigate the limitations of any methods to be used. The limitations of methods summarized in Informative Annex D are described in Table D.1.

NFPA *70E* covers electrical safety in the workplace via an established electrical safety program, not the calculation method for the incident energy. Science and testing have proven that an incident energy of 1.2 cal/cm² is sufficient to cause a second-degree burn to exposed skin. This limit must be the basis for arc flash protection in an electrical safety work program. It is the employer's responsibility to apply the correct equation for the system and equipment being assessed. Regardless of the calculation method, 1.2 cal/cm² must be used to establish the arc flash boundary.

Table D.1 identifies the source for and limitations of the methods of performing calculations to determine the arc flash boundary and incident energy that are demonstrated in Annex D. The table identifies which section of Informative Annex D covers each calculation method.

It is possible that one equation will not be applicable to all the equipment or systems in a facility. Using an equation, software program, or contract company does not absolve employers from making sure that the appropriate equation is used to calculate the incident energy for their specific systems and equipment.

Δ **TABLE D.1** *Limitation of Calculation Methods*

Section	Source	Limitations/Parameters
D.2	Lee, "The Other Electrical Hazard: Electrical Arc Flash Burns"	Calculates incident energy and arc flash boundary for arc in open air; conservative over 600 volts and becomes more conservative as voltage increases
D.3	Doughty, et al., "Predicting Incident Energy to Better Manage the Electrical Arc Hazard on 600 V Power Distribution Systems"	Calculates incident energy for three-phase arc on systems rated 600 volts and below; applies to short-circuit currents between 16 kA and 50 kA
D.4	IEEE 1584, *Guide for Performing Arc Flash Hazard Calculations*	Calculates incident energy and arc flash boundary for 208 volts to 15 kV; three-phase; 50 Hz to 60 Hz; 500 amperes to 106.000 amperes short-circuit current (208 volts to 600 volts); 200 amperes to 65,000 amperes short-circuit current (600 volts to 15.000 volts); and conductor gaps of 6.35 mm to 76.2 mm (0.25 in. to 3 in.) for 208 volts to 600 volts and 13 mm to 152 mm (0.75 in. to 10 in.) for 601 volts to 15,000 volts
D.5	Doan, "Arc Flash Calculations for Exposure to DC Systems"	Calculates incident energy for dc systems rated up to 1000 volts dc

D.2 Ralph Lee Calculation Method.

Δ **D.2.1 Basic Equations for Calculating Arc Flash Boundary Distances.** The short-circuit symmetrical ampacity, I_{sc}, from a bolted three-phase fault at the transformer terminals is calculated with the following formula:

$$I_{sc} = \left\{ \left[MVA \text{ Base} \times 10^6 \right] \div [1.732 \times V] \right\} \times \left\{ 100 \div \%Z \right\} \qquad \text{[D.2.1a]}$$

where I_{sc} is in amperes, V is in volts, and %Z is based on the transformer *MVA*.

A typical value for the maximum power, P (in MW) in a three-phase arc can be calculated using the following formula:

$$P = \left[\text{maximum bolted fault, in } MVA_{bf} \right] \times 0.707^2 \qquad \text{[D.2.1b]}$$

$$P = 1.732 \times V \times I_{sc} \times 10^{-6} \times 0.707^2 \qquad \text{[D.2.1c]}$$

The arc flash boundary distance is calculated in accordance with the following formulae:

$$D_c = \left[2.65 \times MVA_{bf} \times t \right]^{\frac{1}{2}} \qquad \text{[D.2.1d]}$$

$$D_c = \left[53 \times MVA \times t \right]^{\frac{1}{2}} \qquad \text{[D.2.1e]}$$

where:

D_c = distance in feet of person from arc source for a just curable burn (that is, skin temperature remains less than 80°C).

MVA_{bf} = bolted fault MVA at point involved.

MVA = MVA rating of transformer. For transformers with MVA ratings below 0.75 MVA, multiply the transformer MVA rating by 1.25.

t = time of arc exposure in seconds.

The clearing time for a current-limiting fuse is approximately !4 cycle or 0.004 second if the arcing fault current is in the fuse's current-limiting range. The clearing time of a 5-kV and 15-kV circuit breaker is approximately 0.1 second or 6 cycles if the instantaneous function is installed and operating. This can be broken down as follows: actual breaker time (approximately 2 cycles), plus relay operating time of approximately 1.74 cycles, plus an additional safety margin of 2 cycles, giving a total time of approximately 6 cycles. Additional time must be added if a time delay function is installed and operating.

The formulas used in this explanation are from Ralph Lee, "The Other Electrical Hazard: Electrical Arc Flash Burns," in *IEEE Trans. Industrial Applications*. The calculations are based on the worst-case arc impedance. *(See Table D.2.1.)*

TABLE D.2.1 *Flash Burn Hazard at Various Levels in a Large Petrochemical Plant*

(1)	(2)	(3)	(4)	(5)	(6)	(7)	
			System or		Clearing	Arc Flash Boundary Typical Distance*	
Bus Nominal Voltage Levels	System (MVA)	Transformer (MVA)	Transformer (% Z)	Short-Circuit Symmetrical (A)	Time of Fault (cycles)	SI	U.S.
230 kV	9000		1.11	23,000	6.0	15 m	49.2 ft
13.8 kV	750		9.4	31,300	6.0	1.16 m	3.8 ft
Load side of all 13.8-V fuses	750		9.4	31,300	1.0	184 mm	0.61 ft
4.16 kV		10.0	5.5	25,000	6.0	2.96 m	9.7 ft
4.16 kV		5.0	5.5	12,600	6.0	1.4 m	4.6 ft
Line side of incoming 600-V fuse		2.5	5.5	44,000	60.0–120.0	7 m–11 m	23 ft–36 ft
600-V bus		2.5	5.5	44,000	0.25	268 mm	0.9 ft
600-V bus		1.5	5.5	26,000	6.0	1.6 m	5.4 ft
600-V bus		1.0	5.57	17,000	6.0	1.2 m	4 ft

*Distance from an open arc to limit skin damage to a curable second degree skin burn [less than 80°C (176°F) on skin] in free air.

D.2.2 Single-Line Diagram of a Typical Petrochemical Complex. The single-line diagram *(see Figure D.2.2)* illustrates the complexity of a distribution system in a typical petrochemical plant.

Public utility
9000MVA fault
available

FIGURE D.2.2 *Single-Line Diagram of a Typical Petrochemical Complex.*

Δ **D.2.3 Sample Calculation.** Many of the electrical characteristics of the systems and equipment are provided in Table D.2.1. The sample calculation is made on the 4160-volt bus 4A or 4B. Table D.2.1 tabulates the results of calculating the arc flash boundary for each part of the system. For this calculation, based on Table D.2.1, the following results are obtained:

(1) Calculation is made on a 4160-volt bus.
(2) Transformer *MVA* (and base *MVA*) = 10 *MVA*.
(3) Transformer impedance on 10 *MVA* base = 5.5 percent.
(4) Circuit breaker clearing time = 6 cycles.

Using Equation D.2.1(a), calculate the short-circuit current:

$$I_{sc} = \left\{ \left[MVA\,Base \times 10^6 \right] \div \left[1.732 \times V \right] \right\} \times \left\{ 100 \div \%Z \right\} \qquad \text{[D.2.3a]}$$

$$N \qquad = \left\{ \left[10 \times 10^6 \right] \div \left[1.732 \times 4160 \right] \right\} \times \left\{ 100 \div 5.5 \right\}$$

$$= 25{,}000 \text{ amperes}$$

Using Equation D.2.1(b), calculate the power in the arc:

$$P = 1.732 \times 4160 \times 25,000 \times 10^{-6} \times 0.707^2$$ [D.2.3b]
$$= 91 \text{ MW}$$

Using Equation D.2.1(d), calculate the second degree burn distance:

$$D_c = \left\{ 2.65 \times \left[1.732 \times 25,000 \times 4160 \times 10^{-6} \right] \times 0.1 \right\}^{\frac{1}{2}}$$ [D.2.3c]
$$= 6.9 \text{ or } 7.00 \text{ ft}$$

Or, using Equation D.2.1(e), calculate the second degree burn distance using an alternative method:

$$D_c = \left[53 \times 10 \times 0.1 \right]^{\frac{1}{2}}$$ [D.2.3d]
$$= 7.28 \text{ ft}$$

△ D.2.4 Calculation of Incident Energy Exposure Greater Than 600 V for an Arc Flash Hazard Analysis. The equation that follows can be used to predict the incident energy produced by a three-phase arc in open air on systems rated above 600 V. The parameters required to make the calculations follow.

(1) The maximum bolted fault, three-phase short-circuit current available at the equipment.
(2) The total protective device clearing time (upstream of the prospective arc location) at the maximum short-circuit current. If the total protective device clearing time is longer than 2 seconds, consider how long a person is likely to remain in the location of the arc flash. It is likely that a person exposed to an arc flash will move away quickly if it is physically possible, and 2 seconds is a reasonable maximum time for calculations. A person in a bucket truck or a person who has crawled into equipment will need more time to move away. Sound engineering judgment must be used in applying the 2-second maximum clearing time, since there could be circumstances where an employee's egress is inhibited.
(3) The distance from the arc source.
(4) Rated phase-to-phase voltage of the system.

$$E = \frac{793 \times F \times V \times t_A}{D^2}$$ [D.2.4]

where:

E = incident energy, cal/cm^2
F = bolted fault short-circuit current, kA
V = system phase-to-phase voltage, kV
t_A = arc duration, sec
D = distance from the arc source, in.

> This discussion expands on the concept of a person's reaction time during an incident. A person's reaction time is a composite of many factors. When using exposure time as a basis for calculating incident energy, each factor needs to be studied because each has its own eccentricities.

REACTION TIME

Reaction time is complicated. Often, reaction times are used without a good understanding of where the numbers came from, how they were acquired, or the variables that shaped them. A reaction time of 1.5 seconds is commonly quoted by experts in regard to automobile accidents. In regard to arc flash incidents, 2 seconds is a reasonable maximum time to use when calculating the arc flash incident energy, provided the employee's egress is not inhibited. If the total clearing time of the upstream overcurrent protective device is greater than 2 seconds or if egress is restricted, then additional time might be needed to exit the arc flash boundary.

Engineering judgment must be used to determine if the 2-second exposure time is applicable. Reaction time can be broken down into different components or categories—such as perception, decision, and motor response times—each having fairly dissimilar properties.

MENTAL PROCESSING TIME

Mental processing time is the length of time it takes an employee to recognize that an event has happened (perception time) and to decide upon a response (decision time). For example, it might be the time it takes an employee to realize that an arc flash event is underway and decide what action to take. Perception and decision time can be further broken down into subcategories to better understand the hazard response.

Perception time. Perception time can be broken down into the following two subcategories:

- *Sensation time.* The time it takes to detect the sensory input of an event is the sensation time. The greater the signal intensity, the better the visibility and the faster the reaction time. Because reaction times can be faster for acoustic signals than for visual signals, the sound wave associated with an arc blast might lead to a faster response time.
- *Recognition time.* The time it takes to understand the meaning of an event is the recognition time. In some cases, an extremely fast automatic response could kick in, while in others, a controlled response, which can take substantial time, might occur. Training can help to decrease the time it takes to respond.

Decision time. Decision time can be broken down into the following two subcategories:

- *Situational awareness time.* The time it takes to recognize and interpret an event, extract its meaning, and possibly extrapolate it into the future is the situational awareness time. Again, practice or training can decrease the response time.
- *Response selection time.* The time needed to determine what reaction to have and decide what to do is the response selection time. Generally, the response selection time slows when more than one event is perceived or when more than one response is possible (that is, when choice is involved). As with the other categories here, practice or training can decrease the response time.

Additional factors. The following factors might also have an impact on the response time to an event:

- *Movement time.* A number of factors can affect the movement time, such as the number of exit passageways, the length of the passageways, and any obstacles that might be in the way. Generally, the greater the complexity of a movement, the longer it takes. Practice or training can lower movement times. In addition, an emotional stimulus can accelerate gross motor movements but inhibit fine detail movement.

- *Expectation.* It might be possible to get the reaction time down to around 1.4 seconds when the movement time is around 0.7 seconds if an event is expected, practiced for, and rehearsed. The reaction time for an unexpected event could be around 1.75 seconds, including 0.7 seconds of travel time. Extra time might be necessary to interpret an event and decide on the appropriate response when it is a complete surprise. In this case, the best estimate might be around 2.0 seconds, including 1.2 seconds for perception and decision and 0.8 seconds for movement. It might be necessary to study the situation to determine the appropriate reaction time.
- *Other factors.* Factors such as the perceived urgency, the complexity of a task, whether an employee is holding tools, and the employee's age and gender can affect the overall response time. The more complex an employee's task when an event happens, the longer the anticipated response time.

MINIMIZING EXPOSURE

The overcurrent protective device's operating time depends on whether the device is current limiting or not. Depending on the available fault current, an overcurrent protective device might be expected to extinguish an arcing current in anywhere from a ¼ cycle to 30 cycles. Employees cannot outrun arc flash events or minimize their exposure time for such short intervals, but they might be able to minimize their time inside the arc flash boundary when extended tripping times are involved.

Where the tripping time of the overcurrent protective device is longer than the reaction time of the employee, the employee might be able to increase his or her distance from the arcing event or exit the arc flash boundary. Doubling the distance between the source of an arc flash event and the employee decreases the incident energy level by around four (it is an inverse square type of relationship).

If the overcurrent protective device takes longer than 2 seconds to trip in response to an arcing current, consideration should be given to how long a person is likely to remain within the arc flash boundary. The physical layout needs to be considered when the exposure time is used to calculate the incident energy level. The anticipated exposure time might have to be increased if a narrow aisle is the only means of egress. Other factors to consider include whether it is possible for an employee to get stuck in a position and not be able to escape within the anticipated exposure time; whether the employee has studied the exit routes; whether the event is in an enclosed area or an outside switchyard; and whether the employee is in a bucket, in an aerial lift, or on a ladder. Field staff should evaluate and verify that, in the event of arc flash, they can exit the arc flash boundary within the assumed exposure time.

This discussion demonstrates the basic principles and thought processes involved when using exposure time as a basis for calculating the incident energy. Each type of reaction time needs to be studied, as each type has its own characteristics.

D.3 Doughty Neal Paper.

D.3.1 Calculation of Incident Energy Exposure. The following equations can be used to predict the incident energy produced by a three-phase arc on systems rated 600 V and below. The results of these equations might not represent the worst case in all situations. It is essential that the equations be used only within the limitations indicated in the definitions of the variables shown under the equations. The equations must be used only under qualified engineering supervision.

Informational Note: Experimental testing continues to be performed to validate existing incident energy calculations and to determine new formulas.

The parameters required to make the calculations follow.

(1) The maximum bolted fault, three-phase short-circuit current available at the equipment and the minimum fault level at which the arc will self-sustain. (Calculations should be made using the maximum value, and then at lowest fault level at which the arc is self-sustaining. For 480-volt systems, the industry accepted minimum level for a sustaining arcing fault is 38 percent of the available bolted fault, three-phase short-circuit current. The highest incident energy exposure could occur at these lower levels where the overcurrent device could take seconds or minutes to open.)

(2) The total protective device clearing time (upstream of the prospective arc location) at the maximum short-circuit current, and at the minimum fault level at which the arc will sustain itself.

(3) The distance of the worker from the prospective arc for the task to be performed.

Typical working distances used for incident energy calculations are as follows:

(1) Low voltage (600 V and below) MCC and panelboards — 455 mm (18 in.)
(2) Low voltage (600 V and below) switchgear — 610 mm (24 in.)
(3) Medium voltage (above 600 V) switchgear — 910 mm (36 in.)

D.3.2 Arc in Open Air. The estimated incident energy for an arc in open air is as follows:

$$E_{MA} = 5271 D_A^{-1.9593} t_A \begin{bmatrix} 0.0016F^2 \\ -0.0076F \\ +0.8938 \end{bmatrix} \qquad \text{[D.3.2a]}$$

where:

E_{MA} = maximum open arc incident energy, cal/cm^2
D_A = distance from arc electrodes, in. (for distances 18 in. and greater)
t_A = arc duration, sec
F = short-circuit current, kA (for the range of 16 kA to 50 kA)

Sample Calculation: Using Equation D.3.2(a), calculate the maximum open arc incident energy, cal/cm^2, where D_A = 18 in., t_A = 0.2 second, and F = 20 kA.

$$E_{MA} = 5271 D_A^{-1.9593} t_A \begin{bmatrix} 0.0016F^2 - 0.0076F \\ +0.8938 \end{bmatrix} \qquad \text{[D.3.2b]}$$

$$= 5271 \times .0035 \times 0.2 \times [0.0016 \times 400 - 0.0076 \times 20 + 0.8938]$$

$$= 3.69 \times [1.381]$$

$$= 21.33 \, \text{J} / \text{cm}^2 \left(5.098 \, \text{cal} / \text{cm}^2 \right)$$

D.3.3 Arc in a Cubic Box. The estimated incident energy for an arc in a cubic box (20 in. on each side, open on one end) is given in the equation that follows. This equation is applicable to arc flashes emanating from within switchgear, motor control centers, or other electrical equipment enclosures.

$$E_{MB} = 1038.7 D_B^{-1.4738} t_A \begin{bmatrix} 0.0093F^2 \\ -0.3453F \\ +5.9675 \end{bmatrix} \qquad \text{[D.3.3a]}$$

where:

E_{MB} = maximum 20 in. cubic box incident energy, cal/cm^2
D_B = distance from arc electrodes, in. (for distances 18 in. and greater)
t_A = arc duration, sec
F = short-circuit current, kA (for the range of 16 kA to 50 kA)

Sample Calculation: Using Equation D.3.3(a), calculate the maximum 20 in. cubic box incident energy, cal/cm^2, using the following:

(1) D_B = 18 in.
(2) t_A = 0.2 sec
(3) F = 20 kA

$$E_{MB} = 1038.7 D_B^{-1.4738} t_A \begin{bmatrix} 0.0093F^2 - 0.3453F \\ +5.9675 \end{bmatrix}$$ **[D.3.3b]**

$$= 1038 \times 0.0141 \times 0.2 \begin{bmatrix} 0.0093 \times 400 - 0.3453 \times 20 \\ +5.9675 \end{bmatrix}$$

$$= 2.928 \times [2.7815]$$

$$= 34.1 \, \text{J/cm}^2 \left(8.144 \, \text{cal/cm}^2\right)$$

D.3.4 Reference. The equations for this section were derived in the IEEE paper by R. L. Doughty, T. E. Neal, and H. L. Floyd, II, "Predicting Incident Energy to Better Manage the Electric Arc Hazard on 600 V Power Distribution Systems."

D.4 IEEE 1584-2018 Calculation Method.

N **D.4.1 Introduction.** This section provides a summary of the scope and purpose of IEEE 1584-2018, *Guide for Performing Arc Flash Hazard Calculations,* and it also provides an overview of the model range of parameters. Readers are encouraged to consult IEEE 1584-2018 for further information and detailed guidelines for proper application of the standard.

IEEE 1584-2018 is a revision of IEEE 1584-2002 as amended by IEEE 1584a-2004 and IEEE 1584b-2011.

The scope and purpose of IEEE 1584-2018 are in D.4.2 and D.4.3.

> IEEE 1584, *Guide for Performing Arc-Flash Hazard Calculations,* is possibly the most used standard for calculating incident energy. Annex D.4 summarizes IEEE 1584 rather than providing details. The limited information in this annex is not intended to cover all the issues addressed by IEEE 1584 and is insufficient to properly apply the equations. Appropriate use of the equations requires the review and understanding of IEEE 1584.

N **D.4.2 Scope.** This guide provides models and an analytical process to enable calculation of the predicted incident thermal energy and the arc-flash boundary (AFB). The process covers a collection of applicable field data, consideration of power system operating scenarios, and calculation parameters. Applications include electrical equipment and conductors for three-phase alternating current (ac) voltages from 208 volts to 15 kV. Calculations for single-phase ac systems and direct current (dc) systems are not a part of this guide, but some guidance and references are provided for those applications. Recommendations for personal protective equipment (PPE) to mitigate arc-flash hazards are not included in this guide.

N **D.4.3 Purpose.** The purpose of the guide is to enable qualified person(s) to analyze power systems for the purpose of calculating the incident energy (IE) to which employees could be exposed during operations and maintenance work. Contractors and facility owners can use this information to provide appropriate protection for employees in accordance with the requirements of applicable electrical workplace safety standards.

The new arc-flash model is a result of the IEEE/NFPA Arc-Flash Phenomena Collaborative Research Project and is based on over 1800 tests. The tests were performed at five different testing facilities over a 6-year period to ensure consistency and repeatability.

N **D.4.4 Range of the Model.** The range of the IEEE 1584-2018 model is provided in Table D.4.4.

N **TABLE D.4.4**   *Range of Input Parameters for IEEE 1584-2018*

Input parameter	Range
Voltage (Voc)	208 volts to 15,000 volts 3-phase (line-to-line)
Bolted fault curren (I_{bf}): 208 volts to 600 volts — low voltage (LV)	500 amperes to 106 000 amperes (rms symmetrical)
Bolted fault current (I_{bf}): 601 volts to 15,000 volts — medium voltage (MV)	200 to 65 000 A (rms symmetrical)
Gap (G): 208 volts to 600 volts	6.35 mm to 76.2 mm (0.25 in. to 3 in.)
Gap (G): 601 volts to 15,000 volts	19.05 mm to 254 mm (0.75 in. to 10 in.)
Working distance (*D*)	≥ 305 mm (12 in.)
Fault clearing time (*T*)	No limit
Maximum height	1244.6 mm (49 in.)
Maximum width	1244.6 mm (49 in.)
Minimum width	Four times the gap mm (4 x G)
Opening area	1.549 m^2 (2401 in.^{2})
Frequency	50 Hz or 60 Hz

N **D.4.5 Comparison with IEEE 1584-2002.** The following are differences between the IEEE 1584-2018 and the IEEE 1584-2002 arc flash models:

(1) The IEEE 1584-2002 arc-flash model was based on approximately 300 tests.
(2) The IEEE 1584-2018 model was based on over 1800 tests.
(3) IEEE 1584-2002 used two configurations.
(4) IEEE 1584-2018 includes five configurations.
(5) Five different labs were used for performing the tests.
(6) IEEE 1584-2002 test results were also used in new model.
(7) Based on the testing performed it was observed that sustainable arcs are possible but less likely in three-phase systems operating at 240 volts nominal or less with an available short-circuit current less than 2000 amperes.

N **D.4.6 Electrode Configuration.** The orientation and arrangement of the electrodes used in the testing performed for the model development.

The following electrode configurations (test arrangements) in Table D.4.6 are defined and utilized in the incident energy model:

(1) VCB: Vertical conductors/electrodes inside a metal box/enclosure
(2) VCBB: Vertical conductors/electrodes terminated in an insulating barrier inside a metal box/enclosure

(3) HCB: Horizontal conductors/electrodes inside a metal box/enclosure
(4) VOA: Vertical conductors/electrodes in open air
(5) HOA: Horizontal conductors/electrodes in open air

N **TABLE D.4.6**   *Electrode Orientation and Configurations*

E.C.	Standard	Orientation	Configuration	Termination
VOA	2002/2018	Vertical	Open air	Open air
VCB	2002/2018	Vertical	Metal enclosure	Open air
VCBB	2018	Vertical	Metal enclosure	Insulating barrier
HOA	2018	Horizontal	Open air	Open air
HCB	2018	Horizontal	Metal enclosure	Open air

N **D.4.7 Enclosure Size Correction Factor.** The VCB, VCBB, and HCB equations were normalized for a 508 mm x 508 mm x 508 mm (20 in. x 20 in. x 20 in.) enclosure. This model provides instructions on how to adjust incident energy for smaller and larger enclosures using a calculated correction factor.

N **D.4.8 Cautions and Disclaimers.** As an IEEE guide, this document suggests approaches for conducting an arc-flash hazard analysis but does not contain any mandatory requirements that preclude alternate methods. Following the suggestions in this guide does not guarantee safety, and users should take all reasonable, independent steps necessary to reduce risks from arc-flash events.

This information is offered as a tool for conducting an arc-flash hazard analysis. It is intended for use only by qualified persons who are knowledgeable about power system studies, power distribution equipment, and equipment installation practices. It is not intended as a substitute for the engineering judgment and adequate review necessary for such studies.

This guide is based upon testing and analysis of the thermal bum hazard presented by incident energy. Due to the explosive nature of arc-flash incidents, injuries can occur from ensuing molten metal splatters, projectiles, pressure waves, toxic arc by-products, the bright light of the arc, and the loud noise produced. These other effects are not considered in this guide.

This guide is subject to revision as additional knowledge and experience is gained. IEEE, those companies that contributed test data, and those people who worked on the development of this standard make no guarantee of results and assume no obligation or liability whatsoever in connection with this information.

The methodology in this guide assumes that all equipment is installed, operated, and maintained as required by applicable codes, standards, and manufacturers' instructions, and applied in accordance with its ratings. Equipment that is improperly installed or maintained may not operate correctly, possibly increasing the arc flash incident energy or creating other hazards.

D.5 Direct-Current Incident Energy Calculations.

D.5.1 Maximum Power Method. The following method of estimating dc arc flash incident energy that follows was published in the *IEEE Transactions on Industry Applications (see reference 2 of D.5.2)*. This method is based on the concept that the maximum power possible in a dc arc will occur when the arcing voltage is one-half the system voltage. Testing completed for Bruce Power *(see reference 3 of D.5.3)* has shown that this calculation is conservatively high in estimating the arc flash value. This method applies to dc systems rated up to 1000 volts.

$$I_{arc} = 0.5 \times I_{bf}$$
$$IE_m = 0.01 \times V_{sys} \times I_{arc} \times T_{arc} / D^2 \qquad \text{[D.5.1]}$$

where:

I_{arc} = arcing current, amperes

I_{bf} = system bolted fault current, amperes

IE_m = estimated dc arc flash incident energy at the maximum power point, cal/cm^2

V_{sys} = system voltage, volts

T_{arc} = arcing time, sec

D = working distance, cm

For exposures where the arc is in a box or enclosure, it would be prudent to consider additional PPE protection beyond the values shown in Table 130.7(C)(15)(b).

> This maximum power method for calculating the arc flash incident energy for a direct current power source uses principles similar to those used by Ralph Lee in his paper, "The Other Electrical Hazard: Electrical Arc Blast Burns," in *IEEE Transactions on Industrial Applications.*
>
> Without a full appreciation for the intricacies involved, it is possible to incorrectly apply the maximum power method equations. Appropriately determining the arcing time is key when using this method. Under transient conditions, such as at the initiation of an arcing fault, the current in a dc circuit will not change instantaneously. The rate of change is dependent on the L/R time constant of the circuit. The longer the time constant, the longer the circuit will take to reach its new steady-state value. During this time, the root mean square (rms) current value is dependent on the time constant. For devices that trip in response to rms current values, the L/R time constant can affect the total clearing time of the overcurrent protective device used to protect the circuit. It might be necessary to contact the manufacturer of the overcurrent protective device to obtain an appropriate time-current characteristic curve.

D.5.2 Detailed Arcing Current and Energy Calculations Method. A thorough theoretical review of dc arcing current and energy was published in the *IEEE Transactions on Industry Applications.* Readers are advised to refer to that paper (see reference 1) for those detailed calculations.

References:

1. "DC-Arc Models and Incident-Energy Calculations," Ammerman, R.F.; et al.; *IEEE Transactions on Industry Applications,* Vol. 46, No. 5.

2. "Arc Flash Calculations for Exposures to DC Systems," Doan, D.R., *IEEE Transactions on Industry Applications,* Vol. 46, No. 6.

3. "DC Arc Flazard Assessment Phase II", Copyright Material, Kinectrics Inc., Report No. K-012623-RA-0002-R00.

D.5.3 Short Circuit Current. The determination of short circuit current is necessary in order to use Table 130.7(C)(15)(b). The arcing current is calculated at 50 percent of the dc short-circuit value. The current that a battery will deliver depends on the total impedance of the short-circuit path. A conservative approach in determining the short-circuit current that the battery will deliver at 25°C is to assume that the maximum available short-circuit current is 10 times the 1 minute ampere rating (to 1.75 volts per cell at 25°C and the specific gravity of 1.215) of the battery. A more accurate value for the short-circuit current for the speciific application can be obtained from the battery manufacturer.

References:

1. IEEE 946, *Recommended Practice for the Design of DC Auxiliary Powers Systems for Generating Stations.*

Electrical Safety Program

This informative annex is not a part of the requirements of this NFPA document but is included for informational purposes only.

Informative Annex E provides information that can be used as the groundwork for an electrical safety program.

(See 110.5, Electrical Safety Program.)

E.1 Typical Electrical Safety Program Principles.

Electrical safety program principles include, but are not limited to, the following:

(1) Inspecting and evaluating the electrical equipment
(2) Maintaining the electrical equipment's insulation and enclosure integrity
(3) Planning every job and document first-time procedures
(4) De-energizing, if possible (see 120.5)
(5) Anticipating unexpected events
(6) Identifying the electrical hazards and reduce the associated risk
(7) Protecting employees from shock, bum, blast, and other hazards due to the working environment
(8) Using the right tools for the job
(9) Assessing people's abilities
(10) Auditing the principles

E.2 Typical Electrical Safety Program Controls.

Electrical safety program controls can include, but are not limited to, the following:

(1) The employer develops programs and procedures, including training, and the employees apply them.
(2) Employees are to be trained to be qualified for working in an environment influenced by the presence of electrical energy.
(3) Procedures are to be used to identify the electrical hazards and to develop job safety plans to eliminate those hazards or to control the associated risk for those hazards that cannot be eliminated.

(4) Every electrical conductor or circuit part is considered energized until proved otherwise.

(5) De-energizing an electrical conductor or circuit part and making it safe to work on is, in itself, a potentially hazardous task.

(6) Tasks to be performed within the limited approach boundary or arc flash boundary of exposed energized electrical conductors and circuit parts are to be identified and categorized.

(7) Precautions appropriate to the working environment are to be determined and taken.

(8) A logical approach is to be used to determine the associated risk of each task.

E.3 Typical Electrical Safety Program Procedures.

Electrical safety program procedures can include, but are not limited to determination and assessment of the following:

(1) Purpose of task
(2) Qualifications and number of employees to be involved
(3) Identification of hazards and assessment of risks of the task
(4) Limits of approach
(5) Safe work practices to be used
(6) Personal protective equipment (PPE) involved
(7) Insulating materials and tools involved
(8) Special precautionary techniques
(9) Electrical single-line diagrams
(10) Equipment details
(11) Sketches or photographs of unique features
(12) Reference data

Risk Assessment and Risk Control

F

This informative annex is not a part of the requirements of this NFPA document but is included for informational purposes only.

Both installation and work practices impact electrical safety, but they are separate and distinct electrical industries. Safe work practices are not part of a de-energized installation, and installation is not a safe work practice for exposed electrical hazards. To improve electrical safety for persons interacting with electrical equipment, those responsible for electrical safety must use a holistic approach. Designers must consider electrical safety for persons operating the equipment and the safety for persons maintaining that equipment. Employers must conduct risk assessments prior to finalizing the selection and installation of electrical equipment to address both equipment operation and maintenance.

There are thousands of ways to design or install a piece of equipment while complying with product standards and *NEC®* requirements. One design method then one installation method is used to allow the equipment to be safely operated under normal conditions. However, the decision to design or install equipment in a particular manner can have a lasting impact on electrical safety for the life of that equipment. There is no limit to the level of voltage, current, or energy that a safe installation can contain. Once an employee is exposed to those hazards, there can be no hindsight regarding the design or installation.

With a holistic approach to electrical safety, equipment design and installation must consider justified employee exposure to hazards and methods of controlling those hazards. As a result, future employees will be not only protected by the installation itself but protected based on *NFPA 70E®* safe work practices.

This informative annex deals with risk assessment and risk control. Risk assessment is made up of risk estimation and risk evaluation. Risk control utilizes the hierarchy of controls from the highest level to the lowest level to reduce the risk to an acceptable level for the task at hand. The procedure involves an iterative process of risk reduction until an acceptable risk level is attained.

Electrical safety issues (not health issues) are the focus of this standard. However, from an overall safety point of view, both health and safety issues are important. Electrical safety issues need to be assessed and prioritized. Potential electrical safety issues include electrical shock, arc flashes, arc blasts, and burns from hot electrical equipment associated with a particular task; risks associated with those hazards; electrical safety management system deficiencies; the opportunities for improvement; and the appropriate PPE necessary for the assigned task.

F.1 Introduction to Risk Management.

Risk management is the logical, systematic process used to manage the risk associated with any activity, process, function, or product including safety, the environment, quality, and finance. The risk management process and principles can be by organizations of any type or size.

The following risk management principles can readily be applied to electrical safety. Risk management:

(1) Is an integral part of all organizational processes and decision making
(2) Is systematic, structured, and timely
(3) Is based on the best available information
(4) Takes human and cultural factors into account
(5) Is dynamic, iterative, and responsive to change
(6) Facilitates continual improvement of the organization

Informational Note: For more information on risk management principles see ISO 31000:2009, *Risk Management — Principles and Guidelines.*

The risk management process includes the following:

(1) Communication and consultation
(2) Establishing the risk assessment context and objectives
(3) Risk assessment
(4) Risk treatment
(5) Recording and reporting the risk assessment results and risk treatment decisions
(6) Monitoring and reviewing risks

Risk assessment is the part of risk management that involves the following:

(1) Identifying sources of risk
(2) Analyzing the sources of risk to estimate a level of risk
(3) Evaluating the level of risk to determine if risk treatment is required

(*See Figure F.1.*)

FIGURE F.1 *Risk Management Process (Adapted from ISO 31000 figure 3).*

In a general sense, risk can be described as the potential for a chosen action or inaction to lead to some type of loss or injury. For electrical safety, risk is defined as a combination of the likelihood of the occurrence of injury and the severity of the injury that results from a hazard. The type of injury (either direct or indirect) can be caused by contact with exposed energized circuit parts or when an arc flash occurs.

Risk assessment is a step in the risk management process that involves risk estimation and risk evaluation. Risk assessment is the determination of the level of risk related to an actual situation involving a recognized hazard. Two basic approaches to risk assessment—the hazard-based approach and the task-based approach—are briefly addressed in Sections F.4 and F.5. There are many techniques that can be used to conduct a risk assessment. Section F.6 explains three possible methods.

For risk to be properly assessed, the situation must be placed into a specific context and the objective must be defined. A risk assessment could be different if the objective is arc flash protection rather than shock protection. An exposed hazard introduces the risk of injury. If employees are not permitted to enter a room, there is no risk of personal injury. If employees are permitted into that room, the risk of personal injury greatly increases. However, not all tasks close to hazards pose an increased risk of injury. Without context or an objective, a risk assessment is incomplete.

F.1.1 Occupational Health and Safety (OHS) Risk Management. The same logical, systematic process and the same principles apply to risk management in the OHS sphere of activity. However, it is more focused and the terminology more narrowly defined, as follows:

(1) The OHS objective is freedom from harm (i.e., injury or damage to health).
(2) Sources of risk are referred to as hazards.
(3) Analyzing and estimating the level of risk is a combination of the estimation of the likelihood of the occurrence of harm and the severity of that harm.
(4) The level of risk is evaluated to determine if it is reasonable to conclude that freedom from harm can be achieved or if further risk treatment is required.
(5) Risk treatment is referred to as risk control.

Therefore, OHS risk assessment involves the following:

(1) Hazard identification: Find, list, and characterize hazards.
(2) Risk analysis: Sources, causes, and potential consequences are analyzed to determine the following:
   a. The likelihood that harm might result
   b. The potential severity of that harm
   c. Estimate the level of risk
(3) Risk evaluation: The level of risk is evaluated to determine if the objective of freedom from harm can reasonably be met by the risk control that is in place or is further risk control required?

Users of NFPA *70E* will likely follow their own version of the occupational health and safety (OHS) risk management system to conduct the required shock and arc flash risk assessments.

Step 1: Hazard Identification

Hazard identification is possibly the simplest step in the process. The possible source of injury in an electrical safety context is typically obvious. NFPA *70E* currently addresses.

only two hazards directly—electric shock and arc flash burns. As part of a risk assessment, it is necessary to address all the electrical hazards. The definition of *electrical hazard* in Article 100 includes electric shock, arc flash burns, thermal burns, and arc blasts. Other known hazards include flying parts, molten metal, intense light, poisonous oxides, and generated pressure waves (blasts).

Step 2: Risk Analysis

The second step is more difficult to define. The risk level related to an identified hazard is based on the severity of the possible injury and the likelihood of occurrence of that injury. A qualitative rather than quantitative approach might be necessary to estimate the likelihood of harm, the severity of an injury, and the level of risk associated with a hazard. Often, three factors are considered independently to determine the likelihood of harm. The factors are as follows:

1. The frequency and duration of exposure
2. The likelihood of a hazardous event occurring
3. The likelihood of avoiding or limiting injury

The occurrence of a hazardous event influences the likelihood of the occurrence of injury. The risk assessment of a hazardous event should address the likelihood of the event during the use or foreseeable misuse—or both—of an electrical system. Foreseeable characteristics of human behavior that could impact the likelihood of an occurrence are stress (e.g., due to time constraints, work tasks, and perceived damage) and a lack of awareness of information relevant to the hazard. Human behavior is influenced by factors such as skill, training, experience, and the complexity of the equipment or the process.

Subjectivity can have a substantial impact on the result of a risk assessment. The use of subjective information should be minimized as far as is reasonably practicable. When determining the likelihood of a hazardous event, it might be helpful to ask several questions. While it is not intended to be a complete or accurate list of the actual questions that they should ask, employers should consider the following:

1. Does the equipment meet the necessary normal operating conditions?
2. At what point is the equipment in its rated life?
3. Have all the connections been verified to be appropriately tightened (torqued) in accordance with the manufacturer's requirements or the appropriate industry standard?
4. Is any component, device, or equipment loose or damaged?
5. Does the enclosure have all of its bolts and screws installed?
6. Does the equipment have ventilation openings?
7. Is the enclosure arc rated?
8. Are there openings in the enclosure that rodents or other vermin could enter?
9. Has the enclosure been examined for moisture, dust, dirt, soot, and grease?
10. What actions can employees take?
11. What errors might employees make?

The following are some circuit breaker (CB) condition questions:

12. Has the right type of CB been used?
13. Has the CB been applied at its marked rating?
14. Have the proper conductor types and sizes been used?
15. What is the ampere rating?

16. Has the CB been operated in accordance with the manufacturer's instructions or in accordance with standard requirements?
17. Has a calibration sampling program been instituted?
18. Has the CB interrupted high-fault currents or repeatedly interrupted fault currents?
19. Has the operating temperature been checked under normal use conditions?
20. Have insulation resistance or individual pole resistance (millivolt drop) tests been performed?
21. Have inverse-time or instantaneous overcurrent trip tests been conducted?
22. Has a rated hold-in test been conducted?
23. Have accessory devices been tested?
24. Have the surfaces been examined for evidence of overheating, blistering, cracks, dust, dirt, soot, grease, and moisture?
25. Are all the electrical connections clean and secure?
26. Are the external metal parts discolored or flaking or is the adjacent wiring melting or blistering?
27. If the CB has interchangeable trip units, are the trip units loose or overheated?

The likelihood of avoiding injury can be estimated by considering the aspects of an electrical system's design and its intended application. Examples include the following:

1. The sudden or gradual occurrence of a hazardous event
2. An employee's spatial ability to withdraw from a hazard
3. The nature of a component or system—for example, the use of touch-safe components, which reduce the likelihood of contact with energized parts
4. The likelihood of recognizing a hazard

The severity of an injury can be estimated by considering reversible injuries, irreversible injuries, and death.

Step 3. Risk Evaluation

Risk evaluation is a determination whether risk control methods can satisfactorily protect employees from harm. Once a risk has been estimated prior to the application of protective measures, all practicable efforts must be made to reduce the risk of injury. Careful consideration of failure modes is an important part of risk reduction. Care should be taken to ensure that both technical and behavioral failures, which could result in ineffective risk reduction, are taken into account during the risk reduction stage of the risk assessment.

Situations in which hazards cannot be eliminated typically require a balanced approach to reduce the likelihood of injury. For example, controlling access to an electrical system requires the use of barriers, awareness placards, safe operating instructions, qualification and training, and PPE, as well as initial, refresher, or periodic training for all affected personnel. Engineering controls alone are not sufficient to reduce the remaining risk to a tolerable level. Often, all six levels of risk controls in Table F.3 must be used in some form to achieve an adequate risk reduction strategy.

Once the assessment is complete and the protective measures have been determined, it is imperative that the protective measures be implemented prior to initiating electrical work. While this procedure might not result in a reduction of the PPE required, it could improve the understanding of the hazards associated with a task to a greater extent and, thus, ensure the proper implementation of the protective measures.

F.2 Relationship to Occupational Health and Safety Management System (OHSMS).

As discussed in Annex P, the most effective application of the requirements of this standard can be achieved within the framework of an OHSMS. Using a management system provides a methodical approach to health and safety by means of goal setting, planning, and performance measurement.

Risk management shares the six management system process elements of the following:

(1) Leadership. If any venture is to succeed it needs to be sponsored at the highest levels of the organization.
(2) Policy. The organization should articulate its vision and establish relevant, attainable goals.
(3) Plan. A plan is developed in line with the organization's vision and to achieve its goals. The plan must include mechanisms to measure and monitor the success of the plan.
(4) Do. The plan is executed.
(5) Check (Monitor). The success of the plan in achieving the organization's goals is continuously monitored.
(6) Act (Review). The measuring and monitoring results are compared to the organization's goals for the purposes of reviewing and revising goals and plans to improve performance.

As noted in F.1, risk management is iterative. The repeating nature of the management system plan-do-check-act (PDCA) cycle is intended to promote continuous improvement in health and safety performance.

Risk assessment fits into the "plan" and "do" stages of the PDCA cycle, as follows:

(1) Planning: Information used during the planning stage comes from sources that can include workplace inspections, incident reports, and risk assessments.
(2) Do: Risk assessment is an ongoing activity.

F.3 Hierarchy of Risk Control.

The purpose of specifying and adhering to a hierarchy of risk control methods is to identify the most effective individual or combination of preventive or protective measures to reduce the risk associated with a hazard. Each risk control method is considered less effective than the one before it. Table F.3 lists the hierarchy of risk control identified in this and other safety standards and provides examples of each.

TABLE F.3   *The Hierarchy of Risk Control Methods*

Risk Control Method	Examples
(1) Elimination	Conductors and circuit parts in an electrically safe working condition
(2) Substitution	Reduce energy by replacing 120 V control circuitry with 24 Vac or Vdc control circuitry
(3) Engineering controls	Guard energized electrical conductors and circuit parts to reduce the likelihood of electrical contact or arcing faults
(4) Awareness	Signs alerting of the potential presence of hazards
(5) Administrative controls	Procedures and job planning tools
(6) PPE	Shock and arc flash PPE

Although it can never be eliminated, risk can be significantly reduced using the hierarchy of risk controls. Whenever the level of risk is unacceptable, additional safety measures must be used to reduce the risk to an acceptable level.

The hierarchy is listed in order of the most effective to the least effective and must be applied in descending order for each risk assessment. Once a hazard has been identified, it must first be determined if the hazard can be eliminated. During the electrical system design stage, methods should be employed to eliminate the hazard in its entirety. In the electrical system design and equipment selection phase, it might be easier to utilize the most effective controls of elimination and substitution to limit the risk associated with anticipated justified energized work. In this first context, elimination is the removal of a hazard so that it does not exist. This removes the potential for human error when interacting with the equipment.

Elimination of a hazard is often not an option for installed electrical equipment. Although elimination of a hazard can be achieved by applying other controls, such as by establishing an electrically safe work condition, these other controls can introduce the potential for human error. Therefore, the initial attempt should be for full elimination of the hazard or substitution of the equipment to minimize the hazard.

The result of each risk assessment should be evaluated to determine if the hierarchy of risk controls can be further employed to lower the risk or reduce the hazard. Exhibit F.1 illustrates the iterative process of applying the hierarchy of risk controls. Each step is evaluated and controls reapplied as necessary until the risk of injury is reduced to an acceptable level. Only after all the other risk controls have been exhausted should PPE be selected. PPE is considered the least effective and lowest level of safety control for employee protection and should not be the first or only control element used.

F.4 Hazard-Based Risk Assessment.

In a hazard-based risk assessment, workplace hazards are identified and characterized for materials, processes, the worksite, and the environment. Activities that might be affected by those hazards are identified. The risk associated with each activity is analyzed for likelihood of harm and severity of harm. An organization uses this information to prioritize risk reduction decisions.

The information from hazard-based risk assessments is useful to organizations when designing, specifying, and purchasing electrical distribution equipment. Risk control is much more effective when it is applied at the beginning of the equipment or process lifecycle. Risk can be reduced by specifying "substitution" and "engineering" risk control methods that affect the likelihood of occurrence of harm or severity of harm.

F.5 Task-Based Risk Assessment.

In a task-based risk assessment, a job is broken down into discrete tasks. Hazards are identified for each task (often referred to as task-hazard pairs). The risk associated with each hazard is analyzed and evaluated.

The task-based risk assessment is the most commonly used when performing a field level risk assessment.

F.6 Risk Assessment Methods.

There are many risk assessment methods. The method or combination of methods should be chosen based on the following:

(1) The application
(2) The desired result
(3) The skill level of the persons performing the assessment

EXHIBIT F.1

Risk assessment process.

Some risk assessment methods include the following:

(1) Brainstorming. An open group discussion regarding hazards, the associated risk, and risk control methods can be used as part of pre-job planning and during a job briefing session.

(2) Checklists. A list of common hazards and possible control methods is a useful tool for pre-job planning and for job briefing purposes. See Annex I for an example of a job briefing and planning checklist.

(3) Risk assessment matrix. A risk assessment matrix is commonly used to quantify levels of risk. The matrix can be in a multilevel or a simple two-by-two format. See Figure F.6 for an example of a risk assessment matrix.

Informational Note: See ISO 31010. Risk management — *Risk assessment techniques*, and ANSI/ AIHA Z10-2012, *Occupational Health and Safety Management Systems*, for further information regarding risk assessment methods.

Likelihood of Occurrence of Harm	Severity of Harm	
	Energy ≤ [Selected Threshold]	Energy > [Selected Threshold]
Improbable	Low	Low
Possible	Low	High

Legend

Likelihood of Occurrence of Harm	**Severity of Harm**
Improbable: Source of harm is adequately guarded to avoid contact with hazardous energy	Energy ≤ [Selected Threshold]: Level of hazardous energy insufficient to cause harm
Possible: Source of harm is not adequately guarded to avoid contact with hazardous energy	Energy > [Selected Threshold]: Level of hazardous energy insufficient to cause harm

Risk Evaluation

Identify the risk controls in place and evaluate the effectiveness of the controls. Prioritize actions taken to control risk based on the level of risk as follows:

Low: Risk Acceptable — Further risk control discretionary

High: Risk Unacceptable — Further risk control required before proceeding

Δ **FIGURE F.6** *Example of a Qualitative Two-by-Two Risk Assessment Matrix.*

Several methods can be used to qualitatively estimate risk, such as risk assessment matrices, risk ranking, or risk scoring systems. Sample risk assessment matrices are shown in Figure F.6 and Exhibit F.2. A matrix is an ordered presentation of data in a display of rows and columns that defines the cells of the array. A risk assessment matrix is a simple table that groups risk based on severity and likelihood. It can be used to assess the need for remedial action, such as the use of PPE for a given task, and to prioritize safety issues.

The risk assessment matrix that appears in Figure F.6 displays the two factors that must be considered when evaluating risk: the likelihood of the occurrence of harm and the severity of the injury that could result. The columns and rows must then be assigned values, such as low and high. A matrix can become cumbersome if too many columns and rows are used, and it can fail to impart the necessary information if too few are used. Practically speaking, the maximum number of categories for a useful matrix is five. Figure F.6 uses two categories for the rows (improbable and possible) and two for the columns (first energy level and second energy level).

Likelihood of occurrence in period	Severity of the injury (consequences)				
	Slight	Minor	Medium	Critical	Catastrophic
cal/cm²	<1.2	≥1.2 to ≤ 8		>8 to ≤ 40	> 40
Unlikely					
Seldom					
Occassional					
Likely					
Definite					

Notes:
1. Extreme equals 25 through 15.
2. High equals 12 through 9.
3. Moderate equals 8 through 4.
4. Low equals 3 through 1.

The risk assessment matrices in this informational annex and its associated commentary are only illustrations of aids that can be used when prioritizing and determining remedial actions. There are many different risk assessment matrices available, including those in ANSI/AIHA Z10, *Occupational Safety and Health Management Systems*, which offer a different interpretation.

Likelihood of Occurrence of Arc Flash Event and Circuit Breaker Operation

Experience has shown that the likelihood of an arc flash event increases as people interact with electrical equipment, and that some interactions increase the likelihood of an arc flash event occurring. Turning on a circuit breaker (CB) might increase the likelihood of an arc flash event more than turning off a CB, for instance. CBs housed in electrical equipment enclosures that have been properly installed, applied within their ratings, and properly maintained have a lower likelihood of causing an arc flash event than those that have not. Additionally, it is more likely that the actual incident energy level of a maintained CB will be close to the calculated level. The incident energy level available can affect the seriousness of potential harm—the greater the incident energy level, the more harm can be expected.

The risk of injury largely depends on the amount of energy available to a breaker, how old it is, how well it is maintained, and the task to be performed, among other factors. For example, there is little risk when simply operating (turning on and off) a well-maintained breaker in a dwelling with a 240-volt service and 10,000 amperes available. In contrast, a commercial building with an equally well-maintained breaker with 40,000 amperes available poses a greater risk..

Example: Circuit Breaker Operation While Energized

This example illustrates the use of a risk register and the other demonstrates the use of a risk assessment matrix. These examples should not be relied upon for any particular installation. They are simply meant to demonstrate the thinking process required to perform a risk assessment based on the principles included in Informative Annex F.

Background Facts. Using a risk register and a risk assessment matrix, an electrical safety committee must analyze two tasks to determine if they require additional safety controls. The first task is the operation (turning on and off) of a 1600-ampere CB in the main 480Y/277-volt, non-arc-rated switchboard in a building where the short-circuit current is calculated to be 35,000 amperes. The second task scenario is the operation (turning on and off) of a 20-ampere HID CB in a 480Y/277-volt lighting panelboard where the short-circuit current is 25,000 amperes. In both cases, the electrical equipment is under normal operating conditions, the equipment is within its rated life, a damp environment is not involved, and the CBs are being operated while the equipment is in a dead-front configuration.

The switchboard has an incident energy level of 31 cal/cm^2 and the lighting panelboard has an incident energy level of 5.8 cal/cm^2. The 1,600-ampere switchboard CB is operated twice a year when maintenance is scheduled for the facility and the 20-ampere HID CB is operated twice a day to turn the lighting on and off. Of the possible electrical hazards, only a risk assessment for the arc flash hazard must be performed.

Analysis Using the Risk Register. Scenario 1 illustrates the risk evaluation of the 1600-ampere CB in the switchboard, and Scenario 2 illustrates the 20-ampere CB in the panelboard. The following tables, which were selected by the safety committee, are applicable to these evaluations.

Scenario 1: The switchboard is not arc rated, and the incident energy level is 31 cal/cm^2; therefore, the severity value from Commentary Table F.1 is 6. The CB is operated twice a year, so the frequency and duration of exposure value from Commentary Table F.2 is 3. In this scenario, the likelihood of a hazardous event occurring is negligible due to the proper application of the CB and switchboard, and the value selected from Commentary Table F.3 is 1. Finally, since it is not anticipated that the switchboard enclosure will always be breached should an arc flash event occur while operating the CB, the likelihood of avoiding or limiting injury is rare, and the value from Commentary Table F.4 is 3.

Scenario 2: Should an arc flash incident occur, it is assumed that at 8 cal/cm^2 or less, the integrity of the lighting panelboard will not be breached. Based on an incident energy of 5.8 cal/cm^2, the severity of injury value from Commentary Table F.1 is 1. Based on the CB being operated twice per day, the frequency and duration of exposure value from Commentary Table F.2 is 5. For the same reason as for the 1600-ampere switchboard CB, the likelihood of an incident value from Commentary Table F.3 is 1. Finally, since it is assumed that the enclosure's integrity will remain intact, the likelihood of avoiding or limiting injury is probable, and its value from Commentary Table F.4 is 1.

The completed risk register is displayed as Commentary Table F.5. After its evaluation, the electrical safety committee has determined that a risk score higher than 10 requires additional safety controls. However, for the given scenarios and installed equipment, only administrative controls and PPE from the hierarchy of controls must be implemented. Therefore, based on their analysis, the committee has determined that the use of PPE is required when operating the 1600-ampere CB and is not required when operating the 20-ampere HID lighting panelboard CB.

Analysis Using the Risk Assessment Matrix. The electrical safety committee included incident energy levels in their selected risk assessment matrix (Exhibit F.2) based on their assumption that incident energy levels less than or equal to 8 cal/cm^2 will not breach the integrity of the enclosure. Further, they determined that the likelihood of occurrence of an arc flash event is unlikely, as their equipment has been properly selected, installed, and maintained. Scenario 1 illustrates the risk evaluation of the 1600-ampere CB in the switchboard, and Scenario 2 illustrates the risk evaluation of the 20-ampere CB in the panelboard.

Since the incident energy level in Scenario 1 is greater than 8 cal/cm^2 and less than 40 cal/cm^2 and the likelihood of an incident is considered unlikely, the risk is color-coded yellow and is assumed to be moderate. Therefore, based on their analysis, the committee recommends that management consider the additional controls indicated in Commentary Table F.6.

For Scenario 2, the risk assessment level is determined to be low (color code green), as the incident energy level is greater than 4 cal/cm^2 and less than or equal to 8 cal/cm^2 and the likelihood of an incident is considered unlikely. The electrical safety committee recommends that the existing controls remain in place as detailed in Commentary Table F.6.

COMMENTARY TABLE F.1 *Severity of the Possible Injury (Se) Classification*

Severity of Injury	Se Value
irreversible — trauma, death	8
Permanent — skeletal damage, blindness, hearing loss, third-degree burns	6
Reversible — minor impact, hearing damage, second-degree burns	3
Reversible — minor lacerations, bruises, first-degree burns	1

COMMENTARY TABLE F.2 *Frequency and Duration of Exposure (Fr) Classification*

Frequency of Exposure	Fr Value
$\geq$ 1 per hour	5
< 1 per hour to $\geq$ 1 per day	5
< 1 per day to $\geq$ 1 every 2 weeks	4
< 1 every 2 weeks to $\geq$ 1 per year	3
< 1 per year	2

COMMENTARY TABLE F.3 *Likelihood of a Hazardous Event (Pr) Classification*

Likelihood of a Hazardous Event	Pr Value
Very high	5
Likely	4
Possible	3
Rare	2
Negligible	1

COMMENTARY TABLE F.4 *Likelihood of Avoiding or Limiting Injury (Av) Classification*

Likelihood of Avoiding or Limiting Injury	Av Value
Impoossible	5
Rare	3
Probable	1

COMMENTARY TABLE F.5 *Risk Register for Example Scenario 1 (1600-ampere SWB CB) and Scenario 2 (20-ampere HID Lighting Panelboard CB)*

Scenario No.	Hazard	Severity		Likelihood of Occurrence of Harm				Risk Score
		Se (Commentary Table F.l)	Fr (Commentary Table F.2)	Pr (Commentary Table F.3)	Av (Commentary Table F.4)	Po (Fr + Pr + Av)		Se x Po
1	Arc flash	6	3	1	3	1		42
2	Arc flash	1	5	1	1	1		7

COMMENTARY TABLE F. 6   *Definition of Terms and Risk Categories for Use in Risk Assessment Matrix*

Likelihood (Probability) of Occurrence	
Definite	Almost certain to happen
Likely	Can happen at any time
Occasional	Can occur sporadically; from time to time
Seldom	Remote possibility; could happen sometime; most likely will not happen
Unlikely	Rare and exceptional for all practical purposes; can assume it will not happen
Severity of Injury	
Catastrophic	Death or permanent total disability
Critical	Permanent partial disability or temporary total disability for 3 months or longer
Medium	Medical treatment and lost work injury
Minor	Minor medical treatment possible
Slight	First aid or minor treatment
Risk and Risk Controls	
Extreme (Color code red)	Intolerable risk
	Do not proceed
	Immediately introduce further controls
	Detailed action and plan required
High (Color code orange)	Unsupportable risk
	Review and introduce additional controls
	Requires senior management attention
Moderate (Color code yellow)	Tolerable risk
	Introduces some level of risk; unlikely to occur
	Specific management responsibility
	Consider additional controls
	Take remedial action at the appropriate time
Low (Color code green)	Supportable risk
	Monitor and maintain controls in place
	Manage by routine
	Procedures
	Little or no impact

N **F.7 Battery Risk Assessment.**

Multiple hazards may be encountered when working on batteries (shock, arc flash, chemical, thermal). PPE selection should take into account all of the hazards depending on the task. The flow chart displayed in Figure F.7 will assist users to assess all hazards associated with work on batteries.

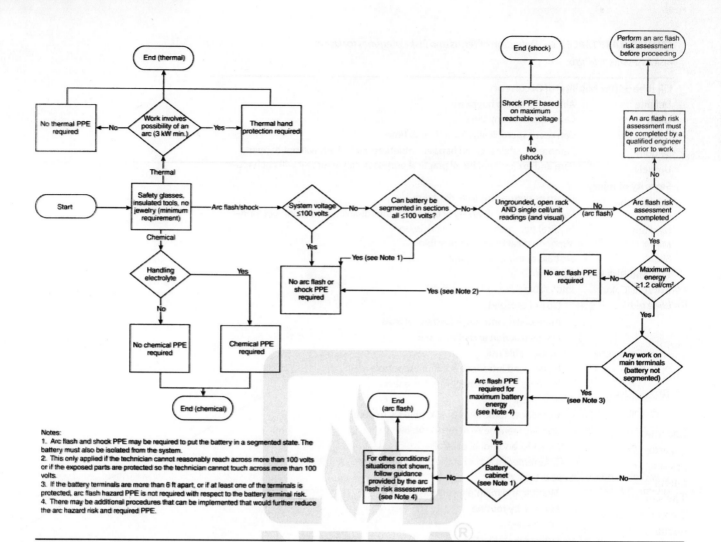

Notes:
1. Arc flash and shock PPE may be required to put the battery in a segmented state. The battery must also be isolated from the system.
2. This only applied if the technician cannot reasonably reach across more than 100 volts or if the exposed parts are protected so the technician cannot touch across more than 100 volts.
3. If the battery terminals are more than 6 ft apart, or if at least one of the terminals is protected, arc flash hazard PPE is not required with respect to the battery terminal risk.
4. There may be additional procedures that can be implemented that would further reduce the arc hazard risk and required PPE.

N **FIGURE F.7** *Assessing Hazards Associated with Work on Batteries.*

Sample Lockout/Tagout Program

This informative annex is not a part of the requirements of this NFPA document but is included for informational purposes only.

Informative Annex G illustrates how a lockout/tagout program can be published. An employer can fill in the blanks and publish the resulting program for an organization. See Supplement 3 for another safety procedure example that demonstrates the types of information that should make up a typical safety procedure.

Lockout is the preferred method of controlling personnel exposure to electrical energy hazards. Tagout is an alternative method that is available to employers. The sample program and procedures that follow are provided to assist employers in developing a lockout/tagout program and procedures that meet the requirements of Article 120 of *NFPA 70E*. The sample program and procedures can be used for a simple lockout/tagout or as part of a complex lockout/tagout. A more comprehensive procedure will need to be developed, documented, and used for the complex lockout/tagout.

LOCKOUT/TAGOUT PROGRAM
FOR [COMPANY NAME]
OR
TAGOUT PROGRAM FOR [COMPANY NAME]

1.0 Purpose.

This procedure establishes the minimum requirements for lockout /tagout of electrical energy sources. It is to be used to ensure that conductors and circuit parts are disconnected from sources of electrical energy, locked (tagged), and tested before work begins where employees could be exposed to dangerous conditions. Sources of stored energy, such as capacitors or springs, shall be relieved of their energy, and a mechanism shall be engaged to prevent the reaccumulation of energy.

2.0 Responsibility.

All employees shall be instructed in the safety significance of the lockout/tagout procedure. All new or transferred employees and all other persons whose work operations are or might be in the area shall be instructed in the purpose and use of this procedure. *[Name(s) of the person(s) or the job title(s) of the employee(s) with responsibility]* shall ensure that appropriate personnel receive instructions on their roles and responsibilities. All persons installing a lockout/tagout device shall sign their names and the date on the tag *[or state how the name of the individual or person in charge will be available].*

3.0 Preparation for Lockout/Tagout.

3.1 Review current diagrammatic drawings (or their equivalent), tags, labels, and signs to identify and locate all disconnecting means to determine that power is interrupted by a physical break and not de-energized by a circuit interlock. Make a list of disconnecting means to be locked (tagged).

3.2 Review disconnecting means to determine adequacy of their interrupting ability. Determine if it will be possible to verify a visible open point, or if other precautions will be necessary.

3.3 Review other work activity to identify where and how other personnel might be exposed to electrical hazards. Review other energy sources in the physical area to determine employee exposure to those sources of other types of energy. Establish energy control methods for control of other hazardous energy sources in the area.

3.4 Provide an adequately rated test instrument to test each phase conductor or circuit part to verify that they are de-energized (see Section G.11.3). Provide a method to determine that the test instrument is operating satisfactorily.

3.5 Where the possibility of induced voltages or stored electrical energy exists, call for grounding the phase conductors or circuit parts before touching them. Where it could be reasonably anticipated that contact with other exposed energized conductors or circuit parts is possible, call for applying ground connecting devices.

4.0 Simple Lockout/Tagout.

The simple lockout/tagout procedure will involve G.1.0 through G.3.0, G.5.0 through G.9.0, and G.11.0 through G.13.0.

5.0 Sequence of Lockout/Tagout System Procedures.

5.1 The employees shall be notified that a lockout/tagout system is going to be implemented and the reason for it. The qualified employee implementing the lockout/tagout shall know the disconnecting means location for all sources of electrical energy and the location of all sources of stored energy. The qualified person shall be knowledgeable of hazards associated with electrical energy.

5.2 If the electrical supply is energized, the qualified person shall de-energize and disconnect the electric supply and relieve all stored energy.

5.3 Wherever possible, the blades of disconnecting devices should be visually verified to be fully opened, or draw-out type circuit breakers should be verified to be completely withdrawn to the fully disconnected position.

5.4 Lockout/tagout all disconnecting means with lockout/tagout devices.

> Informational Note: For tagout, one additional safety measure must be employed, such as opening, blocking, or removing an additional circuit element.

5.5 Attempt to operate the disconnecting means to determine that operation is prohibited.

5.6 A test instrument shall be used. (See G.11.3.) Inspect the instrument for visible damage. Do not proceed if there is an indication of damage to the instrument until an undamaged device is available.

5.7 Verify proper instrument operation on a known source of voltage and then test for absence of voltage.

5.8 Verify proper instrument operation on a known source of voltage after testing for absence of voltage.

5.9 Where required, install a grounding equipment/conductor device on the phase conductors or circuit parts, to eliminate induced voltage or stored energy, before touching them. Where it has been determined that contact with other exposed energized conductors or circuit parts is possible, apply ground connecting devices rated for the available fault duty.

5.10 The equipment, electrical source, or both are now locked out (tagged out).

6.0 Restoring the Equipment, Electrical Supply, or Both to Normal Condition.

6.1 After the job or task is complete, visually verify that the job or task is complete.

6.2 Remove all tools, equipment, and unused materials and perform appropriate housekeeping.

6.3 Remove all grounding equipment/conductors/devices.

6.4 Notify all personnel involved with the job or task that the lockout/tagout is complete, that the electrical supply is being restored, and that they are to remain clear of the equipment and electrical supply.

6.5 Perform any quality control tests or checks on the repaired or replaced equipment, electrical supply, or both.

6.6 Remove lockout/tagout devices. The person who installed the devices is to remove them.

6.7 Notify the owner of the equipment, electrical supply, or both, that the equipment, electrical supply, or both are ready to be returned to normal operation.

6.8 Return the disconnecting means to their normal condition.

7.0 Procedure Involving More Than One Person.

For a simple lockout/tagout and where more than one person is involved in the job or task, each person shall install his or her own personal lockout/tagout device.

8.0 Procedure Involving More Than One Shift.

When the lockout/tagout extends for more than one day, it shall be verified that the lockout/tagout is still in place at the beginning of the next day. When the lockout/tagout is continued on successive shifts, the lockout/tagout is considered to be a complex lockout/tagout.

For a complex lockout/tagout, the person in charge shall identify the method for transfer of the lockout/tagout and of communication with all employees.

9.0 Complex Lockout/Tagout.

A complex lockout/tagout plan is required where one or more of the following exist:

(1) Multiple energy sources (more than one)
(2) Multiple crews
(3) Multiple crafts
(4) Multiple locations
(5) Multiple employers
(6) Unique disconnecting means
(7) Complex or particular switching sequences
(8) Lockout/tagout for more than one shift; that is, new shift workers

9.1 All complex lockout/tagout procedures shall require a written plan of execution. The plan shall include the requirements in G. 1.0 through G.3.0, G.5.0, G.6.0, and G.8.0 through G. 12.0.

9.2 A person in charge shall be involved with a complex lockout/tagout procedure. The person in charge shall be at the procedure location.

9.3 The person in charge shall develop a written plan of execution and communicate that plan to all persons engaged in the job or task. The person in charge shall be held accountable for safe execution of the complex lockout/tagout plan. The complex lockout/tagout plan must address all the concerns of employees who might be exposed, and they must understand how electrical energy is controlled. The person in charge shall ensure that each person understands the electrical hazards to which they are exposed and the safety-related work practices they are to use.

9.4 All complex lockout/tagout plans identify the method to account for all persons who might be exposed to electrical hazards in the course of the lockout/tagout.
    One of the following methods is to be used:

(1) Each individual shall install his or her own personal lockout or tagout device.
(2) The person in charge shall lock his/her key in a lock box.
(3) The person in charge shall maintain a sign-in/sign-out log for all personnel entering the area.
(4) Another equally effective methodology shall be used.

9.5 The person in charge can install locks/tags or direct their installation on behalf of other employees.

9.6 The person in charge can remove locks/tags or direct their removal on behalf of other employees, only after all personnel are accounted for and ensured to be clear of potential electrical hazards.

9.7 Where the complex lockout/tagout is continued on successive shifts, the person in charge shall identify the method for transfer of the lockout and the method of communication with all employees.

10.0 Discipline.

10.1 Knowingly violating the requirements of this program will result in [*state disciplinary actions that will be taken*].

10.2 Knowingly operating a disconnecting means with an installed lockout device (tagout device) will result in [*state disciplinary actions to be taken*].

11.0 Equipment.

11.1 Locks shall be [*state type and model of selected locks*],

11.2 Tags shall be [*state type and model to be used*].

11.3 The test instrument(s) to be used shall be [*state type and model*].

12.0 Review.

This program was last reviewed on [date] and is scheduled to be reviewed again on [date] (not more than 1 year from the last review).

13.0 Lockout/Tagout Training.

Recommended training can include, but is not limited to, the following:

(1) Recognition of lockout/tagout devices
(2) Installation of lockout/tagout devices
(3) Duty of employer in writing procedures
(4) Duty of employee in executing procedures
(5) Duty of person in charge
(6) Authorized and unauthorized removal of locks/tags
(7) Enforcement of execution of lockout/tagout procedures
(8) Simple lockout/tagout
(9) Complex lockout/tagout
(10) Use of single-line and diagrammatic drawings to identify sources of energy
(11) Alerting techniques
(12) Release of stored energy
(13) Personnel accounting methods
(14) Temporary protective grounding equipment needs and requirements
(15) Safe use of test instruments

Guidance on Selection of Protective Clothing and Other Personal Protective Equipment (PPE)

This informative annex is not a part of the requirements of this NFPA document but is included for informational purposes only.

Informative Annex H provides guidance on the selection of clothing and PPE, regardless of whether the arc flash PPE category method or the incident energy method is used to perform an arc flash risk assessment. This annex also provides guidance on the selection of shock protective equipment.

H.1 Arc-Rated Clothing and Other Personal Protective Equipment (PPE) for Use with Arc Flash PPE Categories.

Table 130.5(C), Table 130.7(C)(15)(a), Table 130.7(C)(15)(b), and Table 130.7(C)(15)(c) provide guidance for the selection and use of PPE when using arc flash PPE categories.

H.2 Simplified Two-Category Clothing Approach for Use with Table 130.7(C)(15)(a), Table 130.7(C)(15)(b), and Table 130.7(C)(15)(c).

The use of Table H.2 is a simplified approach to provide minimum PPE for electrical workers within facilities with large and diverse electrical systems. The clothing listed in Table H.2 fulfills the minimum arc-rated clothing requirements of Table 130.7(C)(15)(a), Table 130.7(C)(15)(b), and Table 130.7(C)(15)(c). The clothing systems listed in this table should be used with the other PPE appropriate for the arc flash PPE category *[see Table 130.7(C)(15)(c)]*. The notes to Table 130.7(C)(15)(a), Table 130.7(C)(15)(b), and Table 130.7(C)(15)(c) must apply as shown in those tables.

After an employer develops and publishes a procedure describing how thermal protection can be determined using the arc flash PPE categories method, the employer must develop a system to administer the procedure requirements efficiently and effectively. Section H.2 illustrates one way to efficiently and effectively use the arc flash PPE category method.

TABLE H.2 *Simplified Two-Category, Arc-Rated Clothing System*

Clothing[a]	*Applicable Situations*
Everyday Work Clothing Arc-rated long-sleeve shirt with arc-rated pants (minimum arc rating of 8) *or* Arc-rated coveralls (minimum arc rating of 8)	Situations where a risk assessment indicates that PPE is required and where Table 130.7(C)(15)(a) and Table 130.7(C)(15)(b) specify arc flash PPE category 1 or 2[b]
Arc Flash Suit A total clothing system consisting of arc-rated shirt and pants and/or arc-rated coveralls and/or arc flash coat and pants (clothing system minimum arc rating of 40)	Situations where a risk assessment indicates that PPE is required and where Table 130.7(C)(15)(a) and Table 130.7(C)(15)(b) specify arc flash PPE category 3 or 4[b]

[a] Note that other PPE listed in Table 130.7(C)(15)(c), which include arc-rated face shields or arc flash suit hoods, arc-rated hard hat liners, safety glasses or safety goggles, hard hats, hearing protection, heavy-duty leather gloves, rubber insulating gloves, and leather protectors, could be required. The arc rating for a garment is expressed in cal/cm^2.

[b] The estimated available fault current capacities and fault clearing times or arcing durations are listed in the text of Table 130.7(C)(15)(a) and Table 130.7(C)(15)(b). For power systems with greater than the estimated available fault current capacity or with longer than the assumed fault clearing times, Table H.2 cannot be used and arc flash PPE must be determined and selected by means of an incident energy analysis in accordance with 130.5(G).

H.3 Arc-Rated Clothing and Other Personal Protective Equipment (PPE) for Use with Risk Assessment of Electrical Hazards.

Table H.3 provides a summary of specific sections within the NFPA *70E* standard describing PPE for electrical hazards.

Even when using the arc flash PPE category method, the sections identified in Table H.3 should be reviewed to ensure that the appropriate PPE is being used to protect employees from the identified electrical hazards. This table does not include any clothing below 1.2 cal/cm². There are no requirements to provide the employee with arc flash protection below this incident energy, as an injury from such an incident is expected to be survivable and nonpermanent.

H.4 Conformity Assessment of Personal Protective Equipment (PPE).

Annex A references performance standards for items of PPE. Conformance to these standards is intended to provide employees with the appropriate PPE to ensure that any residual risk associated with their duties remains at an acceptable level. The responsibility of verifying conformance to the appropriate standard is with the employer, purchaser, or person providing PPE to employees.

Section H.4 offers a system of conformity assessment that can augment an employer's PPE approval process. ANSI/ISEA 125, *American National Standard for Conformity Assessment of Safety and Personal Protective Equipment,* is the standard for the conformity assessment methodology, and it provides three levels of conformity assessment ranging from supplier self-declaration to independent third-party certification. In accordance with 130.7(0(14), the level of conformity assessment for any item of PPE can be determined by the manufacturer or can be mandated by the purchaser.

TABLE H.3   *Summary of Specific Sections Describing PPE for Electrical Hazards*

Shock Hazard PPE	**Applicable Section(s)**
Rubber insulating gloves and leather protectors, unless the requirements of ASTM F496 are met	130.7(C)(7)(a)
Rubber insulating sleeves as needed	130.7(C)(7)(a)
Class G or E hard hat as needed	130.7(C)(3)
Safety glasses or goggles as needed	130.7(C)(4)
Dielectric overshoes as needed	130.7(C)(8)
Incident Energy Exposures Greater than or Equal to 1.2 cal/cm² (5 J/cm²)	
Clothing: Arc-rated clothing system with an arc rating appropriate to the anticipated incident energy exposure	130.7(C)(1), 130.7(C)(2), 130.7(C)(6), 130.7(C)(9)(d)
Clothing underlayers (when used): Arc-rated or nonmelting untreated natural fiber	130.7(C)(9)(c), 130.7(C)(11), 130.7(C)(12)
Gloves: Exposures greater than or equal to 1.2 cal/cm² (5 J/cm²) and less than or equal to 8 cal/cm² (33.5 J/cm²): heavy-duty leather gloves Exposures greater than 8 cal/cm² (33.5 J/cm²): rubber insulating gloves with their leather protectors or arc-rated gloves	130.7(C)(7)(b), 130.7(C)(10)(d)
Hard hat: Class G or E	130.7(C)(1), 130.7(C)(3)
Face shield: Exposures greater than or equal to 1.2 cal/cm² (5 J/cm²) and less than or equal to 12 cal/cm² (50.2 J/cm²): Arc-rated face shield that covers the face, neck, and chin and an arc-rated balaclava or an arc-rated arc flash suit hood Exposures greater than 12 cal/cm² (50.2 J/cm²): arc-rated arc flash suit hood	130.7(C)(1), 130.7(C)(3), 130.7(C)(10)(a), 130.7(C)(10)(b), 130.7(C)(10)(c)
Safety glasses or goggles	130.7(C)(4), 130.7(C)(10)(c)
Hearing protection	130.7(C)(5)
Footwear: Exposures less than or equal to 4 cal/cm² (16.75 J/cm²): Heavy-duty leather footwear (as needed) Exposures greater than 4 cal/cm² (16.75 J/cm²): Heavy-duty leather footwear	130.7(C)(10)(e)

H.4.1 Introduction. Section 130.7(C)(14) requires personal protective equipment (PPE) provided by a supplier or manufacturer to conform to appropriate product standards by one of three methods. Additional information for these conformity assessment methods can be found within ANSI/ISEA 125, *American National Standard for Conformity Assessment of Safety and Personal Protective Equipment.* ANSI/ISEA 125 establishes criteria for conformity assessment of safety and PPE that is sold with claims of compliance with product performance standards. ANSMSEA 125 contains provisions for data collection, product verification, conformation of quality and manufacturing production control, and roles and responsibilities of suppliers, testing organizations, and third-party certification organizations.

> Delivery of a conformity method to a purchaser of PPE does not absolve the employer from determining the validity of the claim. The employer must be competent to determine which standard applies to the purchased equipment, the correctness of the claim, and the validity of the test results. It might be necessary for the purchaser to specify exactly which standards the equipment must comply with.

H.4.2 Level of Conformity. ANSI/ISEA 125 provides for three different levels of conformity assessment: Level 1, Level 2, and Level 3.

Level 1 conformity is where the supplier or manufacturer is making a self-declaration that a product meets all of the requirements of the standard(s) to which conformance is claimed. A supplier Declaration of Conformity for each product is required to be made available for examination upon request.

Level 2 conformity is where the supplier or manufacturer is making a self-declaration that a product meets all of the requirements of the standard(s) to which conformance is claimed, the supplier or manufacturer has a registered ISO 9001 Quality Management System or equivalent quality management system, and all testing has been carried out by an ISO 17025 accredited testing laboratory. A supplier Declaration of Conformity for each product is required to be made available for examination upon request.

Level 3 conformity is where the products are certified by an ISO 17065 accredited independent third-party certification organization (CO). All product testing is directed by the CO, and all changes to the product must be reviewed and retested if necessary. Compliant products are issued a Declaration of Conformity by the CO and products are marked with the CO's mark or label.

H.4.3 Equivalence. While there are three levels of conformity assessment described in ANSI/ISEA 125, the levels are not to be considered as equivalent. Users are cautioned that the level of rigor required to demonstrate conformity should be based on the potential safety and health consequence of using a product that does not meet a stated performance standard. A higher potential safety and health consequence associated with the use of a noncompliant product should necessitate a higher level of conformity assessment.

> When employees are put at risk of injury when their employer authorizes energized work, PPE is the last line of defense available to limit injury or prevent their death. The effectiveness of protective equipment might not be evident until that equipment is called upon to perform its safety function. Employers must not supply their employees with substandard, counterfeit, or inappropriate PPE. Such gear could increase the severity of an injury if an incident occurs.
>
> Level 1 conformity is a variation of the Declaration of Conformity (DoC) system used in the European Union (EU). Within the EU and in some other locations, the DoC is a legal document declaring that equipment complies with the specific laws of the governing country. However, Level 1 conformity is not tied to a legal system and has no external oversight. It is the employer's responsibility to determine the validity of the declaration.
>
> An accredited laboratory in a Level 2 conformity is not necessarily an independent testing laboratory. Many companies are registered under the ISO 9000 series of standards for management systems. These companies might have on-site laboratories to conduct evaluations and to test their products with no external oversight. It is the employer's responsibility to determine the validity of product declarations.
>
> Level 3 conformity involves an independent organization testing products to the applicable standards. Within the United States, OSHA has a process for accrediting

organizations to perform evaluations using specific standards. Within NFPA *70E®*, equipment evaluated under this system is considered to be listed. It is the employer's responsibility to determine the validity of product declarations.

H.4.4 Supplier's Declaration of Conformity. A Declaration of Conformity should be issued by the supplier and made available for examination upon request from a customer, user, or relevant authority. The Declaration of Conformity should, at a minimum:

(1) List the supplier name and address.
(2) Include a product model number or other identification details.
(3) List the product performance standard or standards (designation and year) to which conformance is claimed.
(4) Include a statement of attestation.
(5) Be dated, written on supplier letterhead, and signed by an authorized representative. The name and title of the authorized representative should also be printed.

Additional information should include:

(1) The level of conformity followed
(2) Whether the ISO 17025 testing facility is an independent or in-house laboratory (owned or partially owned by an entity within the supplier's corporate structure or within the manufacturing stream for the applicable product, including subcontractors and sub-suppliers)
(3) Reference to the test report (title, number, date, etc.) that serves as the basis of determining conformity

For an example of a Supplier's Declaration of Conformity see Figure H.4.4.

```
┌─────────────────────────────────────────────────────────────┐
│            Supplier's Declaration of Conformity               │
│ No. _____                                    │
│ Issuer's name: _____             │
│ Issuer's address: _____           │
│ Object of the declaration: _____           │
│ _____             │
│ _____             │
│                                                               │
│ The object of the declaration described above is in conformity with the │
│ following documents:                                          │
│ Documents No.      Title               Edition/Date of issue  │
│                                                               │
│ _____    _____        _____    │
│ _____    _____        _____    │
│ _____    _____        _____    │
│                                                               │
│ Additional information:                                       │
│ _____             │
│ _____             │
│ _____             │
│                                                               │
│ Signed for and on behalf of:                                  │
│ _____             │
│ _____             │
│ Place and date of issue                                       │
│ _____             │
│ (Name, function)    (Signature or equivalent authorized by the issuer) │
└─────────────────────────────────────────────────────────────┘
```

FIGURE H.4.4 *Supplier's Declaration of Conformity.*

H.4.5 References. ANSI/ISEA contains detailed information and guidance on the application of the different conformity assessment levels. Copies of ANSI/ISEA 125 are available free of charge by emailing the International Safety Equipment Association at ISEA@Safetyequipment.org and requesting a complimentary copy.

Job Briefing and Job Safety Planning Checklist

This informative annex is not a part of the requirements of this NFPA document but is included for informational purposes only.

The employer is required by 110.5(A) to implement and document an overall electrical safety program (ESP). Job briefings must be included among the ESP elements. Before starting each job, the employee in charge must conduct a job briefing. The briefing must cover such subjects as the hazards associated with the job, work procedures involved, special precautions, energy source controls, PPE requirements, and information on the energized electrical work permit. The job briefing must be performed before employees begin the work tasks.

The job planning checklist in Figure 1.2 contains examples of items that must be addressed during job planning. The planning checklist can help when documenting the hazards and the appropriate protection necessary. The job briefing checklist in Figure I.1 contains examples of subjects that should be discussed during the job briefing. The briefing checklist can help facilitate this conversation. These checklists are not intended to be an all-inclusive list of subjects that should be considered. For example, job planning should include identifying the proper practices and procedures for an assigned task. Flowever, other subjects might need to be considered based on specific circumstances.

Δ **1.1 Job Briefing Checklist.**

Figure 1.1 illustrates considerations for a job briefing checklist.

N **1.2 Job Safety Planning Checklist**

Figure 1.2 illustrates considerations for a job safety planning checklist.

Identify
- ❏ Hazards
- ❏ Voltage levels involved
- ❏ Skills required
- ❏ Any "foreign" (secondary source) voltage source
- ❏ Any unusual work conditions
- ❏ Number of people needed to do the job
- ❏ Shock protection boundaries
- ❏ Available incident energy
- ❏ Potential for arc flash (Conduct an arc flash risk assessment.)
- ❏ Arc flash boundary
- ❏ Any evidence of impending failure?

Ask
- ❏ Can the equipment be de-energized?
- ❏ Are backfeeds of the circuits to be worked on possible?
- ❏ Is an energized electrical work permit required?
- ❏ Is a standby person required?
- ❏ Is the equipment properly installed and maintained?

Check
- ❏ Job plans
- ❏ Single-line diagrams and vendor prints
- ❏ Status board
- ❏ Information on plant and vendor resources is up to date
- ❏ Safety procedures
- ❏ Vendor information
- ❏ Individuals are familiar with the facility

Know
- ❏ What the job is
- ❏ Who else needs to know — Communicate!
- ❏ Who is in charge

Think
- ❏ About the unexpected event . . . What if?
- ❏ Lock — Tag — Test — Try
- ❏ Test for voltage — FIRST
- ❏ Use the right tools and equipment, including PPE
- ❏ Install and remove temporary protective grounding equipment
- ❏ Install barriers and barricades
- ❏ What else . . . ?

Prepare for an emergency
- ❏ Is the standby person CPR/AED trained?
- ❏ Is the required emergency equipment available? Where is it?
- ❏ Where is the nearest telephone?
- ❏ Where is the fire alarm?
- ❏ Is confined space rescue available?
- ❏ What is the exact work location?
- ❏ How is the equipment shut off in an emergency?
- ❏ Are the emergency telephone numbers known?
- ❏ Where is the fire extinguisher?
- ❏ Are radio communications available?
- ❏ Is an AED available?

△ **FIGURE I.1** *Sample Job Briefing Checklist.*

Job Safety Planning Checklist			
Equipment:			
Task:			
Location:			
Qualified submitter:		**Date:**	

Section A, General			
Mark "Y" or "N" as appropriate			

No.	Item	Yes	No	Instructions
1.	Is there justification for the energized work? a. Equipment operating at less than 50 volts b. Additional hazard or increased risk c. Infeasible to de-energize d. Normal operating condition			If **No**, the equipment must be placed in an electrically safe working condition. If **Yes**, complete 1a, 1b, and 1c, and shock and arc flash risk assessments are required to determine the appropriate hazard controls. *Proceed to Line 2.*
2.	Will the worker be exposed to energized parts?			If **No**, a shock risk assessment is discretionary and completing Sections B and C is optional. *Proceed to Line 3.*
3.	Is there an arc flash hazard?			If **No**, arc flash risk assessment is discretionary and completing Sections D or E and F is optional. *Proceed to Line 4.*
4.	Were any of the answers to Questions 3 or 4 yes?			If **No**, further risk assessment is discretionary. If **Yes**, proceed to Line 5.
5.	Did the arc flash risk assessment determine that additional protective measures are required?			If **No**, completing Parts D or E and F is discretionary. If **Yes**, Part D or E is required to be completed. *Proceed to Line 6.*
6.	Is the required working distance available?			If **Yes**, proceed to Line 7. If **No**, additional risk assessment is required before completing Section D or E or performing any work. *Proceed to Line 7.*

Section B, Shock Hazard Information	
Use Table 130.4(D)(a) for ac system boundaries or Table 130.4(D)(b) fordo system boundaries	

7.	Voltage between phases: Limited approach boundary: Restricted approach boundary:	Establish the shock boundaries. *Proceed to Line 8.*

Section C, Shock Hazard Information			
Mark "Y" or "N" as appropriate			

No.	Item			Instructions
8.	Will the task require the worker to cross the restricted approach boundary?			If **No**, shock protection controls are discretionary. *Proceed to Section D or E as appropriate.* If **Yes**, shock protection controls are required. *Proceed to Line 9.*
9.	Will rubber insulating gloves and leather protectors be used for the task?			If **Yes**, proceed to Line 10. If **No**, proceed to Line 11.
10.	Minimum glove class required for insulating gloves			Establish minimum glove class. *Proceed to Line 11.*
11.	Will insulating blankets be used for the task?			If **Yes**, proceed to Line 12. If **No**, proceed to Line 13.
12.	Minimum voltage rating for insulating blankets			Establish minimum voltage rating. *Proceed to Line 13.*

© 2020 National Fire Protection Association

NFPA 70E (p. 1 of 2)

N **FIGURE I.2** *Sample Job Safety Planning Checklist.*

	Mark "Y" or "N" as appropriate			
13.	Are insulated or insulating hand tools required for the task?			If **Yes**, proceed to Line 14. If **No**, proceed to Section D or E as applicable.
14.				Identify the hand tools, including the minimum voltage rating required. Proceed to Section D or E as applicable.

	Section D, Arc Flash Control Information — Incident Energy Analysis Method *Use information from incident energy study*		
15.	Incident energy:	Working distance:	**Include:** the arc flash boundary **and** at least one of the following: the incident energy and the working distance **or** the level of PPE **or** the minimum arc rating of clothing. Proceed to Section F.
	Level of PPE:		
	Minimum arc rating of clothing:		
	Arc flash boundary:		

	Section E, Arc Flash Hazard Control Information — Arc Flash PPE Category Method *Use Table 130.5(C)(15)(a) for ac systems or Table 130.7(C)(15)(b) for dc systems*		
16.	Determine the estimated available fault current and clearing times for the task.		
	Available *fault* current:	Overcurrent device clearing time:	
	Mark "Y" or "N" as appropriate		
17.	Do the estimated available fault current and clearing times for the task exceed the maximum allowed by Table 130.7(C)(15)(a) or Table 130.7(C)(15)(b)?		If **Yes**, an incident energy analysis is required. If **No**, proceed to Line 18.
18.	Arc flash boundary:		Proceed to Line 19.
19.	Arc flash PPE category:	Working distance:	Proceed to Line 20 and 21, Section F.

	Section F, Arc-Rated Clothing and Other Arc Flash Protection Equipment Information	
20.	Minimum arc rating in cal/cm² for protective clothing and other PPE	Establish the required arc-rated clothing and other PPE.
21.		List the required arc-rated clothing and other arc flash PPE. **PPE Category Method:** Use 130.7(C)(15)(c) and Table 130.7(C)(15)(c). **Incident Energy Analysis Method:** Use 130.5(G) and Table 130.5(G).

	Section G, Energy Source Controls	
22.		List all sources of electrical supply to the specific equipment. Include location and method to lock or tag. Include method to verify and test for absence of voltage. List temporary protective grounding equipment.

	Section H, Work Procedures and Special Precautions	
23.		List specific work procedures required to complete the task. List any special precautions needed to safely complete the task (i.e., discharge time for capacitors).

© 2020 National Fire Protection Association   NFPA 70E (p. 2 of 2)

N **FIGURE I.2** *Sample Job Safety Planning Checklist. (Continued)*

Energized Electrical Work Permit

This informative annex is not a part of the requirements of this NFPA document but is included for informational purposes only.

Under both NFPA *70E*® and OSHA regulations, work is required to be performed in a verified de-energized state (an electrically safe work condition) unless energized work can be justified. There are only three conditions in 110.4 under which energized work is permitted.

If an employee will be exposed to an electrical hazard during justified energized electrical work, the hierarchy of risk controls must be employed to lower the incident energy level or to provide additional protection for the employee prior to the start of the task. The use of PPE is considered the least effective form of risk control available, and it must not be the first or only control method used to protect the employee.

Once energized electrical work is properly justified, the hierarchy of risk controls has been employed, and the justified work has been approved, the elements of a work permit required by 130.2(B) must be provided on the energized work permit form. The format of this work permit example is not a fixed requirement, although many employers have used this template successfully.

The purpose of a work permit is to ensure that people in responsible positions are involved in the decision whether to accept the increased risk of injury to an employee assigned an energized electrical task. Employers can also use the work permit to review the decision to perform energized work.

J.1 Energized Electrical Work Permit Sample.

Figure J. 1 illustrates considerations for an energized electrical work permit.

J.2 Energized Electrical Work Permit.

Figure J.2 illustrates items to consider when determining the need for an energized electrical work permit.

ENERGIZED ELECTRICAL WORK PERMIT

PART I: TO BE COMPLETED BY THE REQUESTER:

Job/Work Order Number _____

(1) Description of circuit/equipment/job location: _____
_____

(2) Description of work to be done: _____
_____

(3) Justification of why the circuit/equipment cannot be de-energized or the work deferred until the next scheduled outage:
_____
_____

_____   _____
Requester/Title   Date

PART II: TO BE COMPLETED BY THE ELECTRICALLY QUALIFIED PERSONS *DOING* THE WORK:

Check when complete

(1) Detailed description of the job procedures to be used in performing the above detailed work: ☐
_____

(2) Description of the safe work practices to be employed: _____ ☐
_____

(3) Results of the shock risk assessment: _____
    (a) Voltage to which personnel will be exposed _____ ☐

    (b) Limited approach boundary _____ ☐

    (c) Restricted approach boundary _____ ☐

    (d) Necessary shock, personal, and other protective equipment to safely perform assigned task ☐
_____

(4) Results of the arc flash risk assessment: _____
    (a) Available incident energy at the working distance or arc flash PPE category _____ ☐
_____

    (b) Necessary arc flash personal and other protective equipment to safely perform the assigned task ☐
_____

    (c) Arc flash boundary _____ ☐

(5) Means employed to restrict the access of unqualified persons from the work area: _____ ☐

(6) Evidence of completion of a job briefing, including discussion of any job-related hazards: _____ ☐

(7) Do you agree the above-described work can be done safely?   ☐ Yes ☐ No (If *no*, return to requester.)

_____   _____
Electrically Qualified Person(s)   Date

_____   _____
Electrically Qualified Person(s)   Date

PART III: APPROVAL(S) TO PERFORM THE WORK WHILE ELECTRICALLY ENERGIZED:

_____   _____
Manufacturing Manager   Maintenance/Engineering Manager

_____   _____
Safety Manager   Electrically Knowledgeable Person

_____   _____
General Manager   Date

Note: Once the work is complete, forward this form to the site Safety Department for review and retention.

© 2020 National Fire Protection Association   NFPA 70E

Δ **FIGURE J.1** *Sample Permit for Energized Electrical Work.*

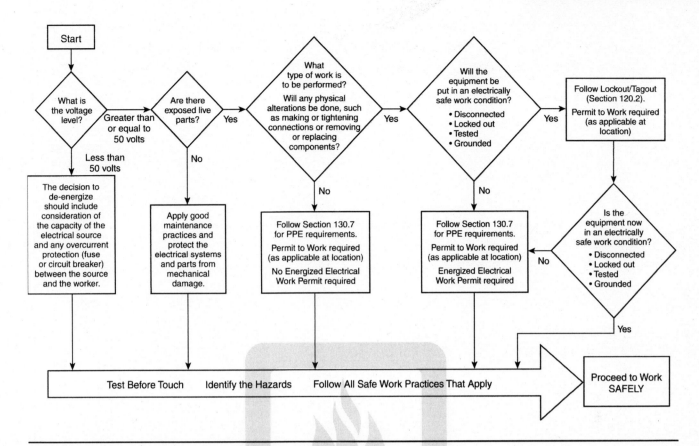

△ **FIGURE J.2** *Energized Electrical Work Permit Flow Chart.*

K

General Categories of Electrical Hazards

This informative annex is not a part of the requirements of this NFPA document but is included for informational purposes only.

Informative Annex K provides an abbreviated discussion of known electrical hazards. Critical information is included for employees to use in support of an improved electrical safety program.

K.1 General.

Electrical injuries represent a serious workplace health and safety issue to electrical and non-electrical workers. Data from the U.S. Bureau of Labor Statistics (BLS) indicate that there were nearly 6000 fatal electrical injuries to workers in the United States from 1992 through 2012. BLS data also indicate that there were 24,100 non-fatal electrical injuries from 2003 through 2012. From 1992 to 2013, the number of fatal workplace electrical injuries has fallen steadily and dramatically from 334 in 1992 to 139 in 2013. However, the trend with non-fatal electrical injuries is less consistent. Between 2003 and 2009, non-fatal injury totals ranged from 2390 in 2003 to 2620 in 2009, with a high of 2950 injuries in 2005. Non-fatal injury totals between 2010 through 2012 were the lowest over this 10-year period, with 1890 non-fatal injuries in 2010, 2250 in 2011, and 1700 in 2012.

There are two general categories of electrical injury: electrical shock and electrical burns. Electrical burns can be further subdivided into burns caused by radiant energy (arc burns), burns caused by exposure to ejected hot gases and materials (thermal bums), and burns caused by the conduction of electrical current through body parts (conduction burns). In addition, hearing damage can occur from acoustic energy, and traumatic injury can be caused by toxic gases and pressure waves associated with an arcing event.

About 98 percent of fatal occupational electrical injuries are electrical shock injuries. A corporate case study examining electrical injury reporting and safety practices found that 40 percent of electrical incidents involved 250 volts or less and were indicative of a misperception of electrical safety as a high-voltage issue. In addition, electrical incidents once again were found to involve a large share of non-electrical workers, with approximately one-half of incidents involving workers from outside electrical crafts. Research of electrical fatalities in construction found that the highest proportion of fatalities occurred in establishments with 10 or fewer employees and pointed out that smaller employers could have fewer formal training requirements and less structured training in safety practices.

Electrical workers are exposed to risk of injury not only from electrical hazards but other hazards as well. A risk assessment should address all the potential hazards. Commentary Table K.1 lists fatalities by employment according to the US Bureau of Labor Statistics (BLS) from 2003 to 2018.

COMMENTARY TABLE K.1 *Number of Fatalities by Employment, 2003 to 2018*

Occupation	Number of Fatalities
Electricians	1287
Electrician helpers	46
Electrical contractors and other wiring installation contractors	1197
Nonresidential electrical contractors and other wiring installation contractors	421
Residential electrical contractors and other wiring installation contractors	129
Electric power-line installers and repairers	462
Electrical power generation, transmission, and distribution	368
Electrical and electronic equipment mechanics, installers, and repairers	336

K.2 Electric Shock.

Over 40 percent of all electrical fatalities in the U.S. involved overhead power line contact. This includes overhead power line fatalities from direct contact by a worker, contact through hand-carried objects, and contact through machines and vehicles. Comparing the ratio of total electrical fatalities to total electrical injuries (fatal and nonfatal), it was noticed that electrical injuries are more often fatal than many other injury categories. For example, from 2003 to 2009 there were 20,033 electrical injuries of which 1573 were fatalities. One worker died for every 12.74 electrical injuries. For the same period there were 1,718,219 fall injuries of which 5279 were fatalities — one worker died for every 325 injuries.

Of those, 1573 were electrical fatalities. A more detailed look at the demographics for 168 electrical fatalities in 2009 showed that 99 percent of deaths were the result of electrocution, and 70 percent occurred while the worker was performing a constructing, repairing, or cleaning activity.

Electrical contact fatalities are not exclusive to the electrical industry. Employees in all occupations must be protected from exposure to shock hazards. Protection against electric shock exposure and incidents was the original mission of NFPA *70E®*. Establishing an electrically safe work condition is the desired approach to mitigating electric shock exposure, but where tasks are permitted on energized electrical conductors and circuit parts, the requirements in Article 130 provide protection strategies that allow employees to safely work on energized electrical equipment.

Although 110.4(C) establishes 50 volts and higher as the threshold at which shock protection for personnel is required, voltages lower than 50 volts can be hazardous under certain conditions. Wet, damp, and submersed conditions lower the body's resistance to electric current, and voltages lower than 50 volts in these conditions are potentially dangerous. The lower voltage levels might not necessarily pose an injurious electric shock hazard, but the effects of electric current on muscular control can be dangerous if an employee is partially or completely immersed in a body of water. Swimming pool maintenance is one activity that could pose this threat.

According to the BLS, exposure to electricity accounted for 2948 fatalities from 2003 to 2018. Electrocutions by occupation from 2011 to 2018 are shown in Commentary Table K.2. Electrical employees are not the only employees that can be fatally injured by electricity in the workplace. Employees in nonelectrical occupations, such as production line workers and groundskeepers, who do not expect to be exposed to electrical hazards are being fatally injured due to exposure to electrical current in the course of conducting their assigned tasks.

The need for electrical contract employers to establish safe work practices is demonstrated by the 390 electrical exposure fatalities at private residences, which are covered workplaces under NFPA *70E* and OSHA. By comparison, 352 fatalities occurred on industrial premises for the same 2011 to 2018 period.

Fatalities by voltage level are shown in Commentary Table K.3. Commentary Table K.4 lists the number of fatalities by electrical part. Additional data and information regarding electrical safety can be found in the resource library of the Electrical Safety Foundation International (ESFI) at www.esfi.org.

COMMENTARY TABLE K.2　*Number of Fatalities from Contact with Electricity by Occupation, 2011 to 2018*

Occupation	Number of Fatalities
Construction and extraction	546
Installation, maintenance, and repair	271
Building and grounds cleaning and maintenance	150
Production	54
Transportation and material moving	47
Management	42

COMMENTARY TABLE K.3　*Electrical Fatalities by Voltage Level, 2011 to 2018*

Activity	Number of Fatalities
Exposure to electricity, 220 volts or less	254
Exposure to electricity, greater than 220 volts	861

COMMENTARY TABLE K.4　*Electrical Fatalities by Equipment 2011 to 2018*

Electric Part	Number of Fatalities
All electric parts	1301
• Power lines, transformers, and converters	768
• Electrical wiring	193
• Power cords, electrical cords, and extension cords	131
• Switchboards, switches, and fuses	102
• Generators	57
• Batteries, other than automotive	4

K.3 Arc Flash.

In the recently issued 29 CFR Subpart V, OSHA identified 99 injuries that involved bums from arcs from energized equipment faults or failures, resulting in 21 fatalities and 94 hospitalized injuries for the period January 1991 through December 1998.

Based on this data, OSHA estimated that an average of at least eight bum injuries from arcs occur each year involving employees doing work covered by OSHA rules, leading to 12 non-fatal injuries and two fatalities per year. Of the reports indicating the extent of the burn injury, 75 percent reported third-degree burns.

During the period involved, Federal OSHA only required non-fatal injuries to be reported when there were three or more workers hospitalized. OSHA found that there were six injuries for every fatality in California, which requires the reporting of every hospitalized injury.

Using that data, OSHA estimated that would be at least 36 injuries to every fatality, and probably many more. Also, many non-fatal electric shocks involve burns from associated electric arcs.

Starting January 1, 2015, Federal OSHA requires every hospitalized injury to be reported.

> The BLS database does not indicate fatalities caused by an arc flash. However, during the 2011 to 2018 period, electrical burns accounted for 23 fatalities. While 16 burn fatalities were associated with third- and fourth-degree burns, one fatality was associated with a second-degree burn.

K.4 Arc Blast.

The tremendous temperatures of the arc cause the explosive expansion of both the surrounding air and the metal in the arc path. For example, copper expands by a factor of 67,000 times when it turns from a solid to a vapor. The danger associated with this expansion is one of high pressures, sound, and shrapnel. The high pressures can easily exceed hundreds or even thousands of pounds per square foot, knocking workers off ladders, rupturing eardrums, and collapsing lungs. Finally, material and molten metal are expelled away from the arc at speeds exceeding 1120 km/hr (700 mph), fast enough for shrapnel to completely penetrate the human body.

> Protection against the arc flash hazards described in Section K.3 can prevent incurable burns to employees. Extremely dangerous concussive forces, sounds, and shrapnel can occur during arc blast events. Although arc-rated garments are available, they are not intended to provide arc blast protection.
>
> Arc terminal temperature is estimated to be in excess of 35,000°F (19,430°C). The plasma of vaporizing metal has a temperature of 23,000°F (12,760°C). For comparison, after 0.3 seconds, an atomic bomb reaches only 12,600°F (6980°C), and the surface of the sun is only 10,000°F (5540°C). The superheating of the air during an arcing incident creates an acoustic wave similar to the generation of thunder by lightning.
>
> The acoustic and pressure waves from arcs are caused by the expansion of boiling metal and the superheating of air by the arc passing through it. Vaporizing copper expands 67,000 times in volume, whereas water expands 1670 times when becoming steam. This expansion accounts for the expulsion of molten metal droplets from the arc, which can be thrust up to distances around 10 ft (3 m). This pressure generates ionized vapor (plasma) outward from the arc for distances that are proportional to the arc power. Fifty-three kW of power will vaporize 0.05 in.³ (0.328 cm³) of copper into 3350 in.³ (54,907 cm³) of vapor, and 1 in.³ (16.39 cm³) of copper will vaporize into 1.44 yd³ (1.098 m³) of vapor.
>
> Before the hot vapor that forms an arc starts to cool, it combines with the oxygen in the air to become an oxide of the metal vapor. It solidifies as it cools and becomes minute particles that appear as smoke—copper and iron are black and aluminum is grey. These particles are poisonous if inhaled, are quite hot, and will cling to any surface they touch.
>
> Arc blasts have propelled large objects—like personnel, switchboard doors, and busbars—several feet at high rates of speed. Arc blasts can create enough pressure to collapse lungs and rupture eardrums if hearing protection is not used.
>
> In his paper "Pressures Developed by Arcs" from *IEEE Transactions on Industry Applications*, Ralph H. Lee provides information regarding arc blast pressures. The following equation from Lee's paper can be used to estimate the arc blast pressure. However, it should be noted that this equation has not been generally adopted and additional testing is required.

$$P = (11.5 \times I_a)/D^{0.9}$$

where:
P = pressure (lb/ft^2)
I_a = arcing current (kA)
D = distance from the center of the arc (ft)

According to this equation, the pressure from a 100-kA arc can reach around 400 lb/ft^2 (1950 kg/m^2) at a distance of 3.3 ft (1 m). A 25-kA arc at a distance of 2 ft (0.6 m) can produce a pressure of around 160 lb/ft^2 (780 kg/m^2). The average man's upper body has about 2.2 ft^2 (0.2 m^2) of body area. A 25-kA arc at 2 ft (0.6 m) is sufficient to exert a total pressure of about 352 lb (2.2 ft^2 x 160 lb/ft^2) on the average man's chest.

K.5 Other Information.

For additional information, the following documents are available:

Occupational Injuries From Electrical Shock and Arc Flash Events Final Report, by Richard Campbell, and David Dini, Sponsored by The Fire Protection Research Foundation, Quincy, MA.

Occupational Electrical Injuries in the US, 2003-2009, by James Cawley and Brett C. Banner, ESFI.

Technical paper ESW 2012-24 presented at IEEE ESW conference, *Arc Flash Hazards, Incident Energy, PPE Ratings and Thermal Burn Injury — A Deeper Look,* by Tammy Gammon, Wei-Jen Lee, and Ben Johnson.

Technical Paper ESW 2015-17 presented at IEEE ESW conference, OSHA Subpart V, *Electric Power and Distribution,* April 11, 2014.

Typical Application of Safeguards in the Cell Line Working Zone

This informative annex is not a part of the requirements of this NFPA document but is included for informational purposes only.

Informative Annex L discusses and illustrates the application of typical safeguards in a process area associated with a dc electrical system that cannot be de-energized.

L.1 Application of Safeguards.

This informative annex permits a typical application of safeguards in electrolytic areas where electrical hazards exist. Take, for example, an employee working on an energized cell. The employee uses manual contact to make adjustments and repairs. Consequently, the exposed energized cell and grounded metal floor could present an electrical hazard. Safeguards for this employee can be provided in the following ways:

(1) Protective boots can be worn that isolate the employee's feet from the floor and that provide a safeguard from the electrical hazard.

(2) Protective gloves can be worn that isolate the employee's hands from the energized cell and that provide a safeguard.

(3) If the work task causes severe deterioration, wear, or damage to personal protective equipment (PPE), the employee might have to wear both protective gloves and boots.

(4) A permanent or temporary insulating surface can be provided for the employee to stand on to provide a safeguard.

(5) The design of the installation can be modified to provide a conductive surface for the employee to stand on. If the conductive surface is bonded to the cell, a safeguard will be provided by voltage equalization.

(6) Safe work practices can provide safeguards. If protective boots are worn, the employee should not make long reaches over energized (or grounded) surfaces such that his or her elbow bypasses the safeguard. If such movements are required, protective sleeves, protective mats, or special tools should be used. Training on the nature of electrical hazards and proper use and condition of safeguards is, in itself, a safeguard.

(7) The energized cell can be temporarily bonded to ground.

L.2 Electrical Power Receptacles.

Power supply circuits and receptacles in the cell line area for portable electric equipment should meet the requirements of 668.21 of *NFPA 70, National Electrical Code.* However, it is recommended that receptacles for portable electric equipment not be installed in electrolytic cell areas and that only pneumatic-powered portable tools and equipment be used.

Section 668.21 of *NFPA 70®, National Electrical Code®* (*NEC®*), addresses circuit isolation, receptacle configuration, and marking requirements for circuits supplying power to ungrounded receptacles for handheld, cord-connected equipment in the cell line.

Layering of Protective Clothing and Total System Arc Rating

M

This informative annex is not a part of the requirements of this NFPA document but is included for informational purposes only.

Informative Annex M discusses how layering protective clothing can impact the overall rating of layered protection. The total arc rating of a layered clothing system must be determined by testing the multilayer system as it would be worn in the field. The total system arc rating cannot be determined simply by adding together the arc ratings of the individual layers. Exhibit M.1 shows an arc-rated PPE system of clothing.

When layers of clothing are worn, some air is captured between the layers. Air is a good thermal insulator and modifies the protective nature of the sum of the protective clothing. The resulting protection offered by the layers of clothing can be greater or less than the sum of the protection afforded by the individual layers. Although this annex covers layering protective clothing without testing the entire system, employers should consult the clothing manufacturer.

An arc-rated PPE system of clothing. (Courtesy of Salisbury by Honeywell)

M.1 Layering of Protective Clothing.

M.1.1 Layering of arc-rated clothing is an effective approach to achieving the required arc rating when the layers have been tested together to determine the composite rating. The use of all arc-rated clothing layers will result in achieving the required arc rating with the lowest number of layers and lowest clothing system weight. Garments that are not arc rated should not be used to increase the arc rating of a garment or of a clothing system.

M.1.2 A total system of protective clothing can be determined to take credit for the protection provided by all the layers of clothing that are worn if tested as a combination. For example, to achieve an arc rating of 40 cal/cm^2 (167.5 J/cm^2), an arc flash suit with an arc rating of 40 cal/cm^2 (167.5 J/cm^2) could be worn over a cotton shirt and cotton pants. Alternatively, an arc flash suit with a 25 cal/cm^2 (104.7 J/cm^2) arc rating could be worn over an arc-rated shirt and arc-rated pants with an arc rating of 8 cal/cm^2 (33.5 J/cm^2) to achieve a total system arc rating of 40 cal/cm^2 (167.5 J/cm^2). This latter approach provides the required arc rating at a lower weight and with fewer total layers of fabric and, consequently, would provide the required protection with a higher level of worker comfort.

The arc rating of a layered system of PPE is not simply a matter of adding together the ratings of the individual pieces; some manufacturers provide data on the arc ratings of individual layers. Exhibit M.2 is an example of how a manufacturer might supply such data.

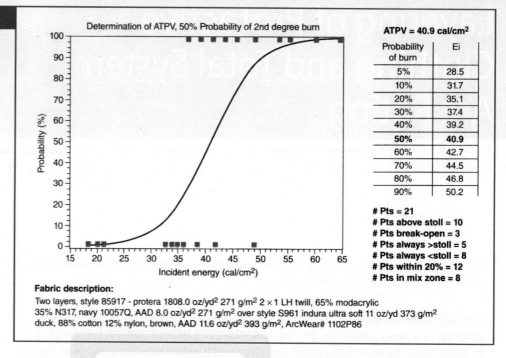

Determination of ATPV, 50% Probability of 2nd degree burn

Fabric description:
Two layers, style 85917 - protera 1808.0 oz/yd² 271 g/m² 2 × 1 LH twill, 65% modacrylic 35% N317, navy 10057Q, AAD 8.0 oz/yd² 271 g/m² over style S961 indura ultra soft 11 oz/yd 373 g/m² duck, 88% cotton 12% nylon, brown, AAD 11.6 oz/yd² 393 g/m², ArcWear# 1102P86

ATPV = 40.9 cal/cm²

Probability of burn	Ei
5%	28.5
10%	31.7
20%	35.1
30%	37.4
40%	39.2
50%	**40.9**
60%	42.7
70%	44.5
80%	46.8
90%	50.2

Pts = 21
Pts above stoll = 10
Pts break-open = 3
Pts always >stoll = 5
Pts always <stoll = 8
Pts within 20% = 12
Pts in mix zone = 8

M.2 Layering Using Arc-Rated Clothing over Natural Fiber Clothing Underlayers.

M.2.1 Under some exposure conditions, natural fiber underlayers can ignite even when they are worn under arc-rated clothing.

M.2.2 If the arc flash exposure is sufficient to break open all the arc-rated clothing outerlayer or underlayers, the natural fiber underlayer can ignite and cause more severe burn injuries to an expanded area of the body. This is due to the natural fiber underlayers burning onto areas of the worker's body that were not exposed by the arc flash event. This can occur when the natural fiber underlayer continues to burn underneath arc-rated clothing layers even in areas in which the arc-rated clothing layer or layers are not broken open due to a "chimney effect."

M.3 Total System Arc Rating.

M.3.1 The total system arc rating is the arc rating obtained when all clothing layers worn by a worker are tested as a multilayer test sample. An example of a clothing system is an arc-rated coverall worn over an arc-rated shirt and arc-rated pants in which all of the garments are constructed from the same arc-rated fabric. For this two-layer arc-rated clothing system, the arc rating would typically be more than three times higher than the arc ratings of the individual layers; that is, if the arc ratings of the arc-rated coverall, shirt, and pants were all in the range of 5 cal/cm² (20.9 J/cm²) to 6 cal/cm² (25.1 J/cm²), the total two-layer system arc rating would be over 20 cal/cm² (83.7 J/cm²).

M.3.2 It is important to understand that the total system arc rating cannot be determined by adding the arc ratings of the individual layers. In a few cases, it has been observed that the total system arc rating actually decreased when another arc-rated layer of a specific type was added to the system as the outermost layer. The only way to determine the total system arc rating is to conduct a multilayer arc test on the combination of all of the layers assembled as they would be worn.

> A total system arc rating is not simply a matter of adding together the ratings of the individual pieces; the layered system as a whole requires testing to obtain an arc rating.

Example Industrial Procedures and Policies for Working Near Overhead Electrical Lines and Equipment

This informative annex is not a part of the requirements of this NFPA document but is included for informational purposes only.

Informative Annex N illustrates electrical safety measures that might be appropriate when working near overhead lines. Although the content of this informative annex is not enforceable, the measures contained here are effective. See Supplement 3 for another safety procedure example that illustrates the types of information that should make up a typical safety procedure.

N.1 Introduction.

This informative annex is an example of an industrial procedure for working near overhead electrical systems. Areas covered include operations that could expose employees or equipment to contact with overhead electrical systems.

When working near electrical lines or equipment, avoid direct or indirect contact. Direct contact is contact with any part of the body. Indirect contact is when part of the body touches or is in dangerous proximity to any object in contact with energized electrical equipment. The following two assumptions should always be made:

(1) Lines are "live" (energized).
(2) Lines are operating at high voltage (over 1000 volts).

As the voltage increases, the minimum working clearances increase. Through arc-over, injuries or fatalities could occur, even if actual contact with high-voltage lines or equipment is not made. Potential for arc-over increases as the voltage increases.

N.2 Overhead Power Line Policy (OPP).

This informative annex applies to all overhead conductors, regardless of voltage, and requires the following:

(1) That employees not place themselves in close proximity to overhead power lines. "Close proximity" is within a distance of 3 m (10 ft) for systems up to 50 kV, and should be increased 100 mm (4 in.) for every 10 kV above 50 kV.
(2) That employees be informed of the hazards and precautions when working near overhead lines.

(3) That warning decals be posted on cranes and similar equipment regarding the minimum clearance of 3 m (TO ft).

(4) That a "spotter" be designated when equipment is working near overhead lines. This person's responsibility is to observe safe working clearances around all overhead lines and to direct the operator accordingly.

(5) That warning cones be used as visible indicators of the 3 m (10 ft) safety zone when working near overhead power lines.

> Informational Note: "Working near," for the purpose of this informative annex, is defined as working within a distance from any overhead power line that is less than the combined height or length of the lifting device plus the associated load length and the required minimum clearance distance [as stated in N.2(1)]. Required clearance is expressed as follows:
>
> Required clearance = lift equipment height or length + load length + at least 3 m (10 ft)

(6) That the local responsible person be notified at least 24 hours before any work begins to allow time to identify voltages and clearances or to place the line in an electrically safe work condition.

N.3 Policy.

All employees and contractors shall conform to the OPP. The first line of defense in preventing electrical contact accidents is to remain outside the limited approach boundary. Because most company and contractor employees are not qualified to determine the system voltage level, a qualified person shall be called to establish voltages and minimum clearances and take appropriate action to make the work zone safe.

N.4 Procedures.

N.4.1 General. Prior to the start of all operations where potential contact with overhead electrical systems is possible, the person in charge shall identify overhead lines or equipment, reference their location with respect to prominent physical features, or physically mark the area directly in front of the overhead lines with safety cones, survey tape, or other means. Electrical line location shall be discussed at a pre-work safety meeting of all employees on the job (through a job briefing). All company employees and contractors shall attend this meeting and require their employees to conform to electrical safety standards. New or transferred employees shall be informed of electrical hazards and proper procedures during orientations.

On construction projects, the contractor shall identify and reference all potential electrical hazards and document such actions with the on-site employers. The location of overhead electrical lines and equipment shall be conspicuously marked by the person in charge. New employees shall be informed of electrical hazards and of proper precautions and procedures.

Where there is potential for contact with overhead electrical systems, local area management shall be called to decide whether to place the line in an electrically safe work condition or to otherwise protect the line against unintentional contact. Where there is a suspicion of lines with low clearance [height under 6 m (20 ft)], the local on-site electrical supervisor shall be notified to verify and take appropriate action.

All electrical contact incidents, including "near misses," shall be reported to the local area health and safety specialist.

N.4.2 Look Up and Live Flags. In order to prevent unintentional contact with all aerial lifts, cranes, boom trucks, service rigs, and similar equipment shall use look up and live flags. The flags are visual indicators that the equipment is currently being used or has been returned to its "stowed or cradled" position. The flags shall be yellow with black lettering and shall state in bold lettering "LOOK UP AND LIVE."

The procedure for the use of the flag follows.

(1) When the boom or lift is in its stowed or cradled position, the flag shall be located on the load hook or boom end.

(2) Prior to operation of the boom or lift, the operator of the equipment shall assess the work area to determine the location of all overhead lines and communicate this information to all crews on site. Once completed, the operator shall remove the flag from the load hook or boom and transfer the flag to the steering wheel of the vehicle. Once the flag is placed on the steering wheel, the operator can begin to operate the equipment.

(3) After successfully completing the work activity and returning the equipment to its stowed or cradled position, the operator shall return the flag to the load hook.

(4) The operator of the equipment is responsible for the placement of the look up and live flag.

N.4.3 High Risk Tasks.

N.4.3.1 Heavy Mobile Equipment. Prior to the start of each workday, a high-visibility marker (orange safety cones or other devices) shall be temporarily placed on the ground to mark the location of overhead wires. The supervisors shall discuss electrical safety with appropriate crew members at on-site tailgate safety talks. When working in the proximity of overhead lines, a spotter shall be positioned in a conspicuous location to direct movement and observe for contact with the overhead wires. The spotter, equipment operator, and all other employees working on the job location shall be alert for overhead wires and remain at least 3 m (10 ft) from the mobile equipment.

All mobile equipment shall display a warning decal regarding electrical contact. Independent truck drivers delivering materials to field locations shall be cautioned about overhead electrical lines before beginning work, and a properly trained on-site or contractor employee shall assist in the loading or off-loading operation. Trucks that have emptied their material shall not leave the work location until the boom, lift, or box is down and is safely secured.

N.4.3.2 Aerial Lifts, Cranes, and Boom Devices. Where there is potential for near operation or contact with overhead lines or equipment, work shall not begin until a safety meeting is conducted and appropriate steps are taken to identify, mark, and warn against unintentional contact. The supervisor will review operations daily to ensure compliance.

Where the operator's visibility is impaired, a spotter shall guide the operator. Hand signals shall be used and clearly understood between the operator and spotter. When visual contact is impaired, the spotter and operator shall be in radio contact. Aerial lifts, cranes, and boom devices shall have appropriate warning decals and shall use warning cones or similar devices to indicate the location of overhead lines and identify the 3 m (10 ft) minimum safe working boundary.

N.4.3.3 Tree Work. Wires shall be treated as live and operating at high voltage until verified as otherwise by the local area on-site employer. The local maintenance organization or an approved electrical contractor shall remove branches touching wires before work begins. Limbs and branches shall not be dropped onto overhead wires. If limbs or branches fall across electrical wires, all work shall stop immediately and the local area maintenance organization is to be called. When climbing or working in trees, pruners shall try to position themselves so that the trunk or limbs are between their bodies and electrical wires. If possible, pruners shall not work with their backs toward electrical wires. An insulated bucket truck is the preferred method of pruning when climbing poses a greater threat of electrical contact. Personal protective equipment (PPE) shall be used while working on or near lines.

N.4.4 Underground Electrical Lines and Equipment. Before excavation starts and where there exists reasonable possibility of contacting electrical or utility lines or equipment, the local area supervision (or USA DIG organization, when appropriate) shall be called and a request is to be made for identifying/marking the line location(s).

When USA DIG is called, their representatives will need the following:

(1) Minimum of two working days' notice prior to start of work, name of county, name of city, name and number of street or highway marker, and nearest intersection
(2) Type of work
(3) Date and time work is to begin
(4) Caller's name, contractor/department name and address
(5) Telephone number for contact
(6) Special instructions

Utilities that do not belong to USA DIG must be contacted separately. USA DIG might not have a complete list of utility owners. Utilities that are discovered shall be marked before work begins. Supervisors shall periodically refer their location to all workers, including new employees, subject to exposure.

N.4.5 Vehicles with Loads in Excess of 4.25 m (14 ft) in Height. This policy requires that all vehicles with loads in excess of 4.25 m (14 ft) in height use specific procedures to maintain safe working clearances when in transit below overhead lines.

The specific procedures for moving loads in excess of 4.25 m (14 ft) in height or via routes with lower clearance heights are as follows:

(1) Prior to movement of any load in excess of 4.25 m (14 ft) in height, the local health and safety department, along with the local person in charge, shall be notified of the equipment move.
(2) An on-site electrician, electrical construction representative, or qualified electrical contractor should check the intended route to the next location before relocation.
(3) The new site is to be checked for overhead lines and clearances.
(4) Power lines and communication lines shall be noted, and extreme care used when traveling beneath the lines.
(5) The company moving the load or equipment will provide a driver responsible for measuring each load and ensuring each load is secured and transported in a safe manner.
(6) An on-site electrician, electrical construction representative, or qualified electrical contractor shall escort the first load to the new location, ensuring safe clearances, and a service company representative shall be responsible for subsequent loads to follow the same safe route.

If proper working clearances cannot be maintained, the job must be shut down until a safe route can be established or the necessary repairs or relocations have been completed to ensure that a safe working clearance has been achieved.

All work requiring movement of loads in excess of 4.25 m (14 ft) in height are required to begin only after a general work permit has been completed detailing all pertinent information about the move.

N.4.6 Emergency Response. If an overhead line falls or is contacted, the following precautions should be taken:

(1) Keep everyone at least 3 m (10 ft) away.

(2) Use flagging to protect motorists, spectators, and other individuals from fallen or low wires.

(3) Call the local area electrical department or electric utility immediately.

(4) Place barriers around the area.

(5) Do not attempt to move the wire(s).

(6) Do not touch anything that is touching the wire(s).

(7) Be alert to water or other conductors present.

(8) Crews shall have emergency numbers readily available. These numbers shall include local area electrical department, utility, police/fire, and medical assistance.

(9) If an individual becomes energized, DO NOT TOUCH the individual or anything in contact with the person. Call for emergency medical assistance and call the local utility immediately. If the individual is no longer in contact with the energized conductors, CPR, rescue breathing, or first aid should be administered immediately, but only by a trained person. It is safe to touch the victim once contact is broken or the source is known to be de-energized.

(10) Wires that contact vehicles or equipment will cause arcing, smoke, and possibly fire. Occupants should remain in the cab and wait for the local area electrical department or utility. If it becomes necessary to exit the vehicle, leap with both feet as far away from the vehicle as possible, without touching the equipment. Jumping free of the vehicle is the last resort.

(11) If operating the equipment and an overhead wire is contacted, stop the equipment immediately and, if safe to do so, jump free and clear of the equipment. Maintain your balance, keep your feet together and either shuffle or bunny hop away from the vehicle another 3 m (10 ft) or more. Do not return to the vehicle or allow anyone else for any reason to return to the vehicle until the local utility has removed the power line from the vehicle and has confirmed that the vehicle is no longer in contact with the overhead lines.

Safety-Related Design Requirements

This informative annex is not a part of the requirements of this NFPA document but is included for informational purposes only.

Both installation and work practices impact electrical safety, but they are separate and distinct electrical industries. Safe work practices are not part of a de-energized installation, and installation is not a safe work practice for exposed electrical hazards. The design of a facility, equipment, or circuit can help determine if a work task can be performed safely. Facility and circuit design determine if an employee is or might be exposed to an electrical hazard when performing the tasks necessary to troubleshoot, repair, or maintain a facility. For electrical safety to progress for anyone interacting with electrical equipment, it must follow a holistic approach. The decision to design or install equipment in a particular manner can have a lasting impact on electrical safety for the lifetime of equipment, as there is no limit to the level of voltage, current, or energy in a safe installation.

Once an employee is exposed to a hazard, hindsight regarding the design is ineffective. The circuit and equipment design determines the amount of incident energy that might be available at various points in the system and whether an electrically safe work condition can be created for sectors of the circuit. The location of components and isolating or insulating barriers determines whether or how an employee might be exposed to shock or electrocution. With a holistic approach to electrical safety, the design and installation consider employee exposure to hazards and the methods of controlling them. As a result, future employees will be protected by the design and installation of equipment and by NFPA *70E®* safe work practices when they are exposed to hazards.

O.1 Introduction.

This informative annex addresses the responsibilities of the facility owner or manager or the employer having responsibility for facility ownership or operations management to perform a risk assessment during the design of electrical systems and installations.

O.1.1 This informative annex covers employee safety-related design concepts for electrical equipment and installations in workplaces covered by the scope of this standard. This informative annex discusses design considerations that have impact on the application of the safety-related work practices only.

O.1.2 This informative annex does not discuss specific design requirements. The facility owner or manager or the employer should choose design options that eliminate hazards or reduce risk and enhance the effectiveness of safety-related work practices.

O.2 General Design Considerations.

O.2.1 Employers, facility owners, and managers who have responsibility for facilities and installations having electrical energy as a potential hazard to employees and other personnel should ensure that electrical hazard risk assessments are performed during the design of electrical systems and installations.

O.2.2 Design option decisions should facilitate the ability to eliminate hazards or reduce risk by doing the following:

(1) Reducing the likelihood of exposure
(2) Reducing the magnitude or severity of exposure
(3) Enabling achievement of an electrically safe work condition

O.2.3 Incident Energy Reduction Methods. The following methods have proved to be effective in reducing incident energy:

(1) Zone-selective interlocking. This is a method that allows two or more circuit breakers to communicate with each other so that a short circuit or ground fault will be cleared by the breaker closest to the fault with no intentional delay. Clearing the fault in the shortest time aids in reducing the incident energy.

(2) Differential relaying. The concept of this protection method is that current flowing into protected equipment must equal the current out of the equipment. If these two currents are not equal, a fault must exist within the equipment, and the relaying can be set to operate for a fast interruption. Differential relaying uses current transformers located on the line and load sides of the protected equipment and fast acting relay.

(3) Energy-reducing maintenance switching with a local status indicator. An energy-reducing maintenance switch allows a worker to set a circuit breaker trip unit to operate faster while the worker is working within an arc flash boundary, as defined in NFPA *70E*, and then to set the circuit breaker back to a normal setting after the work is complete.

(4) Energy-reducing active arc flash mitigation system. This system can reduce the arcing duration by creating a low impedance current path, located within a controlled compartment, to cause the arcing fault to transfer to the new current path, while the upstream breaker clears the circuit. The system works without compromising existing selective coordination in the electrical distribution system.

(5) Energy-reducing line side isolation. This is equipment that encloses the line side conductors and circuit parts and has been listed to provide both shock and arc flash protection from events on the line side of a circuit breaker or switch.

(6) Arc flash relay. An arc flash relay typically uses light sensors to detect the light produced by an arc flash event. Once a certain level of light is detected, the relay will issue a trip signal to an upstream overcurrent device.

(7) High-resistance grounding. A great majority of electrical faults are of the phase-to-ground type. High-resistance grounding will insert an impedance in the ground return path and will typically limit the fault current to 10 amperes and below (at 5 kV nominal or below), leaving insufficient fault energy and thereby helping reduce the arc flash hazard level. High-resistance grounding will not affect arc flash energy for line-to-line or line-to-line-to-line arcs.

(8) Current-limiting devices. Current-limiting protective devices reduce incident energy by clearing the fault faster and by reducing the current seen at the arc source. The energy reduction becomes effective for current above the current-limiting threshold of the current-limiting fuse or current limiting circuit breaker.

(9) Shunt-trip. Adding a shunt-trip that is signaled to open from an open-fuse relay to switches 800 amperes and greater reduces incident energy by opening the switch immediately when the first fuse opens. The reduced clearing time reduces incident energy. This is especially helpful for arcing currents that are not within the current-limiting threshold of the three current-limiting fuses.

O.2.4 Additional Safety-by-Design Methods. The following methods have proven to be effective in reducing risk associated with an arc flash or shock hazard:

The following is a list of commonly used engineering controls to either reduce available current, restrict access to energized conductors and circuit parts, or reduce the likelihood of initiating an arc flash hazard.

(1) Installing finger-safe components, covers, and insulating barriers reduces exposure to energized parts.

Finger-safe components, often called IP-20 components, make it more difficult for employees to accidentally contact an energized part, thereby reducing the likelihood of them receiving an electric shock or creating an arcing fault.

(2) Installing disconnects within sight of each motor or driven machine increases the likelihood that the equipment will be put into an electrically safe work condition before work has begun.

NFPA 70®, National Electrical Code® (NEC®), has allowances for a disconnecting means being out of sight of a motor. However, installing a disconnecting means within sight of a motor increases the probability that an employee will utilize it to put the equipment into an electrically safe work condition.

(3) Installing current limiting cable limiters can help reduce incident energy. Additionally, cable limiters can be used to provide short-circuit protection (and therefore incident energy reduction) for feeder tap conductors that are protected at up to 10 times their ampacity, a situation where the tap conductor can easily vaporize.

(4) Installing inspection windows for noncontact inspection reduces the need to open doors or remove covers.

Infrared and viewing windows eliminate the high-risk task of opening energized electrical equipment when employees perform periodic diagnostic inspections to evaluate the equipment's condition. Eliminating this task reduces the employee's likelihood of initiating an incident.

(5) Installing a single service fused disconnect switch or circuit breaker provides protection for buses that would be unprotected if six disconnect switches are used.

A main disconnecting means provides an easy way to de-energize all but the incoming terminals. The use of the six-disconnect rule permitted by the NEC can leave an unprotected energized bus inside the enclosure. The presence of an unprotected energized bus increases the likelihood of an employee accidentally contacting the bus or initiating an arc flash incident.

(6) Installing metering to provide remote monitoring of voltage and current levels reduces exposure to electrical hazards by placing the worker farther away from the hazard.

(7) Installing Type 2 "no damage" current limiting protection to motor controllers reduces incident energy whenever the arcing current is within the current limiting threshold of the current-limiting fuse or current-limiting circuit breaker

In order to achieve Type 2, no damage protection of a motor controller, it is generally necessary to utilize overcurrent devices with the highest degree of current limitation. For example, most motor controllers cannot achieve Type 2 protection with Class RK5 fuses; a Class RK1, Class J, or Class CC fuse must be used. This very high degree of current limitation can also reduce the incident energy during an arc flash incident if the fault current is high enough to be within the overcurrent protective device's current-limiting threshold.

(8) Installing adjustable instantaneous trip protective devices and lowering the trip settings can reduce the incident energy.

(9) Installing arc-resistant equipment, designed to divert hot gases, plasma, and other products of an arc-flash out of the enclosure so that a worker is not exposed when standing in front of the equipment with all doors and covers closed and latched, reduces the risk of arc flash exposure.

When its doors and covers are closed and latched, arc-resistant switchgear provides protection for employees energizing or de-energizing equipment. Products of an arcing incident are diverted out of the enclosure and away from the employee. Arc-resistant equipment does not protect the worker when the doors and covers are not properly closed and latched.

(10) Installing provisions that provide remote racking of equipment, such as remote-controlled motorized remote racking of a circuit breaker or an MCC bucket, allows the worker to be located outside the arc-flash boundary. An extended length hand-operated racking tool also adds distance between the worker and the equipment, reducing the worker's exposure.

(11) Installing provisions that provide remote opening and closing of circuit breakers and switches could permit workers to operate the equipment from a safe distance, outside the arc flash boundary.

(12) Class C, D, and E special purpose ground fault circuit interrupters exist for circuits operating at voltages outside the range for Class A GFCI protection. See UL 943C for additional information.

The reader should be aware of the following documents:

- ANSI/IEEE C37.20.7-2007, *IEEE Guide for Testing Metal-Enclosed Switchgear Rated Up to 38 kV for Internal Arcing Faults.* This guide includes a procedure for testing and evaluating the performance of metal-enclosed switchgear for internal arcing faults.

It also includes a method for identifying the capabilities of such equipment and covers the service conditions, installation, and application of equipment.

- ANSI/IEEE C37.20.7-2007/Cor. 1-2010, *IEEE Guide for Testing Metal-Enclosed Switchgear Rated up to 38 kV for Internal Arcing Faults Corrigendum 1*. This corrects technical errors found in IEEE C37.20.7-2007 concerning the current values and arc initiation in low-voltage testing and the supply frequency for equipment used in laboratories.

Aligning Implementation of This Standard with Occupational Health and Safety Management Standards

P

This informative annex is not a part of the requirements of this NFPA document but is included for informational purposes only.

ANSI/AIHA Z10, *American National Standard for Occupational Health and Safety Management Systems,* defines the minimum basic requirements for an organization's overall occupational health and safety management system. The standard addresses management leadership, employee participation, planning, implementation, evaluation, corrective action, and management review. It covers basic activities such as incident investigation, inspections, and training.

The system in ANSI/AIHA Z10 allows for the continual improvement of health and safety management. The standard includes the interrelated processes suitable for continual improvement that aligns with the Deming Cycle. The Deming Cycle, plan - do - check - act, or PDCA, is an iterative, four-step management process also known as the Shewhart Cycle or PDSA (plan - do - study - act). The Deming Cycle is shown in Exhibit P.1.

PDCA is a successive cycle that starts off with a known base and tests small potential effects on the process, then gradually leads to larger and more targeted change based on a continuous process. The cycle is comprised of the following phases:

- Plan phase —The objectives and processes necessary to deliver results in accordance with the expected output or goal are established.
- Do phase — The new process is implemented on a small scale to test its possible effects.
- Check phase—The new process is measured, and the results of the do phase are compared to the expected results to determine any differences.
- Act phase — The differences are analyzed to determine their cause. Under this phase, the changes to be made and where they apply are determined.

When a cycle through these four steps does not result in improvement, employers can return to the original base and process it again until there is improvement.

A fundamental principle of PDCA is reiteration. Reiterating the PDCA cycle can bring a company, organization, group, or production area closer to its goals. PDCA needs to be repeated in ever-tightening circles that represent increasing knowledge of the system, ultimately ending on or near the fundamental goals of that system. Small steps from a solid base provide feedback to justify hypotheses and increase the understanding of the system being studied. If a small misstep is taken, it is easy to repeat the previous iteration. The power of this concept lies in its simplicity. The simple cycle can be continually reapplied to the process in question for improvement.

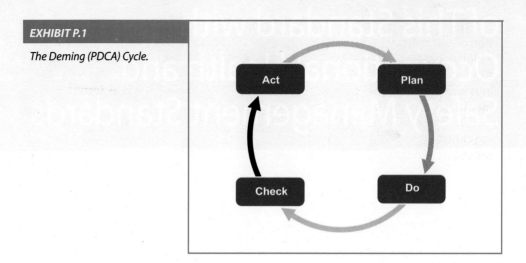

EXHIBIT P.1

The Deming (PDCA) Cycle.

△ P.1 General.

Injuries from electrical energy are a significant cause of occupational fatalities in the workplace in the United States. This standard specifies requirements unique to the hazards of electrical energy. By itself, however, this standard does not constitute a comprehensive and effective electrical safety program. The most effective application of the requirements of this standard can be achieved within the framework of a recognized health and safety management system. ANSI/AIHA Z10, *American National Standard for Occupational Health and Safety Management Systems,* and ISO 45001, *Occupational Health and Safety Management Systems — Requirements with Guidance for Use,* provides comprehensive guidance on the elements of an effective health and safety management system and are recognized standards. ANSI/AIHA Z10 and ISO 45001 are similar to other internationally recognized standards, such as ANSI/ISO 14001, *Environmental Management Systems — Requirements with Guidance for Use.* Some companies and other organizations have proprietary health and safety management systems that are aligned with the key elements of ANSI/AIHA Z10 and ISO 45001.

The most effective design and implementation of an electrical safety program can be achieved through a joint effort involving electrical subject matter experts and safety professionals knowledgeable about safety management systems.

Such collaboration can help ensure that proven safety management principles and practices applicable to any hazard in the workplace are appropriately incorporated into the electrical safety program.

This informative annex provides guidance on implementing this standard within the framework of ANSI/AIHA Z10 and ISO 45001 and other recognized or proprietary comprehensive occupational health and safety management system standards.

According to ANSI/AIHA Z10, a *hazard* is defined as "[a] condition, set of circumstances, or inherent property that can cause injury, illness, or death." *Incident* is defined as" [a]n event in which a work-related injury or illness (regardless of severity) or fatality occurred or could have occurred (commonly referred to as a 'close call' or 'near miss')." Risk is defined as "[a]n estimate of the combination of the likelihood of an occurrence of a hazardous event or exposure(s), and the severity of injury or illness that may be caused by the event or exposures."

ANSI/AIHA Z10 outlines the use of a hierarchy of health and safety controls. The hierarchy of health and safety controls offers a methodical approach to reducing the risk associated with a hazard. ANSI/AIHA Z10 lists the following methods of reducing risk, from most effective to least effective: elimination, substitution, engineering controls, warnings, administrative controls, and PPE. Exhibit P.2 provides a graphical representation of this hierarchy. NFPA 70P specifically covers electrical safety controls.

The highest level of practical control should be used. In many cases, a combination of controls might be the most effective method. This is frequently the case where a higher-order control, such as substitution, is not practical or does not reduce the risk to an acceptable level. In this case, a combination of lower-order controls, such as warnings and PPE, might be most effective when performing tasks such as testing equipment or creating an electrically safe work condition.

The use of arc-resistant switchgear might be considered a substitution or engineering control. Administrative controls include items such as job planning, training, work procedures and practices, temporary barricades, and the like.

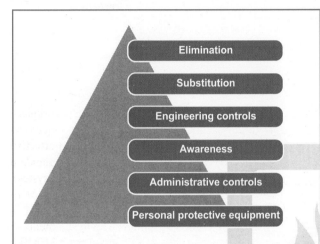

EXHIBIT P.2

The AIHA hierarchy of health and safety controls.

Human Performance and Workplace Electrical Safety

This informative annex is not a part of the requirements of this NFPA document but is included for informational purposes only.

Annex Q introduces the concept of human performance (i.e., human error) and demonstrates how it can apply to workplace electrical safety. The basic principle of human performance is that humans are fallible—even the best-intentioned person errs. The objective of human performance factors is to identify and address human error and its negative consequences on people, programs, processes, work environments, equipment, and organizations. Risk assessment is a fundamental part of NFPA 70P. For a risk assessment to be comprehensive, it must include organizational, leadership, and individual human performance factors that can either lead to or prevent errors and their consequences.

Q.1 Introduction.

This annex introduces the concept of human performance and how this concept can be applied to workplace electrical safety.

Human performance is an aspect of risk management that addresses organizational, leader, and individual performance as factors that either lead to or prevent errors and their events. The objective of human performance is to identify and address human error and its negative consequences on people, programs, processes, the work environment, an organization, or equipment.

Studies by high-risk industries indicate that human error is often a root cause of incidents. The premise of this annex is that human error is similarly a frequent root cause of electrical incidents. In occupational health and safety terms, an incident is an occurrence arising in the course of work that resulted in or could have resulted in an injury, illness, damage to health, or a fatality (see ANSI/AIHA Z10-2012, *Definition of Incident*).

The hierarchy of risk control methods identified in this and other standards is:

(1) Eliminating the hazard
(2) Substituting other materials, processes, or equipment
(3) Using engineering controls
(4) Establishing systems that increase awareness of potential hazards
(5) Setting administrative controls, e.g., training and procedures, instructions, and scheduling
(6) Using PPE, including measures to ensure its appropriate selection, use, and maintenance

The purpose of these controls is to either reduce the likelihood of an incident occurring or to prevent or mitigate the severity of consequence if an incident occurs. No control is infallible. All of the controls are subject to errors in human performance, whether at the design, implementation, or use phase.

Human performance addresses managing human error as a unique control that is complementary to the hierarchy of risk control methods.

Q.2 Principles of Human Performance.

The following are basic principles of human performance:

(1) People are fallible, and even the best people make mistakes.
(2) Error-likely situations and conditions are predictable, manageable, and preventable.
(3) Individual performance is influenced by organizational processes and values.
(4) People achieve high levels of performance largely because of the encouragement and reinforcement received from leaders, peers, and subordinates.
(5) Incidents can be avoided through an understanding of the reasons mistakes occur and application of the lessons learned from past incidents.

Q.3 Information Processing and Attention.

The brain processes information in a series of interactive stages:

(1) Attention — where and to what we intentionally or unintentionally direct our concentration.
(2) Sensing — sensory inputs (hearing, seeing, touching, smelling, etc.) receive and transfer information.
(3) Encoding, storage, thinking — incoming information is encoded and stored for later use in decision making (i.e., what to do with information). This stage of information processing involves interaction between the working memory and long-term memory (capabilities, knowledge, past experiences, opinions, and perspectives).
(4) Retrieval, acting — taking physical human action based on the synthesis of attention, sensation, encoded information, thinking, and decision-making. In a workplace environment this would include changing the state of a component using controls, tools, and computers, including verbal statements to inform or direct others.

According to Rasmussen's model used to classify human error, workers operate in one or more of three human performance modes: rule-based mode, skill-based mode, and knowledge-based mode.

Note: See Rasmussen, J. (1983); Skills, rules, and knowledge; signals, signs, and symbols, and other distinctions in human performance models. *IEEE Transactions on Systems, Man, and Cybernetics,* (3), 257-266.

Reason's Human Performance Generic Error Modeling System is an extension of Rasmussen's model. An individual consciously or subconsciously selects a human performance mode based on his or her perception of the situation. This perception is usually a function of the individual's familiarity with a specific task and the level of attention (information processing) applied to accomplish the activity.

Note: See Reason, J. *Human Error.* Cambridge, UK: Cambridge University Press, 1990.

Most cognitive psychologists agree that humans have a limited pool of attentional resources available to divide up among tasks. This pool of shared attentional resources enables the mind to process information while performing one or sometimes multiple tasks. Some tasks require more attentional resources than others. The amount of attentional resource required to perform a task satisfactorily defines the mental workload for an individual and is inversely proportional to the individual's familiarity with the task. An increase in knowledge, skill, and experience with a task decreases the level of attentional resources required to perform that task and therefore decreases the level of attentional resource allocated to that task.

Critical points in activities when risk is higher (increased likelihood of harm or increased severity of harm, or both) require an increased allocation of attentional resources. Allocation at these critical points can be improved by training, procedures, equipment design, and teamwork.

Each human performance mode has associated errors. Awareness of which human performance mode the individual might be in helps identify the kind of errors that could be made and which error prevention techniques would be the most effective.

Q.4 Human Performance Modes and Associated Errors.

Q.4.1 Rule-Based Human Performance Mode.

Q.4.1.1 General. An individual operates in rule-based human performance mode when the work situation is likely to be one that he or she has encountered before or has been trained to deal with, or which is covered by a procedure. It is called the rule-based mode because the individual applies memorized or written rules. These rules might have been learned as a result of interaction at the workplace, through formal training, or by working with experienced workers.

The level of required attentional resources when in the rule-based mode fits between that of the knowledge- and skill-based modes. The time devoted to processing the information (reaction time) to select an appropriate response to the work situation is in the order of seconds.

The rule-based level follows an IF (symptom X), THEN (situation Y) logic. The individual operates by matching the signs and symptoms of the situation to some stored knowledge structure, and will usually react in a predicable manner.

In human performance theory, rule-based is the most desirable performance mode. The individual can use conscious thinking to challenge whether or not the proposed solution is appropriate. This can result in additional error prevention being integrated into the solution.

Not all activities guided by a procedure are necessarily executed in rule-based mode. An experienced worker might unconsciously default to the skill-based mode when executing a procedure that is normally done in the rule-based mode.

Q.4.1.2 Rule-Based Human Performance Mode Errors. Since the rule-based human performance mode requires interpretation using an "if-then" logic, misinterpretation is the prevalent type error mode. Errors involve deviating from an approved procedure, applying the wrong response to a work situation, or applying the correct procedure to the wrong situation.

Q.4.2 Knowledge-Based Human Performance Mode.

Q.4.2.1 General. A worker operates in knowledge-based human performance mode when there is uncertainty about what to do; no skill or rule is readily identifiable. The individual relies on their understanding and knowledge of the situation and related scientific principles and fundamental theory to develop an appropriate response. Uncertainty creates a need for information. To gather information more effectively, the individual's attentional resources become more focused. Thinking takes more effort and energy, and the time devoted to processing the information to select an appropriate response to the situation can be in the order of minutes to hours.

Q.4.2.2 Knowledge-Based Human Performance Mode Errors. The prevalent error when operating in knowledge-based mode is that decisions are often based on an inaccurate mental picture of the work situation. Knowledge-based activities require decision making based on diagnosis and problem-solving. Humans do not usually perform optimally in high-stress, unfamiliar situations where they are required to "think on their feet" in the absence of rules, routines, and procedures to handle the situation. The tendency is to use only information that is readily available to evaluate the situation and to become enmeshed in one aspect of the problem to the exclusion of all other considerations. Decision-making is erroneous if problem-solving is based on incomplete or inaccurate information.

Q.4.3 Skill-Based Human Performance Mode.

Q.4.3.1 General. A person is in skill-based mode when executing a task that involves practiced actions in a very familiar and common situation. Human performance is governed by mental instructions developed by either practice or experience and is less dependent on external conditions. The time devoted to processing the information is in the order of milliseconds. Writing one's signature is an example of skill-based performance mode. A familiar workplace procedure is typically performed in skill-based performance mode, such as the operation of a low-voltage molded case circuit breaker.

Q.4.3.2 Skill-Based Human Performance Mode Errors. The relatively low demand on attentional resources required when an individual is in skill-based human performance mode can create the following errors:

(1) Inattention: Skill-based performance mode errors are primarily execution errors involving omissions triggered by human variability, or not recognizing changes in task requirements or work conditions related to the task.

(2) Perceived reduction in risk: As familiarity with a task increases, the individual's perception of the associated risk is less likely to match actual risk. A perceived reduction in risk can create "inattentional blindness" and insensitivity to the presence of hazards.

Q.5 Error Precursors.

Error precursors are situations when the demands of the task and the environment it is performed in exceed the capabilities of the individual(s) or the limitations of human nature. Error precursors can also be unfavorable conditions that increase the probability for error during a specific action. Error precursors can be grouped into four broad categories.

(1) Task demands — when specific mental, physical, or team requirements to perform a task either exceed the capabilities or challenge the limitations of the individual assigned to the task.

(2) Work environment — when general influences of the workplace, organizational, and cultural conditions affect individual performance.

(3) Individual capabilities — when an individual's unique mental, physical, and emotional characteristics do not match the demands of the specific task.

(4) Human nature — when traits, dispositions, and limitations common to all persons incline an individual to err under unfavorable conditions.

Table Q.5 provides a list of specific examples for each category.

When error precursors are identified and addressed then the likelihood of human error is reduced.

TABLE Q.5 *Error Precursor Identification and Human Performance Tool Selection (see Q.5 and Q.6.1)*

Error Precursors	Optimal Tools(s)	Human Performance Tools
Task Demands Time pressure (in a hurry) High workload (memory requirements) Simultaneous or multiple tasks Repetitive actions or monotony Critical steps or irreversible acts Interpretation requirements Unclear goals, roles, or responsibilities Lack of or unclear standards		**1 Pre-job briefing** Identify hazards, assess risk and select and implement risk controls from a hierarchy of methods **2 Job site review** Increased situational awareness
Work Environment Distractions/interruptions Changes/departures from routine Confusing displays or controls Workarounds/out of service instrumentation Obscure electrical supplies or configurations Unexpected equipment conditions Lack of alternative indication Personality conflicts		**3 Post-job review** Identify ways to improve and best practices Peer check **4 Procedure use and adherence** Step-by-step procedure read, outcome understood Circle the task to be performed, check off each task as it is completed
Individual Capabilities Unfamiliar with, or first time performing task Lack of knowledge (faulty mental model) New technique not used before Imprecise communication habits Lack of proficiency or experience Indistinct problem-solving skills Unsafe attitudes for critical task Inappropriate values		**5 Self-check with verbalization** Stop, Think, Act, Review (STAR) Verbalize intent before, during, and after each task **6 Three-way communication** Directives are repeated by receiver back to sender; receiver is acknowledged by sender Use of the phonetic alphabet for clarity
Human Nature Stress (limits attention) Habit patterns Assumptions Complacency/overconfidence Mind-set Inaccurate risk perception Mental shortcuts (biases) or limited short-term memory		**7 Stop when unsure** Stop and obtain further direction when unable to follow a procedure or process step or if something unexpected occurs Maintain a questioning attitude **8 Flagging and blocking** Identify (flag) equipment and controls that will be operated Prevent access (block) equipment and controls that should not be operated

Notes: This table may be utilized when identifying workplace hazards. Identify the error precursors in the left-hand column. Select the optimal human performance tool or combination of tools from the right-hand column. List the selected tool(s) in the centre column beside the associated error. This table does not include all possible human performance tools; however, all tools listed can be applied to each error precursor.

Q.6 Human Performance Tools.

Q.6.1 Application. Human performance tools reduce the likelihood of error when applied to error precursors. Consistent use of human performance tools by an organization will facilitate the incorporation of best practice work. The following are some human performance tools. See Table Q.5 for a list of these tools.

Q.6.2 Job Planning and Pre-Job Briefing Tool *[see 110.15(1)].* Creating a job plan and conducting pre-job briefing assists personnel to focus on the performance of the tasks and to understand their roles in the execution of the tasks.

The following is a graded approach that can be used when job planning to identify error precursors and select an appropriate human performance tool, or combination of tools, proportionate to the potential consequences of error:

(1) Summarize the critical steps of the job that, if performed improperly, will cause irreversible harm to persons or equipment, or will significantly impact operation of a process.
(2) Anticipate error precursors for each critical step.
(3) Foresee probable and worst-case consequences if an error occurs during each critical step.
(4) Evaluate controls or contingencies at each critical step to prevent, catch, and recover from errors and to reduce their consequences.
(5) Review previous experience and lessons learned relevant to the specific task and critical steps.

If one or more human performance tools are identified, then each tool should be discussed regarding its advantages, disadvantages, and when and how it should be applied.

Q.6.3 Job Site Review Tool. Incorporating a job site review into job planning facilitates the identification of hazards and potential barriers and delays. A job site review can be performed any time prior or during work.

Q.6.4 Post-Job Review Tool. A post-job review is a positive opportunity to capture feedback and lessons learned from the job that can be applied to future jobs. The use of or lack of use of human performance tools should be incorporated into the review.

The pre-job briefing and the post-job review are effective communication tools.

Q.6.5 Procedure Use and Adherence Tool. Adhering to a written step-by-step sequential procedure is a human performance tool. The worker should proactively read and understand the purpose, scope, and intent of all actions as written and in the sequence specified.

An accurate and current account of progress should be kept by marking each step in the procedure as it is completed. This ensures that if the procedure is interrupted before all the steps are completed, the job site or activity can be left in a safe state and the procedure can be resumed at the point it was interrupted.

If the procedure cannot be used as written, or if the expected result cannot be accurately predicted, then the activity should be stopped and the issues resolved before continuing.

An example of adhering to a written step-by-step sequential procedure is a switching sequence, wherein the sequential order of operation of electrical distribution equipment is identified and documented for the purposes of de-energizing and re-energizing.

Q.6.6 Self-Check with Verbalization Tool. The self-check with verbalization tool is also known by the acronym STAR — Stop, Think, Act, and Review. Before, during, and after performing a task that cannot be reversed, the worker should stop, think, and openly verbalize their actions. Verbalizing permits the individual's brain to slow down to their body speed. It has the effect of keeping the individual focused, thus enabling them to act and then review their actions.

Example: A worker has one more routine task to complete before the end of shift — to approach a group of motor control panels and close a circuit breaker in one of those panels. The error precursors are task demands (in a hurry) and human nature (complacency). If the worker verbalizes each step in the task and the expected outcome of each step, he or she is less likely to operate the wrong circuit breaker and will be prepared in the event that the outcome of an action does not match the expectation. For example, the worker self checks and verbalizes:

(1) Iam at Panel 12 Bravo (12B).

(2) I am about to close Circuit Breaker 4 Bravo (4B).

(3) The pump motor heater indicator light will engage bright red on Panel 10 Bravo (10B).

(4) The pump motor should not start.

(5) If the pump motor starts then I will open Circuit Breaker 4 Bravo.

(6) I am now closing Circuit Breaker 4 Bravo.

Q.6.7 Three-Way Communication Tool. The three-way communication tool facilitates a mutual understanding of the message between the sender and receiver. After a directive or statement is made by the sender, it is repeated by the receiver to confirm the accuracy of the message.

When the message includes the use of letters, then whenever possible the letters should be communicated using the phonetic alphabet.

Example: A sender issues a directive over a radio communication device: "Close circuit breaker 4 Bravo." The receiver repeats the message: "I understand, close circuit breaker 4 Bravo." The sender validates that the proper response was understood: "That is correct" or "Affirmative."

Q.6.8 Stop When Unsure Tool. When a worker is unable to follow a procedure or process step, if something unexpected occurs or if the worker has a "gut feeling" that something is not right, then the worker should stop and obtain further direction. The "stop when unsure" tool requires that the worker maintain a questioning attitude at all times.

Phrases such as "I think" or "I'm pretty sure," whether verbalized or not, indicate that the worker is in knowledge-based mode and needs to transition to rule-based mode. This transition should be communicated to co-workers.

Q.6.9 Flagging and Blocking Tools *[see 130.7(E)]*. Flagging is a method to ensure the correct component is manipulated or worked on at the required time under the required conditions. A flag could be a marker, label, or device.

It should be used when an error-likely situation or condition is present, such as one of the following:

(1) Similar or "look-alike" equipment

(2) Work on multiple components

(3) Frequent operations performed in a short period of time

(4) Interruption of process critical equipment

Blocking is a method of physically preventing access to an area or equipment controls.

Hinged covers on control buttons or switches, barricades, fences or other physical barriers, whether temporary or permanent, are examples of blocking tools.

Blocking can be used in conjunction with flagging.

Q.7 Human Performance Warning Flags.

Q.7.1 General. There are common process, organizational, supervisory, and worker performance weaknesses that serve as human performance warning flags. These warning flags should be identified by the organization and action should be taken to address the root cause.

Q.7.2 Program or Process. The following are program or process human performance warning flags:

(1) Risk management processes are over-relied on, instead of personal ownership and accountability for managing risk.
(2) Risk management processes are inefficient or cumbersome ("more" is often not better).

Q.7.3 Organizational Performance. The following are organizational human performance warning flags:

(1) Personnel in the organization tend to engage in consensus or group thinking, without encouraging counterview points.
(2) Personnel overly defer to managers and perceived experts.
(3) Activities with high risk are not assigned clear owners.
(4) Past success without adverse outcomes becomes the basis for continuing current practices.
(5) The organization assumes that risk management is healthy because a program or process was established (i.e., complacency exists).

Q.7.4 Supervisory Performance. The following are supervisory human performance warning flags:

(1) Delegation is lacking, with a few individuals relied on to make major decisions.
(2) Supervision is physically or mentally separated from the job site and is insufficiently aware of current conditions and attitudes.
(3) Personnel in the organization do not understand how risk is perceived and managed at the worker level.
(4) Past success without adverse outcomes becomes the basis for continuing current practices.
(5) Performance indicators are used to justify existing risk management strategies.

Q.7.5 Worker Performance. The following are worker human performance warning flags:

(1) Individuals or groups exhibit self-imposed production pressure.
(2) Work activities are considered routine.
(3) Individuals are quick to make risky judgments without taking the time to fully understand the situation.
(4) Past success without adverse outcomes becomes the basis for continuing current practices.
(5) Personnel take pride in their ability to work through or with levels of risk that could have been mitigated or eliminated.
(6) Risk is not communicated effectively up the company. Individuals assume that the next level of supervision knows or understands the risk involved or that there are insufficient resources to manage the risk.
(7) Problem reporting is not transparent. Individuals are not willing to report high-risk conditions.

Q.8 Workplace Culture.

Q.8.1 General. The reduction or elimination of electrical incidents requires that all members at the workplace cultivate and consistently exhibit a culture that supports the use of human performance tools and principles. Workers, supervisors, and managers must all work together to implement strong human performance practices.

Q.8.2 Workers. The safe performance of activities by workers is a product of mental processes influenced by factors related to the work environment, the task demands, and the capabilities of the worker. All need to take responsibility for their actions and strive to improve themselves, the task at hand, and the work environment. Five general practices that should be consistently demonstrated by workers include the following:

(1) Communication to support a consistent understanding
(2) Anticipation of error-likely situations and conditions
(3) Desire to improve personal capabilities
(4) Reports on all incidents (including "near-miss" incidents)
(5) A commitment to utilize human performance tools and principles

Q.8.3 Supervisors and Managers. Through their actions, supervisors focus worker and team efforts in order to accomplish a task. To be effective, supervisors must understand what influences worker performance. Supervisors promote positive outcomes into the workplace environment to encourage desired performance and results. Supervisors must demonstrate a passion for identifying and preventing human performance errors. They influence both individual and company performance in order to achieve high levels of workplace electrical safety. Five general practices that should be consistently demonstrated by supervisors include the following:

(1) Promote open communication
(2) Encourage teamwork to eliminate error-likely situations and conditions
(3) Seek out and eliminate broader company weaknesses that may create opportunity for error
(4) Reinforce desired workplace culture
(5) Recognize the value in preventing errors, reporting of near-miss incidents, and the utilization of human performance tools and principles

Q.8.4 The Organization. It is important that an organization's procedures, processes, and values recognize and accept that people make mistakes. The policies and goals of an organization influence worker and supervisor performance. Five general practices that should be consistently demonstrated by an organization include the following:

(1) Promote open communication
(2) Foster a culture that values error prevention and the use of human performance tools
(3) Identify and prevent the formation of error-likely situations and conditions
(4) Support continuous improvement and learning across the entire organization
(5) Establish a blame-free culture that supports incident reporting and proactively identifies and reacts appropriately to risk

N Working with Capacitors

Annex R provides insight and explanation for the application of Article 360, Safety-Related Requirements for Capacitors.

N R.1 Introduction.

Capacitors have the ability to store electrical energy after the source power has been disconnected. While many systems with capacitors are built with bleed resistors that automatically discharge the stored energy within a set time, these systems can sometimes fail, leaving a thermal, shock, arc flash, or arc blast hazard. Some capacitor systems might not have built-in bleed resistors. This informative annex provides detailed guidance on how to properly assess the risk in working with capacitors and implement suitable controls.

N R.2 Qualification and Training.

N R.2.1 Qualifications.
Employees who perform work on electrical equipment with capacitors that exceed the energy thresholds in 360.3 should be qualified persons as required in Chapter 1 and should be trained in, and familiar with, the specific hazards and controls required for safe work.

N R.2.2 Unqualified Persons.
Unqualified persons should be trained in, and familiar with, any electrical safety-related practices necessary for their safety.

N R.3 Shock Hazard.

N R.3.1 General.
The capacitor shock hazard to a person is an impulse shock with an exponential decay curve. The severity of the shock is related to the amount of energy (joules) delivered and the time in which the energy is delivered. Injuries from capacitor shock include severe reflex action, internal and external bums, and heart fibrillation. Reflex injury can occur at energy levels as low as 0.25 joules when the capacitor voltage is over the skin breakdown threshold (about 400 volts), resulting in a very rapid delivery of the energy. Reflex action can result in injuries from falling, involuntarily coming in contact with other hazards, tearing muscles, tendons, and ligaments, or dislocation of joints. Internal bum injuries to nervous system and other tissues can occur at energies as low as 10s of joules. Heart fibrillation can happen when the voltage exceeds 100 volts and the stored energy delivered exceeds 10 joules under certain circumstances. However, even without fibrillation, a high-voltage, high-energy shock can cause serious injuries, either directly or

where:

V = voltage
C = capacitance
R = resistance

FIGURE R.3.1(a) Capacitor Shock Circuit.

through reflex action, down to as low as 0.25 joules. Instances of temporary paralysis, loss of consciousness, hearing damage, temporary loss of eyesight, bums, and dislocated joints have been reported. [See Figure R.3.1(a) for a capacitive shock circuit and Figure R.3.1(b) for a capacitive discharge curve.]

N **R.3.2 Duration of Discharge.** The duration of a capacitive discharge shock is independent of voltage and is generally assumed to be three times the time constant of the shock circuit. After three time constants, the voltage is reduced by 95 percent, and the energy has been reduced by 99.25 percent. The time constant, x, is equal to body shock pathway resistance times capacitance, as follows:

N
$$\tau = RC \qquad\qquad\qquad \text{[R.3.2]}$$

N **R.3.3 Current Delivered.** The current delivered by the shock is independent of capacitance and is proportional to the initial peak voltage and inversely proportional to shock pathway resistance. Assuming that all of the stored energy is delivered in 3x, the rms equivalent current can be expressed as follows:

N
$$I_{rms} = \frac{V_p}{R\sqrt{6}} \qquad\qquad\qquad \text{[R.3.3]}$$

where:
V = voltage
t = time
Vp = peak voltage
τ = time constant
R = resistance
C = capacitance

FIGURE R.3.1(b) *Typical Exponential Discharge Characteristic of a Capacitor Through a Resistor.*

where:

I_{rms} = rms current
V_p = peak voltage
R^p = pathway resistance

N **R.3.4 Shock Pathway.** The shock pathway resistance depends on skin resistance, entry and exit locations, and internal body resistance. The severity of a capacitor discharge shock depends on the time of delivery (quickly or slowly) and the energy delivered. A capacitor disconnected from a live voltage source has only a finite amount of energy and can deliver that energy either quickly or slowly, depending on specific shock pathway resistance. As shock pathway resistance increases, the current lowers but the time to discharge also takes longer, and vice versa. Below 400 volts, skin breakdown is less likely and skin resistance (over 10,000 ohms for intact skin) will significantly reduce the shock current and extend discharge time. For punctured, broken, or very wet skin, the contact resistance is 0 ohms to 100 ohms.

N **R.3.5 Response to Shock Levels.** For a given stored energy, there is a difference in response to whether it is a high-voltage, low-capacitance shock, or a low-voltage, high-capacitance shock. At high voltage and low capacitance, a hazardous shock will fully discharge nearly instantaneously (in microseconds) and could miss the vulnerable part of the heart cycle. However, the full energy is delivered to the person and there could be nerve or other tissue damage.

At low voltage and high capacitance, the total discharge time can extend several seconds (multiple heart beats), behaving more like a dc shock. Both scenarios remain highly hazardous as fibrillation could still occur.

> Informational Note: For more information on impulse shock hazards, see IEC TS 60479-2, *Effects of Current on Humans and Livestock, Part 2, Special Aspects.*

N **R.3.6 Reflex Hazard.** Even when fibrillation does not occur, there remains the potential for serious bodily injury, especially above 400 volts. The reflex action to an impulse shock can be severe, causing persons to fall off of elevated platforms or ladders, knock a body part into nearby objects, or in some cases cause severe muscle clenching, temporary paralysis, or dislocated joints. This reflex hazard extends to lower energies even where fibrillation is unlikely. The lower threshold for hazardous reflex shocks is 0.25 joules for over 400 volts.

N **R.3.7 Shock Hazard Thresholds.** Capacitors connected to conductors or circuit parts operating at voltages equal to or greater than 100 volts and containing a stored energy equal to or greater than 10 joules present a significant risk of shock and fibrillation. Below 10 joules, a significant risk of reflex action leading to injury could exist in the following situations:

(1) 100 volts–400 volts: if the stored energy is greater than 1 joule
(2) >400 volts: if the stored energy is greater than 0.25 joules

N **R.4 Short-Circuit Hazard.**

Capacitors have the unique ability to discharge very rapidly in a shorted condition due to their low internal impedance. In ac power systems, faults typically occur on the order of milliseconds and are limited by transformer impedances. Battery faults take seconds or minutes to discharge. In contrast, capacitors have very little internal impedance and can fully discharge in microseconds, with very high discharge current. This current can cause heating of metals, arc flash injury, and arc blast injury, dependent on the stored energy in the capacitor. The shock injuries, including reflex and fibrillation, are discussed in R.3.7. Additional hazards that can result from capacitor energy include those discussed in R.4.1 through R.4.3.

N **R.4.1 Thermal Hazard.** At around 100 joules, a short through a metal object in contact with the worker, such as a ring or tool, can cause rapid heating and burns to the skin. Above 1 kJ, there can be substantial heating of metal, arcing, and magnetic forces causing mechanical deformation. Above 10 kJ, there is massive conductor melting, massive magnetic/mechanical motion, and an arc blast hazard.

N **R.4.2 Arc Flash Hazard.** At approximately 120 kJ, there exists sufficient stored energy to create an arc flash hazard (greater than 1.2 cal/cm^2 at a working distance of 18 in.). This is a conservative lower bound that assumes all of the stored energy has been converted to radiant heat. The threshold of 120 kJ could be lower for a capacitor in a box. There could be an additional contribution to the arc flash energy from an ac or dc source connected to the capacitor or capacitor bank.

N **R.4.3 Arc Blast Hazard.** Capacitors can have a significant arc blast hazard due to the very high short-circuit current involved. The effects of the acoustic shock wave can rupture eardrums and collapse lungs. While hearing protection should be used above 100 joules to mitigate against hearing damage, there is no PPE for protection against lung collapse, which becomes a hazard above 122 kJ.

N **R.5 Internal Rupture.**

N **R.5.1 High Currents.** When a capacitor is subjected to high currents, such as a short circuit condition, internal stresses could result in violent rupture of the capacitor enclosure.

N **R.5.2 Internal Failure.** When capacitors are used to store large amounts of energy, internal failure of one capacitor in a bank could result in the rupture and explosion of the failed capacitors when all other capacitors in the bank discharge into the fault. Fuses or inductive elements are often used to limit the fault current from a capacitor bank into a faulted individual capacitor. Improperly sized fuses or inductive elements for this application could explode.

N **R.5.3 Fire Hazard.** Rupture of a capacitor can create a fire hazard from ignition of the dielectric fluids. Dielectric fluids can release toxic gases when decomposed by fire or the heat of an electric arc.

N **R.6 Performing a Risk Assessment for Capacitors.**

N **R.6.1 Annex F.** The risk assessment process for capacitors can follow the overall risk management process found in Annex F. This risk assessment should be coordinated with the shock risk assessment of 130.4 and the arc flash risk assessment of 130.5.

N **R.6.2 Exposure to Stored Energy.** Whether there is an exposure to capacitor stored energy hazard should be determined. An exposure would exist when a conductor or circuit part that could potentially remain energized with hazardous stored energy is not properly guarded, enclosed, or insulated. All circuit parts that are electrically connected to a capacitor or capacitor bank could present this hazard. For example, a power factor correction bank could be in a completely separate enclosure; however, should the bank remained charged for some reason, the switchgear to which it is connected could also deliver the stored energy hazard.

N **R.6.3 Determining Shock Hazard.** The shock hazard should be determined using both the voltage and stored energy of the capacitor. A high-voltage capacitor is not a shock hazard below the energy threshold of 0.25 joules. Use the shock risk assessment process of 130.4 and the dc shock approach boundaries (for capacitors above 100 volts and 0.25 joules) and PPE ratings.

N **R.6.4 Determining Total Stored Energy.** The total capacitor stored energy (see R.8) of the system should be determined.

N **R.6.5 Determining Arc Flash.** The arc flash hazard (see R.9) should be determined. If stored energy is greater than 120 kJ, the arc flash incident energy and the arc flash boundary should be determined at the appropriate working distance. Appropriate arc flash PPE should be selected accordingly, but workers should always remain out of the arc blast lung protection boundary (see R.6.6).

N **R.6.6 Determining Arc Blast Hazard.** The arc blast hazard (see R.10) should be determined. Hearing protection should be used where the stored energy exceeds 100 joules. Where the stored energy exceeds 10 kJ, the hearing protection boundary should be calculated. If stored energy is above 122 kJ, determine the arc blast boundary for lung hazards. A lung collapse hazard could exist above 122 kJ. DO NOT ENTER THE LUNG PROTECTION BOUNDARY. There is no PPE for lung protection.

N **R.6.7 Determine the Test and Grounding Method.** (See R. 11.)

N **R.6.8 Determining Discharge Time.** If capacitors are equipped with bleed resistors, or if using a soft grounding system, the required discharge wait time should be determined where applicable (see R.12). After the discharge time a hard ground stick or hard grounding system should be applied.

N **R.6.9 Written Discharge Procedure.** A written discharge procedure should be developed that captures all of the steps to place the equipment into an electrically safe work condition. Information about the amount of stored energy available, how long to wait after de-energization before opening the enclosure, how to test for absence of energy, and what to do if there is still stored energy present should be included.

N **R.6.10 Labeling.** Labeling the equipment with a hazard warning label (see R. 15) should be considered so that qualified persons are made aware of the potential for stored energy and the need for a written discharge procedure. The maximum voltage and stored energy should be included.

N **R.7 Determining the Shock Hazard.**

N **R.7.1 Risk Assessment.** A shock risk assessment should be performed for capacitors exceeding the thresholds in 360.3 in accordance with 130.4. Shock approach boundaries are based on the peak voltage and the dc shock approach boundaries of Table 130.4(E)(b). Appropriately rated shock protection PPE, such as voltage-rated gloves and dielectric insulating sheeting, should be selected. The dc ratings for rubber insulated products should be used. (See ASTM D120, *Standard Specification for Rubber Insulating Gloves,* for dc ratings.) The restricted approach boundary should be used to assist in the selection of the length and voltage rating of the ground stick. Capacitors below the thresholds defined in 360.3 are not shock hazards, and 130.4 does not apply. This includes capacitors from 0 volts to 100 volts and less than 100 joules, capacitors 100 volts to 400 volts and less than 1 joule, and capacitors greater than 400 volts and less than 0.25 joules.

N **R.7.2 Shock PPE.** Shock protection PPE is required for all parts of the body that enter the restricted approach boundary for capacitor shock hazards defined in R.7.1. [See Table 130.4(E)(b).]

N **R.8 Determining Capacitor Stored Energy.**

N **R.8.1 Capacitor Stored Energy.** Determining capacitor stored energy could require detailed examination of schematics or manufacturer's information to properly determine both the peak voltage that will be applied to the capacitors and the total capacitance. The value of capacitance and the capacitor voltage rating can also be obtained from the labels on the capacitor, if done safely. Commercial capacitors often use unit labels of mF for millifarads and MF for microfarads.

N **R.8.2** The stored energy in a capacitor is calculated as follows

N
$$E = \frac{1}{2}CV^2 \qquad\qquad \text{[R.8.2]}$$

where:

E = capacitive stored energy in joules
C = total capacitance in farads
V = peak voltage in volts

R.8.3 Capacitor Calculations. Total capacitance of capacitor banks is calculated as follows:

(1) For capacitors in parallel, add the capacitance as follows:

$$C_{total} = C_1 + C_2 + C_3 + ...$$ **[R.8.3a]**

(2) For capacitors in series, use the following:

$$\frac{1}{C_{total}} = \frac{1}{C_1} + \frac{1}{C_2} + \frac{1}{C_3} + ...$$ **[R.8.3b]**

(3) Capacitor banks used for power factor correction are often labeled with a kVAr value (kilovolt-amperes reactive) to facilitate power engineering calculations. Calculate the capacitance as follows:

$$C = \frac{Q}{2\pi fV^2}$$ **[R.8.3c]**

where:

C = total capacitance in farads
Q = reactive power in VAr (volt-amperes reactive)
f = frequency in hertz
V = phase-to-phase voltage in volts rms

(4) Long high-voltage coaxial cables can have significant capacitance, normally on the order of 45 pF/m-10 pF/m (1 picofarad = 1 x 10^{-12} F) for low-current applications, or 150 pF/m-450 pF/m for utility-grade, medium-insulated cable. Manufacturer's specifications on capacitance per meter should be consulted.

R.8.4 Voltage. For peak voltage, the voltage applied across the capacitors that would cause the maximum charge should be used. For disconnected capacitors in storage or for disposal, the capacitor rated voltage should be used.

R.8.4.1 For dc systems, use the maximum available terminal voltage that could be applied to the capacitor by the system.

R.8.4.2 For ac systems, nominal system voltage is normally expressed in volts rms (root mean square). For capacitor stored energy calculations, use the peak amplitude of the voltage, V_p, as follows:

$$V_{rms} = \frac{1}{\sqrt{2}} V_p = 0.707 V_p$$ **[R.8.4.2a]**

(1) For single-phase ac systems, use peak ac voltage, as follows:

$$V_p = V_{rms} \sqrt{2}$$ **[R.8.4.2b]**

(2) For 3-phase wye-connected systems, use the peak phase-to-neutral ac voltage, as follows:

N $$V_p = V_{\phi-N}\sqrt{2}$$ **[R.8.4.2c]**

(3) For 3-phase delta-connected systems, use the peak phase-to-phase ac voltage, as follows:

N $$V_{cap} = V_{\phi-\phi}\sqrt{2}$$ **[R.8.4.2d]**

Informational Note: For the same capacitance, a delta-connected system will have a total energy three times higher than a wye-connected system. Always check the configuration as design requirements vary.

N **R.9 Determining the Arc Flash Hazard.**

N **R.9.1 Incident Energy.** The maximum theoretical possible arc flash incident energy can be calculated by assuming that all of the stored energy is dissipated as radiant energy in a spherical expansion in open air. While this is unlikely, it helps set a lower bound of stored energy below which an arc flash hazard is unlikely.

N $$IE_{open\ air} = \frac{Energy}{Area} = \frac{\frac{1}{2}CV^2}{4\pi r^2} = \frac{CV^2}{8\pi r^2} J/cm^2$$ **[R.9.1a]**

Converting to cal/cm² (1 cal = 4.184 joules) we obtain the following:

N $$IE_{open\ air} = \frac{CV^2}{105.1r^2} = \frac{E}{52.6r^2} cal/cm^2$$ **[R.9.1b]**

where:

IE = incident energy
E = energy
C = capacitance
V = voltage
r = radius

N **R.9.2 Arc Flash Boundary.** The arc flash boundary, where IE = 1.2 cal/cm², is then as follows

N $$AFB_{open\ air} = 0.126\sqrt{E}\ (cm) = 0.05\sqrt{E}\ (in.)$$ **[R.9.2a]**

In a box, we can apply a three times factor over the open-air incident energy calculation, as follows:

N $$IE_{box} = 3 \times IE_{open\ air}$$ **[R.9.2b]**

N $$AFB_{box} = \sqrt{3} \times AFB_{open\ air}$$ **[R.9.2c]**

where:

AFB = arc flash boundary
IE = incident energy

Thus, the minimum stored energy (lower bound) required to obtain 1.2 cal/cm² at a working distance of 18 in. is roughly 44 kJ in a box or 120 kJ in open air. Extreme caution should be used with the open-air calculation, as the arc flash boundary can fall inside the lung protection boundary for arc blast. A better practice is to always use the box arc flash boundary as a minimum approach distance.

_N_ **R.10 Determining the Arc Blast Hazard.**

_N_ **R.10.1 Hazard.** The arc blast hazard is directly related to the instantaneous (initial) short circuit current. Since capacitors can discharge very rapidly, the shockwave generated by a capacitor discharge can cause barotrauma (overpressure injury) to persons in the area. The most sensitive organs are the ears, lungs, and brain. When a differential pressure across the eardrums exceeds around 20-35 kilopascals (3-5 psi), the eardrum can rupture. At 200 kilopascals (29 psi), lung damage can occur. The following formulas are used to estimate safe boundaries based on total stored energy, where "safe" is less than a 1 percent probability of eardrum rupture or lung injury:

_N_
$$R_{ear} = 49.29 \sqrt[3]{\frac{E}{1000}} - 5.09 \qquad \text{[R.10.1a]}$$

_N_
$$R_{lung} = 31.22 \sqrt[3]{\frac{E}{1000}} - 155.45 \qquad \text{[R.10.1b]}$$

where:

R_{ear} = eardrum rupture boundary (1 percent probability) in cm
R_{lung} = lung collapse boundary (1 percent probability) in cm
E = capacitor stored energy in joules

> Informational Note: For more information about the derivation of these formulas, see Charles R. Hummer, Richard J. Pearson, and Donald H. Porschet, *"Safe Distances From a High-Energy Capacitor Bank for Ear and Lung Protection,"* Army Research Laboratory Report, ARL-TN-608, July 2014.

_N_ **R.10.2 Above 122 kJ.** Above 122 kJ a lung collapse hazard can exist. It is not sufficient to wear arc flash PPE, as this will not protect against lung injury. Remain outside of the lung collapse boundary.

_N_ **R.10.3 Above 448 kJ.** Above 448 kJ, the lung protection boundary will be greater than the arc flash boundary in open air calculated in.R.9. A better practice is to always use the box arc flash boundary as a minimum approach distance. (See Figure R.10.3.)

_N_ **R.11 Selecting the Appropriate Test and Grounding Method.**

_N_ **R.11.1 Method Selection.** The method to safely discharge or verify discharge of a capacitor will vary depending on the degree of hazard. Low-voltage, low-energy capacitors can be verified de-energized with a properly rated test instrument meeting the requirements of 110.8 and/or hard grounded. At higher energy and voltage, soft grounding through a resistor could

FIGURE R.10.3 Plot of Arc Flash and Blast Protection Boundaries.

be needed to limit the discharge current. At very high energies (>100 kJ), manual testing or grounding can become a serious arc blast hazard, and remote metering and grounding should be performed.

N **R.11.2 Bleed Systems.** For systems with permanently installed bleed systems, testing for absence of voltage after the prescribed discharge time can be performed instead of applying grounds. Testing can also be performed as a means to verify absence of voltage after an automatically switched bleed system has grounded the system. In all cases, the test device must be rated for the system. (See Table R. 11.9 for the appropriate test method.)

N **R.11.2.1** Below 1000 volts and below 10 kJ, a properly rated, high-impedance digital voltmeter (DVM) can be used.

N **R.11.2.2** Above 1000 volts and below 100 joules, a properly rated, high-impedance digital voltmeter (DVM) can be used with an approved attachment for measuring high-voltage dc on non-utility systems. On utility systems, a utility-grade, dc, resistive-type voltmeter must be used with a live-line tool.

N **R.11.2.3** Above 1000 volts and between 100 joules and 100 kJ, a utility-grade, dc, resistive-type voltmeter can be used with a live-line tool.

N **R.11.2.4** Above 100 kJ, engineered method can be used only for verifying absence of voltage.

N **R.11.3 Hard Grounding.** Hard grounding is the practice of shorting a capacitor from terminal to terminal and then directly to ground. Since the resistance is typically <0.1 ohm, the discharge time is rapid and the discharge current can be high. An intense spark and a loud noise can happen at higher energies. Above 100 joules there is a hearing damage hazard. The voltage reversal associated with using a hard ground can put excessive voltage stress on the capacitor. Since this is an equipment issue, check with the manufacturer for their recommendations.

N **R.11.4 Soft Grounding.** Soft grounding is the practice of discharging a capacitor through a resistor rated for the power. The resistor raises the time constant ($\tau = RC$) and reduces the peak discharge current ($I = V/R$) to safer levels. Soft discharge is necessary above 1000 joules.

N **R.11.5 End of Discharge Time.** At the conclusion of the specified discharge time, there is still voltage on the capacitors. A properly matched resistor and capacitor will reduce the voltage to less than 50 volts and the energy to less than 5 joules. At this point hard grounding is applied to fully short the capacitors to ground.

N **R.11.6 Resistor Connection Point.** Sometimes the grounding resistor is attached directly to the grounding stick. Other times, there are two separate grounding points built into the equipment itself. The grounding point labeled "High-Z" is the soft grounding point, where "High-Z" stands for high impedance. The grounding point labeled "Low-Z" is the hard grounding point, directly to ground. In this case the same ground stick is applied, first to the High-Z point, then to the Low-Z ground point. See Figure R.11.9.

N **R.11.7 Lung Protection Boundary.** The grounding method should keep all personnel clear of the lung protection boundary. For this reason, above 100 kJ, remote soft grounding is necessary.

N **R.11.8 Ground Sticks.** All ground sticks should meet the construction and periodic inspection requirements of R.16.

N **R.11.9 Use of Table for Method Selection.** See Table R.11.9, Figure R. 11.9(a), and Figure R. 11.9(b) for selection of the proper test and grounding methods.

TABLE R.11.9 *Capacitor Test and Grounding Matrix to Establish Safe Discharge*

	Test Method				**Grounding Method**		
	0-100 volts	**100-1 kV**	**>1 kV**		**0-100 volts**	**100-1 kV**	**>1 kV**
< 0.25 joules	Not applicable	Not applicable	Not applicable	< 0.25 joules	Not applicable	Not applicable	Not applicable
0.25-100 joules	Not applicable	DVM	DVM with HV adapter	0.25-100 joules	Not applicable	Hard ground ok	Hard ground ok
100 joules-1 kJ	DVM	DVM	HV utility grade dc voltmeter	100 joules -1 kJ	Hard ground ok	Hard ground ok	Hard ground ok
1 kJ-100 kJ	DVM	DVM	HV utility grade dc voltmeter	1 kJ-100 kJ	Soft ground then hard ground	Soft ground then hard ground	Soft ground then hard ground
>100 kJ	Engineered method	Engineered method	Engineered method	>100 kJ	Remote grounding only	Remote grounding only	Remote grounding only

	Hard grounding: An insulating stick with a grounding tip is used to discharge a capacitor between its two terminals and then to ground.
	Soft grounding 1: An insulating stick with a mounted resistor is used to perform a controlled discharge of the capacitor charge using the High-Z tip first. Then, after the prescribed wait time, hard grounding is applied with the second (Low-Z) tip that bypasses the resistor.
	Soft grounding 2: An insulating stick with a grounding tip is first applied to the High-Z point to perform a controlled discharge of the capacitor. Then, after the prescribed wait time, the grounding tip is applied to the Low-Z point to bypass the resistor and hard-ground the capacitor.

FIGURE R.11.9(a) *Illustration of Hard and Soft Grounding Examples.*

FIGURE R.11.9(b) *Flowchart of Capacitor Test and Grounding Methods to Establish Safe Discharge*

N **R.11.10 Other Considerations.** Other considerations are as follows:

(1) Charge transfer: Grounding capacitors in series may transfer charge between capacitors rather than discharge the stored energy. Special precaution should be taken in selecting the tools and sequence necessary to discharge capacitors connected in series. Improper grounding can result in moving charge around and not fully discharging to ground. Capacitor cases are not always grounded and should be considered charged unless otherwise determined.

(2) Dielectric absorption: Not all the energy in a capacitor is dissipated when it is short-circuited for a short time. Although the charge on the plates may be initially removed, dielectric polarization can cause charge to accumulate after the ground is removed. A voltage recharge of up to 10 percent can occur a few minutes after the grounding or shorting device has been removed. This can occur in capacitors with liquid dielectrics, such as an electrolytic capacitor, and in capacitors with solid dielectrics, such as polyethylene film capacitors.

(3) High-voltage capacitors can build a charge in the presence of high electric fields.

(4) A momentary hazardous voltage can exist at the moment of contact across the inductance of a few feet of the grounding cable of a ground stick at the moment of contact with a charged capacitor. This is why a worker should never hold the grounding cable during a discharge event.

N **R.12 Determining the Capacitor Discharge Time.**

N **R.12.1 Discharge Time.** The discharge time, T_d of a capacitor is the time it takes to reduce to less than 100 volts. It is related to the time constant, τ. The discharge resistance can be permanently installed on the capacitors (e.g., a bleeder resistor), automatically switched in after power shutoff (e.g., a resistor dump bank), or applied through a soft grounding stick.

N **R.12.2 Voltages 1000 Volts and Less.** For voltages up to 1000 volts, it is sufficient to wait three times the time constant, or one minute, whichever is greater. That is because after 3τ, the residual voltage is less than 5 percent of the initial voltage.

N **R.12.3 Voltages Greater Than 1000 Volts.** For voltages greater than 1000 volts, the discharge time will need to be longer than 3x and should be calculated. Use the following formula to determine the minimum wait time:

N
$$\tau = RC \qquad\qquad\qquad\qquad \textbf{[R.12.3a]}$$

N
$$T_d = -\ln\left(\frac{100}{V_p}\right)\tau \qquad\qquad\qquad\qquad \textbf{[R.12.3b]}$$

where:

τ = time constant
R = discharge path resistance
C = total capacitance
T_d = discharge time (wait time)
V_p = peak voltage

N **R.13 Establishing an Electrically Safe Work Condition.**

N **R.13.1 Written Discharge Procedure.** Where a conductor circuit part is operating at or above 100 volts and 10 joules, a written discharge procedure (such as a complex LOTO procedure) should be used to document the necessary steps to place the equipment in an electrically safe work condition. The written discharge procedure should incorporate the results of the risk assessment performed in R.6 and specify the following at a minimum:

(1) Voltage in volts
(2) Energy in joules
(3) Specific steps to safely discharge the capacitor or verify that it is discharged
(4) Specific tool(s) (e.g.. ground stick) or engineering system to discharge the capacitors, if necessary
(5) Specific test instruments (e.g., DVM) or engineered systems used to verify a de-energized state

N **R.13.2 Electrically Safe Work Condition.** In order to place the equipment with stored hazardous energy in an electrically safe work condition, a qualified person should follow the steps in 120.5 as well as the specific sequence outlined in the written discharge procedure. The process to remove stored energy in a capacitor is a part of the overall process to establish an electrical safe work condition in 120.5. These would then be as follows:

(1) Review the scope of work and the written discharge procedure. Determine all safe approach boundaries and necessary PPE and tools for the task.
(2) Perform a job briefing with the personnel involved and notify affected persons that the equipment will be de-energized.
(3) After properly interrupting the supply current, open the disconnecting device(s) for each source feeding the equipment.
(4) Wherever possible, visually verify that all blades of the disconnecting devices are fully open or that drawout-type circuit breakers are withdrawn to the fully disconnected position.
(5) Apply lockout/tagout devices in accordance with a documented and established policy, or use plug control on smaller equipment.
(6) If bleed resistors or automatic discharge systems are applicable, wait the prescribed time for the capacitors to fully discharge to less than thresholds in 360.3.
(7) Perform the test and ground method selected in R. 11.

To ensure that recharging does not occur, all of the capacitor terminals should be connected together (shorted) and grounded with a non-insulated wire of sufficient gauge to withstand handling. For series capacitors these shorting wires should be attached across each individual capacitor and to case. For single capacitors or for a parallel capacitor bank, the grounding device should be permitted to be left hanging on the capacitor terminal during the work (e.g., a ground stick/hook).

N **R.14 Storage and Disposal.**

N **R.14.1 Residual Charge.** Any residual charge from capacitors should be removed by discharging the terminals before servicing or removal.

N **R.14.2 Stored Capacitors.** All uninstalled capacitors capable of storing energy exceeding the thresholds of 360.3 at their rated voltage should be short-circuited with a conductor of appropriate size.

N **R.14.3 Capacitors Without Shorting Wire.** When an uninstalled capacitor is discovered without a shorting wire attached to the terminals, it should be treated as energized and charged to its full rated voltage until determined otherwise. A qualified person should be contacted to determine the appropriate steps to safely discharge the capacitor.

N **R.14.4 Change in Initial Capacitance.** Large, high-voltage capacitors are often formed of a network of smaller capacitor elements connected inside a case. When such a capacitor develops an internal open circuit, it can retain a substantial charge internally even though the external terminals are short-circuited. Such a capacitor can be hazardous to transport because the damaged internal wiring can reconnect and discharge the capacitor through the short-circuiting wires. Any capacitor that shows a significant change in capacitance after a fault can have this problem. Action should be taken to reduce the risk associated with this hazard when it is discovered.

N **R.15 Capacitor Hazard Labeling.**

N **R.15.1 Labeling.** Electrical equipment operating at or above 100 volts and 10 joules should be field marked with a label containing all the following information:

(1) A warning about the potential for capacitive stored energy, with the word "WARNING" on an orange colored background
(2) Stored energy in joules and the maximum voltage for that stored energy
(3) The required wait time before opening the enclosure (the wait time needs to be greater than the discharge time)
(4) Date of the stored energy hazard analysis
(5) An instruction that a qualified person is necessary and that they should use a written discharge procedure

N **R.15.2** Labeling should conform to the requirements of ANSI Z535.4, *Product Safety Signs and Labels.*

N **R.16 Ground Sticks.**

N **R.16.1 Use of Ground Sticks.** Ground sticks should be provided for qualified persons to safely discharge any residual stored energy contained in capacitor(s). The ground sticks should be designed, constructed, installed, and periodically inspected so that the full energy of a capacitor(s) can be safely discharged. See Table R.11.9 for selection guidance.

N **R.16.2 Construction.** Design and construction are as follows:

(1) Ground stick rod: When built of fiber reinforced plastic (FRP), the rod in the ground stick assembly should meet ASTM F711, *Standard Specification for Fiberglass-Reinforced Plastic (FRP) Rod and Tube Used in Live Line Tools,* specifications. Other insulating materials may be used provided they are of acceptable insulation and durability for the application. The stick should be long enough to be handled effectively and also to keep a person's hands out of the restricted approach boundary. This should include a non-moveable hand stop to remind the worker during use where to hold the ground stick.
(2) Ground stick tip: The ground stick connection to discharge points may be chain links, bare conductor, or solid copper bar in various geometries. The selection of the grounding tip should match the requirements of the intended application and ensure that all necessary circuit parts are fully discharged and grounded at the same time in order to avoid

charge transfer. The grounding tips can be designed to remain applied (e.g., a hook) in order to safely prevent recharging from dielectric absorption. Alternatively, shorting straps may be applied while the grounding sticks are applied. Discharge points should be clearly marked and caution should be used to prevent transferring charge to other capacitors or reversing the charge on affected capacitors.

(3) Ground stick resistor: Soft grounding should be provided where stored energy exceeds 1000 joules. The resistor used to soft ground a capacitor(s) should be fully rated to handle power, voltage, and current. An engineering safety margin would be to calculate peak power, voltage and current, and double the resistor rating for each parameter. The resistor should be able to discharge the capacitor bank to less than 50 volts and less than 5 joules in less than 1 minute (less than 1000 volts) or less than 5 minutes (greater than 1000 volts). Ideally, the current should be limited to 500 amperes peak in order to reduce the magnetic force on the ground stick and its cable. This can require a discharge time longer than 5 minutes. Note that soft grounding is always followed by hard grounding to complete the discharge.

(4) Ground stick cable: The cable should be grounding or welding cable, flexible rope lay, soft drawn copper. The individual strands should not be larger than #30 AWG. Grounding cables have flexible, transparent elastomer or thermoplastic jackets primarily for mechanical protection of the conductor it covers and to allow visual examination of stranding degradation. Connections should be crimped according to manufacturer instructions. The lugs should be rated for the cables to be clamped. In permanent equipment installations the cable conductor size should be sized no smaller than #10 AWG stranded and capable of safely carrying the potential discharge current. For temporary or benchtop situations, the conductor should be capable of safely carrying any potential discharge current. Ground sticks should never be fused.

N **R.16.3 Installation.** Installation is as follows:

(1) Connection to building grounding system: Ground sticks should be connected to the building grounding electrode system where practicable. A qualified engineer should evaluate the connection point to the building grounding system to ensure the integrity of the ground stick system. This connection should be in a location accessible to and visible to the operator of the ground stick. Ground sticks should be connected such that impedance is less than 0.1 ohms to ground. High-Z ground sticks should be connected such that impedance is less than 0.1 ohms between the resistor and the ground connection.

(2) Operator access: The ground sticks should be permanently grounded and stored in the immediate area of the equipment in a manner that ensures they are used. The approach path to the equipment being grounded should be perpendicular to the equipment and clear of debris or obstructions. The ground stick operator will then always be facing the potential hazard and have the grounded conductor between them and the potentially energized equipment. For cases of capacitors in a field situation, or in portable equipment, a portable ground stick may be used. The ground stick must be effectively connected to the system ground, by a bolt or heavy-duty clamp, before opening the enclosure.

N **R.16.4 Visual Inspection.** Visual inspection is as follows:

(1) The ground stick should be visually inspected for defects before use each day.
(2) If any defect or contamination that could adversely affect the insulating qualities or mechanical integrity of the ground stick is present, the tool should be removed from service. All mechanical connections should be examined for loose connections. Ground sticks should have a hand guard that reduces the risk of improper hand position.
(3) If the defect or contamination exists on the grounding stick, then it should be replaced.
(4) If the defect or contamination exists on the cable, then it should be replaced or repaired and tested before return to service.

N **R.16.5 Biennial Testing (every 2 years).** A ground stick system places a grounded conductor at the end of the rod between the operator and the electrical hazard. The low impedance (Low-Z) ground stick system is not a live line tool, and there will not be a voltage potential at the end of the ground stick rod. High-impedance (High-Z) ground sticks can have a voltage potential at the end of the rod and should be treated as live line tools.

(1) For all ground sticks: The ground stick system should be tested to verify that impedance is less than 0.1 ohms to ground. This test should be performed annually when it is located outside or under any other adverse conditions.

(2) All High-Z ground stick insulating rods should be removed from service to be recertified to the ASTM F711, *Standard Specification for Fiberglass-Reinforced Plastic (FRP) Rod and Tube Used in Live Line Tools,* standard or equivalent.

(3) High-Z ground sticks with resistors: The resistor on the High-Z ground stick should be measured and compared to the specified value.

N **R.17 References.** IEC TS 60479-1, 4th Edition (2005), *Effects of Current on Human Beings and Livestock, Part 1, General Aspects,* Geneva, Switzerland.

IEC TS 60479-2, 3rd Edition (2007), *Effects of Current on Human Beings and Livestock, Part 2, Special Aspects,* Geneva, Switzerland.

DOE-HDBK-1092-2013, *DOE Handbook for Electrical Safety,* U.S. Department of Energy, Washington, DC.

Dalziel, Charles F., "A Study of the Hazards of Impulse Currents," *Transactions of the American Institute of Electrical Engineers. Part III: Power Apparatus and Systems,* Volume 72, Issue 2, 1953, DOI: 10.1109/AIEEPAS.1953.4498738.

Gordon, Lloyd B. and Cartelli, Laura, "A Complete Electrical Hazard Classification System and Its Application," IEEE *Transactions on Industry Applications,* Vol. 54, pp. 6554—6565, November/December 2018.

Hummer, Charles R., Pearson, Richard J., and Porschet, Donald H., "Safe Distances From a High-Energy Capacitor Bank for Ear and Lung Protection," Army Research Laboratory Report, ARL-TN-608, July 2014.

Richmond, D.R., Yelverton, J.T., Fletcher, E.R., and Phillips, YY, "Physical Correlates of Eardrum Rupture," *Annals of Otology Rhinology and Laryngology,* Vol. 109 (May 1989): 35-41.

Scott, Mark, "Working Safely with Hazardous Capacitors: Establishing Practical Thresholds for Risks Associated With Stored Capacitor Energy," IEEE *Industry Applications Magazine,* Vol. 25, Issue 3, 2019: 44–53.

PART 2

Supplements

The three supplements included in Part 2 of the *Handbook for Electrical Safety in the Workplace* provide additional information as well as supporting reference material to assist users of NFPA *70E®, Standard for Electrical Safety in the Workplace®*. These supplements are not part of the NFPA *70E* standard.

Supplement 1   *National Electrical Code®* Requirements Associated with Safety-Related Work Practices

Supplement 2   Electrical Preventive Maintenance Programs

Supplement 3   Typical Safety Procedure (Procedure for Selection, Inspection, and Care of Rubber Insulating Gloves and Leather Protectors)

National Electrical Code Requirements Associated with Safety-Related Work Practices

Editor's Note: This supplement consists of a list of requirements from the 2020 edition of NFPA 70®, National Electrical Code® (NEC®), that directly impact the implementation of safety-related work practices from NFPA 70E®, Standard for Electrical Safety in the Workplace®. This list is not intended to be all-inclusive of the applicable NEC requirements for any of the indicated equipment. Although the requirements are listed and categorized as applicable to employees, employers, or electrical system designers, the employer and designer must be aware of each requirement.

NEC Requirements for Employees

Employees should be able to identify these requirements when they are put at risk of injury from the use of electricity.

Disconnecting Means and Where to Find Them

225.31	Feeders passing through the building or structure
225.32	Location for outside feeders
225.33	Maximum number of outside feeder disconnects
225.34	Grouping of outside feeder disconnects
225.51	Isolating switches for outside feeders
225.52	Outside feeders over 1000 volts
240.40	Fuses
410.130(G)	Electric-discharge lighting systems of 1000 volts or less
410.141	Electric-discharge lighting systems of more than 1000 volts
422.30	Appliances
422.31	Permanently connected appliances
422.33	Cord-and-plug-connected appliances
424.19	Fixed electric space-heating equipment
424.20	Thermostatically controlled switching devices
424.65	Fixed electric duct space heater controller equipment
425.19	Fixed industrial process heating equipment
425.65	Fixed industrial process duct heater controller equipment
426.50	Fixed outdoor deicing and snow-melting equipment
427.55	Fixed electric pipeline or vessel heating equipment
430.75	Motor control circuits
430.102	Motor controller
430.111	Switch or circuit breaker as both controller and disconnecting means
430.112	Motors served by single disconnecting means
430.113	Motors with energy from more than one source
430.227	Motor controller over 1000 volts, nominal
440.14	Air-conditioning or refrigerating equipment
440.63	Single-phase room air conditioner
450.14	Transformers
455.8	Phase converters
455.20	Utilization equipment — phase converters
480.7	Stationary battery system over 60 volts dc

(continues)

Disconnecting Means and Where to Find Them (Continued)

514.13	Maintenance and service of fuel dispensing equipment	665.12	Dielectric heating, induction heating, induction melting, and induction welding equipment
525.21(A)	Rides, tents, and concessions	668.13	Direct-current cell line
547.9	Electrical supply to agricultural building(s) or structure(s)	669.8	Electroplating, anodizing, electropolishing, and electrostripping
555.4	Shore power connections for buildings	670.4(B)	Industrial machinery
555.36	Shore power connections for boats	680.13	Swimming, wading, therapeutic, and decorative pools; fountains; hot tubs; spas; and hydromassage bathtubs
590.4(E)	Temporary circuits disconnecting means		
600.6(A)	Signs and outline lighting systems		
610.32	Cranes and monorail hoists	690.13	Building or other structure supplied by a photovoltaic system
620.51	Elevator, dumbwaiter, escalator, moving walk, platform lift, or stairway chairlift		
		690.15	Photovoltaic equipment
620.52	Single-car and multicar elevator	692.17	Fuel cell system
620.53	Elevator car light, receptacle(s), and ventilation	694.22(C)	Wind electric systems
620.54	Elevator heating and air-conditioning	694.24	Wind electric system equipment
620.55	Elevator utilization equipment	694.26	Wind electric systems — fuses
625.43	Electric vehicle charging	695.4(B)	Electric motor-driven fire pumps
630.13	Arc welder equipment	705.20	Interconnected electric power production sources
630.33	Resistance welder and control equipment		
660.5	X-ray equipment	706.15	Energy storage systems
660.24	Multi x-ray equipment independent control	712.34	Direct current microgrids

Working Space Necessary to Conduct Tasks Safely

110.26	Access and working space for electrical equipment	480.10(C)	Stationary storage battery systems
		530.62	Television and motion picture studio portable substations
110.30	Working space for electrical equipment over 1000 volts, nominal		
		620.5	Elevators, dumbwaiters, escalators, moving walks, platform lifts, and stairway chairlifts
110.32	Access and work space for electrical equipment over 1000 volts, nominal		
		646.20	Modular data centers
110.34	Equipment likely to require examination, adjustment, servicing, or maintenance while energized	646.21	Modular data center battery systems
		646.22	Routine service and maintenance — modular data center
425.8(B)	Fixed resistance and electrode industrial process heating equipment	668.10	Electrolytic cell line working zone
		706.20(C)	Energy storage systems

Guarding Employees from Injury

110.25	Locking requirements for disconnecting means	422.4	Appliances — live parts
110.27	Guarding of live parts operating at 50 to 1000 volts, nominal	426.12	Outdoor electric deicing and snow-melting equipment — thermal protection
110.33	Entrance to enclosures and access to working space	427.12	Pipeline and vessel heating equipment — thermal protection
110.75	Access to manholes	427.25	Pipeline and vessel heating equipment — personnel protection
110.76	Access to vaults and tunnels		
230.62	Service equipment — enclosed or guarded	427.36	Pipeline and vessel heating equipment induction coils — personnel protection
240.41	Guarded or isolated arcing or suddenly moving parts		
		430.232	Guarding exposed live parts of motors and controllers
408.20	Location of switchboards and switchgear		
410.5	Live parts of luminaires, portable luminaires, lampholders, and lamps	430.233	Motors — guards for attendants
		445.14	Generator — protection of live parts

Guarding Employees from Injury *(Continued)*

445.15	Generators — guards for attendants
450.8	Transformers — guarding
450.13	Transformers — accessibility
460.3	Capacitors — enclosing and guarding
470.18(B)	Resistors and reactors — isolated by enclosure or elevation
480.10(B)	Stationary storage battery locations
490.21(A)	Power fuses and fuseholders — equipment operating at more than 1000 volts, nominal
490.32	Guarding of high-voltage energized parts within a compartment
490.33	Guarding of energized parts operating at 1000 volts, nominal, or less within compartments
490.35	Accessibility of energized parts operating at more than 1000 volts, nominal
490.42	Interlocks — interrupter switches operating at more than 1000 volts, nominal
490.45	Circuit breaker interlocks operating at more than 1000 volts, nominal
490.46	Circuit breaker operating at more than 1000 volts, nominal — locking
490.53	Enclosures for equipment operating at more than 1000 volts, nominal
490.55	Power cable connections to mobile machines operating at more than 1000 volts, nominal
525.10(A)	Services for carnivals, circuses, fairs, and similar functions
590.7	Temporary wiring over 600 volts, nominal — guarding
620.4	Elevators, dumbwaiters, escalators, moving walks, platform lifts, and stairway chairlifts — live parts enclosed
620.71	Elevators, dumbwaiters, escalators, moving walks, platform lifts, and stairway chairlifts — guarding equipment
665.22	Induction and dielectric heating equipment — access to internal equipment

Identifying Hazards and Other Identification Requirements

110.15	Four-wire, delta-connected system high-leg marking
110.16	Arc flash hazard warning
110.22	Disconnecting means
200.6	Grounded conductors
210.5	Branch circuits
215.12	Feeders
225.30	Outside feeders — number of supplies
225.37	Services, feeders, or branch circuits supplying building or structure
408.3(F)	Switchboard, switchgear, or panelboard
408.4	Switchboard, switchgear, or panelboard circuit directory
409.110	Industrial control panel marking
424.86	Electrode-type boiler markings
425.86	Fixed industrial process electrode-type boiler markings
490.25	Backfeed of equipment operating at more than 1000 volts, nominal
665.23	Induction and dielectric heating equipment warning labels or signs
690.56	Solar photovoltaic (PV) systems — identification of power sources
692.56	Fuel cell system — stored energy
694.50	Interactive system point of interconnection
694.52	Wind electric systems employing energy storage
694.54	Wind electric systems — identification of power sources
700.7	On-site emergency power source signs
701.7	On-site legally required standby power source signs
702.7	On-site optional standby power source signs
705.10	Electric power production sources directory
705.12(C)	Electric power production sources — load side of service disconnect
706.15(C)	Energy storage system directory

NEC Requirements for Employers

An employer must ensure that these requirements are applied to reduce the risk of electrical injuries to employees.

Responsibility for Installation

90.1	*NEC* purpose		400.12	Flexible cords and flexible cables uses not permitted
90.4	Enforcement of the *NEC*			
90.7	Examination of equipment for safety		400.13	Flexible cords and flexible cables splices
110.2	Equipment approval		400.17	Flexible cords and flexible cables protection from damage
110.3	Examination, identification, installation, and use of equipment		400.36	Flexible cords and flexible cables splices and terminations
210.8	Ground-fault circuit-interrupter protection for personnel		406.10(E)	Grounding-type attachment plugs
225.56	Inspections and tests for outside branch circuits and feeders		410.82	Portable luminaire wiring
			450.48	Storage in vaults
250.34	Portable and vehicle-mounted generator grounding electrodes		522.7	Permanent amusement attraction maintenance
			590.3	Temporary electric power and lighting installation time constraints
250.188	Grounding of systems supplying portable ormobile equipment			
			590.6	Temporary wiring installation ground-fault protection for personnel
400.10	Flexible cords and flexible cables uses permitted			

Disconnecting Means

230.70	Service		404.8	Accessibility and grouping of switches and circuit breakers used as switches
230.71	Maximum number of service disconnects			
230.72	Grouping of service disconnects		409.22	Industrial control panel short-circuit current rating
230.74	Simultaneous opening of poles of all ungrounded service conductors		424.21	Switch and circuit breaker indicating type
230.77	Indicating the open (off) or closed (on) position		430.103	Open all ungrounded supply conductors
230.82	Equipment permitted to be connected to the supply side of service disconnect		430.128	Adjustable-speed drive systems
			460.8(C)	Capacitor bank
230.91	Location of service overcurrent device		460.24(B)	Isolation of capacitor, capacitor bank
230.92	Service overcurrent devices accessible to the occupant		490.22	Isolating means for equipment over 1000 volts, nominal
230.200	Services exceeding 1000 volts, nominal		490.39	Gas discharge from interrupting devices
230.204	Isolating switches for oil switches or air, oil, vacuum, or sulfur hexafluoride circuit breakers		490.40	Visual inspection windows for equipment over 1000 volts, nominal
230.205	Service disconnecting means		490.45	Circuit breakers — interlocks for equipment over 1000 volts, nominal
240.24	Location for service disconnecting means exceeding 1000 volts, nominal		490.51(D)	Mobile and portable high-voltage equipment
404.6	Position and connection of single-throw knifes witches		665.7	Induction and dielectric heating equipment remote control
404.7	General-use and motor-circuit switches, circuit breakers, and molded case switches indicating open (off) or closed (on) position		669.8	Electroplating
			692.13	Fuel cell systems
			694.20	Wind electric systems
			694.28	Installation and service of a wind turbine
			705.20	Electric power production source

Working Space

110.31	Enclosure for electrical installations over 1000 volts, nominal	425.8(B)	Fixed industrial process heating equipment
110.70	Manholes and other electrical enclosures intended for personnel entry	610.57	Cranes and hoists
110.74	Conductors installed in manholes and other enclosures intended for personnel entry	680.9	Overhead conductor clearances for swimming pools, fountains, and similar installations

Equipment Marking

110.21	Equipment marking requirements	490.48	Substation design, documentation, and required diagram for equipment over 1000 volts, nominal
110.24	Service equipment available fault current		
230.56	Service conductor with higher voltage to ground	692.54	Fuel cell systems fuel shut-off
		694.56	Instructions for disabling turbine

NEC Requirements for Designers

Electrical system designers must use these requirements to reduce the risk of electrical injuries to employees.

110.9	Interrupting rating of equipment intended to interrupt current at fault levels	230.26	Service point of attachment
		230.75	Disconnection of service grounded conductor
110.10	Overcurrent protective device circuit impedance, short-circuit current ratings, and other characteristics	230.76	Manually or power-operable service disconnecting means
		230.95	Ground-fault protection of equipment
110.72	Cabling workspace	240.8	Fuses or circuit breakers in parallel
110.73	Equipment work space	240.12	Electrical system coordination
210.13	Branch circuit ground-fault protection of equipment	240.82	Nontamperable circuit breaker
		240.67	Arc energy reduction — fuses
215.5	Diagram of feeders	240.86	Series ratings
215.10	Feeder ground-fault protection of equipment	240.87	Arc energy reduction — circuit breakers
225.18	Outside branch circuit and feeder clearance for overhead conductors and cables	250.6	Grounding arrangement to prevent objectionable current
225.19	Outside branch circuit and feeder clearances from buildings for conductors of not over 1000 volts, nominal	430.74	Electrical arrangement of control circuits
		440.12	Hermetic refrigerant motor-compressor disconnecting means rating and interrupting capacity
225.60	Outside branch circuit and feeder clearances over roadways, walkways, rails, water, and open land	440.13	Cord-connected air-conditioning and refrigerating equipment
225.61	Outside branch circuit and feeder clearances over buildings and other structures	460.6	Capacitors — discharge of stored energy
		460.28	Capacitor — means for discharge
230.2	Number of services	490.21	Circuit-interrupting devices for equipment over 1000 volts, nominal
230.3	One building or other structure not to be supplied through another	490.48	Substation design, documentation, and required diagram
230.9	Service conductor clearances on buildings		
230.24	Service conductor clearances		

(continues)

517.17	Ground-fault protection for hospitals and other buildings with Category 1 spaces or utilizing electrical life-support equipment
690.7	PV system dc circuits maximum voltage
700.31	Ground-fault protection of equipment for alternate source for emergency systems
707.31	Ground-fault protection of equipment for alternate source legally required standby systems

Electrical Preventive Maintenance Programs

Editor's Note: *This supplement contains extracts from Chapters 4, 5, and 6 of the 2019 edition of NFPA 70B, Recommended Practice for Electrical Equipment Maintenance. Entire sections of NFPA 70B are not included in all cases. The associated commentary explains the subjects of the referenced sections. Refer to NFPA 70B for the full text of each section and chapter.*

NFPA 70B provides detailed information on the maintenance of electrical equipment. Chapter 4 explains the benefits of an electrical preventative maintenance program, and Chapters 5 and 6 provide specific information on how to set up a maintenance program. Scheduled maintenance tends to be systematic and orderly, while breakdown maintenance is often performed under stressful conditions that could tempt workers to take dangerous safety shortcuts.

Businesses can no longer tolerate equipment failure as the signal that maintenance of equipment is necessary. Just-in-time (JIT) manufacturing and Six Sigma programs dictate the need for effective preventive maintenance programs that ensure the continuity of operations and prevent equipment breakdowns. Breakdowns affect quality and production schedules, but they also disrupt customers' supply chains. JIT falls apart when suppliers cannot perform.

CHAPTER 4 Why an Effective Electrical Preventive Maintenance (EPM) Program Pays Dividends

4.1 Why EPM?

4.1.1 Electrical equipment deterioration is normal, and equipment failure is inevitable. However, equipment failure can be delayed through appropriate EPM. As soon as new equipment is installed, a process of normal deterioration begins. Unchecked, the deterioration process can cause malfunction or an electrical failure. Deterioration can be accelerated by factors such as a hostile environment, overload, or severe duty cycle. An effective EPM program identifies and recognizes these factors and provides measures for coping with them.

4.1.2 In addition to normal deterioration, other potential causes of equipment degradation can be detected and corrected through EPM. Among these are load changes or additions, circuit alterations, improperly set or improperly selected protective devices, and changing voltage conditions.

4.1.3 Without an EPM program, management assumes a greatly increased risk of a serious electrical failure and its consequences.

4.2 Value and Benefits of a Properly Administered EPM Program.

4.2.1 A well-administered EPM program reduces accidents, saves lives, and minimizes costly breakdowns and unplanned shutdowns of production equipment. Impending troubles can be identified — and solutions applied — before they become major problems requiring more expensive, time-consuming solutions.

4.2.2 Benefits of an effective EPM program fall into two general categories. Direct, measurable economic benefits are derived from reduced cost of repairs and reduced equipment downtime. Less measurable but very real benefits result from improved safety. To understand fully how personnel and equipment safety are served by an EPM program, the mechanics of the program — inspection, testing, and repair procedures — should be understood. Such an understanding explains other intangible benefits such as improved employee morale, better workmanship and increased productivity, reduced absenteeism, reduced interruption of production, and improved insurance considerations. Improved morale comes with employee awareness of a conscious management effort to promote safety by reducing the likelihood of electrical injuries or fatalities, electrical explosions, and fires. Reduced personnel injuries and property loss claims can help keep insurance premiums at favorable rates.

4.2.3 Some of the benefits that result from improved safety are difficult to measure. However, direct and measurable economic benefits can be documented by equipment repair cost and equipment downtime records after an EPM program has been implemented.

4.2.4 Dependability can be engineered and built into equipment, but effective maintenance is required to keep it dependable. Experience shows that equipment is reduced when it is covered by an EPM program. In many cases, the investment in EPM is small compared with the cost of accidents, equipment repair, and the production losses associated with unexpected outages.

4.2.5 Careful planning is the key to the economic success of an EPM program. With proper planning, maintenance costs can be held to a practical minimum, while production is maintained at a practical maximum.

4.2.6 An EPM program requires the support of top management, because top management provides the funds that are required to initiate and maintain the program. The maintenance of industrial electrical equipment is essentially a matter of business economics. Maintenance costs can be placed in either of two basic categories: preventive maintenance or breakdown repairs. The money spent for preventive maintenance will be reflected as less money required for breakdown repairs. An effective EPM program holds the sum of these two expenditures to a minimum.

4.2.7 An EPM program is a form of protection against accidents, lost production, and loss of profit. An EPM program enables management to place a monetary value on the cost of such protection. An effective EPM program satisfies an important part of management's responsibility for keeping costs down and production up.

CHAPTER 5   What Is an Effective Electrical Preventive Maintenance (EPM) Program?

5.1 Introduction. An effective electrical preventive maintenance (EPM) program should enhance safety and also reduce equipment failure to a minimum consistent with good economic judgment.

5.2 Essential Elements of an EPM Program. An EPM program should consist of the following essential elements:

(1) Responsible and qualified personnel

(2) Regularly scheduled inspection, testing, and servicing of equipment

(3) Survey and analysis of electrical equipment and systems to determine maintenance requirements and priorities

(4) Programmed routine inspections and suitable tests

(5) Accurate analysis of inspection and test reports so that proper corrective measures can be prescribed

(6) Performance of necessary work

(7) Concise but complete records

NFPA 70B contains detailed information about each of these elements. A survey and analysis of essential equipment can evaluate its operating parameters and current condition to determine if any repairs are necessary as well as the nature and frequency of the required inspection and testing. Analysis of the inspection reports requires follow-through with the necessary repairs, replacement, and adjustment of an effective electrical preventive maintenance (EPM) program. A facility might not have qualified personnel to perform the maintenance duties, so qualified contractors might be necessary to follow the EPM program. Programmed inspection and testing might require coordination between maintenance and production to schedule outages of production equipment under the maintenance program. Records should be kept not only of the condition and repair of equipment but also of the training and skills of the employees that conduct the maintenance.

5.3 Planning an EPM Program. The following factors should be considered in the planning of an EPM program.

(1) *Personnel Safety:* Will an equipment failure endanger or threaten the safety of any personnel? What can be done to ensure personnel safety?

(2) *Equipment Loss:* Is installed equipment — both electrical and mechanical — complex or so unique that required repairs would be unusually expensive?

(3) *Production Economics:* Will breakdown repairs or replacement of failed equipment require extensive downtime? How many production dollars will be lost in the event of an equipment failure? Which equipment is most vital to production?

A plan that prioritizes essential equipment can determine how, where, and when each piece fits into a maintenance program. An effective EPM program needs to consider not only equipment loss but the economics of lost production and the impact of an equipment failure on employee safety.

Effective EPM programs begin with good design. A conscious effort to ensure optimum maintainability should be part of the design of new facilities. For example, auxiliary power sources might make it easier to schedule and perform maintenance work with minimal interruption of production.

CHAPTER 6   Planning and Developing an Electrical Preventive Maintenance (EPM) Program

6.1 Introduction.

6.1.1 The purpose of an EPM program is to reduce hazard to life and property resulting from the failure or malfunction of electrical systems and equipment. This chapter explains the planning and development considerations that can be used to establish such a program.

6.1.2 The following four basic steps should be taken in the planning and development of an EPM program:

(1) Compile a listing of all equipment and systems.
(2) Determine which equipment and systems are most critical.
(3) Develop a system for monitoring.
(4) Determine the internal and/or external personnel needed to implement and maintain the EPM program.

6.1.5 The work center of each maintenance work group should be conveniently located. This work center should contain the following:

(1) Copies of all the inspection and testing procedures for that zone
(2) Copies of previous reports
(3) Single-line diagrams
(4) Schematic diagrams
(5) Records of complete nameplate data
(6) Vendors' catalogs
(7) Facility stores' catalogs
(8) Supplies of report forms

6.2 Survey of Electrical Installation.

6.2.1 Data Collection.

6.2.1.1 The first step in organizing a survey should be to examine available resources. Will the available personnel permit the survey of an entire system, process, or building, or should it be divided into segments?

6.2.1.2 Where the project will be divided into segments, a priority should be assigned to each segment. Segments found to be related should be identified before the actual work commences.

6.2.1.3 The third step should be the assembling of all documentation. This might necessitate a search of desks, cabinets, computers, and such, and might also require that manufacturers be contacted, to replace lost documents. All of the documents should be centralized, controlled, and maintained. The documentation should include recommended practices and procedures for some or all of the following:

(1) Installation
(2) Disassembly/assembly (interconnections)
(3) Wiring diagrams, schematics, bills of materials
(4) Operation (set-up and adjustment)
(5) Maintenance (including parts list and recommended spares)
(6) Software program (if applicable)
(7) Troubleshooting

6.2.2 Diagrams and Data. The availability of up-to-date, accurate, and complete diagrams is the foundation of a successful EPM program. The diagrams discussed in 6.2.2.1 through 6.2.2.8.2 are some of those in common use.

Single-line, circuit-routing, and schematic diagrams are just a few of the diagrams covered by 6.2.2. These diagrams can assist maintenance personnel by providing information such as equipment ratings, the physical location of conductors and equipment, and the access points for raceways or pull boxes. The manufacturer's service manuals and instructions are also important components for the diagrams and recommended practices and procedures. Another important aspect of an EPM program is ensuring that equipment installation changes are highlighted and noted or revised in an appropriate manner to keep documentation current.

6.2.3 System Diagrams. System diagrams should be provided to complete the data being assembled. The importance of the system determines the extent of information shown. The information can be shown on the most appropriate type of diagram but should include the same basic information, source and type of power, conductor and raceway information, and switching and protective devices with their physical locations. It is vital to show where the system might interface with another system, such as with emergency power; hydraulic, pneumatic, or mechanical systems; security and fire-alarm systems; and monitoring and control systems. Some of the more common of these are described in 6.2.3.1 through 6.2.3.3.

System diagrams for lighting; heating, ventilation, and air-conditioning; and control and monitoring are also important. Lighting diagrams might show lighting that is used for night security personnel or the location of emergency lighting. Diagrams of ventilation systems should show interfaces with other systems, such as those for smoke removal. Control and monitoring systems are often complicated, and diagrams should describe how these systems function. The referenced sections of NFPA 70B provide further information on these system diagrams.

6.2.5 Test and Maintenance Equipment.

6.2.5.1 All maintenance work requires the use of proper tools and equipment to properly perform the task to be done. In addition to their ordinary tools, maintenance personnel (such as carpenters, pipe fitters, and machinists) use special tools or equipment based on the nature of the work to be performed. The electrician is no exception, but for EPM, special-use tools should be readily available. The size of the facility, the nature of its operations, and the extent of its maintenance, repair, and test facilities are all factors that determine the use frequency of the equipment. Economics seldom justify purchasing an infrequently used, expensive tool when it can be rented. However, a corporation having a number of facilities in the area might well justify common ownership of the same device for joint use, making it quickly available at any time to any facility. Typical examples might be high-current test equipment, infrared thermography equipment, or a ground-fault locator.

6.2.5.2 Because a certain amount of mechanical maintenance is often a part of the EPM program being conducted on associated equipment, the electrical maintenance personnel should have ready access to such items as the following:

(1) Assorted lubrication tools and equipment
(2) Various types and sizes of wrenches
(3) Nonmetallic hammers and blocks to protect against injury to machined surfaces
(4) Feeler gauges to function as inside- and outside-diameter measuring gauges
(5) Instruments for measuring torque, tension, compression, vibration, and speed
(6) Standard and special mirrors with light sources for visual inspection

(7) Industrial-type portable blowers and vacuums having insulated nozzles for removal of dust and foreign matter

(8) Nontoxic, nonflammable cleaning solvents

(9) Clean, lint-free wiping cloths

6.2.5.3 The use of well-maintained safety equipment is essential and should be mandatory for work on energized electrical conductors or circuit parts. Prior to performing maintenance on energized electrical conductors or circuit parts, NFPA *70E* should be used to identify the degree of personal protective equipment (PPE) required. Some of the more important equipment that should be provided includes the following:

(1) Heavy leather gloves

(2) Insulating gloves, mats, blankets, baskets, boots, jackets, and coats

(3) Insulated hand tools such as screwdrivers and pliers

(4) Nonmetallic hard hats with suitable arc-rated face protection

(5) Poles with hooks and hot sticks to safely open isolating switche

> Paragraphs 6.2.5.4 through 6.2.5.9 of NFPA 70B further describe various test and maintenance equipment.

6.3 Identification of Critical Equipment.

6.3.1 Equipment (electric or otherwise) should be considered critical if its failure to operate normally and under complete control will cause a serious threat to people, property, or the product. Electric power, like process steam, water, and so forth, might be essential to the operation of a machine, but unless loss of one or more of these supplies causes the machine to become hazardous to people, property, or production, that machine might not be critical. The combined knowledge and experience of several people might be needed to make this determination. In a small facility, the facility engineer or master mechanic working with the operating superintendent should be able to make this determination.

> Section 6.3 describes some systems or segments of systems that might be critical to the operation of a facility. The equipment's relation to the entire operation and the effect of its loss on safety and production should be considered. An entire system might be critical but, due to its size or complexity, could be segmented.

6.4 Establishment of a Systematic Program. The purpose of any inspection and testing program is to establish the condition of equipment to determine what work should be done and to verify that it will continue to function until the next scheduled servicing occurs. Inspection and testing are best done in conjunction with routine maintenance. In this way, many minor items that require no special tools, training, or equipment can be corrected as they are found. The inspection and testing program is probably the most important function of a maintenance department in that it establishes what should be done to keep the system in service to perform the function for which it is required.

> Several aspects of an installation can have an impact on the frequency of inspection and testing. Section 6.4 points out that the atmosphere or environment, as well as the load the equipment is operating under, should be taken into consideration for the EPM program. For example, dust could impede a motor's ability to dissipate heat, or a motor

designed for continuous operation but installed with an intermittent load could over-heat the motor windings. Section 6.4 also expands on considerations for inspection frequency, such as those for equipment that is operating continuously or that is considered critical.

6.5 Methods and Procedures.

6.5.1 General.

6.5.1.1 If a system is to operate without failure, not only should the discrete components of the system be maintained, but the connections between these components also should be covered by a thorough set of methods and procedures. Overlooking this important link in the system causes many facilities to suffer high losses every year.

6.5.1.2 Other areas where the maintenance department should develop its own procedures are shutdown safeguards, interlocks, and alarms. Although the individual pieces of equipment can have testing and calibrating procedures furnished by the manufacturer, the equipment application is probably unique, so the system should have an inspection and testing procedure developed.

Section 6.5 breaks methods and procedures into five categories: forms and reports, planning, analysis of safety procedures, records, and emergency procedures. Forms can come in many varieties, and Section 6.5 lists items that should be included on a form. Some examples of forms for inspection, testing, and repair are provided in Annex H of NFPA 70B. The planning stage is where inspection schedules should be set to reduce production downtime. Many details involved in setting safety procedures are beyond the scope of NFPA 70B. Nonetheless, general considerations are covered in Section 6.5. Records are important to provide a way to evaluate the results of the EPM program, including the cost not only of the program but of the estimated cost of business interruption. Lastly, Section 6.5 recognizes the need for maintenance personnel to be prepared for emergencies.

6.8 Outsourcing of Electrical Equipment Maintenance.

6.8.1 General. This section describes the process for a facility to request the services of qualified contractors to perform maintenance on electrical equipment.

6.8.2 Contract Elements. Elements in a contract for outsourcing electrical maintenance service are to include, but are not limited to, the following:

(1) Define project scope of work, what is included and not included, along with equipment specifications on any new or replacement parts, and the time period(s) in which the activities are to be performed.
(2) Determine if it is a performance-based or detailed (step-by-step) specification.
(3) Determine which safety and maintenance codes and standards are to be followed, including appropriate permits.
(4) Determine methodology for pricing: lump sum or unit price.
(5) Determine the qualifications of potential contractors and develop and maintain a list of such.
(6) Obtain appropriate liability, insurance coverage, and warranty information.

(7) Assemble the appropriate up-to-date and accurate facility and equipment specific documents, such as, but not limited to, the following:

    (a) Facility one line diagrams

    (b) Facility layout drawings showing location of substations and major facility electrical equipment

    (c) Facility equipment list (if facility drawings show equipment, facility drawings may be used in lieu of specific equipment lists)

    (d) Equipment manufacturers' requirements (these include equipment service manuals, equipment drawings, etc.)

    (e) Risk assessment, short circuit analysis, and time-current coordination studies

(8) Conduct a pre-bid/negotiation walk through with the potential contractor.

(9) Conduct a post-work walk-through to verify proper completion of scope of work, and review written report from the contractor on findings and recommendations, as applicable.

Often, facilities do not have qualified personnel to conduct inspections, tests, or repairs of all or some of the equipment installed. NFPA *70E®* provides guidance on host and contractor relationships from the worker safety aspect. NFPA 70B addresses items that should be included in a service contract for outsourced equipment maintenance.

Typical Safety Procedure (Procedure for Selection, Inspection, and Care of Rubber Insulating Gloves and Leather Protectors)

Editor's Note: *To help users develop their own safety procedures, this supplement describes a typical safety procedure regarding a common subject in electrical safety programs—rubber insulating gloves and leather protectors. It illustrates the type of information and format that can be used to develop an electrical safety procedure. Each electrical safety procedure must be uniquely identified. This sample is provided for reference only to illustrate the types of information that should comprise a typical safety procedure.*

Title: Procedure for Selection, Inspection, and Care of Rubber Insulating Gloves and Leather Protectors		Doc. ID No.: ESP.100.000.003.01 Page: 001 of 010
Eff. Date: 10/23/2020	Revision No. : 001 Revision Date: 10/06/2020	Supersedes: N/A
Reviewer: MK Rev. Date: 10/05/2020	Approved by: MDF Approval Date. 10/05/2020	Covers: All Personnel Within Restricted Approach Boundary

1.0 **Purpose:** The purpose of this procedure is to detail the selection, inspection, and care requirements for rubber insulating gloves and leather protectors.

2.0 **Scope:** This procedure covers all rubber insulating gloves regardless of Class and Type.

3.0 **Revision History:** This is the first revision and is a general upgrade.

4.0 **Background:** This procedure is required to meet Occupational Safety and Health Administration (OSHA) regulations and the requirements contained in NFPA 70£®.

5.0 **Definitions:**

5.1 **Class.** A rubber insulating glove class defines the maximum ac rms and dc use values in volts and the ac rms and dc proof test voltage values to be used in volts. There are six voltage classes as follows:

   a. 00, 0, 1,2, 3, and 4, with cuff labels colored beige, red, white, yellow, green, and orange, respectively.

5.2 **Work Instruction.** A work instruction tells the reader the necessary steps and the order in which the steps are to be taken to safely perform the required task, and is action oriented.

   a. Each step is stated simply in a clear and concise manner that is easy to read and understand.
   b. Work instructions can be prepared using an outline type format, a flow chart format, a playscript format, or a question and answer format.
   c. The format selected is to be the one that is best suited for the situation.

5.3 **Type.** A rubber insulating glove *type* defines whether the material is ozone (natural) resistant - Type I, or non-ozone (synthetic) resistant - Type II.

6.0 **Work Instructions:**

6.1 **Cleaning:**

   a. General:

   1) Cleaning should be done under good lighting conditions.

   2) Cleaning can uncover damage that may be hidden under soiled surfaces as contamination may mask color or hide defects..

   3) Cleaning removes contaminants (chemicals) that are less obvious or cannot be seen but that can degrade rubber such as fertilizers, herbicides, and pesticide residues.

   4) Contaminants may be conductive, especially when wet.

   5) Regular cleaning is good practice.

This sample is for illustrative purposes only. Users should develop their own safety procedures.

Title: Procedure for Selection, Inspection, and Care of Rubber Insulating Gloves and Leather Protectors		Doc. ID No.: ESP.100.000.003.01 Page: 002 of 010
Eff. Date: 10/23/2020	Revision No. : 001 Revision Date: 10/06/2020	Supersedes: N/A
Reviewer: MK Rev. Date: 10/05/2020	Approved by: MDF Approval Date. 10/05/2020	Covers: All Personnel Within Restricted Approach Boundary

  b. Hands Prior to Inspection, Handling, or Use:

   1) Prior to wearing or handling rubber insulating gloves or leather protectors, hands are to be cleaned using a non-petroleum based hand cleaner or towelettes made specifically for workers who wear rubber gloves.
   2) The cleaner is to be capable of dissolving and removing grease, oil, ink, tar, pipe dope, creosote, paint, etc., without harming natural or synthetic rubber.
   3) The cleaner is to be capable of cleaning hands with or without water.
   4) Workers should be aware that the cleaner may contain skin conditioners or perfume.
   5) Only approved hand cleaner is to be used.
   6) Approved hand cleaner for those using rubber insulating gloves or leather protectors is to be obtained from inventory control.

  c. Rubber Insulating Gloves:

   1) Prior to inspection or use, as necessary, rubber insulating gloves should be cleaned to ensure that only clean gloves are used.
   2) Rubber insulating gloves are generally to be cleaned by washing with a mild soap and water combination.
   3) The label area may be cleaned using soapy water or denatured alcohol.
   4) After washing, the gloves are to be thoroughly rinsed with water.
   5) Finally, the gloves are to be air-dried in an area away from direct sunlight and other sources (ozone) and where the temperature is less than 120°F (49°C).
   6) The cleaning is to be done, as necessary, prior to use to ensure that only clean gloves are used.
   7) The mild soap to be used is to be a concentrated detergent with a special grease release formula that removes oils, grease, and dirt from both natural and synthetic rubber.
   8) Only an approved cleaner for use on rubber insulating gloves obtained from inventory control is to be used.

6.2 **Use of Sunscreen:**

  a. Only approved sunscreen is to be used.
  b. If sunscreen is used by those handling or using rubber insulating gloves and leather protectors, it must be of a non-oily type that leaves no residue or slippery hands.
  c. It must be of a type made specifically for use with rubber protectors and rubber insulating gloves (e.g., it must be safe for use with leather protectors and rubber insulating gloves).
  d. Approved sunscreen for those using or handling rubber insulating gloves and leather protectors is to be obtained from inventory control.

6.3 Determine that the rubber insulating gloves have an adequate voltage rating (class) for the nominal system voltage.

  a. This is done by examining the glove label and the NFPA *70E* equipment label.
  b. Verify that the glove class is suitable for the maximum possible rms voltage in accordance with the ANSI C84.1 "B" range, based on nominal system voltage designated on the NFPA *70E* equipment label and the location of use within the system:

This sample is for illustrative purposes only. Users should develop their own safety procedures.

Title: Procedure for Selection, Inspection, and Care of Rubber Insulating Gloves and Leather Protectors		Doc. ID No.: ESP.100.000.003.01 Page: 003 of 010	
Eff. Date: 10/23/2020	Revision No. : 001 Revision Date: 10/06/2020	Supersedes: N/A	
Reviewer: MK Rev. Date: 10/05/2020	Approved by: MDF Approval Date. 10/05/2020	Covers: All Personnel Within Restricted Approach Boundary	

      1) 508 V for a 480 V nominal system at the service location

    c. Refer to the Electrical Safety Procedure (ESP) on *Matching Rubber Insulating Goods to Nominal System Voltage at Point of Use* for further information.

6.4 Use only properly sized gloves:

    a. Glove size is measured by using a soft tape measure.

    b. Measure the dominant hand around the palm, not including the thumb, at its widest point in inches and the distance from the base of the palm to the tip of the index finger in inches of the dominant hand.

    c. The glove size is the longer of the above two measurements taken to the closest ½ inch above the measured value (e.g., 8" = 8, 8¼" = 8.5). Gloves come in sizes from 7 to 11 inches depending on the class, type, and length specified.

    d. If cotton glove liners are used, the glove size is to be increased one half-size (e.g., for 8.5, use 9).

6.5 Each rubber insulating glove is labeled in a color denoting the "class" and the maximum-voltage the glove can be used for as indicated in the following table:

Class	Label Color[1]	Proof Test Voltage		Max. Use Voltage	
N/A	N/A	ac (rms)	dc	ac (rms)[2]	dc[2]
00	Beige	2,500	10,000	500	750
0	Red	5,000	20,000	1,000	1,500
1	White	10,000	40,000	7,500	11,250
2	Yellow	20,000	50,000	17,000	25,500
3	Green	30,000	60,000	26,500	39,750
4	Orange	40,000	70,000	36,000	54,000

Notes:

1. Rubber insulating gloves are to have a color-coded label that meets the requirements contained in ASTM D120.
2. Maximum use voltage when worn with leather protectors.

6.6 Verify that the rubber insulating gloves are the right type (category) for the use location (e.g., ozone resistant or non-ozone resistant):

    a. Type I - natural rubber - non-ozone resistant - indoor use

    b. Type II - synthetic - ozone resistant - outdoor or indoor use

    c. Where Type I gloves are used in outdoor locations, the amount of time they are exposed to sunlight (ozone) is to be minimized

This sample is for illustrative purposes only. Users should develop their own safety procedures.

Title: Procedure for Selection, Inspection, and Care of Rubber Insulating Gloves and Leather Protectors	Doc. ID No.: ESP.100.000.003.01 Page: 004 of 010
Eff. Date: 10/23/2020	**Revision No. :** 001 **Revision Date:** 10/06/2020	**Supersedes:** N/A
Reviewer: MK **Rev. Date:** 10/05/2020	**Approved by:** MDF **Approval Date.** 10/05/2020	**Covers:** All Personnel Within Restricted Approach Boundary

6.7 The following table and notes indicate a breakdown of rubber insulating gloves that are generally available:

Breakdown of Generally Available Rubber Insulating Gloves[1]					
Class	**Length in. (mm)[2]**	**Type[3]**	**Cuff Type[4]**	**Color[5,6]**	**Sizes[7,8]**
00	11 (279), 14(356)	I	SC	R, B	7, 8, 8H, 9, 9H, 10, 10H, 11, 12
00	11 (279), 14 (356)	II	SC	BL, BLO	7, 8, 8H, 9, 9H, 10, 10H, 11, 12
0	11 (279), 14 (356)	I	SC	R, B, Y, BY	7, 8, 8H, 9, 9H, 10, 10H, 11, 12
0	11 (279), 14 (356)	II	SC	BL, BLO	7, 8, 8H, 9, 9H, 10, 10H, 11, 12
1	14 (356), 16 (406), 18 (457)	I	SC, BC, CC	B, YB, RB	7, 8, 8H, 9, 9H, 10, 10H, 11, 12
2	14 (356), 16 (406), 18 (457)	I	SC, BC, CC	B, YB, RB	7, 8, 8H, 9, 9H, 10, 10H, 11, 12
3	14 (356), 16 (406), 18 (457)	I	SC, BC, CC	B, YB, RB	7, 8, 8H, 9, 9H, 10, 10H, 11, 12
4	14 (356), 16 (406), 18 (457)	I	SC, BC, CC	B, YB, RB	9, 9H, 10, 10H, 11, 12

Notes:

1. This chart is intended to provide guidance on the types of rubber insulating gloves that are generally available. The various manufacturers and suppliers of rubber insulated gloves and leather protectors should be consulted to determine the types and characteristics of gloves that are readily available.
2. Contour cuff (CC) gloves are available only on 18 in. (457 mm) gloves.
3. Type I equals natural rubber, which is non-ozone resistant; Type II equals synthetic rubber, which is ozone resistant.
4. Rubber insulating gloves come in one of three types of cuffs styles — straight cuff, contour cuff, or bell cuff:
    a. SC equals straight cuff, which is the default cuff style.
    b. CC equals a contour cuff, which is angled to prevent bunching or binding at the elbow when bent, and is only available on 18 in. gloves.
    c. BC equals a bell cuff, which accommodates heavier winter clothing and allows for greater air flow in warmer weather.

This sample is for illustrative purposes only. Users should develop their own safety procedures.

Title: Procedure for Selection, Inspection, and Care of Rubber Insulating Gloves and Leather Protectors		Doc. ID No.: ESP.100.000.003.01 Page: 005 of 010	
Eff. Date: 10/23/2020	**Revision No. :** 001 **Revision Date:** 10/06/2020		**Supersedes:** N/A
Reviewer: MK **Rev. Date:** 10/05/2020	**Approved by:** MDF **Approval Date.** 10/05/2020		**Covers:** All Personnel Within Restricted Approach Boundary

Notes (continued):

5. Color code is as follows:

    a. R equals Red.
    b. B equals Black.
    c. Y equals Yellow.
    d. O equals Orange.
    e. RB equals Red on the inside and Black on the outside.
    f. YB equals Yellow on the inside and Black on the outside,
    e. BLO equals Blue inner color and Orange outer color.

6. The contrast between the outer color and the inner color makes inspection for cuts and tears easier when the glove is inflated or stretched.
7. Bell cuff (BC) gloves are not available in sizes 7, 8, or 8H.
8. The H in the size designation stands for a half (½) size.

6.8 Verify that the voltage insulation certification is still current:

    a. Check the marked test date and issue date or expiration date, as appropriate, to confirm that glove voltage insulation certification is still current.
    b. Rubber insulating gloves must be issued from inventory by inventory control within 1 year of the date they are voltage tested or they must be retested, and they must be retested no later than 6 months after issue.
    c. The gloves must be returned to inventory control to be sent for retesting at the time their replacement is obtained.

6.9 Ensure that hand jewelry, or other objects which could damage the gloves, are removed prior to inspection or use of the gloves.

6.10 Perform a visual inspection prior to each use, paying particular attention to the body of the glove, between the fingers, and each finger, inspecting both the inside surface and the outside surface for:

    a. Holes
    b. Rips
    c. Tears
    d. Cuts
    e. Cracks
    f. Punctures
    g. Snags
    h. Ozone cutting, checking, cracking, breaks, or pitting
    i. UV checking
    j. Embedded material, such as wire or metal shavings, that could cause punctures
    k. Textural changes, such as the following:

This sample is for illustrative purposes only. Users should develop their own safety procedures.

Title: Procedure for Selection, Inspection, and Care of Rubber Insulating Gloves and Leather Protectors	Doc. ID No.: ESP.100.000.003.01 Page: 006 of 010
Eff. Date: 10/23/2020	**Revision No. :** 001 **Revision Date:** 10/06/2020	**Supersedes:** N/A
Reviewer: MK **Rev. Date:** 10/05/2020	**Approved by:** MDF **Approval Date.** 10/05/2020	**Covers:** All Personnel Within Restricted Approach Boundary

      1) Swelling
      2) Softening
      3) Hardening
      4) Stickiness
      5) Inelasticity

  l. Oil contamination

  m. Other such defects that may damage the insulating properties

    Note: Surface irregularities may be present on all rubber goods because of imperfections on forms or molds or because of inherent difficulties in the manufacturing process. They may appear as indentations, protuberances, or imbedded foreign materials that are acceptable under the following conditions:

    1) The indentation or protuberance blends into a smooth slope when the material is stretched.
    2) Foreign material remains in place when the insulating material is folded and stretches with the insulating material surrounding it.

    If defects are found that cannot be rectified, cut a finger off of each glove and turn into inventory control for proper disposal.

6.11 Perform an air leak test to test for punctures for each glove that may not be caught by the visual inspection by one of the following means or methods:

  a. Inflating gloves makes checking for cuts, tears, or ozone easier.
  b. The roll test:

    1) Hold the glove downward and grasp the cuff.
    2) Roll the glove cuff tightly, forcing air into the palm and finger area.
    3) Apply pressure to the various areas of the glove.
    4) Hold the glove close to the face and ear to listen for or feel leaking air from holes while the glove is inflated and pressure applied.

  c. Check for air leaks by means of a glove inflator:

    1) Inflate the glove following the instructions included with the glove inflator.
    2) Hold the glove close to the face and ear to listen for or feel leaking air from holes in the inflated glove.

  d. Do not over inflate:

    1) Type I - natural rubber - maximum of 1.5 times normal
    2) Type II - synthetic rubber - maximum of 1.25 times normal

This sample is for illustrative purposes only. Users should develop their own safety procedures.

Title: Procedure for Selection, Inspection, and Care of Rubber Insulating Gloves and Leather Protectors		**Doc. ID No.:** ESP.100.000.003.01 **Page:** 007 of 010	
Eff. Date: 10/23/2020	**Revision No. :** 001 **Revision Date:** 10/06/2020	**Supersedes:** N/A	
Reviewer: MK **Rev. Date:** 10/05/2020	**Approved by:** MDF **Approval Date.** 10/05/2020	**Covers:** All Personnel Within Restricted Approach Boundary	

6.12 Use leather protectors over rubber insulating gloves:

    a. Leather protectors must be sized for the rubber insulating gloves (e.g., size 10 for size 10).

    b. Perform a visual inspection of the leather protectors, checking for

        1) Cuts

        2) Tears

        3) Rips

        4) Abrasions

        5) Holes

        6) Contaminants, such as oil or petroleum products, or

        7) Other such damage

        8) If damaged discard by cutting off at least one glove finger on each glove and turn it into in inventory control

        9) Leather protectors are not to be used as work gloves and work gloves are not to be used as leather protectors

6.13 Verify that the distance between the end of the cuff of the rubber insulating glove and the cuff of the leather protector is not less than the distance required by ASTM F496, as shown in the following table:

Class	Distance (inches)
00	½
0	½
1	1
2	2
3	3
4	4

6.14 Use of Glove Liners and Glove Dust:

    a. Only approved glove liners of an appropriate material, such as cotton, cotton with Lycra, or wool blends with substantial wool content, can be used for perspiration control or to provide additional warmth.

    b. Glove liners come only in one size (e.g., one size fits all).

    c. Glove liners can have a knit or straight cuff.

    d. Where glove liners are used, glove size is required to be increased one half (½) size.

    e. Only approved glove dust may be used to control perspiration.

    f. Do not use talc, baby powder, or similar products as they may contain acids and dyes that can cause the rubber insulating gloves to deteriorate.

    g. The glove dust is to be a type suggested or approved by the manufacturer of the gloves.

    h. Only approved glove liners are to be used, and they are to be obtained from inventory control.

    I. Only approved glove dust is to be used, and it may be obtained from inventory control.

This sample is for illustrative purposes only. Users should develop their own safety procedures.

Title: Procedure for Selection, Inspection, and Care of Rubber Insulating Gloves and Leather Protectors		**Doc. ID No.:** ESP.100.000.003.01 **Page:** 008 of 010	
Eff. Date: 10/23/2020	**Revision No. :** 001 **Revision Date:** 10/06/2020	**Supersedes:** N/A	
Reviewer: MK **Rev. Date:** 10/05/2020	**Approved by:** MDF **Approval Date.** 10/05/2020	**Covers:** All Personnel Within Restricted Approach Boundary	

- j. The request to inventory control is to indicate whether the liners are to be used for perspiration control or warmth. The request may be made for more than one pair of glove liners.
- k. Damaged or soiled glove liners are not to be used.
- l. Damaged glove liners must have a finger cut off and be returned to inventory control for replacement.
- m. The cleaner is to be diluted in accordance with the manufacturer's instructions prior to use and applied by means of a clean rag or sponge obtained from inventory control.
- n. Only cleaners tested for compatibility with the type of rubber compound employed in accordance with ASTM D471 and ASTM F496 are to be used.

6.15 Properly store:

- a. Store in a canvas storage bag with ventilation holes in bottom for proper ventilation.
- b. Do not store more than a single pair of rubber insulating gloves or leather protectors in a single bag that has a storage compartment for only one glove.

  1) Where the rubber insulating glove manufacturer permits, leather protectors may be stored over rubber insulating gloves inside a single glove bag storage compartment.

- c. Bags with multiple storage compartments designed to store more than one pair of gloves may be used to store both the rubber insulating gloves and the leather protectors.
- d. Store rubber insulating gloves with the cuffs down and the fingers up.
- e. Ensure that gloves lay flat in the bag.
- f. Store only in properly sized canvas storage bag(s).
- g. Do not store inside out, as storing inside out strains the rubber severely and promotes early ozone cutting.
- h. Do not allow gloves to be stored in a folded condition, as folds and creases strain rubber and cause it to crack from ozone prematurely.
- i. Do not store near sources of heat; store in cool, dry areas only.

6.16 Follow the manufacturer's instructions regarding inspection, storage, and use.

6.17 Training:

- a. Employees are to receive training on the proper use, care, storage, and replacement of rubber insulating gloves prior to issue of their first pair. This training is to include at least the following:

  1) How to determine proper size
  2) How to determine proper voltage class
  3) How to determine proper glove category
  4) How to determine the certification is current
  5) How to properly inspect prior to use
  6) How to clean properly
  7) How to store properly
  8) How to take damaged gloves out of service properly
  9) How to request a new or replacement pair of rubber insulating gloves

This sample is for illustrative purposes only. Users should develop their own safety procedures.

Title: Procedure for Selection, Inspection, and Care of Rubber Insulating Gloves and Leather Protectors		Doc. ID No.: ESP.100.000.003.01 Page: 009 of 010
Eff. Date: 10/23/2020	Revision No. : 001 Revision Date: 10/06/2020	Supersedes: N/A
Reviewer: MK Rev. Date: 10/05/2020	Approved by: MDF Approval Date. 10/05/2020	Covers: All Personnel Within Restricted Approach Boundary

      b. After training, the employee must demonstrate to the satisfaction of the trainer that the employee is competent in the above procedures.

      c. The training, the content of the training, and demonstrated ability are to be documented for each employee.

      d. This training is to be done on at least a yearly basis or any time it is determined that an employee is failing to comply with this procedure.

6.18 Rubber insulating gloves, leather protectors, and glove liners must conform to company specifications.

7.0 Responsibilities:

      a. Supervisors are responsible for seeing that this procedure is followed and enforced.

      b. Trainers are responsible for seeing:

          1) That workers are properly trained

          2) That workers show demonstrated ability in the selection, use, and care of rubber insulating gloves and leather protectors

          3) That training is properly documented

8.0 References:

      a. Company specifications:

          1) Specifications for rubber insulating gloves

          2) Specifications for leather protectors

          3) Specifications for cotton glove liners

          4) Specifications for canvas carrying bags for rubber insulating gloves

          5) Specifications for cleaning products for rubber insulating goods

      b. Governmental standards:

          1) Occupational Safety and Health Administration (OSHA):

              a) 29 CFR 1910.137, *Occupational Safety and Health Standards, Personal Protective Equipment, Electrical Protective Devices*

      c. Industry standards:

          1) American Society of Testing and Materials (ASTM):

              a) ASTM D120, *Standard Specification for Rubber Insulating Gloves*

              b) ASTM F496, *Standard Specification for In-Service Care of Insulating Gloves and Sleeves*

              c) ASTM F696, *Standard Specification for Leather Protectors for Insulating Gloves and Mittens*

              d) ASTM F2675, *Test Method For Determining Arc Ratings of Hand Protective Products Developed and Used for Electrical Arc Flash Protection*

This sample is for illustrative purposes only. Users should develop their own safety procedures.

Title: Procedure for Selection, Inspection, and Care of Rubber Insulating Gloves and Leather Protectors	Doc. ID No.: ESP.100.000.003.01 Page: 010 of 010	
Eff. Date: 10/23/2020	Revision No. : 001 Revision Date: 10/06/2020	Supersedes: N/A
Reviewer: MK Rev. Date: 10/05/2020	Approved by: MDF Approval Date. 10/05/2020	Covers: All Personnel Within Restricted Approach Boundary

    2) National Fire Protection Association (NFPA):

        a) NFPA *70E, Standard for Electrical Safety in the Workplace*

  d. Company electrical safety procedures:

    1) ESP-100.000.001.01, *Matching Rubber Insulating Goods to Nominal System Voltage at Point of Use*

    2) ESP-100.000.002.01, *Purchasing Procedures for Rubber Insulating Gloves and Leather Protectors*

    3) ESP-100.000.004.01, *Limitations on Use of Rubber Insulating Gloves without Leather Protectors*

    4) ESP-100.000.005.01, *Issue and Replacement of Electrical Protective Equipment*

    5) ESP-100.000.006.01, *After Issue Storage of Rubber Insulating Goods*

    6) ESP-100.000.007.01, *Inventory Storage of Electrical Protective Equipment*

    7) ESP-100.000.008.01, *Cleaning of Rubber Insulating Goods*

    8) ESP-100.000.009.01, *Proper Disposal of Electrical Protective Equipment*

    9) ESP-100.000.010.01, *Electrical Safety Training on the Issue, Inspection, Use, Cleaning, Replacement, and Proper Disposal of Rubber Insulating Gloves and Leather Protectors*

    10) ESP-100.000.011.01, *Procedure for Having Rubber Insulating Goods Retested*

    11) ESP-100.000.012.01, *Repair Procedure for Allowable Repairs to Rubber Insulating Gloves*

9.0 Attachments:

  a. 29 CFR 1910.137, *Occupational Safety and Health Standards, Personal Protective Equipment, Electrical Protective Devices*

This sample is for illustrative purposes only. Users should develop their own safety procedures.

Index

A

Accessible (as applied to equipment), 120.4(B)(6), 330.4(A)
  Definition, Art. 100
Access plates, 230.2
Aerial lifts, 130.9(F)(1)
Alarms, battery operation, 320.3(A)(5)
Approach distances, *see also* Boundary
  Limits of, Annex C
  Preparation for, C.l
  Qualified persons, 130.4(F)(3), 130.4(G), C. 1.1, C.l.2
  Unqualified persons, 130.4(F), 130.9(E), C.l.1
Approved (definition), Art. 100
Arc blast, 360.4(B), K.4
Arc blast hazard, R.4.1, R.4.3, R.6.6, R.10, R.11.l
  Definition, 360.2
Arc flash boundary, *see* Boundary, arc flash
Arc flash hazard, 130.2, K.3, O.2.3
  Battery room warning signs, 320.3(A)(6)
  Capacitors, R.4.2, R.6.5, R.9
  Cell line working zone, 310.5(C)(4)
  Definition, Art. 100
  Protection from see Arc flash protective equipment
Arc flash protective equipment, 130.5, 130.7, 360.4(B),
    Annex H, R.10.2
  Qualified persons, use by, C.1.2.1, C.1.2.3
  Unqualified persons, use by, C. 1.1
Arc flash risk assessment, 130.2(B), 130.5, O.2.4
  Batteries, 320.3(A)(2)
  Capacitors, 360.4(B)
  Electrolytic cell line working zones, 310.5(C)
Arc flash suit, 130.7(C)(10), 130.7(C)(13), 130.7(C)(15)
  Definition, Art. 100
Arc rating
  Definition, Art. 100
  Total system arc rating, protective clothing, M.3
Arc-resistant equipment, 0.2.4, 130.5(C), 130.7(C)(15)
  Definition, Art. 100
Attachment plug (plug cap) (plug), 110.9(B). 110.9(C)
  Definition, Art. 100
  Maintenance, 245.1
Attendants, to warn and protect employees, 130.7(E)(3)
Auditing, 110.5(M)
Authority having jurisdiction (definition), Art. 100
Authorized person
  Battery rooms or areas restricted to, 320.3(A)(3)
  Definition, 320.2
Automatic (definition), Art. 100

B

Balaclava, 130.5(G), 130.7(C)(10), 130.7(C)(15)
  Definition, Art. 100
Barricades, 130.7(E)(2)
  Definition, Art. 100
Barriers, *see also* Protective barriers
  Definition, Art. 100
  Electrolytic cells, safe work practices, 310.5(D)(3)
  Laser systems, 330.5(D)
  Maintenance of, 250.1
  Physical or mechanical, 130.7(D)(2), 130.8(F), O.2.4
  Rotating equipment, 230.2
Batteries
  Abnormal conditions, alarms for, 320.3(A)(5)
  Cell flame arresters, 320.3(D)
  Definition, 320.2
  Electrolyte hazards, 320.3(B)
  Maintenance requirements, safety-related, Art. 240
  Personal protective equipment (PPE), use of, 320.3(A)(6)
  Safety requirements, Art. 320
  Tools and equipment, use of, 320.3(C)
  Valve-regulated lead acid cell (definition), 320.2
  Vented cell (definition), 320.2
  Ventilation, 240.1, 320.3(D)
  VRLA (valve-regulated lead acid cell) (definition), 320.2
Battery effect (definition), 310.2
Battery enclosures, 320.3(A)(3)
Battery rooms
  Definition, 320.2
  Requirements, 320.3(A)(3)
Bleed resistors, 360.4(B), 360.5(B), R.6.8, R.13.2
  Definition, 360.2
Bleed systems, testing, R. 11.2
Blind reaching, electrical safety program, 130.8(B)
Body wash apparatus, 240.2
Bonded (bonding)
  Definition, Art. 100
  Maintenance of bonding, 205.6
Bonding conductor or jumper (definition), Art. 100
Boundary, 120.4(B)(6); see also Approach distances
  Approach boundaries to energized conductors or circuits, 130.2,
    C.l.1,C.1.2
  Arc flash, 130.2(B), 130.5(C), 130.5(E), 130.5(H), C.1.2.1,
    R.10.3
    Calculations, Annex D, R.9.2
    Definition, Art. 100
    Protective equipment, use of, 130.7(C)(15), C.l.1, C.l.2.1, C. 1.2.3

Limited approach, 110.3, 110.4(B), 130.2(B), 130.4(E), 130.4(F), 130.7(D)(1), 130.9, C.1.1, C.1.2.2; *see also* Approach distances
  Definition, Art. 100
Restricted approach, 130.2, 130.4(E), 130.4(G), 130.7(C), 130.7(D), C.1.1, C.l.2.3, R.7; *see also* Approach distances
  Definition, Art. 100
Shock protection, 130.4(C), 130.4(E), R.7
Building (definition), Art. 100

C
Cabinets (definition), Art. 100
Cable
  Flexible see Flexible cords and cables
  Maintenance of, 205.13
Cable trays, maintenance, 215.3
Capacitors
  Arc blast hazard see Arc blast hazard
  Arc flash hazard, R.4.2, R.6.5, R.9
  Definitions, 360.2
  Discharge time *see* Discharge time
  Grounding *see* Grounded (grounding)
  Ground sticks *see* Ground sticks
  Hazard warning labeling, R.6.10, R.15
  Internal rupture, R.5
  Risk assessment, 360.4(B), 360.5(A), R.6, R.7.1
  Safety-related requirements for, Art. 360
  Shock hazard, R.3, R.7
  Short-circuit hazard, R.4
  Storage and disposal, 360.6(C), R.14
  Stored energy, 360.3, R.8
  Testing *see* Testing
  Working with, Annex R
Cell
  Definition, 320.2
  Electrolytic *see* Electrolytic cell
Cell line, *see* Electrolytic cell line
Charge transfer, R.11.10, R.16.2
  Definition, 360.2
Chemical hazard, 320.3(A)(2), 320.3(A)(6)
Circuit breakers
  Definition, Art. 100
  Molded-case, 225.2
  Reclosing circuits after operation, 130.8(M)
  Routine opening and closing of circuits, 130.8(L)
  Safety-related maintenance requirements, Art. 225
  Testing, 225.3
Circuits
  De-energized see De-energized
  Energized, working on or near parts that are or might become *see* Working on energized electrical conductors or circuit
  Identification, maintenance of, 205.12
  Impedance, 120.5
  Interlocks, re-energizing by, 120.2(D)
  Reclosing after protective device operation, 130.8(M)
  Routine opening and closing of, 130.8(L)
Clear spaces, 130.8(H), 205.9
Combustible dust, 130.8(J)
Competent person, 350.4(B), 350.5
  Definition, 350.2
Complex lockout/tagout procedure, 120.2(H), 120.4(A)(5), Annex G
Condition of maintenance, 110.5(C)
  Definition, Art. 100

Conductive (definition), Art. 100
Conductive work locations, 110.9(D)
Conductors
  Bare (definition), Art. 100
  Covered (definition), Art. 100
  Cutting, removing, or rerouting, 130.12
  De-energized see De-energized
  Energized see Working on energized electrical conductors or circuit
  Grounding conductors, equipment (EGC), 110.9(B)
    Definition, Art. 100
  Identification see Identified/identification
  Insulated
    Definition, Art. 100
    Integrity of insulation, maintenance of, 210.4
  Maintenance of, 205.13, 210.3
Contractors, relationship with, 110.7
Control devices, 120.2(E)
Controllers (definition), Art. 100
Cord- and plug-connected equipment, 110.9
  Connecting attachment plugs, 110.9(C), 110.9(E)
  Grounding-type equipment, 110.9(B)
  Handling, 110.9(A)
  Safety-related maintenance requirements, Art. 245
  Visual inspection, 110.9(C)
Cords, flexible, *see* Flexible cords and cables
Covers, 215.1
Cranes, 310.5(D)(9)
Current-limiting overcurrent protective device (definition), Art. 100
Cutout
  Definition, Art. 100
  Portable cutout-type switches, 310.5(D)(8)
Cutting, 130.11, 130.12

D
De-energized, *see also* Electrically safe work condition
  Conductors or circuit parts that have lockout/tagout devices applied, 120.4(A)(4), 120.4(B)(6)
  Definition, Art. 100
  Equipment operating at less than 50 volts, 110.4(C)
  Failure of equipment, 130.8(K)
  Infeasibility of task in de-energized state, 110.4(B)
  Process to de-energize equipment, 120.4(B)(1), 120.4(B)(3), R.6.9
  Protective device operation, reclosing circuits after, 130.8(M)
  Testing of parts, 120.4(B)(6), 120.5, R.13.1
  Uninsulated overhead lines, 130.9(C)
Definitions, Art. 100
  Batteries and battery rooms, 320.2
  Electrolytic cells, 310.2
  Lasers, 330.2
  Power electronic equipment, 340.2
  Research and development laboratories, 350.2
Device (definition), Art. 100
Dielectric absorption, 360.5(B), R.l 1.10, R.16.2
  Definition, 360.2
Discharge procedure, capacitors, R.6.9, R.6.10, R.13.1, R.13.2, R. 15.1
Discharge time, R.6.8, R.12
  Definition, 360.2
Disconnecting means, 120.2(E), 120.5; *see* also Circuit breakers
  Definition, Art. 100
  Lockout/tagout devices, use of, 120.4(B)(3), 120.4(B)(11)

Reclosing circuits after operation, 130.8(M)
Routine opening and closing of circuits, 130.8(L)
Disconnecting (or isolating) switches (disconnector, isolator), *see also* Disconnecting means
Definition, Art. 100
Safety-related maintenance requirements, Art. 210
Documentation
Arc flash risk assessment, 130.5(D)
Capacitors, electrically safe work condition for, 360.5(A)
Electrical safety program, 105.3(A), 110.5(A), 110.5(M)(4), 110.7(C)
Equipment labeling, 130.5(H)
Laboratory, unlisted equipment for, 350.7(A)
Of maintenance, 205.3
Shock risk assessment, 130.4(D)
Training, employees, 110.6(C)(4)
Doors, secured, 130.8(G)
Drilling, 130.11
Dust, combustible, 130.8(J)
Dwelling unit (definition), Art. 100

E
Electrical hazard, Art. 130; *see also* Arc flash hazard; Risk; Shock hazard
Alerting techniques, 130.7(E)
Categories of
General, Annex K
Personal protective equipment required for *see* Personal protective equipment (PPE)
Definition, Art. 100
Electrical safety program procedures, identification of, 110.5(G)
Elimination, 110.1
Lasers, 330.3, 330.5
Risk assessment, F.4
Electrically safe work condition, Art. 120; *see also* Lockout/tagout
For capacitors, 360.5, R.6.9, R.13.1
Definition, Art. 100
Laboratory, 350.10
For lasers, 330.5(B)
Policy, inclusion of, 110.5(K)
Process for establishing and verifying, 120.5
Temporary protective grounding equipment, 120.5
Verification of, 120.4(B)(5), 120.5
Work involving electrical hazards, 130.1
Electrical safety (definition), Art. 100
Electrical safety authority, 350.4
Electrical safety program, 110.5, Annex E
Auditing, 110.5(M)
Awareness and self-discipline, 110.5(D)
Contractors, relationship with, 110.7
Controls, 110.5(F), E.2
Definition, Art. 100
Documentation of, 105.3(A), 110.5(A), 110.5(M)(4), 110.7©
General, 110.5(A)
Incident investigations, 110.5(J)
Inspection, 110.5(B)
Job briefing, 110.5(1)
Maintenance, 110.9(C)
Principles, 110.5(E), E.1
Procedures, 110.5(G), E.3
Risk assessment procedure, 110.5(H), Annex F
Electrolyte (definition), 320.2

Electrolyte hazards, storage battery, 320.3(B)(1)
Electrolytic cell, Art. 310
Auxiliary nonelectric connections, 310.6(B)
Employee training, 310.3, 310.4, 310.5(D)(6)
Electrolytic cell line working zone
Attachments, 310.5(D)(10)
Cranes and hoists, 310.5(D)(9)
Employee safeguards, 310.5, Annex L
Employee training, 310.3, 310.4(A), 310(4)(B)(2 310.5(D)(6)
Portable equipment and tools, use of, 310.6
Elevated equipment, 130.9(F)(1)
Emergency response, training in, 110.6(C)
Employees
Electrical safety program, 110.5
Lockout/tagout procedure, 120.1, 120.2(A), 120.4
Responsibilities, 105.3(B), 130.9(D)
Lasers, 330.6
Power electronic equipment, 340.5(B)
Special equipment, 300.2
Safeguarding see Safeguarding
Training *see* Training, employees
Employers
Electrical safety program, 110.5
Responsibilities, 105.3(A), 120.4
Host and contract employers, 110.7
Lockout/tagout procedure, 120.1
Power electronic equipment, 340.5(A)
Safety-related design requirements, Annex O
Special equipment, 300.2
Uninsulated overhead lines, work on or near, 130.9(D)
Enclosed (definition), Art. 100
Enclosures
Definition, Art. 100
Maintenance of, 205.6, 205.7, 210.1, 210.2
Energized
Definition, Art. 100
Electrical conductors or circuit see Working on energized electrical conductors or circuit
Electrolytic cells *see* Electrolytic cell; Electrolytic cell line working zone
Lasers, testing of, 330.5(C)
Energized electrical work permit, 130.2(B), Annex J
Energy thresholds, laboratory, 350.9
Equipment, *see also* specific equipment
Arc-resistant, 0.2.4, 130.5(C), 130.7(C)(15)
Definition, Art. 100
Batteries, for work on, 320.3(C)
Definition, Art. 100
Grounding
Portable equipment within energized cell line wor¹ zone, 310.6(A)
Vehicle or mechanical equipment, 130.9(F)(3)
Grounding-type, 110.9(B)
Overhead see Overhead lines and equipment
Spaces about, maintenance of, 205.5, 205.9
Special see Special equipment
Use of, 110.8
Equipment grounding conductors (EGC), 110.9(B)
Definition, Art. 100
Explanatory material, 90.4
Exposed (as applied to energized electrical conductors or circuit parts), 105.1, 120.4(A)(2), 120.4(B)(6), 130.2
Definition, Art. 100

Safe work practices see Working on energized electrical conductors or circuit; Work practices, safety-related

Exposed (as applied to wiring methods) (definition), Art. 100

Extension cords, *see* Flexible cord sets

Eye wash apparatus, 240.2

F

Fault current, *see also* Short circuit current
  Available, 130.7(C)(15), 210.3, 210.5
    Definition, Art. 100
  Definition, Art. 100

Fiberglass-reinforced plastic rods, 130.7(D)(1)

Fiber or flyings, combustible, 130.8(J)

Field evaluated, 330.5(E), 350.2, 350.6
  Definition, 330.2

Field work audit, 110.5(M)(2)

Fittings (definition), Art. 100

Flame arresters, battery cell, 320.3(D)

Flammable gases, 130.8(J)

Flammable liquids, 130.8(J)

Flexible cords and cables
  Grounding-type utilization equipment, 110.9(B)
  Handling, 110.9(A)
  Maintenance of, 205.14

Flexible cord sets, 110.9
  Connecting attachment plugs, 110.9(C), 110.9(E)
  Visual inspection, 110.9(C)

Formal interpretation procedures, 90.5

Fuses, 130.8(b), 130.8(M)
  Current-limiting fuses, calculating arc-flash energies for use with, D.2.1
  Definition, Art. 100
  Fuse or fuse-holding handling equipment, 130.7(D)(1)
  Safety-related maintenance requirements, 225.1

G

Gases, flammable, 130.8(J)

Ground (definition), Art. 100

Grounded (grounding), 120.4(B)(2)
  Capacitors, 360.4(B), 360.6, R.11, R.13.2
  Definition, Art. 100
  Equipment
    Portable equipment within energized cell line working zone, 310.6(A)
    Vehicle or mechanical equipment, 130.9(F)(3)
  Lockout/tagout procedures, 120.4(B)(7)
  Maintenance of, 205.6
  Safety grounding equipment, maintenance of, 250.3
  Solidly grounded (definition), Art. 100

Grounded conductors (definition), Art. 100

Ground fault (definition), Art. 100

Ground-fault circuit-interrupters (GFCIs), 110.9(D), 110.10
  Definition, Art. 100
  Testing, 110.10(D)

Grounding conductors, equipment (EGC), 110.9(B)
  Definition, Art. 100

Grounding electrode (definition), Art. 100

Grounding electrode conductors (definition), Art. 100

Grounding-type equipment, 110.9(B)

Ground sticks, 360.6, R.6.8, R.11.6, R.11.8, R.11.10, R.16
  Definition, 360.2

Guarded, 205.7; *see also* Barriers; Enclosures
  Definition, Art. 100
  Lasers, 330.5(A)
  Rotating equipment, 230.2
  Uninsulated overhead lines, 130.9(C),130.9(D)

H

Handlines, 130.7(D)(1)

Hard grounding (Low-Z), 360.5(B), R.6.8, R.11.1, R. 11.3, R.11.6, R.11.9
  Definition, 360.2

Hazard (definition), Art. 100; *see also* Electrical hazard

Hazardous (definition), Art. 100

Hazardous (classified) locations, maintenance requirements for, Art. 235

Hazard warning labeling, R.6.10, R.15

Hearing protection boundary
  Definition, 360.2

Hinged panels, secured, 130.8(G)

Hoists, 310.5(D)(9)

Human performance and workplace electrical safety, Annex Q

I

Identified/identification
  Equipment, field marking of, 130.5(H)
  Laboratory, unlisted equipment for, 350.7(A)
  Maintenance of identification, 205.10
  Temporary protective grounding equipment, 120.5

Illumination
  Battery rooms, 320.3(A)(3)
  Working on energized electrical conductors or circuits, 130.8(C)

Implanted pacemakers and metallic medical devices, 310.5(D)(11)

Incident energy
  Calculation methods. Annex D, R.9
  Definition, Art. 100
  Equipment, labeling of, 130.5(H)
  Reducing, 0.2.3

Incident energy analysis, 130.5(F), 130.5(G), 130.7(C)(15)
  Definition. Art. 100

Incident investigations, 110.5(J)

Informative publications, Annex A

Inspection
  Electrical safety program, 110.8(D), 110.9(C)
  Visual
    Capacitors, ground sticks for, 360.6(A), R.16.4
    Cord- and plug-connected equipment, 110.9(C)
    Electrical hazards, work involving, 130.2(C), 130.7(B)
    Return to service after lockout/tagout, 120.4(B)(13)
    Safety and protective equipment, 130.7(B), 250.2(A)
    Safety grounding equipment, 250.3(A)
    Test instruments and equipment, 110.8(D)

Insulated (definition), Art. 100

Insulated conductors, maintenance of, 210.4

Insulated tools and equipment, 110.6(A)(1), 130.7(D)(1), C.1.2.3

Insulating floor surface, L.1

Insulation, electrolytic cells, 310.5(D)(1)

Insulation rating, overhead lines, 130.9(B)

Interlocks
  Circuit, 120.2(D)
  Safety, 130.8(N), 205.8

Interrupter switch (definition), Art. 100

Interrupting rating (definition), Art. 100
Investigations, incident, 110.5(J)
Isolated (as applied to location)
  Definition, Art. 100
  Electrolytic cells, 310.5(D)(5)
Isolating switches
  Definition, Art. 100
  Safety-related maintenance requirements, Art. 210

J
Job briefing, 110.5(1), 130.2(B), 350.5(A). R.13.2
  Checklist, Annex I

L
Labeled (definition), Art. 100
Labeling of equipment, 130.5(H), R.6.10
Laboratory
  Approval requirements, 350.6
  Custom built unlisted equipment
    Greater than 1000 volts, 350.8
    1000 volts or less, 350.7
  Definitions, 350.2
  Electrical safety authority, 350.4
  Energy thresholds, 350.9
  Safety-related work requirements, Art. 350
Lasers
  Definition, 330.2
  Energy source (definition), 330.2
  Radiation (definition), 330.2
  System (definition), 330.2
  Work practices, safety-related, Art. 330
    Responsibility for, 330.6
    Safeguarding persons in operating area, 330.5
    Training, 330.4
Limited approach boundary, see Boundary, limited approach
Listed
  Definition, Art. 100
  Lasers, 330.5(E)
  Research and development laboratory equipment or systems. 350.6
Live parts
  Guarding of see Guarded
  Safe work conditions see Electrical safety program; Working on energized electrical conductors or circuit; Work practices, safety-related
Lockout/tagout
  Accountability for personnel, 120.4(B)(10)
  Audit, program and procedure, 110.5(M)(3)
  Capacitors, 360.5(B), R.13.2
  Control, elements of, 120.4(B)
  Control devices, use of, 120.2(E)
  Control of energy, 120.2(C)
  Coordination, 120.2(G), 120.4(B)(9)
  Equipment, 120.3
  Grounding, 120.4(B)(7)
  Hazardous electrical energy control, forms of, 120.2(H); see also Complex lockout/tagout procedure; Simple lockout/tagout procedure
  Identification of devices, 120.2(F)
  Maintenance of devices, 205.8
  Person in charge, 120.2(H), 120.4(A)(3), 120.4(A)(5)
  Plans for, 120.4(A)

Principles, 120.2
Procedures, 120.2(B), 120.2(G), 120.4, 120.5, Annex G
Programs, 110.5(L), 110.5(M)(3), 120.1
Release
  For return to service, 120.4(B)(13)
  Temporary, 120.4(B)(14)
Removal of devices, 120.4(B)(12)
Responsibility, 120.1, 120.4
Shift change, 120.4(B)(8)
Testing, 120.4(B)(6)
Training, 110.6(B)
Luminaires (definition), Art. 100
Lung protection boundary, 360.4(B), R.6.5, R.6.6, R.9.2, R.10.3, R.11.7
  Definition, 360.2

M
Maintenance, condition of, 110.5(C)
  Definition, Art. 100
Maintenance requirements, Chap. 2, 110.5(C)
  Batteries and battery rooms, Art. 240
  Controller equipment, Art. 220
  Fuses and circuit breakers, Art. 225
  General, Art. 205
  Hazardous (classified) locations, Art. 235
  Introduction, Art. 200
  Laboratory, unlisted equipment for, 350.7(B)
  Personal safety and protective equipment, Art. 250
  Portable electric tools and equipment. Art. 245
  Premises wiring, Art. 215
  Rotating equipment, Art. 230
  Substation, switchgear assemblies, switchboards, panelboards, motor control centers, and disconnect switches, Art. 210
Mandatory rules, 90.4
Marking, see Identified/identification
Mechanical equipment, working on or near uninsulated overhead lines, 130.9(F)
Motor control centers
  Definition, Art. 100
  Personal protective equipment required for tasks, 130.7(C)(15)
  Safety-related maintenance requirements, Art. 210
Multi-employer relationship, 120.4(A)(5)

N
Nominal voltage (definition), 320.2
Nonelectric equipment connections, electrolytic cell line, 310.6(B)

O
Occupational health and safety management standards, alignment with, Annex P
Open wiring protection, 215.2
Outdoors, GFCI protection, 110.10(C)
Outlets (definition), Art. 100
Overcurrent (definition), Art. 100
Overcurrent protection
  Arc flash risk assessment, 130.5(B)
  Maintenance of devices, 205.4, 210.5
  Modification, 110.11
Overhead lines and equipment, 120.3(D)(5)
  Clearances, maintenance of, 205.15

Industrial procedures and policies for working near overhead systems, example of, Annex N
Insulation rating, 130.9(B)
Working within limited approach boundary of uninsulated, 130.9
Overload (definition), Art. 100

P

Pacemakers, implanted, 310.5(D)(11)
Panelboards
Definition, Art. 100
Personal protective equipment required for tasks, 130.7(C)(15)
Safety-related maintenance requirements, Art. 210
Permissive rules, 90.4
Personal protective equipment (PPE), 130.2(B), 130.2(C), 130.10, 130.11, L.l; *see also* Protective clothing
Arc flash protection see Arc flash protective equipment
Batteries and battery rooms, 320.3(A)(6), 320.3(B)(1)
Body protection, 130.7(C)(6)
Capacitors, 360.4(B), 360.5(B)
Care of, 130.7(B)
Electrical equipment labeling for, 130.5(H)
Eye protection, 130.7(C)(4)
Foot and leg protection, 130.7(C)(8)
Hand and arm protection, 130.7(C)(7)
Head, face, neck, and chin protection, 130.7(C)(3)
Hearing protection, 130.7(C)(5)
Maintenance, Art. 250
Required for various tasks, 130.7(C)(15)
Safeguarding of employees in electrolytic cell line working zone, 310.5(C)(1), 310.5(D)(2)
Selection of, 130.7(C)(15), Annex H
Shock protection, 130.4(A), 130.4(C), 130.7, C.1.1, R.7.1, R.7.2
Standards for, 130.7(C)(14)
Pilot cell (definition), 320.2
Planning checklist, Annex I
Portable electric equipment, 110.9
Conductive or wet work locations, 110.9(D)
Connecting attachment plugs, 110.9(C), 110.9(E)
Electrolytic cells, 310.6(A), L.2
Grounding-type, 110.9(B)
Handling and storage, 110.9(A)
Manufacturer's instructions, 110.9(F)
Safety-related maintenance requirements, Art. 245
Visual inspection, 110.9(C)
Power electronic equipment, safety-related work practices, Art. 340
Definitions, 340.2
Hazards associated with, 340.4
Specific measures, 340.5
Power supply
Cell line working area, L.2
Portable electric equipment, circuits for, 310.6(A)
Premises wiring (system)
Definition, Art. 100
Maintenance of, Art. 215
Prohibited approach boundary, *see* Boundary
Prospective fault current (definition), 320.2
Protective barriers, 130.7(D)(2), 130.8(F), 250.1,330.5(D)
Definition, 330.2
Protective clothing, 130.7(C), L.1
Arc flash protection, 130.7(C)(9), 130.7(C)(10), 130.7(C)(13), 130.7(C)(15), C.1.1, Annex H
Care and maintenance, 130.7(C)(13)

Characteristics, 130.7(C)(11)
Layering of, M.l, M.2
Prohibited clothing, 130.7(C)(12)
Selection of, 130.7(C)(9), Annex H
Total system arc rating, M.3
Protective equipment, 130.7, 130.9(D), 130.9(F)(2)
Alerting techniques, 130.7(E)
Arc flash protection see Arc flash protective equipment
Barricades, 130.7(E)(2)
Barriers see Barriers
Batteries, maintenance of, 320.3(A)(6)
Care of equipment, 130.7(B)
Insulated tools, 130.7(D)(1)
Look-alike equipment, 130.7(F)
Maintenance, Art. 250
Nonconductive ladders, 130.7(D)(1)
Personal see Personal protective equipment (PPE)
Reclosing circuits after protective device operation, 130.8(M)
Rubber insulating equipment, 130.7(D)(2)
Safety signs and tags, 130.7(E)(1)
Shock protection, 130.4(C), 130.7, C.1.1
Standards for, 130.7(G)
Voltage-rated plastic guard equipment, 130.7(D)(2)
Purpose of standard, 90.1

Q

Qualified persons, 130.2(C)
Approach distances, 130.4(F)(3), 130.4(G), C.1.1, C.1.2
Capacitors. R.14.3, R.16.1
Safe work practices for, 360.5(B), R.13.2
Training for, 360.4(A), R.2.1
Definition, Art. 100
Electrical safety authority, 350.4
Electrolytic cells, training for, 4(B)(2), 310, 310.4(A)
Lockout/tagout procedures, 120.2(H), 120.4(A)(4), 120.4(B)(14)
Maintenance, performance of, 205.1
Overhead lines, determining insulation rating of, 130.9(B)
Training of, 110.6(A)(1)
For capacitors, 360.4(A), R.2.1
For electrolytic cells, 4(B)(2), 310, 310.4(A)

R

Raceways
Definition, Art. 100
Maintenance, 215.3
Radiation worker (definition), 340.2
Receptacles
Definition, Art. 100
Electrolytic cell lines, L.2
Maintenance, 245.1
Portable electric equipment, 110.9(B), 110.9(C), 110.9(E)
Research and development
Definition, 350.2
Safety-related work requirements for laboratories, Art. 350
Restricted approach boundary, *see* Boundary, restricted approach
Risk
Control, 110.1, F.3
Definition, Art. 100
Risk assessment
Arc flash, 130.2(B), 320.3(A)(2)
Capacitors, 360.4(B), 360.5(A), R.6
Definition, Art. 100

Hazard-based, F.4
Methods, F.6
Procedure, 110.5(H), Annex F
Shock, 130.2(B), 130.4, 320.3(A)(2)
Task-based, F.5
Ropes, 130.7(D)(1)
Rules, mandatory and permissive, 90.4

S

Safeguarding
In cell line working zone, 310.5, Annex L
Definition, 310.2
In laser operating area, 330.5
Safety grounding equipment, maintenance of, 250.3
Safety interlocks, 130.8(N), 205.8
Safety-related design requirements, Annex O
Safety-related maintenance requirements, *see* Maintenance requirements
Safety-related work practices, *see* Work practices, safety-related
Scope of standard, 90.2
Service drop (definition), Art. 100
Service lateral (definition), Art. 100
Service point (definition), Art. 100
Shock hazard, K.2
Battery room warning signs, 320.3(A)(6)
Battery terminals, 320.3(A)(3)
Capacitors, R.3. R.7
Determination of hazard, R.6.3
Personal protective equipment for, 360.4(B)
Definition, Art. 100
Protection from, 130.7, 360.4(B), C.1.1, O.2.4
Shock protection boundaries, 130.4(E), R.7
Shock risk assessment, 130.2(B), 130.4, 320.3(A)(2), O.2.4
Short circuit, O.2.3
Short-circuit current
Calculations, Annex D
Capacitors, R.4.3, R.10.1
Prospective, 320.3(A)(6)
Definition, 320.2
Rating (definition), Art. 100
Short-circuit hazard, R.4
Signs, electrolytic cell areas, 310.5(B)
Simple lockout/tagout procedure, 120.2(H). 120.4(A)(4), Annex G
Single-line diagram
Definition, Art. 100
Maintenance of, 205.2
Soft grounding (High-Z), 360.2, 360.6(B), R.6.8, R.11.1, R.11.4, R.11.6, R.11.9
Special equipment, Chap. 3; *see also* Batteries; Electrolytic cell; Laser; Power electronic equipment
Battery rooms
Definition, 320.2
Requirements, 320.3(3)
Organization, 300.3
Responsibility, 300.2
Special permission (definition), Art. 100
Standard arrangement, 90.3
Step potential (definition), Art. 100
Stored energy, 120.4(B)(2), 120.5, 330.3(B), 360.4(B), R.6.9
Determining, R.6.4, R.8
Exposure to, R.6.2
Ground sticks, use of see Ground sticks
Hazard thresholds, 360.3

Labeling of equipment, R.6.10, R.15.1
Written discharge procedure, R.6.9
Structure (definition), Art. 100
Substations, safety-related maintenance requirements, Art. 210
Supervisory performance, Q.7.1, Q.7.4, Q.8.3
Switchboards
Definition, Art. 100
Safety-related maintenance requirements, Art. 210
Switches, *see also* Switching devices
Disconnecting (or isolating) switches (disconnector, isolator) *see also* Disconnecting means
Definition, Art. 100
Safety-related maintenance requirements, Art. 210
Isolating
Definition, Art. 100
Safety-related maintenance requirements, Art. 210
Load-rated, 130.8(L)
Portable cutout type, 310.5(D)(8)
Switchgear
Arc-resistant, 130.7(C)(15)
Metal-clad, 130.7(C)(15)
Definition, Art. 100
Metal-enclosed, 130.7(0(15)
Definition, Art. 100
Personal protective equipment required for tasks, 130.7(C)(15)
Safety-related maintenance requirements, Art. 210
Switching devices (definition), Art. 100; see also Circuit breakers; Disconnecting means; Switches

T

Tagout, *see* Lockout/tagout
Temporary protective grounding equipment, 120.5, 250.3(B)
Terminals, maintenance of, 230.1
Testing
Capacitors, 360.4(B), 360.6(B), R.6.9. R.11, R.13.1, R.13.2, R.16.5
De-energized parts, 120.4(B)(6), 120.5
Energized equipment, 130.2(C)
Equipment safeguards, 310.5(D)(12)
Ground-fault circuit-interrupters, 110.10(D)
Ground sticks, R.16.5
Lockout/tagout procedure, 120.4(B)(6)
Personal protective equipment, 310.5(D)(2)
Safety and protective equipment, insulation of, 250.2(B)
Safety grounding equipment, 250.3(B), 250.3(C)
Test instruments and equipment, 110.8
Cell line working zone, 310.6(D)
Maintenance of, 250.4
Visual inspection, 110.8(D)
Thermal hazard, 320.3(A)(6), 360.4(B), R.4.1
Time constant, R.3.2, R. 11.4, R. 12
Definition, 360.2
Tools
Batteries, for work on, 320.3(C)
Electrolytic cells, safe work practices, 310.5(D)(7), 310.6, L.2
Insulated, 110.6(A)(1), 130.7(D)(1), C.1.2.3
Laboratory equipment, maintenance and operation of, 350.7(B)
Touch potential (definition), Art. 100
Training, employees
Documentation, 110.6(C)(4)
Emergency responses, 110.6(C)

Laboratory equipment, maintenance and operation of, 350.7(B)
Lockout/tagout practices, 120.1(A), Annex G
Work practices, safety-related, 105.3(A), 110.6, 110.7(B)(1), 310.3, 310.4, 310.5(D)(6), 330.4, 360.4(A), R.2

U

Underground electrical lines and equipment, 130.10
Ungrounded (definition), Art. 100
Uninsulated overhead lines, working within limited approach boundary of, 130.9(A)
Unqualified persons, 130.2(B)
   Approach distances, 130.4(F), 130.9(E), C.1.1
   Definition, Art. 100
   Training of, 110.6(A)(2)
      Capacitors, 360.4(A), R.2.2
      Electrolytic cells, 310.4(B)
Utilization equipment
   Definition, Art. 100
   Grounding-type, 110.9(B)

V

Valve-regulated lead acid cell (definition), 320.2
Vehicular equipment, working on or near uninsulated overhead lines, 130.9(F)
Ventilation, batteries, 240.1, 320.3(D)
Voltage
   Capacitors, 360.4(B), R.8.4
   (Of a circuit) (definition), Art. 100
   Electrolytic cells, voltage equalization, 310.5(D)(4)
   Equipment operating at less than 50 volts, working on energized, 110.4(C)
   Lasers, 330.3(A)
   Nominal (definition), Art. 100
VRLA (valve-regulated lead acid cell) (definition), 320.2

W

Warning signs
   Battery rooms and enclosures, 320.3(A)(6)
   Lasers, 330.5(D)
   Maintenance of, 205.11
Welding machines, 310.6(C)
Wet work locations, 110.9(D)
Wiring, premises
   Definition, Art. 100
   Maintenance of, Art. 215
Working distance, 130.2(B), 130.5(H), 130.7(C)(15), D.3.1, D.4.4
   Definition, Art. 100

Working on energized electrical conductors or circuit parts, Art. 130; *see also* Work practices, safety-related
   Alerting techniques, 130.7(E)
   Alertness of personnel, 130.8(A)
   Approach boundaries see Boundary
   Blind reaching by employees, 130.8(B)
   Conductive articles being worn, 130.8(D)
   Conductive materials, tools, and equipment being handled, 130.8(E)
   Confined or enclosed work spaces, 130.8(F)
   De-energized state, infeasibility of task in, 110.4(B)
   Definition, Art. 100
   Electrically safe working conditions, 130.2
   Energized electrical work permit, 130.2(B)
   Equipment operating at less than 50 volts, 110.4(C)
   Failure, anticipation of, 130.8(K)
   Flash risk assessment, 130.5
   Hazards, additional, 110.4(A)
   Housekeeping duties, 130.8(I)
   Illumination, 130.8(C)
   Insulated tools and equipment, 130.7(D)(1)
   Normal operating condition, 110.4(D)
   Occasional use of flammable materials, 130.8(J)
   Opening and closing of circuits, routine, 130.8(L)
   Overhead lines, working within limited approach boundary of, 130.9
   Portable ladders, 130.7(D)(1)
   Protective shields, 130.8(F)
   Reclosing circuits after protective device operation, 130.8(M)
   Risk, increased, 110.4(A)
Working spaces
   Clear spaces, 130.8(H), 205.9
   Maintenance of, 205.5, 205.9
Work permit, energized electrical, 130.2(B), Annex J
Work practices, safety-related, Chap. 1; *see also* Electrically safe work condition; Working on energized electrical conductors or circuit
   Approach distances see Approach distances
   Batteries and battery rooms, Art. 320
   Capacitors, 360.5(B)
   Contractors, relationship with, 110.7
   De-energized equipment see Electrically safe work condition
   Electrical safety program, 110.5
   Electrolytic cells. Art. 310, Annex L
   General requirements. Art. 110
   Lasers, Art. 330
   Power electronic equipment, Art. 340
   Purpose, 105.2
   Research and development laboratories, Art. 350
   Responsibility for, 105.3
   Scope, 105.1
   Special equipment see Special equipment
   Training requirements, 105.3(A), 110.6, 110.7(B)(1)
   Use of equipment, 110.8

IMPORTANT NOTICES AND DISCLAIMERS CONCERNING NFPA® STANDARDS

NOTICE AND DISCLAIMER OF LIABILITY CONCERNING THE USE OF NFPA STANDARDS

NFPA® codes, standards, recommended practices, and guides ("NFPA Standards"), of which the document contained herein is one, are developed through a consensus standards development process approved by the American National Standards Institute. This process brings together volunteers representing varied viewpoints and interests to achieve consensus on fire and other safety issues. While the NFPA administers the process and establishes rules to promote fairness in the development of consensus, it does not independently test, evaluate, or verify the accuracy of any information or the soundness of any judgments contained in NFPA Standards.

The NFPA disclaims liability for any personal injury, property or other damages of any nature whatsoever, whether special, indirect, consequential or compensatory, directly or indirectly resulting from the publication, use of, or reliance on NFPA Standards. The NFPA also makes no guaranty or warranty as to the accuracy or completeness of any information published herein.

In issuing and making NFPA Standards available, the NFPA is not undertaking to render professional or other services for or on behalf of any person or entity. Nor is the NFPA undertaking to perform any duty owed by any person or entity to someone else. Anyone using this document should rely on his or her own independent judgment or, as appropriate, seek the advice of a competent professional in determining the exercise of reasonable care in any given circumstances.

The NFPA has no power, nor does it undertake, to police or enforce compliance with the contents of NFPA Standards. Nor does the NFPA list, certify, test, or inspect products, designs, or installations for compliance with this document. Any certification or other statement of compliance with the requirements of this document shall not be attributable to the NFPA and is solely the responsibility of the certifier or maker of the statement.

ADDITIONAL NOTICES AND DISCLAIMERS

Updating of NFPA Standards
Users of NFPA codes, standards, recommended practices, and guides ("NFPA Standards") should be aware that these documents may be superseded at any time by the issuance of new editions or may be amended from time to time through the issuance of Tentative Interim Amendments or corrected by Errata. An official NFPA Standard at any point in time consists of the current edition of the document together with any Tentative Interim Amendments and any Errata then in effect. In order to determine whether a given document is the current edition and whether it has been amended through the issuance of Tentative Interim Amendments or corrected through the issuance of Errata, consult appropriate NFPA publications such as the National Fire Codes® Subscription Service, visit the NFPA website at www.nfpa.org, or contact the NFPA at the address listed below.

Interpretations of NFPA Standards
A statement, written or oral, that is not processed in accordance with Section 6 of the Regulations Governing the Development of NFPA Standards shall not be considered the official position of NFPA or any of its Committees and shall not be considered to be, nor be relied upon as, a Formal Interpretation.

Patents
The NFPA does not take any position with respect to the validity of any patent rights referenced in, related to, or asserted in connection with an NFPA Standard. The users of NFPA Standards bear the sole responsibility for determining the validity of any such patent rights, as well as the risk of infringement of such rights, and the NFPA disclaims liability for the infringement of any patent resulting from the use of or reliance on NFPA Standards.

NFPA adheres to the policy of the American National Standards Institute (ANSI) regarding the inclusion of patents in American National Standards ("the ANSI Patent Policy"), and hereby gives the following notice pursuant to that policy:

> **NOTICE:** The user's attention is called to the possibility that compliance with an NFPA Standard may require use of an invention covered by patent rights. NFPA takes no position as to the validity of any such patent rights or as to whether such patent rights constitute or include essential patent claims under the ANSI Patent Policy. If, in connection with the ANSI Patent Policy, a patent holder has filed a statement of willingness to grant licenses under these rights on reasonable and nondiscriminatory terms and conditions to applicants desiring to obtain such a license, copies of such filed statements can be obtained, on request, from NFPA. For further information, contact the NFPA at the address listed below.

Law and Regulations
Users of NFPA Standards should consult applicable federal, state, and local laws and regulations. NFPA does not, by the publication of its codes, standards, recommended practices, and guides, intend to urge action that is not in compliance with applicable laws, and these documents may not be construed as doing so.

Copyrights
NFPA Standards are copyrighted. They are made available for a wide variety of both public and private uses. These include both use, by reference, in laws and regulations, and use in private self-regulation, standardization, and the promotion of safe practices and methods. By making these documents available for use and adoption by public authorities and private users, the NFPA does not waive any rights in copyright to these documents.

Use of NFPA Standards for regulatory purposes should be accomplished through adoption by reference. The term "adoption by reference" means the citing of title, edition, and publishing information only. Any deletions, additions, and changes desired by the adopting authority should be noted separately in the adopting instrument. In order to assist NFPA in following the uses made of its documents, adopting authorities are requested to notify the NFPA (Attention: Secretary, Standards Council) in writing of such use. For technical assistance and questions concerning adoption of NFPA Standards, contact NFPA at the address below.

For Further Information
All questions or other communications relating to NFPA Standards and all requests for information on NFPA procedures governing its codes and standards development process, including information on the procedures for requesting Formal Interpretations, for proposing Tentative Interim Amendments, and for proposing revisions to NFPA standards during regular revision cycles, should be sent to NFPA headquarters, addressed to the attention of the Secretary. Standards Council, NFPA, 1 Batterymarch Park, P.O. Box 9101, Quincy, MA 02269-9101; email: stds_admin@nfpa.org

For more information about NFPA, visit the NFPA website at www.nfpa.org. All NFPA codes and standards can be viewed at no cost at www.nfpa.org/docinfo.